Standard Catalogue of British Coins

COINS OF ENGLAND

AND THE UNITED KINGDOM

37th Edition

SPINK
LONDON

A Catalogue of the Coins of Great Britain
and Ireland
first published 1929

Standard Catalogue of British Coins
Coins of England and the United Kingdom
37th edition, 2002

69 Southampton Row, Bloomsbury
London WC1B 4ET

Typeset by Data Layout Ltd,
24 Greenwich Centre Business Park, Norman Road, London SE10 9QF
Printed in Great Britain by
Cromwell Press
Trowbridge
Wiltshire

ISBN 1 902040 449

CONTENTS

PREFACE

The past year has busy at Spink, and we have now settled into our new premises at 69 Southampton Row, Bloomsbury, just around the corner from the British Museum.

Our website is now well-established at www.spink-online.com and visitors will find a large selection of coins and books offered for sale.

In this year's edition we have included a fascinating survey of what has happened in the UK coin market since last year's edition was published. As always we have looked at every section and, in particular, at prices, and these have been amended in all areas to reflect the current market for British coins.

In the hammered series the coins of the Kings of Northumbria and the Archbishops of York have been re-classified. The descriptions of the halfpennies and farthings of James I and Charles I have been re-catalogued, incorporating a full listing of the mintmarks. New illustrations have been included throughout the hammered section.

In the milled section, we have revised all prices where necessary and have updated all areas to reflect the changing market over a year that has seen a rebirth in the hobby. Many new illustrations have been included here as well.

All new issues of the Royal Mint have been included.

Whilst the major part of the work in revising this edition has fallen on the coin specialists at Spink-May Sinclair, for hammered, and Steve Hill for milled, many collectors have contributed invaluable information.

We welcome comments and suggestions from collectors, and you are all invited to write to: The Editor, Standard Catalogue of British Coins, Spink & Son Ltd., 69 Southampton Row, Bloomsbury, London WC1B 4ET.

Douglas Saville.

Arrangement

The arrangement of this catalogue is not completely uniform, but generally it is divided into metals (gold, silver, copper, etc) under each reign, then into coinages, denominations and varieties. In the Celtic section the uninscribed coins are listed before the dynastic coins; under Charles II all the hammered coins precede the milled coinage; the reign of George III is divided into coins issued up to 1816 and the new coinage from 1816 to the end of the reign; and under Elizabeth II the decimal issues are separated from the pre-decimal (*£.s.d.*) coinages.

Every major coin type is listed though not every variety. We have endeavoured to give rather more coverage to the varieties of relatively common coins, such as the pennies of Edward I, II and III, than to the very much rarer coins of, for instance, King Offa of Mercia.

Values

The values given represent the range of retail prices at which coins are being offered for sale at the time of going to press and **not** the price which a dealer will pay for those coins. These prices are based on our knowledge of the numismatic market, the current demand for particular coins, recent auction sale prices and, in those cases where certain coins have not appeared for sale for some years, our estimation of what they would be likely to sell at today, bearing in mind their rarity and appeal in relation to somewhat similar coins where a current value is known. Values are given for two grades of preservation from the Celtic period onwards and three to four grades of preservation for coins of the 17th to the 20th century.

Collectors normally require coins in the best condition they can afford and, except in the case of a really rare coin, a piece that is considerably worn is not wanted and has little value. The values given in the catalogue are for the exact state of preservation stated at the head of each column and bearing in mind that a score of identical coins in varying states of wear could be lined up in descending order from mint condition (FDC, *fleur de coin*), through very fine (VF) to *poor* state. It will be realized that only in certain instances will the values given apply to particular coins. A 'fine' (F) coin may be worth anything between one quarter and a half of the price quoted for a 'very fine' (VF); on the other hand, a piece in really mint condition will be valued substantially higher than the price quoted for 'extremely fine' (EF). The designation BV has been adopted for coins whose value on the market has yet to exceed its bullion value. Purchasing sovereigns, catalogued as BV, will attract a dealers' premium.

We emphasize again that the purpose of this catalogue is to give a general value for a particular class of coin in a specified state of preservation, and also to give the collector an idea of the range and value of coins in the English series. The value of any particular piece depends on three things:

Its exact design, legend, mintmark or date.

Its exact state of preservation; this is of prime importance.

The demand for it in the market at any given time.

Some minor varieties are much scarcer than others and, as the number of coins issued varies considerably from year to year, coins of certain dates and mintmarks are rarer and of more value than other pieces of similar type. The prices given for any type are for the commonest variety, mintmark or date of that type.

The Scope

Coin collecting, numismatics, is a fascinating hobby. It requires very little physical exertion and only as much mental effort as one wishes or is able to put into it at any time. There is vast scope and boundless ramifications and byways encompassing not only things historical and geographical, but also touching on economics, metallurgy, heraldry, literature, the fine arts, politics, military history and many other disciplines. This catalogue is solely concerned with British coinage from its earliest times right up to date. From the start the beginner should appreciate that the coinage of our own nation may be seen as a small but very important part of the whole story of world currency.

The first coins, made of electrum, a natural alloy of gold and silver, were issued in western Asia Minor (Lydia) in the later seventh century B.C. Over the next century or so coinage of gold and silver spread across the Aegean to mainland Greece, southwards to the eastern Mediterranean lands and eventually westward to the Greek colonies in southern Italy, Sicily (Magna Graecia) and beyond. The coins of the Greeks are noted for their beautiful, sometimes exquisite craftsmanship, with many of the coin types depicting the patron deities of their cities. Coins of Philip II of Macedon (359-336 B.C.), father of Alexander the Great, circulated amongst the Celtic peoples of the Danubian Basin and were widely copied through central Europe and by the Gauls in France. Gold Gaulish staters were reaching Britain around the beginning of the first century B.C. and the earliest gold to be struck in the island must have been produced shortly afterwards. Although their types and designs copy the Apollo head and racing charioteer of Philip II's gold coins, they are stylistically much removed from the original representation and very individually Celtic in concept.

The coins of the Romans cover some seven centuries and include an enormous number of different types that were current throughout a major part of the civilized world from Spain to Syria and from the Rhine in the north to the Sudan in the south. The Roman province of Britain was part of this vast empire for four hundred years from AD 43 until the early fifth century. Innumerable Roman coins have been recovered from sites in this country, most being made of brass or bronze. Many of these are quite inexpensive and very collectable. In recent years many hoards of gold and silver coins have been found, usually by use of metal detectors.

Following the revival of commerce after the Dark Ages, coinage in Western Europe was virtually restricted to silver until the thirteenth century, though gold was still being minted in Byzantium and in the Islamic world. In the Middle Ages many European cities had their own distinctive coinage and money was issued not only by the kings but also by nobles, bishops and abbots. From the time of the later Crusades gold returned to the West, and the artistic developments of the Renaissance in the fifteenth century brought improved portraiture and new minting techniques.

Large silver crown-size thalers were first minted at Joachimsthal in Bohemia early in the sixteenth century. The substantial shipments of silver coming to Europe from the mines of Spanish America over the next couple of centuries led to a fine series of larger coins being issued by the European states and cities. The larger size allowed greater artistic freedom in the designs and the portraits on the coins.

Both Germany and Italy became unified nation states during the later nineteenth century, thereby substantially reducing the number of mints and coin types. Balancing the reduction in European minting authorities were the new coins that were issued by the independent states of South and Central America. Since the 1950s many new nations have established their independence and their coinage provides a large field for the collector of modern coins.

It can be seen that the scope for the collector is truly vast, but besides the general run of official coinage there is also the large series of token coins—small change unofficially produced to supplement the inadequate supply of authorized currency. These tokens were issued by merchants, innkeepers and manufacturers in many towns and villages in the seventeenth, eighteenth and nineteenth centuries and many collectors specialize in their local issues.

Some coins have designs of a commemorative nature; an example being the Royal Wedding crown of 1981, but there are also large numbers of commemorative medals which, though never intended for use as coinage, are sometimes confused with coins because they are metal objects of a similar shape and sometimes a similar size to coins. This is another interesting field for collectors as these medals often have excellent portraits of famous men or women, or they may commemorate important events or scientific discoveries. Other metallic objects of coin-like appearance that can be confusing for the beginner are reckoning counters, advertising tickets, various other tickets and passes, and items such as brass coin weights.

Minting processes

From the time of the earliest Greek coins in the late seventh century BC to about the middle of the sixteenth century AD, coins were made by hand. The method of manufacture was simple. The obverse and reverse designs were engraved or punched into the prepared ends of two bars of bronze or iron, shaped or tapered to the diameter of the required coin. The obverse die, known as the *pile,* was usually spiked so that it could be anchored firmly into a block of wood or metal. The reverse die, the *trussel,* was held by hand or grasped by tongs.

The coin was struck by placing a metal blank between the two dies and striking the trussel with a hammer. Thus, all coinage struck by this method is known as 'hammered'. Some dies are known to have been hinged so there would be an exact register between the upper and lower die. Usually a 'pair of dies' consisted of one obverse die (normally the more difficult to make because it had the finer detail, such as the ruler's portrait) and two reverse dies. This was because the shaft of iron bearing the reverse design eventually split under the constant hammering; two reverse dies were usually needed to last out the life of the obverse die.

Some time toward the middle of the sixteenth century, experiments, first in Germany and later in France, resulted in the manufacture of coins by machinery.

The term 'milled', which is applied to all machine-made coins, comes from the type of machinery used – the mill and screw press. With this machinery the obverse die was fixed as the lower die and the reverse die brought down into contact with the blank by heavy vertical pressure applied by a screw or worm-drive connected to a cross bar with heavy weights at each end. These weights usually had long leather thongs attached which allowed a more powerful force to be applied by the operators who revolved the arms of the press. New blanks were placed on the lower die and the struck coins were removed by hand. The screw press brought more pressure to bear on the blanks and this pressure was evenly applied, producing a far better and sharper coin.

Various attempts were made during the reigns of Elizabeth I and Charles I to introduce this type of machinery with its vastly superior products. Unfortunately problems associated with the manufacture of blanks to a uniform weight greatly reduced the rate of striking and the hand manufacture of coins continued until the Restoration in 1660, when Charles II brought to London from Holland the Roettiers brothers and their improved screw press.

The first English coins made for circulation by this new method were the silver crowns of 1662, which bore an inscription on the edge, DECVS ET TVTAMEN, 'an ornament and a safeguard', a reference to the fact that the new coins could not be clipped, a crime made easy by the thin and often badly struck hammered coins.

The mill and screw press was used until new steam-powered machinery made by Boulton and Watt was installed in the new mint on Tower Hill in London. This machinery had been used most successfully by Boulton to strike the large 'cartwheel' two- and one-penny pieces of 1797 and other coins, including 'overstriking' Spanish *eight-reale* pieces into Bank of England 'dollars' since the old Mint presses were not able to exert sufficient power to do this. This new machinery was first used at the Mint to strike the 'new coinage' halfcrowns of 1816, and it operated at a far greater speed than the old type of mill and screw presses and achieved a greater sharpness of design.

The very latest coining presses now operating at the Royal Mint at Llantrisant in South Wales, are capable of striking at a rate of up to 800 coins a minute.

Condition

One of the more difficult problems for the beginner is to assess accurately the condition of a coin. A common fault among collectors is to overgrade and, consequently, to overvalue their coins.

Most dealers will gladly spare a few minutes to help new collectors. Many dealers issue price lists with illustrations, enabling collectors to see exactly what the coins look like and how they have been graded.

Coins cannot always be graded according to precise rules. Hammered coins often look weak or worn on the high parts of the portrait and the tops of the letters; this can be due to weak striking or worn dies and is not always attributable to wear through long use in circulation. Milled coins usually leave the Mint sharply struck so that genuine wear is easier to detect. However a x5 or x10 magnifying glass is essential, especially when grading coins of Edward VII and George V where the relief is very low on the portraits and some skill is required to distinguish between an uncirculated coin and one in EF condition.

The condition or grade of preservation of a coin is usually of greater importance than its rarity. By this we mean that a common coin in superb condition is often more desirable and more highly priced than a rarity in poor condition. Coins that have been pierced or mounted as a piece of jewellery generally have little interest to collectors.

One must also be on the lookout for coins that have been 'plugged', i.e. that have been pierced at some time and have had the hole filled in, sometimes with the missing design or letters re-engraved.

Badly cleaned coins will often display a complexity of fine interlaced lines and such coins have a greatly reduced value. It is also known for coins to be tooled or re-engraved on the high parts of the hair, in order to 'increase' the grade of coin and its value. In general it is better to have a slightly more worn coin than a better example with such damage.

Cleaning coins

Speaking generally, *do not* clean coins. More coins are ruined by injudicious cleaning than through any other cause, and a badly cleaned coin loses much of its value. A nicely toned piece is usually considered desirable. Really dirty gold and silver can, however, be carefully washed in soap and water. Copper coins should never be cleaned or washed, they may be lightly brushed with a brush that is not too harsh.

Buying and selling coins

Exchanging coins with other collectors, searching around the antique shops, telling your relatives and friends that you are interested in coins, or even trying to find your own with a metal detector, are all ways of adding to your collection. However, the time will come when the serious collector needs to acquire specific coins or requires advice on the authenticity or value of a coin.

At this point an expert is needed, and the services of a reputable coin dealer are necessary. There are now a large number of coin dealers in the UK, many of whom belong to the B.N.T.A. (The British Numismatic Trade Association) or the I.A.P.N. (The International Association of Professional Numismatists) and a glance through the 'yellow pages' under 'coin dealer' or 'numismatist' will often provide local information. Many dealers publish their own lists of coins. Studying these lists is a good way for a collector to learn about coins and to classify and catalogue their own collections.

The Standard Catalogue of Coins of England and the UK has been published since 1929. It serves as a price guide for all coin collectors. Spink also publish books on many aspects of English, Greek, Roman and Byzantine coins and on British tokens which serve as a valuable source of information for coin collectors. Our books are available directly from Spink or through reputable booksellers. Many branches of W. H. Smith, and other High Street booksellers, stock copies of *The Standard Catalogue*.

Numismatic Clubs and Societies

There are well over one hundred numismatic societies and clubs in the British Isles. For details of how to contact them see page 466. Joining one is the best way to meet fellow enthusiasts, learn about your coins and other series and acquire coins in a friendly and informative way.

Useful suggestions

Security and insurance. The careful collector should not keep valuable coins at home unless they are insured and have adequate protection. Local police and insurance companies will give advice on what precautions may be necessary.

Most insurance companies will accept a valuation based on *The Standard Catalogue*. It is usually possible to have the amount added to a householder's contents policy but particularly valuable individual coins may have to be separately listed. A 'Fire, Burglary and Theft' policy will cover loss only from the insured's address, but an 'All Risks' policy will usually cover accidental damage and loss anywhere within the U.K.

For coins deposited with a bank or placed in a safe-deposit box a lower insurance premium is usually payable.

Keeping a record. All collectors are advised to have an up-to-date record of their collection and, if possible, photographs of the more important and more easily identifiable coins. This should be kept in a separate place from the collection so that a list and photographs can be given to the police should loss occur. Note the price paid, from whom purchased, the date of acquisition and the condition of the coin.

Storage and handling. New collectors should get into the habit of handling coins by the edge. This is especially important as far as highly polished proof coins are concerned.

Collectors may initially keep their coins in paper or plastic envelopes housed in boxes, albums or special containers. Many collectors will eventually wish to own a hardwood coin cabinet in which the collection can be properly arranged and displayed. If a home-made cabinet is being constructed avoid using oak and cedar wood; mahogany, walnut and rosewood are ideal. It is important that coins are not kept in a humid atmosphere; especial care must be taken with copper and bronze coins which are very susceptible to damp or condensation which may result in a green verdigris forming on them.

From beginner to numismatist

The new collector can best advance to becoming an experienced numismatist by examining as many coins as possible, noting their distinctive features and by learning to use the many books of reference that are available. It will be an advantage to join a local numismatic society, as this will provide an opportunity for meeting other enthusiasts and obtaining advice from more experienced collectors. Most societies have a varied programme of lectures, exhibitions and occasional auctions of members' duplicates.

Those who become members of one or both of the national societies, the Royal Numismatic Society and the British Numismatic Society, receive an annual journal containing authoritative papers and have access to the societies' library and programme of lectures.

Many museums have coin collections available for study, although they may not always be displayed, and a number of museum curators are qualified numismatists.

ABBREVIATIONS

Archb.	Archbishop
Æ	bronze
Æ	silver
AV	gold
Bp.	Bishop
BV	bullion value
cuir.	cuirassed
d.	penny, pence
diad.	diademed
dr.	draped
ex.	exergue
grs.	grains
hd.	head
i.c.	inner circle
illus.	illustration
l.	left
laur.	laureate
mm.	*mintmark*
mon.	monogram
O., obv.	obverse
p.	new penny, pence
pl	plume
quat.	quatrefoil
qtr.	quarter
rad.	radiate
R., *rev.*	reverse
r.	right
s.	shillings
trun.	truncation
var.	variety
wt.	weight

SOME NUMISMATIC TERMS EXPLAINED

Obverse	That side of the coin which normally shows the monarch's head or name.
Reverse	The side opposite to the obverse, the 'Tails'.
Blank	The coin as a blank piece of metal, i.e. before it is struck.
Flan	The whole piece of metal after striking.
Type	The main, central design.
Legend	The inscription. Coins lacking a legend are called 'mute' or anepigraphic.
Field	That flat part of the coin between the main design and the inscription or edge.
Exergue	That part of the coin below the main design, usually separated by a horizontal line, and normally occupied by the date.
Die	The block of metal, with design cut into it, which actually impresses the coin blank with the design.
Die variety	Coin showing slight variation of design.
Mule	A coin with the current type on one side and the previous (and usually obsolete) type on the other side, or a piece struck from two dies that are not normally used together.
Graining or reeding	The crenellations around the edge of the coin, commonly known as 'milling'.
Proof	Carefully struck coin from special dies with a mirror-like or matt surface. (In this country 'Proof' is *not* a term used to describe the state of preservation, but the method of striking.)
Hammered	Refers to the old craft method of striking a coin between dies hammered by hand.
Milled	Coins struck by dies worked in a coining press. The presses were hand powered from 1560-1800, powered by steam from 1790 and by electricity from 1895.

MARKET TRENDS

A refreshing breeze of optimism is blowing through the English coin market. For the first time for almost a generation collectors feel confident and all the signs of an established bull market are in place. This confidence is not misplaced.

Last year Market Trends set out in broad terms the price movements for English coins over the last century. In part it will bear restating. In the early 1950's a collectors' boom began and, gathering momentum, continued for twenty five years. Average prices rose fortyfold. In the late 1970's this market was supplanted by an investor boom which drove out the collectors and peaked in 1980. Prices, left unsupported by demand, fell for a decade to a half or even to a third of their 1980 peak. In the early 1990's a nucleus of established and new collectors, attracted by historically low prices, finally stabilized the market. Prices have now been rising, with increasing confidence, for five years.

Predicting the future is more an art than a science. Even a well set market can be blown off course, ironically often by too much demand rather than too little. It is often overlooked how small the market in English coins is. The London turnover is no more than a few million pounds a year. The 2002 VF catalogue value of every priced hammered gold coin including the Henry III gold penny amounts to £1,347,000 (2001 £1,231,000). Such a collection would take a lifetime to assemble yet the price would purchase only a few square inches of an old master drawing. Too much money coming in can destroy the equilibrium. Fortunately there is no sign of this at the moment.

In 2001 the market passed two benchmarks. Individual price rises in the Standard Catalogue outnumbered falls by more than ten to one. The market is far from monolithic. Individual series move to different tempi and are often in different stages of their cycle. In even the strongest market some individual prices will be falling. However it is many years since such a high proportion of prices have been moving in the same direction. More significantly the average catalogue value has now risen through the record highs set in 1980. In the July 2001 sale of the Manville collection of Commonwealth coins, there was an EF pattern 1651 halfcrown by Blondeau, lot 21. This coin has appeared at auction four times in the last twenty years, on each occasion in a named Spink sale. In 1983 (Agricola) it sold for £2,835, in 1989 (Selig) for £1,540, in 1999 (Hughes) for £2,200, in 2001 (Manville) for £3,450. Many examples of this price pattern could be quoted. It is a pattern which underlies, more or less amplified, most of the price movements in the Standard Catalogue whether they be gold or silver, hammered or milled.

In almost any other field such a performance would be derisory. In the last two decades of the 20th century the FTSE All share rose from 230 to 3,242, an appreciation of fourteen fold. The UK house price index has performed almost as well. The psychological importance of breaking through such a long established price ceiling, however, is considerable. Once breached there is no limit to immediate progress and the expectation is that the rising trend will continue. A similar mood prevailed in the mid 1950's. Prices had then recovered to the levels set in the 1949 Korean war boom. They went on to triple in the next five years.

The Blondeau halfcrown has appreciated by 50% over the last two years. Other pieces have done as well. An Edward VI 1552 halfcrown which realised £2,185 in the Shuttlewood collection in March 2001, lot 267, cost only £1,325 when purchased in the Ashby sale in July 2000. However genuine rises of this magnitude are unusual. The overall catalogue price increase in VF grade between 2001 and 2002 is around 10%, though this conceals individual increases of up to 40% and some actual falls.

The pattern of increases is most interesting. As a rule the more expensive coins have considerably outperformed the less expensive. Coins with a VF price of under £100 have risen, on average, by only 2.5%, while those with a VF price of over £1,000 have risen, on average, by over 10%. This is exactly the movement expected early in a bull market. As confidence returns the better material is suddenly seen as historically cheap. Collectors are prepared to 'reach' to obtain the more desirable pieces, partly because they expect the cost to rise when the next piece becomes available. This expectation is self fulfilling and EF prices outperform VF, VF outperform F. Desirable rarities outperform more readily available types.

If the Catalogue listed a price for hammered coins in EF grade it would show a rather more marked increase than for VF, possibly 25%. EF hammered coins are not priced as, for the vast majority, a standard EF example does not exist in the way that it does for milled coins. A coin graded EF in the sense of having no wear from circulation can often be ill-struck and worth less than a pleasing VF example. As a rough rule of thumb, and allowing for exceptions, the EF price will be the same multiple of the VF price as the VF is of the F.

It is clearly important when buying better grade material to check the true condition. There are many more or less apparent defects – mis-striking, cleaning, repairs, mounting etc. which have a detrimental effect on values and should be taken into account. On the other hand the experienced eye will pick out a 'desirable' specimen. In the Manville Commonwealth collection there were two anchor initial mark halfcrowns, 1658 and 1660, of not dissimilar rarity, both graded VF and estimated £1,200-1,500. The 1658, a full round specimen, sold for £3,220. The 1660, slightly double-struck and on a smaller flan, sold for £1,200. The premium is large but the first is undoubtedly the more pleasing.

There is also a considerable variation in price movements across the coinage. In the last year Celtic coins have risen overall by about 7%. In many ways Celtic coins reflect the international market in ancient coins where rarities in premium condition are fetching record prices but where the run-of-the-mill material is difficult to sell. It has been pointed out that under S.395 the 2001 footnote read 'chipped or cracked specimens are often encountered and are worthless', this should read 'worth less', but there is a germ of truth in the original. This is a market where quality and artistic style is of particular importance. The sceat and styca series is quiet. A very strong market a few years ago, it has run out of steam. The coins are physically small and tend not to be attractive in the lower grades. Early Saxon pennies have now begun to recover after a long decline and are up 5% overall. This is very much a two tier market. Good old provenanced material is in strong demand and increasingly difficult to obtain. Recent finds, typically damaged and porous specimens, are not wanted. Late Saxon is stable.

Norman coins are in an interesting position, up 12.5% on the year. For a long time the huge Conte collection has overhung the market. This has now been purchased almost en bloc by the Fitzwilliam Museum, Cambridge. It is always sad to see such large group permanently taken off the market, though in this case it has gone to a good home. It may not yet be generally realised how much this has depleted the body of material available to collectors.

Hammered gold coins continue to be a strong market and some of the largest rises in the Catalogue are in this field, though the overall rise in VF is only 10%. In part this is because the catalogue price of some of the heavier pieces was not reduced as far as it might have been in the recession and is only now begining to rise. Little hammered gold is coming onto the market which suggests that collectors feel that it is undervalued.

In the mediaeval, Tudor and Stuart series the denomination is as important as the series. Shillings have performed best, rising on average by almost 20%, both halfcrowns and groats have risen by 12.5%. These are all denominations with specialist denomination collectors. Sixpences have generally risen by 10%, and crowns by only 5%. Crowns have been neglected as a popular series for some time. The small series of Charles I silver pounds and halfpounds have actually fallen slightly in value. These are not as rare as is sometimes believed and they were pushed up very sharply a couple of years ago. Charles I provincial issues generally continue to appreciate, up 10% in a year, as are siege pieces from an already high historical level.

Milled gold has benefitted from an overflow of unsatisfied demand for hammered gold. Five Guineas, which are still far below their highs, are at last in demand, particularly in the higher grades. They suffer from being apparently readily available but once the supply begins to diminish, as has happened in the case of triple unites, it will release unexpected demand.

Milled silver, copper and bronze is flat in the lower grades, F and VF, but strong in EF. This very much reflects the trend in the huge market for USA coins. These series have often swung between emphasis on quality and rarity. Currently the early rarities in lower, but collectable, condition look quite attractive.

Movements in the English coin market are not coupled to the general state of the economy. If anything it moves contra-cyclically. A very small amount of extra money from the overall economy finding its home in coins has a quite disproportionate impact on values. It is more a matter of confidence and, as the performance at recent auction shows, Manville selling for 17% over high estimate, Shuttlewood for 28% over high estimate, that confidence has now returned.

CELTIC COINAGE

The Celtic or Ancient British issues are amongst the most interesting and varied of all British coins. They are our earliest coins and are the product of a society that left no historical sources of its own. It is therefore often difficult to be specific about for whom, when or where they were produced. Despite only being used for approximately a hundred and fifty years they do provide a rich variety of designs and types in gold, silver and bronze. Collectors looking for a theme to concentrate on may find the coins of one tribe, an individual ruler or a particular phase in the coinage interesting.

Grading Celtic Coins

The majority of Celtic coins were struck by hand, sometimes resulting in a loss of definition through weak striking. In addition, the design on the dies was often bigger than the blank flan employed, resulting in the loss of some of the design. Coins with full legends are generally more valuable than examples with incomplete legends. Bronze coins in good condition (VF or better) and especially toned examples attract a premium. Factors that detract from a coins value are chips, scratches and verdigris on bronze coins. It is important to take into account these factors as well as the amount of wear on a coin when assessing its grade.

Cunobelin Bronze Unit — Epatticus Silver Unit — Cunobelin Gold Stater

Fine

Very Fine

Plated Coins

Plated gold staters, quarter staters and silver units are recorded for many known types. They vary considerably in the quality of their production and are usually priced at around a quarter of the substantive types value. Their exact purpose or relation to the type they copy is not fully understood.

References and Select Bibliography.

M Mack, R.P. (1975) 3rd edition, The Coinage of Ancient Britain.
V Van Arsdell, R.D. (1989), Celtic Coinage of Britain.
BMC Hobbs, R. (1996), British Iron Age Coins in the British Museum.

de Jersey, P. (1996), Celtic Coinage in Britain. *A good general introduction to the series.*
Nash, D. (1987), Coinage in the Celtic World. *Sets the coinage in its social context.*

The layout of the following list is derived from the standard works by Mack, Van Arsdell and the British Museum Catalogue by Richard Hobbs. References are made to these works where possible, in the case of the last work it should be noted that the British Museum collection is not exhaustive, and therefore should not be used to assess the rarity of a coin. More detailed information than that given here can be gained from these works.

IMPORTED COINAGE

The earliest coins to circulate in Britain were made in northern Gaul (Belgica) and imported into the south-east of England from around 150 B.C. onwards. They were principally the product of two tribal groups in this region, the Ambiani and Suessiones. In Britain these types are known as Gallo-Belgic A to F. The first type Gallo-Belgic A is ultimately derived from the Macedonian gold staters (M) of Philip II (359-336 B.C.)

The reasons why they were imported are not fully understood. However, the context for their importation is one of close social, political and economic ties between Britain and Gaul. Within this cross-channel relationship they undoubtedly had various functions, such as payment for military service or mercenaries, in exchanges between the elite of each society: in cementing alliances for example, or as gifts in a system of exchange.

Numbers in brackets following each entry refer to numbers employed in previous editions of this catalogue.

GALLO-BELGIC ISSUES

GOLD

M 2 3 5 7

From *c.*150 B.C. – *c.*50 B.C.

No.		*F* £	*VF* £
1	**Stater.** Gallo-Belgic A. (Ambiani). Good copy of Macedonian stater, large flan. Laureate head of Apollo r. R. Horse r. *M. 1; V. 10. (1)*...........	450	1750
2	Similar, but head and horse l. *M. 3; V. 12. (1)*..	300	1250
3	B. (Ambiani). Somewhat similar to 1, but small flan and 'defaced' *obv.* die. R. Horse r. *M. 5; V. 30. (3)*...	225	600
4	— Similar, but with lyre between horse's legs. *M. 7; V. 33. (3)*	300	750
5	C. (Ambiani), *Stater.* Disintegrated Apollo head. R. horse. *M. 26; V. 44. (5)*..	200	525
6	**Quarter Stater.** Gallo-Belgic A. Similar to 1. *M. 2; V .15. (2)*..............	225	550
7	— Similar to 2. *M. 4; V. 20. (2)*..	200	525
8	B. Similar to 3. *M. 6; V. 35. (4)*	175	450
9	— Similar. R. Two horses l. with lyre between legs. *M. 8; V. 37. (4)*......	175	475
10	D. Portions of Apollo head R. A mixture of stars, crescents, pellets, zig-zag lines; often referred to as 'Geometric' types,(See also British 'O', S. 46.). *M. 37, 39, 41, 41a, 42; V. 65/7/9/146. (6)*	65	130

From *c.*50 B.C.

11

		F £	VF £
11	**Stater.** Gallo-Belgic E. (Ambiani). Blank obv. R. Disjointed curved horse r., pellet below, zig-zag in exergue. *M. 27; V. 52, 54. (7)*	130	235
12	F. (Suessiones). Devolved Apollo head r. R. Disjointed horse r. With triple-tail. *M. 34a; V. 85. (8)*	225	525
13	Xc. Blank except for VE monogram at edge of coin, R. S below horse r. *M. 82; V. 87-1. (9)*	250	600

BILLON

Armorican (Channel Islands and N.W. Gaul, *c.*75-50 B.C.)

14

15

14	**Stater.** Class I. Head r. R. Horse, boar below, remains of driver with Victory above, lash ends in or two loops, or 'gate'. *(12)*	35	100
15	— Class II. Head r. R. Horse, boar below, remains of Victory only, lash ends in small cross of four pellets. *(13)*	30	90
16	— Class III. Head r., anchor-shaped nose. R. Somewhat similar to Class I. *(14)*	30	95
17	— Class IV. Head r. R. Horse with reins, lyre shape below, driver holds vertical pole, lash ends in three prongs. *(15)*	35	100
18	— Class V. Head r. R. Similar to last, lash ends in long cross with four pellets. *(16)*	40	110
19	— Class VI. Head r. R. Horse, boar below, lash ends in 'ladder' *(17)*	45	125
20	**Quarter Stater.** Similar types to above. *(18)*	50	125

20

CELTIC COINS STRUCK IN BRITAIN

Coin production in Britain began at the very end of the second century B.C. with the cast potin coinage of Kent (Nos 62-64). Inspired by Gaulish issues and ultimately derived from the potin coins of Massalia (Marseilles) in southern Gaul, the precise function and period of use of this coinage is not fully understood. The domestic production of gold coins started around 70 B.C., these issues are traditionally known as British A-P and are derived from imported Gallo-Belgic issues. Broadly contemporary with these issues are quarter staters, silver units, and bronze units. Recent work by John Sills has further enhanced our understanding of this crucial early period with the identification of two new British staters (Insular Belgic C or Kentish A and the Ingoldisthorpe type) and their related quarters and a Westerham quarter stater. The Insular Belgic C or Kentish A type derived from Gallo-Belgic C now becomes the first British stater.

EARLY UNINSCRIBED COINAGE

GOLD

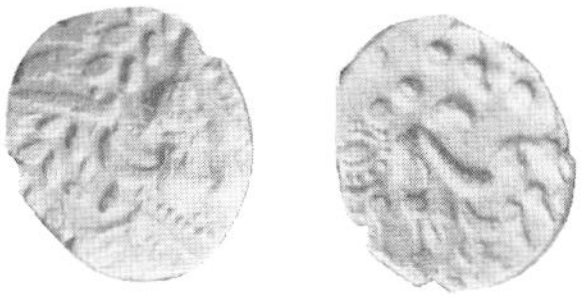

20A

20B

		F £	VF £
20A	**Stater.** Insuler Belgic C/Kentish A type. Devolved Apollo head r. R. Disjointed horse r, a rosette behind or in front, or both. *M. —; V. —; BMC —*	400	950
20B	Ingoldisthorpe type. Similar to last, as illustration. *M.—; V.—; BMC—..*	375	900

21

22

23

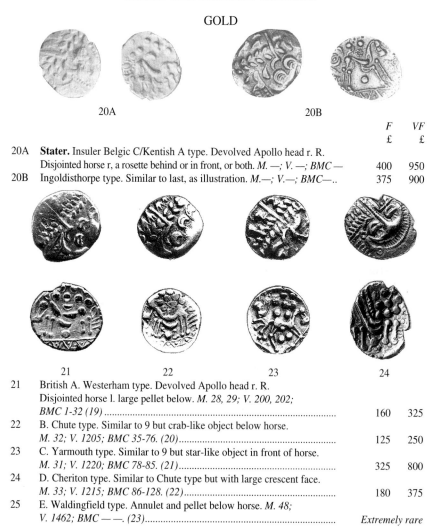

24

		F	VF
21	British A. Westerham type. Devolved Apollo head r. R. Disjointed horse l. large pellet below. *M. 28, 29; V. 200, 202; BMC 1-32 (19)*	160	325
22	B. Chute type. Similar to 9 but crab-like object below horse. *M. 32; V. 1205; BMC 35-76. (20)*	125	250
23	C. Yarmouth type. Similar to 9 but star-like object in front of horse. *M. 31; V. 1220; BMC 78-85. (21)*	325	800
24	D. Cheriton type. Similar to Chute type but with large crescent face. *M. 33; V. 1215; BMC 86-128. (22)*	180	375
25	E. Waldingfield type. Annulet and pellet below horse. *M. 48; V. 1462; BMC ——. (23)*	*Extremely rare*	

26

27

No.	Description	F £	VF £
26	F. Clacton type 1. Similar to Westerham type but rosette below horse. *M. 47; V. 1458; BMC 137-44. (24)*	250	625
27	G. Clacton type 2. Similar but horse r., with pellet, or pellet with two curved lines below. *M. 46, 46a; V. 30, 1455; BMC 145-79. (25)*	250	600

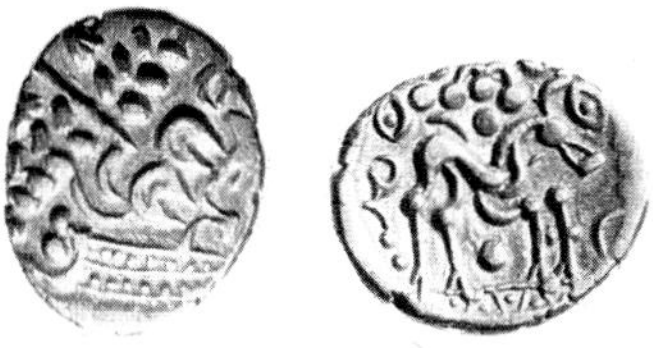

28

30

No.	Description	F £	VF £
28	H. North-East Coast type. Variety of 9, pellet or rosette below horse to r. *M. 50, 50a, 51, 51a; V. 800; BMC 182-191. (26)*	175	385
29	I. — Similar, horse l., pellet, rosette or star with curved rays below. *M. 52-57; V. 804, 805, 807; BMC 193-211. (27)*	160	350
30	J. Norfolk Wolf type. R. Crude wolf to r. *M. 49; V. 610-1; BMC 212-16. (28)*	200	475
31	— Similar but wolf to l. Usually base gold. *M. 49a/b; V. 610-2/3; BMC 217-78. (28A)*	125	275
32	L. Whaddon Chase type. R. Spirited horse r. of new style, various symbols below. *M. 133-138a, 139a; V. 1470-6; 1485/7/9/93; BMC 279-343. (31)*	175	385
33	— Plain. R. Horse r. With ring ornament below or behind. *M. 140-143; V. 1498-1505; BMC 344-46. (32)*	185	425
34	Lx. NorthThames group. Blank apart from reversed SS. R. Similar to last. *M. 146; V. 1509; BMC 350. (33)*	750	2000
35	Lz. Weald group. Blank with some traces of Apollo head. R. Horse r., large wheel ornament below. *M. 144-145; V. 1507; BMC 347-49. (36)*	350	900

36

No.	Description	F £	VF £
36	Ma. Wonersh type. Crossed wreath design with crescents back to back in centre. R. Spiral above horse, wheel below. *M. 148; V. 1520; BMC 351-56. (37)*	325	850

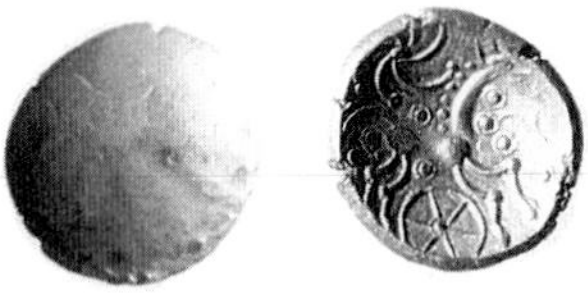

37

38

		F £	VF £
37	Mb. Savernake Forest type. Similar but *obv.* plain or almost blank. *M. 62; V. 1526; BMC 361-64*	175	425
38	Qa. British 'Remic' type. Crude laureate head. R. Triple-tailed horse, wheel below. *M. 58, 60, 61; V. 210-124; BMC 445-58. (41)*	185	450
39	Qb. — Similar, but *obv.* blank. *M. 59; V. 216; BMC 461-76. (42)*	150	300
39A	**Quarter Stater.** Insuler Belgic C/Kentish A type. Similar to Gallo-Belgic D, but with rosette in field on obverse. *M. —; V.—; BMC—*	165	450
39B	Ingoldisthorpe type. Similar to last but with sperm-like objects in field. *M.—; V.—; BMC—*	175	475
39C	British A. Westerham type. Similar to last but of cruder style, or with L-shapes in field on rev. *M.—; V.—; BMC—*	150	400
40	British D. Cheriton type. Similar to Stater, large crescent face. R. Cross motif with pellets. *M. —; V. 143 var; BMC 129-136*	135	325
41	F/G. Clacton type. Plain, traces of pattern. R. Ornamental cross with pellets. *M. 35; V. 1460; BMC 180-1. (43A)*	135	325
42	H. Crescent design and pellets. R. Horse r. *M. —; V. —; BMC 192*	110	275
43	Lx. N.Thames group. Floral pattern on wreath. R. Horse l. or r. *M. 76; V. 234; BMC 365-370. (44)*	135	300

43

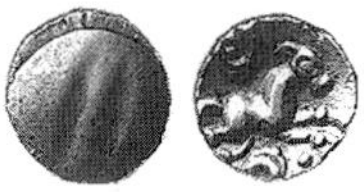

44

45

44	Ly. N.Kent group. Blank. R. Horse l. or r. *M. 78; V. 158; BMC 371-3. (45)*	100	250
45	Lz. Weald group. Spiral design on wreath. R. Horse l. or r. *M. 77; V. 250; BMC 548-50. (46)*	100	250

46

47

48

46	O. Geometric type. Unintelligible patterns (some blank on obv.). *M. 40, 43-45; V. 143, 1225/27/29; BMC 410-32. (49)*	70	150
47	P.Trophy type. Blank. R. Trophy design. *M. 36, 38; V. 145-7; BMC 435-44. (50)*	90	190
48	Qc.British 'Remic' type. Head or wreath pattern. R. Triple-tailed horse, l. or r. *M. 63-67; 69-75; V. 220-32, 36, 42-6, 56; BMC 478-546. (51)*	100	225
49	Xd. Head l. of good style, horned serpent behind ear. R. Horse l. *M. 79; V. 78; BMC 571-575. (11)*	225	550

SILVER

Units (unless otherwise stated)

50

52

		F £	*VF* £
50	Lx. Head l.or r. R. Horse l. or r. *M. 280, 435, 436, 438, 441; V. 80, 1546, 1549, 1555; BMC 376-382. (53)*	70	200
51	— Head l. R. Stag r. with long horns. *M. 437; V. 1552; BMC 383-7. (54)*	95	275
52	— **Half Unit.** Two horses or two beasts. *M. 272, 442, 443, 445; V. 474, 1626, 1643, 1948; BMC 389-400. (55)*	100	280
53	Lz. Danebury group. Head r. with hair of long curves. R. Horse l., flower above. *M. 88; V. 262; BMC 580-82*	80	225

54

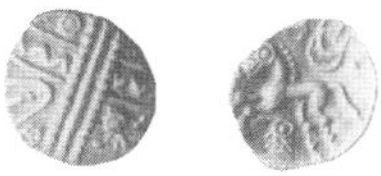

54A

		F £	*VF* £
54	— Helmeted head r. R. Horse r. wheel below. *M. 89; V. 264; BMC 583 -592. (58)*	90	250
54A	Cruciform pattern with ornaments in angles. R. Horse l., ear of corn between legs, crescents and pellets above, *M.—; V.—; BMC—*	90	250
55	— **Quarter Unit.** As last. *M. 90; V. 268; BMC 642-43. (59)*	50	135
56	— Head r. R. Horse r. star above, wheel below. *M. –; V. 280; BMC 595-601*	100	275
57	— Head l., pellet in ring in front. R. Horse l. or r. *M. –; V. 284; BMC 610-630*	65	200
58	— Serpent looking back. R. Horse l. *M. –; V. 286; BMC 631-33*	110	275
59	— **Quarter Unit.** Cross pattern. R. Two-tailed horse. *M. 119; V. 482; BMC 654-56. (56C). (Formerly attributed to Verica)*	50	140

BRONZE

		F £	*VF* £
60	**Unit.** Lx. Winged horse l. R. Winged horse l. *M. 446; V. 1629; BMC 401 (78)*	80	325
61	Chichester Cock type. Head r. R. Head r. surmounted by cock. *M. –; V. — BMC 657-59*	45	175

POTIN
(Cast Copper/Tin alloy)

62

		F £	VF £
62	**Unit.** Thurrock type.Head l. R. Bull butting l. or r. *M. —; V. 1402-42; BMC 660-666. (84A)*	30	100

63

64

63	Class I type. Crude head. R. Lines representing bull *(Allen types A-L.) M. 9-22a; V. 104, 106, 108, 112, 114, 115, 117, 119, 120, 122, 123, 125, 127, 129, 131, 133; BMC 667-714. (83)*	30	75
64	Class II type. Smaller flan, large central pellet. *(Allen types M-P.) M. 23-25; V. 135-39; BMC 715-23. (84)*	35	80

CELTIC DYNASTIC AND LATER UNINSCRIBED COINAGE

From Julius Caesars expeditions to Britain in 55/54 B.C. and his conquest of Gaul in 52 B.C. to the Claudian invasion in 43 A.D., southern Britain was increasingly drawn into the orbit of the Roman world. This process is reflected not only in the coins but also in what we know about their issuers and the tribes they ruled. Latin legends begin to appear for the first time and increasingly accompany objects and designs drawn from the classical world. A lot of what we know about the Celtic tribes and their rulers, beyond just their names on coins, is drawn from contemporary and slightly later Roman historical sources. A great deal however is still uncertain and almost all attributions to either tribes or historically attested individuals have to be seen as tentative.

The coin producing tribes of Britain can be divided into two groups, those of the core and those of the periphery. The tribes of the core, the Atrebates/Regni, Trinovantes/Catuvellauni and Cantii, by virtue of their geographical location controlled contact with the Roman world. Unlike the tribes of the periphery they widely employed Latin legends, classical designs and used bronze coinage in addition to gold and silver.

Following the Roman invasion of 43 A.D. it is likely that some coinage continued to be produced for a short time. However in 61 A.D. with the death of King Prasutagus and the suppression of the Boudiccan revolt that followed, it is likely that Celtic coinage came to an end.

TRIBAL/MINT MAP

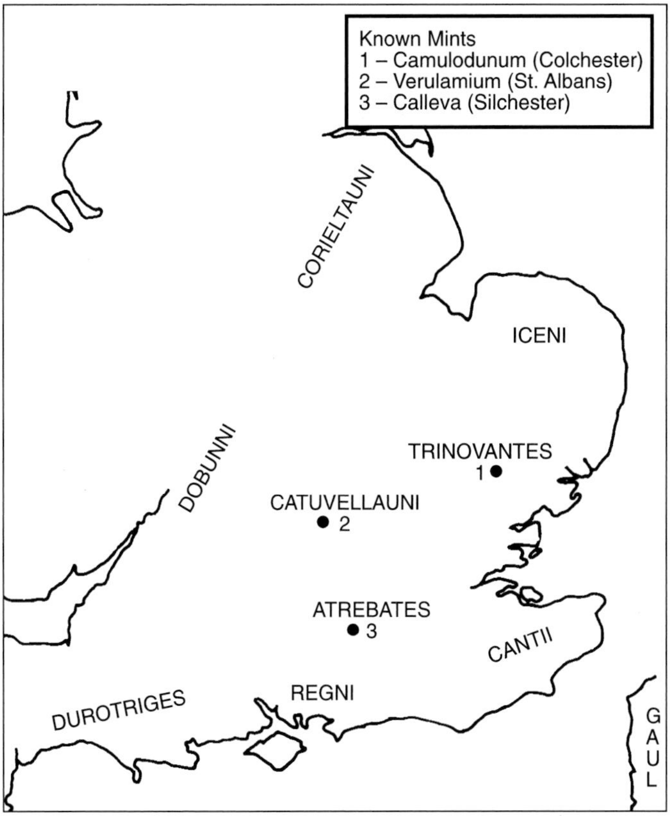

ATREBATES AND REGNI

The joint tribal area of these two groups corresponds roughly with Berkshire and Sussex and parts of northern and eastern Hampshire. The Atrebatic portion being in the north of this region with its main centre at Calleva (Silchester). The Regni occupying the southern part of the region centred around Chichester.

COMMIUS

(Mid to Late 1st Century B.C.)

The first inscribed staters to appear in Britain, closely resemble British Q staters (no.38) and are inscribed 'COMMIOS'. Staters and silver units with an inscribed 'E' are also thought to be related. Traditionally this Commius was thought to be the Gaulish chieftain who Caesar refers to in De Bello Gallico, as firstly serving him in his expeditions to Britain and finally fleeing to Britain c.50 B.C. This attribution does however present chronological problems, and the appearance of a few early staters reading 'COM COMMIOS' suggests that the Commius who issued coins is more likely to have been the son of Caesar's Commius.

GOLD

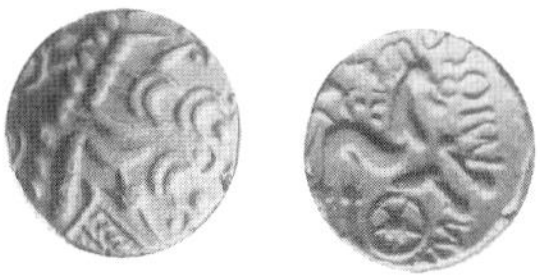

65

		F £	*VF* £
65	**Stater.** Devolved Apollo head r. R. COMMIOS around triple tailed horse r., wheel below. *M. 92; V. 350; BMC 724-29. (85)*	325	900

66

67

66	Similar, but 'E' symbol above horse instead of legend. *M. —;V. 352. BMC 730*	375	950
67	**Quarter Stater.** Blank except for digamma. R. Horse l. *M. 83; V. 353-5; BMC —. (10)*	125	300

SILVER

69

69	**Unit.** Head l. R. Horse l. Mostly with 'E' symbol above. *M. —;V. 355; BMC 731-58. (57)*	40	125

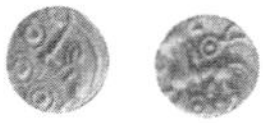

70

		F £	VF £
70	**Minim.** Similar to Unit. *M. —; V. 358-5; BMC 759-60*	30	95

TINCOMARUS or TINCOMMIUS

(Late 1st Century B.C. – Early 1st Century A.D.)

Successor to Commius and on his coins styled as 'COM.F' (son of Commius). Early coins of the reign like his predecessors are very obiviously Celtic in their style. However later coins exhibit an increasing tendancy towards Roman designs. Indeed Tincommius is recorded as a supliant king of the Roman emperor Augustus (Res Gestae, xxxii), finally fleeing to Rome in the early 1st century A.D. The discovery of the Alton Hoard in 1996 brought to light gold staters with the new legend TINCOMARVS.

GOLD

71

73

		F £	VF £
71	**Stater.** *Celtic style.* Devolved Apollo head r. R. TINC COMM. F. around horse. *M. 93; V. 362; BMC —. (86)*	425	1100
72	Similar but legend reads TINCOMARVS. *M. 94; V. 363; BMC 761-765. (86)*	375	950
73	**Quarter Stater.** Spiral with pellet centre. R. Horse r. T above. *M. 81; V. 366; BMC 781-797. (46)*	85	210

74

75

		F £	VF £
74	TINCOM, zig-zag ornament below. R. Horse l. *M. 95; V. 365; BMC 798-810. (87)*	160	425
75	**Stater.** *Classical style.* TINC(O) on a sunk tablet. R. Horseman with javelin r. often with CF in field. *M. 96-98; V. 375-76; BMC 765-769. (88)*	235	575

76

77

		F £	VF £
76	COM.(F). on a sunk tablet. R. Horseman with javelin r. TIN in field *M. 100; V. 385; BMC 770-774. (88)*..	225	550
77	**Quarter Stater.** TINC on a tablet, C above, A or B below. R. Winged head (Medusa?) facing. *M. 97; V. 378; BMC 811-826. (89)*....................	200	500
78	TIN on tablet. R. Boar l. *M. 99; V. 379; BMC 827-837. (90)*..................	100	240

79

83

		F £	VF £
79	COMF on tablet. R. Horse r. TIN around. *M. 101; V. 387; BMC 838-841. (90)*..	110	250
80	— R. Horse l. TIC around. *M. 102; V. 388; BMC 842-851. (90)*............	110	250
81	COM on tablet. R. Horse l. T above. *M. 103; V. 389; BMC 852-3. (90)*.	125	275
82	COMF on tablet. R. Horse r. TINC around. *M. 104; V. 390; BMC 854-879. (90)*..	90	225

SILVER

		F £	VF £
83	**Unit.** Laureate head r. TINCOM in front, V behind. R. Eagle stg. on snake. *M. 105; V. 397; BMC 880-905. (91)*..	40	120
84	Laureate head l. R. Bull l. TINC around. *M. 106; V. 396; BMC 906-910. (91A)*..	45	140
85	Laureate head r. R. Bull r. TIN(C) around. *M. —; V. 381; BMC 911-925. (92B)*..	35	100
86	Facing head. R. Bull l. TINC around. *M. —; V. 370; BMC 926-29 (92)*..	45	140

87

91

		F £	VF £
87	TINC in angles of cross, R. Lion l. *M. —; V. 372; BMC 930-45. (93B)*..	40	135
88	Star. R. Boy riding dolphin r. TINC in field. *M. —; V. 371; BMC 946-977. (93C)*..	40	110
89	TINC around pellet. R. Lion l. *M. 106a; V. 382; BMC 978-80. (93)*.......	45	150
90	Head l. TINCOMMIVS in front. R. Horse l. lyre above. *M. 131b; V. 473; BMC —. (92C) (Formerly attributed to Verica)*..................................	45	140
91	**Minim.** CF within two interlinked squares. R. Boar? r. TINC. *M. 118; V. 383-1; BMC 981-82. (94)*..	35	110
92	As above but CO. R. Bull r. TI. *M. —; V. 383-5; BMC —*.....................	40	125

		F £	VF £
93	C inside box, box above and below. R. Bull r. TIN. *M. —; V. 383-7; BMC 983*	40	135
94	Cross, T? in angles. R. uncertain object. *M. 120; V. 483; BMC 984-85. (Formerly attributed to Verica)*	40	120

EPPILLUS

(Later 1st Century B.C. – Early 1st Century A.D.)

His reign is likely to have coincided with that of Tincommius's, who also claimed to be a son of Commius. Two coinages appear in his name, one for Kent and one minted at Calleva (Silchester, Hants.) in the northern part of the territory of the Atrebates and Regni. The coins of Calleva conform to the southern denominational structure of gold and silver with fractions of each, whilst the Kentish series is distinctly tri-metallic, replacing the silver minim with bronze. A joint coinage was issued by Eppillus and Verica. It is not understood if Eppillus held both territories simultaneously.

COINAGE STRUCK AT CALLEVA

GOLD

95 **Stater.** Devolved Apollo head r. R. EPPI COMMI F around horse. *M. —; V. 405; BMC —* ...... *Extremely rare*

96

		F £	VF £
96	**Quarter Stater.** CALLEV, star above and below. R. Hound r. EPPI. *M. 107; V. 407-08; BMC 986-1005. (95)*	90	200

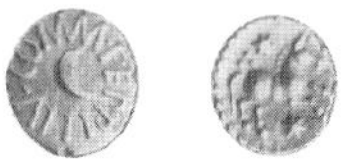

97

98

		F £	VF £
97	COMM F EPPILV, around crescent. R. Horse r. *M. —; V. 409; BMC 1006-1009. (95A)*	120	300
98	EPPI COMF in two lines. R. Winged horse r. *M. 302; V. 435; BMC 1010-15. (129)*	100	250

SILVER

99

100

		F £	VF £
99	**Unit.** Crescent REX CALLE above and below. R. Eagle r. EPP. *M. 108; V .415. BMC 1016-1060. (96)*	35	110
100	Bearded hd. r. in wreath. R. Boar r. EPPI(L) F CO(M). *M. —; V. 416; BMC 1061-87. (96A)*	40	125

		F £	VF £
101	Bearded hd. in pellet border. R. Lion r. EPP COMF. *M. 305; V. 417; BMC 1088-1115. (131)*	35	115
102	**Minim.** Floral cross. R. Eagle r. EPPI. *M. —; V. 420; BMC 1116-17*	40	125
103	Spiral and pellets. R. Ram r. EPP. *M. —; V. 421; BMC 1118-20. (96C)*	45	145
104	Bulls head facing. R. Ram r. EPP. *M. —; V. 422; BMC 1121-24. (96D)*	50	150
105	Wreath pattern. R. Boar r. EPP. *M. —; V. 423; BMC —*	60	175
106	Crescent cross. R. Hand holding trident. *M. —; V. 487; BMC —. (111C)*	60	175

KENTISH TYPES

GOLD

		F £	VF £
107	**Stater.** COMF within wreath. R. Horseman l. EPPILLVS above. *M. 300; V. 430; BMC 1125-26. (127)*	*Extremely rare*	

108

107

		F £	VF £
108	Victory holding wreath l., within wreath. R. Horseman r. holding carnyx, F EPPI COM below. *M. 301; V. 431; BMC 1127-28. (128)*	*Extremely rare*	
109	**Quarter Stater.** Crossed wreaths, EPPI in angles. R. Horse l. *M. 303; V. 436; BMC 1129. (130)*	225	625
110	COMF in pellet border. R. Horse r. EPPI. *M. 304; V. 437; BMC 1130-31. (130)*	200	475

SILVER

		F £	VF £
111	**Unit.** Head l. EPPIL in field. R. Horseman holding carnyx, EPPILL. *M. 306; V. 441; BMC 1132. (131)*	125	350

BRONZE

		F £	VF £
112	**Unit.** Bow cross, EPPI COMF around. R. Eagle facing. *M. 309; V. 450; BMC 1137-38. (134)*	65	275
113	Bull r., EPPI COF around. R. eagle facing. *M. 310; V. 451; BMC 1139-41. (134)*	65	275
114	Head l., EPPI in front. R. Victory l. holding wreath and standard. *M. 311; V. 452; BMC 1142. (133)*	80	325
115	Bearded hd. r., EPPI CF. R. Biga r. CF. *M. 312; V. 453; BMC —*	85	350

JOINT TYPES OF EPPILUS AND VERICA

SILVER

		F £	VF £
116	**Unit.** Head l. CO VIR in front. R. Victory, EP. *M. 307; V. 442; BMC 1133-34. (132)*	225	575

117

		F £	VF £
117	Head r. VIR CO in front. R. Capricorn l. EPPI COMF. *M. 308/a; V. 443; BMC 1135-36. (132)*	175	475

VERICA

(*c.*10.-*c.*40 A.D.)

The exact details of Verica's succession and relationship to Eppillus and Tincommius are not fully understood. However by c.10 A.D. it seems likely that Verica was the sole ruler of the southern region. His close contact with Rome, both political and economic, seen in the increasing use of classical designs on his coins, culminated in his flight to Rome in c.42 A.D. to seek assistance from Claudius.

GOLD

		F £	VF £
118	**Stater.** COM:F on tablet. R. Horseman r. holding spear, VIR below. *M. 109; V. 460; BMC 1143-44. (97)*	225	625
119	COM.F. on tablet, pellet in ring ornament above and below. R. Similar to last. *M. 121; 461; BMC 1146-53. (97)*	200	600

120

121

		F £	VF £
120	COM.F on tablet. R. Horseman r. holding spear, VIR above, REX below. *M. 121 var; V. 500; BMC 1155-58. (98)*	160	425
121	Vine-leaf dividing VI RI. R. Horseman r. with shield and spear. COF in field. *M. 125; V. 520-1; BMC 1159-73. (99)*	190	475
122	Similar, reads VE RI. *M. 125; V. 520-5/7; BMC 1174-76. (99)*	225	575
123	**Quarter Stater.** COMF on tablet. R. Horse l. VIR. *M. 111; V. 465; BMC 1177-78. (100)*	110	225

124

		F £	VF £
124	COMF on tablet, pellet in ring ornament above and below R. Horse r. VI. *M. 112; V. 466; BMC 1179-1206. (100)*	95	200

		F £	VF £
125	COMF on tablet, pellet border. R. Horse r. VI above. *M. 113; V. 467; BMC 1207-16. (100)*	95	200

126

128

		F £	VF £
126	COM FILI. in two lines, scroll in between. R. Horse r. VIR(I) above. *M. 114; V. 468; BMC 1217-22. (100)*	100	225
127	VERI COMF, crescent above, star below. R. Horse r. REX below. *M. 122; V. 501; BMC 1223-36. (101)*	100	225
128	VERI beneath vine-leaf. R. Horseman r. with sword and shield, FRX in field. *M. 124; V. 525; BMC 1237-38. (102)*	200	625
129	COM, horseman r. R. Seated figure, VERICA around. *M. 126; V. 526; BMC 1239. (103)*	250	750
130	Similar to last. R. Laureate bust r., VIRI in front. *M. 127; V. 527; BMC 1240. (103)*	250	750

SILVER

		F £	VF £
131	**Unit.** COMF, crescent and or pellet in ring above and below. R. Boar r. VI(RI) below. *M. 115; V. 470/72; BMC 1241-1331. (104)*	40	125

132

133

		F £	VF £
132	VERICA COMMI F around pellet in ring. R. Lion r. REX below. *M. 123; V. 505; BMC 1332-1359. (105)*	30	120
133	COMMI F, horseman with shield r. R. VERI CA, mounted warrior with spear r. *M. 128; V. 530; BMC 1360-92. (106)*	30	120

134

137

		F £	VF £
134	Two cornucopiae, COMMI F. R. Figure seated r. VERICA. *M. 129; V. 531; BMC 1393-1419. (107)*	30	90
135	Bust r. VIRI. R. Figure seated l. *M. 130; V. 532; BMC 1420. (108)*	75	275
136	Naked figure l. R. Laureate bust r., COMMI F. *M. 131; V. 533; BMC 1421-49. (108)*	35	120
137	VERICA REX, bull r. R. Figure stg. l., COMMI F. *M. —; V. 506; BMC 1450-84. (108B)*	35	125
138	COMF, in tablet and scroll. R. Eagle facing, VI RI. *M. —; V. 471; BMC 1485-1505. (104A)*	35	120

		F £	*VF* £
139	VIRIC across field,ornaments above and below. R. Pegasus r., star design below. *M. —; V. —; BMC —. (104B)*	65	250
140	Head r. Verica. R. COMMI F., eagle l. *M. 131A; V. 534; BMC —. (108A)*	75	275
141	**Minim.** COF in tablet, R. Facing head (Medusa?), VE below. *M. —; V. 384; BMC 1506.(94A). (Formerly attributed to Tincommius)*	45	165
142	Head r. R. Horse r., VIRICO. *M. 116; V. 480; BMC —. (109)*	35	125
143	Pellet and ring pattern. R. Lion r. VIR. *M. 120a/c; V. 484; BMC 1514-17. (109)*	30	100
144	VIRIC reversed. R. Boar r. *M. —; V. 485; BMC 1518*	30	95
145	Cross. R. Trident. *M. —; V. 486-1; BMC —-*	54	160
146	Uncertain. R. Boar r. *M. 120b; V. 510-1; BMC —. (109)*	30	95
147	Crescent cross. R. Boar r. *M. —; V. 510-5; BMC 1521-23. (109)*	35	110
148	VIR VAR in tablets. R. Winged horse r. CO. *M. 120d; V. 511; BMC 1507-12. (109)*	35	110

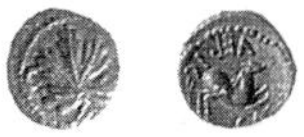

149

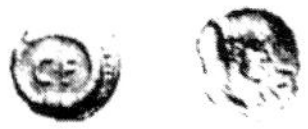

150

149	Vine-leaf, CFO. R. Horse r. VERI CA. *M. —; V. 550; BMC 1524-25*	35	125
150	CF in torc. R. Head r. VERIC. *M. 132; V. 551; BMC 1526-33. (111A)*	30	110
151	Altar, CF, R. Bulls head facing, VERICA. *M. 120e; V. 552; BMC 1534-37. (109)*	45	165
152	Temple, CF. R. Bull r, VER REX. *M. —; V. 553; BMC 1538-41*	30	95

153

154

153	Cornucopia, VER COM. R. Lion r. *M. —; V. 554; BMC 1542*	40	135
154	Two cornucopiae. R. Eagle l. *M. —; V. 555; BMC 1543-58*	25	75
155	Floral pattern, CF. R. Lion r. *M.—; V. 556; BMC 1559-63. (111E)*	35	125
156	Sphinx r., CF, R. dog curled up, VERI. *M. —; V. 557; BMC 1564-68. (109B)*	30	110
157	VERI. R. Urn, COMMI F. *M. —; V. 559; BMC —*	35	130
158	A in star. R. Bird r. *M. 316; V. 561; BMC 1569-71*	40	140
159	Urn, Rex. R. Eagle r., VERRICA COMMI F. *M. —; V. 563; BMC 1572-78. (109C)*	30	100
160	VIR inside tablet. R. Boars head r. *M. 117; V. 564; BMC 1579-81. (109A)*	30	110
161	Cross. R. bull l. *M. —; V. —; BMC 1582*	35	125
162	Boars head r., CF, R. Eagle, VE. *M. —; V. —; BMC 1583-86*	30	100

163

163	Head r, COMM IF., R. Sphinx, R VE. *M. —; V. —; BMC 1587-89*	35	125

		F £	*VF* £
164	A in tablet. R. Boar r. VI CO. *M. —; V. —; BMC 1590*	40	150
	The two following coins are possibly issues of Epatticus.		
165	Bull r. R. Eagle with snake l. *M. —; V. 512; BMC 2366-70*	30	110
166	Bust r. R. dog r. *M. —; V. 558; BMC 2371-74*	30	110

CANTII

The Cantii who gave their name to Kent, occupied a similar area to that of the modern county. Caesar considered this the most civilised part of Britain and the early production of potin units in Kent can be seen as an indicator of this. A number of Kentish rulers for whom we have coins, appear to be dynasts from the two neighbouring kingdoms, who were involved in struggles to acquire territory. Eppillus (see Atrebates and Regni) produced coins specifically for circulation in Kent and like those of Cunobelin they circulated widely.

EARLY UNINSCRIBED

GOLD

167	**Stater.** Ly. Blank. R. Horse l. numerous ring ornaments in field. *M. 293; V. 142; BMC 2472. (34)*	325	750
168	Blank. R. Horse r. numerous ornaments in field. *M. 294; V. 157; BMC— (34)*	300	725

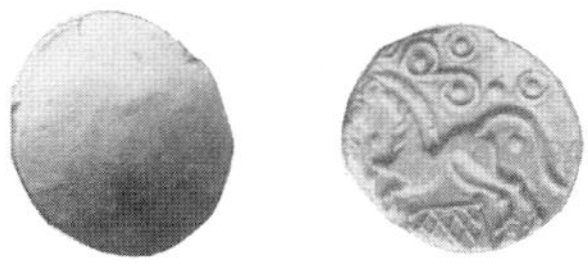

169

169	Lz. Blank. R. Horse l., box with cross hatching below. *M. 84, 292; V. 150, 144; BMC 2466-68. (35)*	375	950

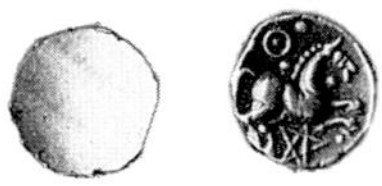

170

171

170	**Quarter Stater.** Ly. Blank. R. Horse r., pentagram below. *M. 285; V. 163; BMC 2473-74. (45)*	95	200
171	Blank. R. Horse r., 'V' shape above. *M. 284; V. 170; BMC 2475-77. (45)*	90	190
172	Lz. Blank. R. Horse l., 'V' shape above. *M. 85; V. 151; BMC 2469-70. (47)*	95	200

SILVER

173	**Unit.** Curved star. R. Horse r. Pentagram below. *M. 272a; V. 164; BMC—. (56)*	100	325
174	Serpent torc. R. Horse r., box with cross hatching below. *cf Mossop 8; BMC 2478*	125	475
175	**Half Unit.** Spiral of three arms. R. Horse l. *M. —; V. —; BMC 2479*	50	185

BRONZE

176 **Unit.** Various animal types, R. Various animal types. *M. 295-96, 316a-d; V. 154/167; BMC 2480-91. (80/141-44)* 60 225

DUBNOVELLAUNUS

(Late 1st Century B.C.)

Likely to be the same Dubnovellaunus recorded on coins in Essex (see Trinovantes / Catuvellauni). The two coinages share the same denominational structure and have some stylistic similarities. It has been suggested that Dubnovellaunus is the British king of that name mentioned along with Tincommius as a client king in the Res Gestae of the Roman emperor Augustus.

GOLD

177

		F £	*VF* £
177	**Stater.** Blank. R. Horse r., bucranium above, serpent like object below, DUBNOV[ELLAUNUS] or similar around. *M. 282; V. 169; BMC 2492-96. (118)*	185	425
178	— R. Horse r., but without bucranium and with wheel below. *M. 283; V. 176; BMC 2497-98. (118)*	275	650

SILVER

179 **Unit.** Winged animal r. R. Horse l., DVBNO. *M. 286; V. 171; BMC 2499-2501. (119)* 100 325

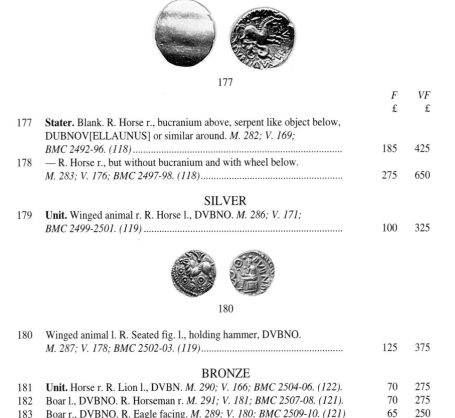

180

180 Winged animal l. R. Seated fig. l., holding hammer, DVBNO. *M. 287; V. 178; BMC 2502-03. (119)* 125 375

BRONZE

181 **Unit.** Horse r. R. Lion l., DVBN. *M. 290; V. 166; BMC 2504-06. (122).* 70 275

182 Boar l., DVBNO. R. Horseman r. *M. 291; V. 181; BMC 2507-08. (121).* 70 275

183 Boar r., DVBNO. R. Eagle facing. *M. 289; V. 180; BMC 2509-10. (121)* 65 250

VOSENOS

(Late 1st Century B.C./ Early 1st Century A.D.)

Little is known of this ruler who issued coins in a characteristically Kentish style similar to those of Dubnovellaunus.

GOLD

		F £	*VF* £
184	**Stater.** Blank. R. Horse l., bucranium above, serpent like object below., [VOSE]NOS. *M. 297; V. 184; BMC 2511-12. (123)*	*Extremely rare*	

185

185	**Quarter Stater.** Blank. R. Horse r., VOSI below. *M. 298; V. 185; BMC 2514-15. (124)*	325	900

SILVER

186	**Unit.** Horse and griffin. R. Horse r., retrograde legend. *M. 299a; V. 186; BMC —. (125)*	175	475

"SA" or "SAM"

(Late 1st Century B.C./ Early 1st Century A.D.)

An historically unattested individual whose coins are stylistically associated with those of Dubnovellaunus and Vosenos. His coins have been predominantly found in north Kent

SILVER

187	**Unit.** Head l., R. Horse l., SA below. *M. —; V. —; BMC —*	185	525

BRONZE

187A	**Unit.** Boar l., R. Horse l., SA below. *M. 299; V. 187; BMC 2516-19. (126)*	110	350

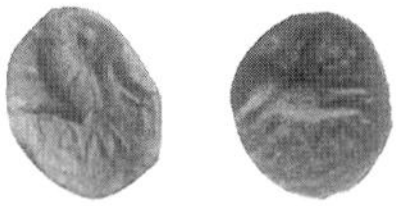

187B

187B	Horse l., SAM below. R. Horse l., SAM below. *M. —; V. —; BMC —* ...	120	375

AMMINUS

(Early 1st Century A.D.)

Issued a coinage stylistically distinct from other Kentish types and with strong affinities to those of Cunobelin. Indeed it has been suggested that he is the Adminius recorded by Suetonius, as a son of Cunobelin. The enigmatic legend DVN or DVNO may be an unknown mint site.

SILVER

188

		F £	*VF* £
188	**Unit.** Plant, AMMINIUS around. R. Winged horse r., DVN. *M. 313; V. 192; BMC 2522-23. (136)*	125	350

190

190	A in wreath. R. Capricorn r., S AM. *M. 314; V. 194; BMC 2520-21. (137)*	125	350

BRONZE

189

189	AM in wreath. R. Horse r., DVNO. *M. —; V. 193; BMC* ——.................	135	375
191	**Unit.** Head r. R. Hippocamp r., AM. *M. 315; V. 195; BMC 2524. (139).*	125	350

TRINOVANTES AND CATUVELLAUNI

Occupying the broad area of Essex, southern Suffolk, Bedfordshire, Buckinghamshire, Hertfordshire, parts of Oxfordshire, Cambridgeshire and Northamptonshire, they are likely to have been two separate tribes for most of their history. The Trinovantes were originally located in the eastern half of this area, with their main centre at Camulodunum (Colchester). The original Catuvellauni heartland being further west, with their main centre at Verulamium (St.Albans). The whole area eventually came under the control of Cunobelin at the end of the period.

TRINOVANTES

ADDEDOMAROS

(Late 1st Century B.C.)

Unknown to history he appears to have been a contemporary of Tasciovanus. The design of his staters is based on the Whaddon Chase type (No.32) which circulated widely in this region.

GOLD

200

		F £	*VF* £
200	**Stater.** Crossed wreath. R. Horse r., wheel below, AθθDIIDOM above. *M. 266; V. 1605; BMC 2390-94. (148)*	185	475

201

202

201	Six armed spiral. R. Horse r., cornucopia below, AθθDIIDOM above. *M. 267; V. 1620; BMC 2396-2404. (148)*	160	350
202	Two opposed crescents. R. Horse r., branch below, spiral or wheel above, AθθDIIDOM. *M. 268; V. 1635; BMC 2405-2415. (149)*	200	525
203	**Quarter Stater.** Circular flower pattern. R. Horse r. *M. 271; V. 1608; BMC 2416. (44)*	135	350
204	Cross shaped flower pattern. R. Horse r. *M. 270; V. 1623; BMC 2417-21. (44)*	110	250
205	Two opposed crescents. R. Horse r., AθθDIIDOM around. *M. 269; V. 1638; BMC 2422-24. (150)*	160	425

BRONZE

206	**Unit.** Head l. R. Horse l. *M. 274; V. 1615/46 BMC 2450-60. (77)*	30	90

DUBNOVELLAUNUS

(Late 1st Century B.C./ Early 1st Century A.D.)

Dubnovellaunus is likely to have been the successor to Addedomaros, with whom his coins are stylistically related. It is not clear if he was the same Dubnovellaunus who also issued coins in Kent (see Cantii) or if he is the same Dumnobeallaunos mentioned in the Res Gestae of the emperor Augustus c.AD14.

GOLD

207

208

		F £	*VF* £
207	**Stater.** Two crescents on wreath. R. Horse l., leaf below, pellet in ring, DVBNOVAIIAVNOS above. *M. 275; V. 1650; BMC 2425-40. (152)*....	200	575
208	**Quarter Stater.** Similar. *M. 276; V. 1660; BMC 2442. (153)*................	125	275

SILVER

209	Unit. Head l., DVBNO. R. Winged horse r., lattice box below. *M. 288; V. 165; BMC 2443-44. (120)*	125	350
210	Head l., legend ?, R. Horse l. DVB[NOV]. *M. 278; V. 1667; BMC 2445. (154)*........	80	225

BRONZE

211	**Unit.** Head l., R. Horse l., DVBNO above. *M. 281; V. 1669; BMC 2446-48. (154)*........	50	165
212	Head r., R. Horse l. *M. 277; V. 1665; BMC 2461-65. (154)*....................	45	150

DIRAS

(Late 1st Century B.C./ Early 1st Century A.D.)

An historically unattested ruler, responsible for a gold stater related stylistically to Dubnovellaunus's.

GOLD

213	**Stater.** Blank. R. Horse r., DIRAS? above, yoke like object above. *M. 279; V. 162; BMC 2449. (151)*........	*Extremely rare*

CATUVELLAUNI

TASCIOVANUS

(Late 1st Century B.C./ Early 1st Century A.D.)

The early gold coins of Tasciovanus like those of his contemporary Addedomaros are based on the Whaddon Chase stater. Verulamium (St.Albans) appears to have been his principal mint, appearing as VER or VERL on the coinage. Staters and quarter staters inscribed CAM (Camulodunum/Colchester) are known and perhaps suggest brief or weak control of the territory to the east. The later coins of Tasciovanus use increasingly Romanised designs. The adoption of the title RICON, perhaps a Celtic equivalent to the Latin REX (King), can be seen as a parallel move to that of his contemporary Tincommius to the south.

GOLD

214

217

		F £	*VF* £
214	**Stater.** Crescents in wreath. R. TASCIAV and bucranium over horse r. *M. 149; V. 1680; BMC 1591-1603. (157)*	250	650
215	— R. Similar reads TAXCIAV. *M. 150; V. 1682; BMC 1604-05. (157).*	250	675
216	— R. Similar reads TASCIOVAN above, CAM below. *M. 186/a; V. 1684; BMC 1606-07. (160)*	375	1100
217	— R. Horseman r. helmeted and with carnyx, TASC in field. *M. 154-55/57; V. 1730-32; BMC 1608-1613. (158)*	250	625
218	Crescents in wreath, with V or VER in design. R. Similar to last. *M. 156-57; V. 1734-35; BMC 1623-24. (158)*	275	675

219

221

		F £	*VF* £
219	TASCIO(V) RICON in panel. R. Horseman l., wearing armour and holding sword and shield. *M. 184; V. 1780; BMC 1628-36. (161)*	475	1250
220	**Quarter Stater.** Floral design. R. Horse r. *M. —; V. —; BMC 1638-39 .*	165	450
221	Crossed Wreath. R. Horse l. *M. 151; V. 1688; BMC 1651-53. (44)*	95	210
222	— R. Horse r., CAM. *M. 187; V. 1694; BMC 1640. (164)*	150	400
223	Similar, TASCI in wreath. R. Horse r., TASC. *M. 153; V. 1692; BMC 1641. (163)*	100	225

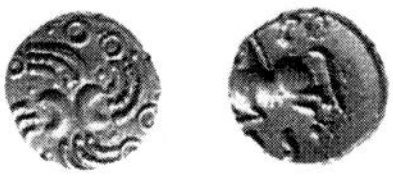

224

226

No.	Description	F £	VF £
224	Similar, VERO in wreath. R. Horse l., TAS. *M. 152; V. 1690; BMC 1642-43. (163)*	95	210
225	TASCIO on tablet. R. Horse l. *M. 195; V. 1848; BMC 1646. (166)*	125	325
226	TASC on tablet. R. Horse l. *M. 185; V. 1786; BMC 1647-50. (165)*	90	200

SILVER

No.	Description	F £	VF £
227	**Unit.** Head l. R. Horse r. *M. —; V. 1698; BMC 1654*	50	140
228	Cross and box. R. Horse r., VER in front. *M. —; V. —; BMC 1655*	60	190
229	Cross and crescent. R. Horse l., TASCI. *M. —; V. —; BMC 1665-57*	60	185
230	Bearded head l. R. Horseman r., TASCIO. *M. 158; V. 1745; BMC 1667-68. (167)*	70	235
231	Winged horse l., TAS. R. Griffin r., within circle of pellets. *M. 159; V. 1790; BMC 1660. (168)*	85	275
232	Eagle stg. l., TASCIA. R. Griffin r. *M. 160; V. 1792; BMC 1658-59. (169)*	75	265
233	VER in beaded circle. R. Horse r., TASCIA. *M. 161; V. 1699; BMC 1670-73. (170)*	70	225
234	— R. Naked horseman. *M. 162; V. 1747; BMC 1674-76. (171)*	80	265

235

238

242

No.	Description	F £	VF £
235	Laureate hd. r., TASCIA. R. Bull l. *M. 163; V. 1794; BMC 1681-82. (172)*	65	200
236	Cross and box, VERL. R. Boar r. TAS. *M. 164; V. 1796; BMC 1661-62. (173)*	75	250
237	TASC in panel. R. Winged horse l. *M. 165; V. 1798; BMC 1664-65. (174)*	55	175
238	— R. Horseman l., carrying long shield. *M. 166; V. 1800; BMC 1677-79. (174)*	50	150
239	Two crescents. R. Winged griffin, VIR. *M. —; V. —; BMC 1666*	75	275
240	Head r., TAS?. R. Horseman r. *M. —; V. —; BMC 1669*	65	225

BRONZE

241

No.	Description	F £	VF £
241	**Double Unit.** Head r., TASCIA, VA. R. Horseman r. *M. 178; V. 1818; BMC 1685-87. (190)*	175	625

		F £	*VF* £
242	**Unit.** Two heads in profile, one bearded. R. Ram l., TASC. *M. 167; V. 1705; BMC 1711-13. (178)*	50	210
243	Bearded head r. VER(L). R. Horse l., VIIR or VER. *M. 168; V. 1707; BMC 1714-21. (179)*	45	185
244	Bearded head r. R. Horse l., TAS. *M. 169; V. 1709; BMC 1722-23. (179)*	45	185
245	Head r., TASC. R. Winged horse l., VER. *M. 170; V. 1711; BMC 1688-89. (180)*	40	175
246	— R. Horseman r., holding carnyx, VIR. *M. 171; V. 1750; BMC 1724-27. (182)*	45	185

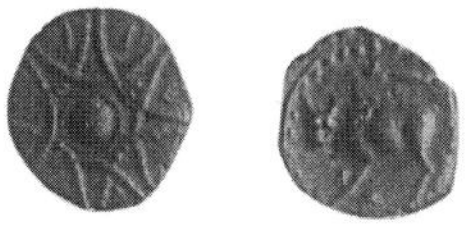

247

		F £	*VF* £
247	VERLAMIO between rays of star. R. Bull l. *M. 172; V. 1808; BMC 1745-51. (183)*	35	150
248	Similar without legend. R. Bull r. *M. 174; V. 1810; BMC 1752-55. (185)*	40	175
249	Similar. R. Horse l., TASCI. *M. 175; V. 1812; BMC 1709-10. (186)*	40	175
250	Head r., TASCIO. R. Lion r., TA SCI. *M. 176; V. 1814; BMC 1736-38. (188)*	35	150
251	Head r. R. Figure std. l., VER below. *M. 177; V. 1816; BMC 1739-44. (189)*	45	185
252	Cross and Crescents. R. Boar r., VER. *M. 179; V. 1713; BMC 1702-05. (191)*	40	160
253	Laureate head r. R. Horse l., VIR. *M. 180; V. 1820; BMC 1706-08. (192)*	45	185
254	Raised band across centre, VER or VERL below. R. Horse grazing r. *M. 183a; V. 1717; BMC —. (193)*	70	275
255	**Fractional Unit.** Animal r. R. Sphinx l. *M. 181; V. 1824; BMC 1760-61. (198)*	35	150
256	Head l., VER. R. Goat r. *M. 182; V. 1715; BMC 1765-68. (199)*	30	125
257	Head r. R. Boar r, *M. 183; V. 1826; BMC 1762-64. (199)*	30	125
258	Head l. R. Animal with curved tail. *M. 183b, c; V. 1822; BMC 1759. (200)*	30	120

ASSOCIATES OF TASCIOVANUS

(Early 1st Century A.D.)

Towards the end of his reign, a number of joint issues bearing his name and the name of either Sego or Dias appear. In addition coins similar in style to those of Tasciovanus appear with either the name Andoco or Rues. It has been suggested that these issues belong to a period of struggle following the death of Tasciovanus and are all rival contestants for the throne. Another theory is that they are associates or sub-kings of Tasciovanus responsible for areas within the wider territory.

SEGO

GOLD

259

		F £	*VF* £
259	**Stater.** TASCIO in tablet, annulets above. R. Horseman with carnyx r., SEGO. *M. 194; V. 1845; BMC 1625-27. (162)*	*Extremely rare*	

SILVER

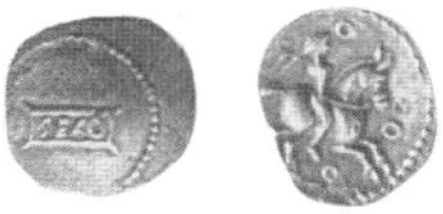

260

260	**Unit.** SEGO on panel. R. Horseman r. *M. 196; V. 1851; BMC 1684. (176)*	200	675

BRONZE

261	**Unit.** Star shaped pattern. R. Winged sphinx l., SEGO. *M. 173; V. 1855; BMC 1690. (184)*..	125	450

ANDOCO

GOLD

262

262	**Stater.** Crescents in wreath. R. Bucranium over horse r., AND below. *M. 197; V. 1860; BMC 2011-14. (202)*..	475	1250

		F £	*VF* £
263	**Quarter Stater.** Crossed wreaths, ANDO in angles. R. Horse l. *M. 198; V. 1863; BMC 2015-17. (203)*	125	350

SILVER

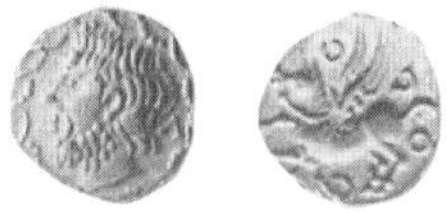

264

264	**Unit.** Bearded head l. R. Winged horse l., ANDOC. *M. 199; V. 1868; BMC 2018. (204)*..	125	350

BRONZE

265

265	**Unit.** Head r., ANDOCO. R. Horse r., ANDOCO. *M. 200; V. 1871; BMC 2019-20. (205)*	60	225
266	Head r., TAS ANDO. R. Horse r. *M. 175a; V. 1873; BMC —. (187)*......	75	265

DIAS

SILVER

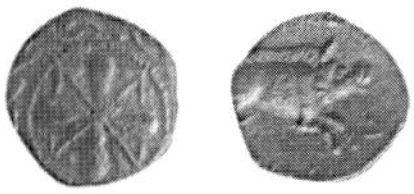

267

268

267	**Unit.** Saltire over cross within square. R. Boar r., TASC DIAS. *M. —; V. —; BMC 1663. (173A)*..	135	400
268	DIAS CO, in star. R. Horse l., VIR. *M. 188; V. 1877; BMC 1683. (177).*	110	300

BRONZE

269

269	**Unit.** Bearded head r., DIAS TASC. R. Centaur r., playing pan pipes. *M. 192; V. 1882; BMC 1728-35. (197)*..	100	350

RUES

BRONZE

		F £	VF £
270	**Unit.** Lion r., RVII. R. Eagle. *M. 189; V. 1890; BMC 1691. (194)*..........	80	325
271	— R. Similar reads RVE. *M. 189; V. 1890-3; BMC 1692. (194)*.............	75	285

272

273

272	Bearded head r., RVIIS. R. Horseman r., VIR. *M. 190; V. 1892; BMC 1698-1701. (195)*...........	85	325
273	RVIIS on tablet. R. Winged sphinx l. *M. 191; V. 1895; BMC 1693-97. (196)*...........	80	300
274	**Fractional Unit.** Annulet within square with curved sides. R. Eagle l., RVII. *M. 193; V. 1903; BMC 1756-58. (201)*..........	65	275

CUNOBELIN

(Early 1st Century A.D. to *c*.40 A.D.)

Styled as son of Tasciovanus on some of his coins, Cunobelin appears to have ruled over the unified territories of the Trinovantes and Catuvellauni, with additional territory in Kent. His aggressive policy of expansion that involved members of family eventually lead to Roman concern over the extent of his power. Following his death just prior to 43 AD, the emperor Claudius took the decision to invade Britain.

During his long reign an extensive issue of gold, silver and bronze coins used ever increasingly Romanised designs. It has been estimated from a study of known dies that around one million of his gold corn ear staters were produced. His main centre and mint was at Camulodunum (Colchester) appearing as the mint signature CAMV. The names SOLIDV and AGR appear on a few coins associated with Cunobelin and are likely to represent personal names.

GOLD

280

281

280	**Stater.** Biga type. CAMVL on panel. R. Two horses l., wheel below, CVNOBELIN. *M. 201; V. 1910; BMC 1769-71. (207)*..........	625	1650
281	Linear type. Corn ear dividing CA MV. R. Horse r., branch above., CVN. *M. 210; V. 1925; BMC 1772-76. (208)*..........	200	425
282	— Similar, privy mark 'x' above a letter in *obv.* legend. *M. 210a; VA 1925-3/5; BMC 1777-81. (208)*..........	225	500

283

285

		F £	VF £
283	Wild type. Corn ear dividing CA MV. R. Horse r., branch above., CVN(O). *M. 211/2; V. 1931/33; BMC 1784-92/1804-08. (208)*	200	400
284	— Similar, heart shaped object between horses forelegs. *M. 211 var; V. 1931-3; BMC 1793. (208)*	250	625
285	— Similar, privy mark pellet or pellet triangle above a letter(s) in *obv.* legend. *M. —; V. 1931-5/7/9; BMC 1797-1803. (208)*	225	450

286

288

		F £	VF £
286	Plastic type. Corn ear dividing CA MV. R. Horse r., branch above., CVNO. *M. 203/13; V. 2010-1/3/5; BMC 1809-11/15-23. (208)*	185	375
287	— Similar, 'B' in front of horse. *M. —; V. 2010-7; BMC 1813. (208)*	250	625

289

290

		F £	VF £
288	Classic type. Corn ear dividing CA MV. R. Horse r., branch above., CVNO. *M. 206-07; V. 2025/27; BMC 1827-31/33. (208)*	265	600
289	— Similar, horse l., lis like object above. *M. 208; V. 2029; BMC 1834-35. (209)*	475	1200
290	**Quarter Stater.** Biga type. Similar to 280. *M. 202; V. 1913; BMC 1836/A. (210)*	180	500

292

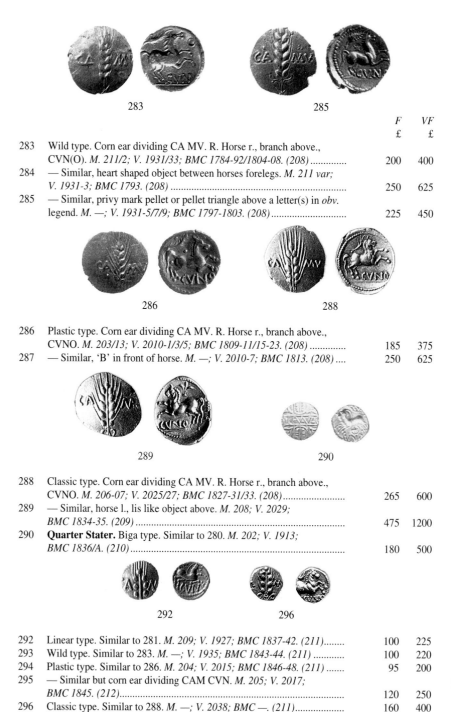

296

		F £	VF £
292	Linear type. Similar to 281. *M. 209; V. 1927; BMC 1837-42. (211)*	100	225
293	Wild type. Similar to 283. *M. —; V. 1935; BMC 1843-44. (211)*	100	220
294	Plastic type. Similar to 286. *M. 204; V. 2015; BMC 1846-48. (211)*	95	200
295	— Similar but corn ear dividing CAM CVN. *M. 205; V. 2017; BMC 1845. (212)*	120	250
296	Classic type. Similar to 288. *M. —; V. 2038; BMC —. (211)*	160	400

SILVER

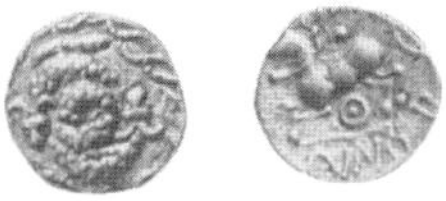

299

No.	Description	F £	VF £
299	**Unit.** Two bull headed serpents, inter twined. R. Horse l., CVNO. *M. 214; V. 1947; BMC 1856. (213)*	90	375
300	Curled serpent inside wheel. R. Winged horse l., CVN. *M. —; V. —; BMC 1857*	90	375
301	CVN on panel R. Horse l., (C)M. *M. 255; V. 1949; BMC 1858-59. (228)*	70	225
302	CVNO BELI on two panels. R. CVN below horseman r. *M. 216/7; V. 1951/53; BMC 1862. (215)*	70	225
303	Head l., CAMVL. R. CVNO beneath Victory std. r. *M. 215; V. 2045; BMV 1863-65. (214)*	75	250

304

305

No.	Description	F £	VF £
304	Two leaves dividing CVN. R. Horseman r., CAM. *M. 218; V. 2047; BMC 1866-67. (216)*	90	350
305	Flower dividing CAMV. R. CVNO below horse r. *M. 219; V. 2049; BMC1867A. (217)*	85	225
306	CVNO on panel. R. CAMV on panel below griffin. *M. 234; V. 2051; BMC 1868-69. (218)*	75	250
307	CAMVL on panel. R. CVNO below centaur l. carrying palm. *M. 234a; V. 1918; BMC —. (219)*	90	325
308	CAMVL on panel. R. Figure seated l. holding wine amphora, CVNOBE. *M. —; V. —; BMC —. (219A)*	75	250
309	Plant, CVNOBELINVS. R. Figure stg. r. holding club and thunderbolt dividing CA MV. *M. —; V .—; BMC 1897. (219B)*	85	300
310	Laur. hd. r., CVNOBELINVS. R. Winged horse springing l., CAMV below. *M. —; V. —; BMC —. (219C)*	85	300
311	CVNO on panel, wreath around. R. Winged horse r., TASC F. *M. 235; V. 2053; BMC 1870. (220)*	80	275

312

313

No.	Description	F £	VF £
312	Head r., CVNOBELINI. R. Horse r., TASCIO. *M. 236; V. 2055; BMC 1871-73. (221)*	65	210
313	Winged bust r., CVNO. R. Sphinx std. l., TASCIO. *M. 237; V. 2057; BMC 1874-78. (222)*	55	175

314

316

		F £	VF £
314	Draped female fig. r., TASCIIOVAN. R. Figure std. r. playing lyre, tree behind. *M. 238; V. 2059; BMC 1879-82. (223)*	80	275
315	Figure stg. l., holding club and lionskin., CVNO. R. Female rider r., TASCIOVA. *M. 239; V. 2061; BMC 1884-85. (224)*	75	250
316	Female head r., CVNOBELINVS. R. Victory r., TASCIO(VAN). *M. —; V. —; BMC 1883. (224A)*	70	225
317	Fig. r. carrying dead animal, CVNOBELINVS. R. Fig. stg. holding bow, dog at side, TASCIIOVANI. *M. 240; V. 2063; BMC 1886-88. (225)*	80	275
318	CVNO on panel, horn above, dolphin below. R. Fig. stg. r. altar behind. *M. 241/41a; V. 2065; BMC 1889-90. (226)*	80	275

319

319	CVN on panel. R. Fig. holding club walking r., CVN. *M. 254; V. 2067; BMC 1891-92. (227)*	85	300
320	CVN in wreath. R. CAM, dog? trampling on serpent r. *M. 256; V. 2069; BMC 1893. (229)*	90	350
321	Winged horse l., CVN. R. Std. fig. r. *M. 258; V. 2071; BMC 1896. (230)*	80	275
322	CVNO in angles of cross. R. Capricorn r., CVNO. *M. —; V. —; BMC 1898*	85	325

BRONZE

323	Head l., CVNO. R. Boar l., branch above. *M. 220; V. 1969; BMC—. (232)*	45	175
324	CVNOB ELINI in two panels. R. Victory std. l., TASC. *M. 221; V. 1971; BMC 1921-27. (233)*	35	150
325	Winged horse l., CAM. R. Winged Victory stg l., CVN. *M. 222; V. 1973; BMC 1938-43. (234)*	35	150

326

326	Bearded head facing R. Boar l., CVN. *M.223; V.1963; BMC 1904-05. (235)*	35	160
327	Ram-headed animal coiled up in double ornamental circle. R. Animal l., CAM. *M. 224; V. 1965; BMC —. (236)*	45	180
328	Griffin r., CAMV. R. Horse r., CVN. *M. 225; V. 2081; BMC 1909-12. (237)*	35	160

		F £	*VF* £
329	Bearded head l., CAMV. R. CVN or CVNO below horse l. *M. 226, 229; V. 2085/2131; BMC 1900-01. (238)*	35	140
330	Laureate head r., CVNO. R. CVN below bull butting l. *M. 227; V. 2083; BMC 1902-03. (239)*	40	170
331	Crude head r., CVN. R. Figure stg. l., CVN. *M. 228; V. 2135; BMC —. (240)*	45	180

332

332	CAMVL / ODVNO in two panels. R. CVNO beneath sphinx crouching l. *M. 230; V. 1977; BMC 1928-30. (241)*	35	150
333	Winged horse l., CAMV. R. Victory stg. r. divides CV NO. *M. 231; V. 1979; BMC 1931-34. (242)*	35	150
334	Victory walking r. R. CVN below, horseman r. *M. 232; V. 1981; BMC 1935. (243)*	40	170
335	Head l., CAM. R. CVNO below eagle. *M. 233; V. 2087; BMC —. (244)*	45	175

336

337

336	Head l., CVNOBELINI. R. Centaur r., TASCIOVANI.F. *M. 242; V. 2089; BMC 1968-71. (245)*	35	150
337	Helmeted bust r. R. TASCIIOVANII above, sow stg. r., F below. *M. 243; V. 2091; BMC 1956-60. (246)*	35	150
338	Horseman galloping r. holding dart and shield, CVNOB. R. Warrior stg. l., TASCIIOVANTIS. *M. 244; V. 2093; BMC 1961-67. (247)*	30	120

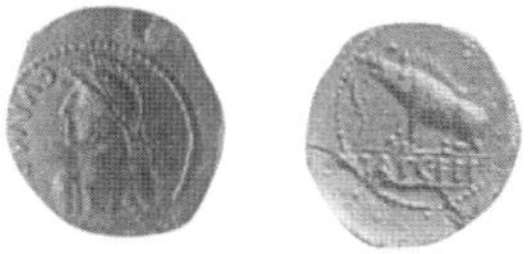

339

339	Helmeted bust l., CVOBELINVS REX. R. TASC FIL below boar l., std. on haunches. *M. 245; V. 1983; BMC 1952-55. (248)*	45	180
340	Bare head r., CVNOBELINVS REX. R. TASC below bull butting r. *M. 246; V. 2095; BMC 1944-51. (249)*	30	140
341	Bare head l., CVNO. R. TASC below bull stg. r. *M. 247; V. 1985; BMC —. (250)*	35	150

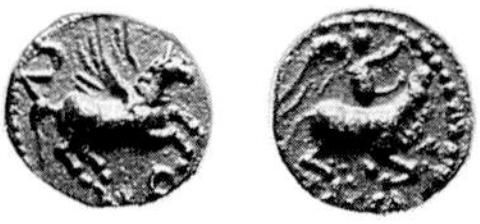

342 343

		F £	VF £
342	Head l., CVNOBELIN. R. Metal worker std. r. holding hammer, working on a vase, TASCIO. *M. 248; V. 2097; BMC 1972-83. (251)*	30	140
343	Winged horse r., CVNO. R. Victory r. sacrificing bull, TASCI. *M. 249; V. 2099; BMC 1913-19. (252)*	30	110
344	CVNO on panel within wreath. R. CAMV below horse, prancing r. *M. 250; V. 2101; BMC 1987-90. (253)*	35	150

345 346

		F £	VF £
345	Bearded head of Jupiter Ammon l., CVNOBELIN. R. CAM below horseman galloping r. *M. 251; V. 2103; BMC 1984-86. (254)*	40	160
346	Janus head, CVNO below. R. CAMV on panel below, sow std. r. beneath a tree. *M. 252; V. 2105; BMC 1998-2003. (255)*	40	170

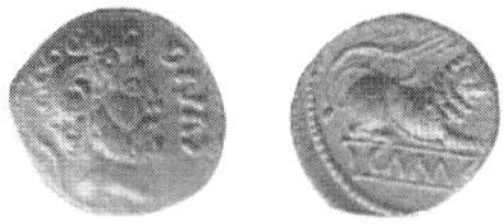

347

		F £	VF £
347	Bearded head of Jupiter Ammon r., CVNOB. R. CAM on panel below lion crouched r. *M. 253; V. 2107; BMC 1991-97. (256)*	35	160
348	Sphinx r., CVNO. R. Fig stg. l. divides CA M. *M. 260; V. 2109; BMC 2004-09. (257)*	35	160
349	Horse r. R. CVN below horseman r. *M. 261; V. 1987; BMC 1936-47. (258)*	40	170
350	Animal l. looking back. R. CVN below horse l. *M. 233a; V. 1967; BMC— . (259)*	60	200
350A	Ship, CVN below. R. Fig. r. dividing S E. *M. —; V. 1989; BMC 2010.* ..	120	475

"SOLIDV"

SILVER

351

		F £	VF £
351	**Unit.** SOLIDV in centre of looped circle. R, Stg. fig. l., CVNO. *M. 259; V. 2073; BMC 1894-95. (231)*	225	675

"AGR"

GOLD

352	Quarter Stater. Corn ear dividing CAM CVN. R. Horse r., branch above., AGR below *M. —; V. —; BMC 1854*	350	900

353

353	— R. Horse r., branch above., cross and A below. *M. —; V. —; BMC 1855*	325	800

SILVER

354	**Unit.** AGR inside wreath. R. Female dog r., AGR below. *M. —; V. —; BMC 1899*	275	750

EPATICCUS

(1st Half 1st Century A.D.)

Epaticcus styled as a son of Tasciovanus on his coins, was most probably a brother of Cunobelin. The corn ear employed on his staters is similar to that of his brother's produced at Colchester. His coins appear in northern Atrebatic territory and conform to the area's denominational structure. It seems likely that Epaticcus's coinage reflects an incursion into Atrebatic territory by the Trinovantian/Catuvellaunian dynasty.

GOLD

355

355	**Stater.** Corn ear dividing TAS CIF. R. Horseman r., with spear and shield. EPATI. *M. 262; V. 575; BMC 2021-23. (112)*	675	1650

SILVER

356

357

		F £	VF £
356	**Unit.** Head of Hercules r., EPAT(I). R. Eagle stg. on snake. *M. 263/a; V. 580; BMC 2024-2268/2270-76. (113)*	25	75
357	Victory seated r. TASCIOV. R. Boar r., EPAT. *M. 263; V. 581; BMC 2294-2328. (114)*	30	95

358

		F £	VF £
358	Bearded head l., TASCIO. R. EPATI below lion r. *M. —; V. 582; BMC 2329*	110	350
359	EPATI inside panel. R. Lion r. *M. —; V. 583; BMC 2330. (114A)*	120	375

360

361

		F £	VF £
360	**Minim.** EPATI. R. Boars head r., TA. *M. 264; V. 585; BMC 2331-46. (115)*	35	110
361	TA inside star. R. Winged horse r., EPA below. *M. —; V. 560; BMC 2351-57. (116)*	40	125
362	Helmeted head r. R. Horse r., E below. *M. —; V. —; BMC 2358-63*	40	130
363	EPATI. R. Winged horse r., cross below. *M. —; V .—; BMC 2365*	50	160

CARATACUS

(1st Half 1st Century A.D.)

Coins inscribed CARA have been traditionally associated with the historically attested son of Cunobelin, Caratacus the leader of British resistance against Rome. His coins appear in the same area as those of Epaticcus and he may have been his successor.

SILVER

364

364A

		F £	VF £
364	**Unit.** Head of Hercules r., CARA. R. Eagle stg. on snake. *M. 265; V. 593; BMC 2376-84. (117)*	110	300
364A	**Minim.** CARA around pellet in ring. R. Winged horse r. *M. —; V. 595; BMC 2385-89. (117A)*	95	235

DUROTRIGES

(Mid 1st Century B.C. to Mid 1st Century A.D.)

The Durotriges inhabited West Hampshire, Dorset and adjoining parts of Somerset and Wiltshire. Their coinage is one of the most distinctive in Britain due to its rapid debasement. The disappearance of precious metals from the coinage should perhaps be linked to the declining trade between the south-west and western Gaul, following the Roman conquest of the Gaul. Hengistbury Head is the probable mint site of the cast bronzes. Coins inscribed CRAB have been traditionally associated with the tribe.

UNINSCRIBED

SILVER

		F £	*VF* £
365	**Stater.** White Gold type. Derived from Westerham stater (no. 21). *M. 317; V. 1235, 52, 54, 55; BMC 2525-2731. (60)*	75	200

366

368

		F £	*VF* £
366	Silver type. Similar. *M. 317; V. 1235, 52, 54, 55; BMC 2525-2731. (60)*	45	110
367	Billon type. Similar. *M. 317; V. 1235, 52, 54, 55; BMC 2525-2731. (60)*	25	65
368	**Quarter Stater.** Geometric type. Crescent design. R. Zig-zag pattern. *M. 319; V. 1242/29; BMC 2734-79. (61). Quality of metal varies, obv. almost blank on later issues*	30	95

369

		F £	*VF* £
369	Starfish type. Spiral. R. Zig-zag pattern. *M. 320; V. 1270; BMC 2780-81 (61A)*	50	160
370	Hampshire Thin Flan type. Crude head of lines and pellets. R. Stylised horse l. *M. 321; V. 1280; BMC 2782-87. (62)*	60	175

BRONZE

		F £	*VF* £
371	**Stater.** Struck Bronze type. Similar to No.365-67. *M. 318; V. 1290; BMC 2790-2859. (81)*	20	45

372

		F £	VF £
372	Cast Bronze type. Many varities, as illustration. *M. 322-70; V. 1322-70; BMC 2860-2936. (82)*	40	115

"CRAB"

SILVER

373

373	**Unit.** CRAB in angles of cross. R. Eagle. *M. 371; V. 1285; BMC 2788. (145)*	*Extremely rare*	
373A	**Minim.** CRAB on tablet. R. Star shape. *M. 372; V. 1286; BMC 2789. (146)*	*Extremely rare*	

DOBUNNI

(Mid 1st Century B.C. to Mid 1st Century A.D.)

Dobunnic territory stretched over Gloucestershire, Hereford and Worcester and into parts of Somerset, Wiltshire and Gwent. The earliest Dobunnic coins are developed from the British Q stater, and have the distinctive tree-like motif of the tribe on the obverse. The inscribed coinage is difficult to arrange chronologically and it may be that some of the rulers named held different parts of the territory simultaneously.

UNINSCRIBED

GOLD

374	**Stater.** Plain except for tree-like object. R. Three tailed horse r., wheel below. *M. 374; V. 1005; BMC 2937-40. (43)*	275	650
375	**Quarter Stater.** Plain with traces of wreath pattern. R. Horse r. *M. 68; V. 1010-3; BMC 2942-46. (52)*	110	265
376	Wreath pattern. R. Horse l., pellet in ring motifs in field. *M. 74; V. 1015; BMC 2949. (51)*	120	275

SILVER

377

378

377 **Unit.** Allen types A-F/I-J. Regular series. Head r. R. Triple-tailed horse l. or r. *M. 374a, b/75/76, 378a-384; V. 1020/45/49/74/78/95/1135/1137; BMC 2950-3011. (63-64). Style becomes progressively more abstract, from-* 25 80

378 Allen types L-O. Irregular series. Similar to last. *M. 377-384d; V. 1170-85; BMC 3012-22. (63-64)* 30 90

INSCRIBED

The following types are not arranged chronologically.

ANTED

GOLD

379 **Stater.** Dobunnic emblem. R. ANTED or ANTEDRIG over triple tailed horse r., wheel below. *M. 385-86; V. 1062-69; BMC 3023-3031. (260)* 350 825

SILVER

380 **Unit.** Crude head r. R. ANTED over horse. *M. 387; V. 1082; BMC 3032-38. (261)* 60 165

EISV

GOLD

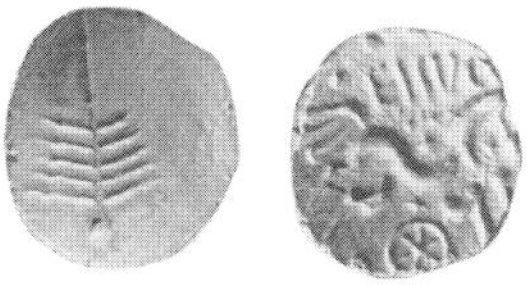

381

381 **Stater.** Dobunnic emblem. R. EISV or EISVRIG over triple tailed horse r., wheel below. *M. 388; V. 1105; BMC 3039-42. (262)* 475 1100

SILVER

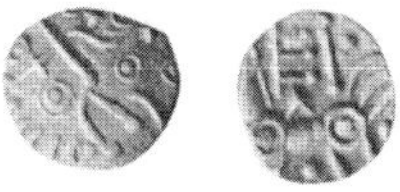

382

382 **Unit.** Crude head r. R. Horse l., EISV. *M. 389; V. 1110; BMC 3043-55. (263)* 50 150

INAM or INARA

GOLD

		F £	VF £
383	**Stater.** Dobunnic emblem. R. INAM or INARA over triple tailed horse r., wheel below. *M. 390; V. 1140; BMC 3056. (264)*	*Extremely rare*	

CATTI

GOLD

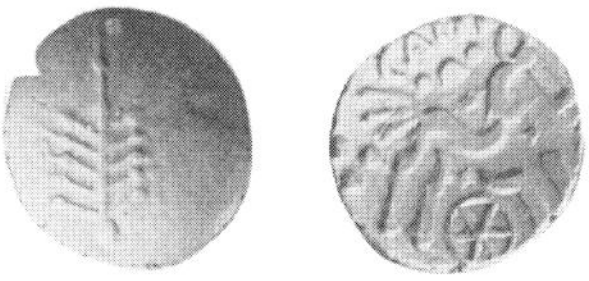

384

384	**Stater.** Dobunnic emblem. R. CATTI over triple tailed horse r., wheel below. *M. 391; V. 1130; BMC 3057-60. (265)*	300	725

COMUX

GOLD

385	**Stater.** Dobunnic emblem. R. COMVX retrograde, over triple tailed horse r., wheel below. *M. 392; V. 1092; BMC 3061-63. (266)*	700	1650

CORIO

GOLD

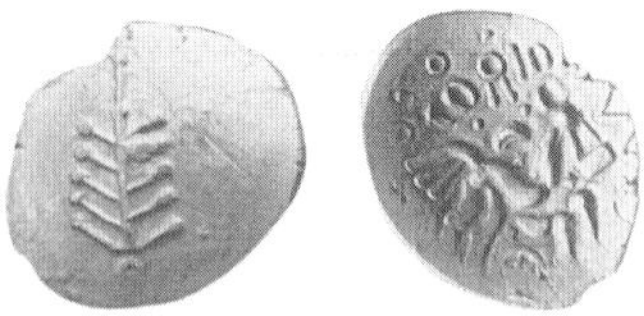

386

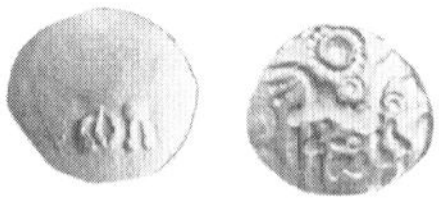

387

386	**Stater.** Dobunnic emblem. R. CORIO over triple tailed horse r., wheel below. *M. 393; V. 1035; BMC 3064-3133. (267)*	325	750
387	**Quarter Stater.** COR in centre. R. Horse r., without legend. *M. 394; V. 1039; BMC 3134. (268)*	525	1350

BODVOC

GOLD

388

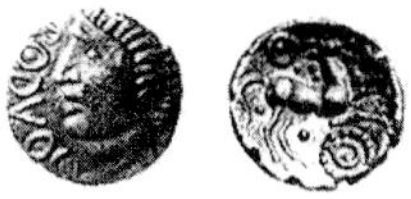

389

		F £	*VF* £
388	**Stater.** BODVOC across field. R. Horse r., without legend. *M. 395; V. 1052; BMC 3135-42. (269)*	650	1500

SILVER

		F £	*VF* £
389	**Unit.** Head l., BODVOC. R. Horse r., without legend. *M. 396; V. 1057; BMC 3143-45. (270)*	120	325

CORIELTAUVI

The Corieltauvi formerly known as the Coritani, occupied Lincolnshire and adjoining parts of Yorkshire, Northamptonshire, Leicestershire and Nottinghamshire. The earliest staters, the South Ferriby type, are developed from Gallo-Belgic C staters, and are associated with the silver Boar/Horse types. The distinctive dish shaped scyphate coinages have no parallels in Britain and stand apart from the main series. The later inscribed issues present a complex system of inscriptions. It has been suggested that some of the later inscriptions refer to pairs of names, possibly joint rulers or moneyers and rulers.

EARLY UNINSCRIBED

(Mid to Late 1st Century B.C.)

GOLD

390

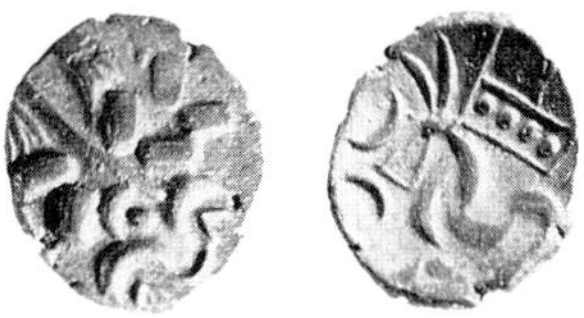

393

		F £	*VF* £
390	**Stater.** South Ferriby type. Crude laureate head. R. Disjointed horse l., rosette or star below, anchor shape and pellets above. *M. 449-50; V. 809-815/19; BMC 3146-3179. (30)*	125	325
391	Wheel type. Similar, but wheel below horse. *M. 449c; V. 817; BMC 3180*	300	750
392	Kite type. Similar to 390, but diamond shape containing pellets above, spiral below horse. *M. 447; V. 825; BMC 3181-84. (29)*	200	450
393	Domino type. Similar to last, but with rectangle containing pellets. *M. 448; V. 829; BMC 3185-86. (29)*	185	400

394

395

		F	VF
		£	£
394	Trefoil type. Trefoil with central rosette of seven pellets. R. Similar to 390. *M. 450a; V. 821; BMC —. (30A)*	*Extremely rare*	
395	North Lincolnshire Scyphate type. Stylised boar r. or l. R. Large S symbol with pellets and rings in field. *M. —; V. —; BMC 3187-93*	275	650

** chipped or cracked specimens are often encountered and are worth less*

SILVER

396

396	**Unit.** Boar/Horse type I.Boar r., large pellet and ring motif above, reversed S below. R. Horse l. or r., pellet in ring above. *M. 405-06, 451; V. 855-60, 864, 867; BMC 3194-3214. (66)*	60	175
397	Boar Horse type II. Vestiges of boar on obv. R. Horse l. or r. *M. 410, 452-53; V. 875-877; BMC 3214-27. (68)*	50	115

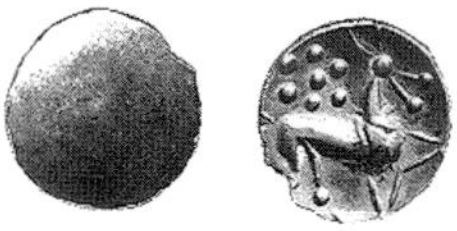

398

399

398	Boar Horse type III. Blank. R. Horse l.or r. *M. 453-54; V. 884-77; BMC 3228-35. (69)*	40	90
399	**Fractional Unit.** Similar to 396-97. *M. 406a, 451a; V. 862/66; BMC 3236-3250. (67)*	40	110
400	Similar to 398. *M. —; V. 877-81; BMC 3251-55. (70/71)*	20	65
401	Pattern/Horse. Flower pattern. R. Horse l. *M. —; V. —; BMC 3256-57*	60	175

INSCRIBED

(Early to Mid 1st Century A.D.)
The following types are not arranged chronologically.

AVN COST

GOLD

		F £	*VF* £
402	**Stater.** Crude wreath design. R. Disjointed horse l., AVN COST. *M. 457; V. 910; BMC 3258. (286)*	525	1350

SILVER

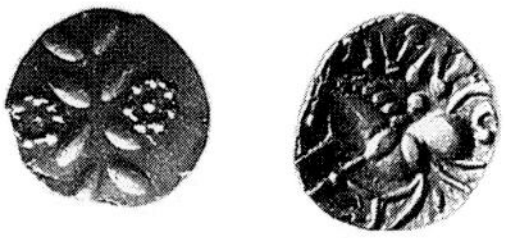

403

403	**Unit.** Remains of wreath or blank. R. AVN COST, horse l. *M. 458; V. 914; BMC 3261-66. (287)*	35	85
404	**Fractional Unit.** Similar. *M. —; l V. 918; BMC 3267-68. (288)*	30	75

ESVP RASV

GOLD

405	**Stater.** Crude wreath design. R. Disjointed horse l., IISVP RASV. *M. 456b; V. 920; BMC 3269. (289)*	375	850

SILVER

406	**Unit.** Similar. *M. 456c; V. 924; BMC 3272-73. (290)*	75	200

VEP

GOLD

407	**Stater.** Blank or with traces of wreath. R. Disjointed horse l., VEP. *M. —; V. 905; BMC 3274-75. (296)*	525	1300

SILVER

408	**Unit.** Blank or with traces of wreath. R. VEP, horse r. *M. —; V. 963; BMC 3277-82. (297)*	60	130
409	**Half Unit.** Similar. *M. 464b; V. 967; BMC 3283-3295. (298)*	45	110

VEP CORF

GOLD

410

		F £	*VF* £
410	**Stater.** Crude wreath design. R. Disjointed horse l., VEP CORF. *M. 459, 460; V. 930/40/60; BMC 3296-3304. (291)*	350	850

SILVER

411	**Unit.** Similar. *M. 460b/464; V. 934/50; BMC 3305-14. (292)*	40	110

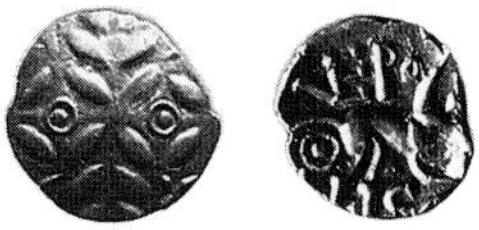

412

412	Similar but VEPOC (M)ES, pellet in ring below horse. *M. —; V. 955; BMC —. (294)*	55	140
413	**Half Unit.** Similar. *M. 464a; V. 938/58; BMC 3316-24. (293/95)*	35	100

DVMNO TIGIR SENO

GOLD

414

414	**Stater.** DVMN(OC) across wreath. R. Horse l., TIGIR SENO. *M. 461; V. 972; BMC 3325-27. (299)*	575	1500

SILVER

415

415	**Unit.** DVMNOC in two lines. R. Horse r., TIGIR SENO. *M. 462; V. 974; BMC 3328-29. (300)*	175	500

VOLISIOS DVMNOCOVEROS

GOLD

416

		F £	VF £
416	**Stater.** VOLISIOS between three lines in wreath. R. Horse r. or l., DVMNOCOVEROS. *M. 463/a; V. 978-80; BMC 3330-3336. (301)*.......	375	850

SILVER

417	**Unit.** Similar. R. Horse r., DVMNOCO. *M. 463a; V. 980; BMC 3339. (302)*..........	140	375
418	**Half Unit.** Similar. *M. 465; V. 984; BMC 3340-41. (303)*..........	65	225

VOLISIOS DVMNOVELLAUNOS

GOLD

419	**Stater.** VOLISIOS between three lines in wreath. R. Horse r. or l., DVMNOVELAVNOS. *M. 466; V .988; BMC 3342-43. (304)*..........	700	1850

SILVER

420	**Half Unit.** As last but DVMNOVE. *M. 467; V. 992; BMC 3344-46. (305).*	150	450

VOLISIOS CARTIVEL

SILVER

421	**Half Unit.** VOLISIOS between three lines in wreath. R. Horse r., CARTILEV. *M. 468; V. 994; BMC 3347-48. (306)*..........	175	525

IAT ISO E

SILVER

422	**Unit.** IAT ISO (retrograde)on tablet, rosettes above and below. R. Horse r., E above. *M. 416; V. 998; BMC 3349-51. (284)*..........	200	475

CAT

SILVER

422A	**Unit.** Boar r., pellet ring above, CAT above. R. Horse r. *M. —; V. —; BMC 3352*..........	*Extremely rare*

LAT ISON

GOLD

423

		F	VF
		£	£
423	**Stater.** LAT ISO(N) in two lines retrograde. R. Horse r., ISO in box above, N below. *M. —; V. —; BMC —. Only recorded as an AE/AV plated core, as illustrated.*	*Extremely rare*	

ICENI

The Iceni centered on Norfolk but also occupying neighbouring parts of Suffolk and Cambridgeshire, are well attested in the post conquest period as the tribe who under Boudicca revolted against Roman rule. Their earliest coins are likely to have been the British J staters, Norfolk Wolf type (no.30/31), replaced around the mid first century B.C. by the Snettisham, Freckenham and Irstead type gold staters and quarter staters. Contemporary with these are silver Boar/Horse and Face/Horse units and fractions. The introduction of legends around the beginning of the millennia led to the adoption of a new obverse design of back to back crescents. The continuation of the coinage after the Roman invasion is attested by the coins of King Prasutagus. Some of the Face/Horse units (no.434) have been attributed to Queen Boudicca.

EARLY UNINSCRIBED

(Mid to Late 1st Century B.C.)

GOLD

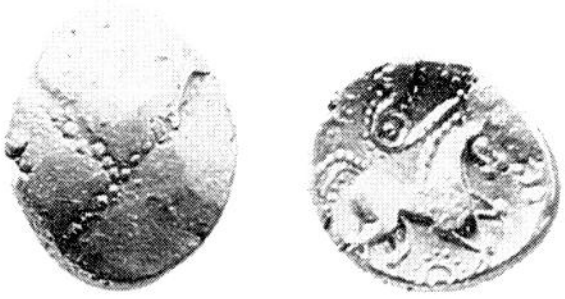

424

425

424	**Stater.** Snettisham type. Blank or with traces of pellet cross. R. Horse r., serpent like pellet in ring motif above. *M. —; V .—; BMC 3353-59*....	225	550
425	Similar. Blank or with 3 short curved lines. R. Horse r., symbol above more degraded. *M. —; V. —; BMC 3360-83*	200	450

426

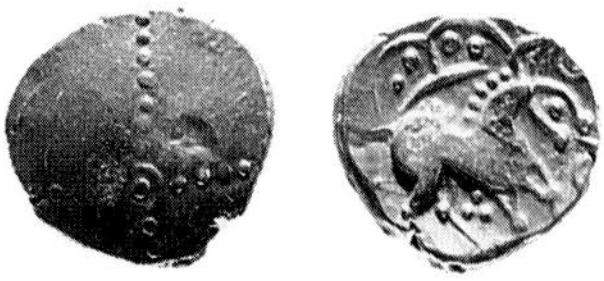

427

		F £	*VF* £
426	Freckenham type. Two opposed crescents with stars or pellets in field. R. Horse r., various symbols in field. *M. 397/99; V. 620; BMC 3384-89. (38)*	225	500
427	Similar. Blank or with traces of pellet cross. R. Horse r., wheel or arch containing pellets above. *M. 400; V. 624; BMC 3390-95. (40)*	200	475

428

428	Similar. Trefoil on cross design. R. Similar. *M. 401-03; V. 626; BMC 3396-3419. (39)*	225	500

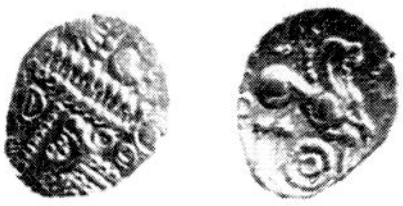

429

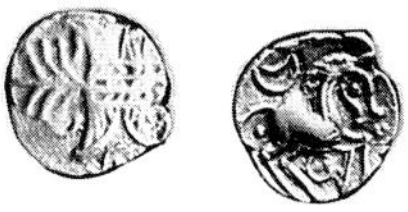

430

429	**Quarter Stater.** Snettisham type. Wreath cross. R. Horse r. *M. —; V. —; BMC 3420-35*	100	275
430	Irstead type. Hatched box, wreaths at sides. R. Horse r. *M. 404; V. 628; BMC 3436-39. (48)*	85	175

SILVER

431

432

431	**Unit.** Boar / Horse type. Boar r. R. Horse r. *M. 407-09; V. 655-59; BMC 3440-3512. (72)*	25	65
432	Bury type. Head l. or r. R. Horse l. or r. *M. —; V. —; BMC 3524-35*	70	185

433

433

No.	Description	F £	VF £
433	Early Face / Horse type. Celticised head l. or r. R. Horse l. or r. *M. 412/413a-c/e; BMC 3536-3555. (74)*	65	175

434

435

No.	Description	F £	VF £
434	Face / Horse Regular type. Head r. R. Horse r. *M. 413/d; V. 790-94; BMC 3556-3759. (74). Attributed to Queen Boudicca by R.D. van Arsdell*	40	135
435	Early Pattern / Horse type. Cross of two opposed crescents. R. Horse l. or r. *M. 414-15; V. 675-79; BMC 3763-74. (75)*	25	75

436

No.	Description	F £	VF £
436	ECEN symbol type. Two opposed crescents. R. Horse r. *M. 429; V. 752; BMC 4297-4325*	20	55
437	**Half Unit.** Boar / Horse type. Similar to 431. *M. 411; V. 661; BMC 3513-20. (73)*	20	55
438	**Fractional Unit.** Early Pattern / Horse type. Similar to 435. *M. 417/a; V. 681-83; BMC 3775-89. (76/A)*	25	60

INSCRIBED

(Early to Mid 1st Century A.D.)

The following types are not arranged chronologically.

CAN DVRO

SILVER

439

No.	Description	F £	VF £
439	**Unit.** Boar. R. Horse r., CAN(S) above, DVRO below. *M. 434; V. 663; BMC 3521-23. (271)*	85	250

ANTED

GOLD

440

No.	Description	*F* £	*VF* £
440	**Stater.** Triple crescent design. R. Horse r., ANTED monongram below. *M. 418; V. 705; BMC 3790. (272)*	525	1200

SILVER

441

No.	Description	*F* £	*VF* £
441	**Unit.** Two opposed crescents. R. Horse r., ANTED. *M. 419-21; V. 710-11/15; BMC 3791-4025. (273)*	25	65
442	**Fractional Unit.** Similar to last. *M. 422; V. 720; BMC 4028-31. (274)*	30	70

ECEN

GOLD

443

No.	Description	*F* £	*VF* £
443	**Stater.** Triple crescent design. R. Horse r., ECEN below. *M. —; V. 725; BMC 4032.*	1250	3250

SILVER

No.	Description	*F* £	*VF* £
443A	**Unit.** Two opposed crescents. R, Horse r., ECEN. *M. 424; V. 730; BMC 4033-4215. (275)*	20	50
443B	**Half Unit.** Similar to last. *M. 431; V. 736; BMC 4216-17. (276)*	25	55

EDN

SILVER

		F £	VF £
444	**Unit.** Two opposed crescents. R, Horse r., ED, E, EI or EDN. *M. 423, 425b; V. 734/40; BMC 4219-81. (277)*	25	60

ECE

GOLD

		F £	VF £
444A	**Stater** Triple crescent design R. Horse r., ECE *M. — ; V. — ;*	1350	3500

SILVER

445

		F £	VF £
445	**Unit.** Two opposed crescents. R, Horse r., ECE. *M. 425-28; V. 761-66; BMC 4348-4538. (278-80)*	25	60

SAENU

SILVER

		F £	VF £
446	**Unit.** Two opposed crescents. R. Horse r., SAENV. *M. 433; V. 770; BMC 4540-57. (281)*	40	95

AESU

SILVER

447

		F £	VF £
447	**Unit.** Two opposed crescents. R. Horse r., AESV. *M. 432; V. 775; BMC 4558-72. (282)*	45	100

ALE SCA

SILVER

		F £	VF £
448	**Unit.** Boar r., ALE. R. Horse r., SCA. *M. 469; V. 996; BMC 4576*	150	375

AEDIC SIA

SILVER

	F	VF
	£	£
449 **Unit.** AEDIC in two lines. R. Horse r., SIA? below. *M.—; V.—; BMC 4581*	*Extremely rare*	

PRASUTAGUS

SILVER

450

	F	VF
450 **Unit.** Romanised head l., SUB RII PRASTO. R. Rearing horse r., ESICO FECIT. *M. 434a; V. 780; BMC 4577-80. (283)*	525	1450

This legend translates as "Under King Prasto, Esico made me", giving the name of both King and moneyer.

The systematic conquest of Britain by the Romans began in A.D. 43 when the Emperor Claudius (41-54), anxious to enhance his military reputation, authorized an invasion in which he personally participated, albeit in a purely symbolic role. The initial military contact between the two cultures had taken place almost a century before when Julius Caesar, during the course of his conquest of Celtic Gaul, led expeditions to the island in 55 and 54 B.C. Although no actual Roman occupation of Britain resulted from Caesar's reconnoitring campaigns commercial intercourse was certainly accelerated, as evidenced by the 'Romanization' of the British Celtic coinage in the final decades of its production.

The Claudian conquest, commencing in A.D. 43, brought about a complete change in the nature of the currency circulating in Britain and ushered in a period lasting more than three and a half centuries during which Roman coinage was the only official medium of exchange. Local copies of the money brought with them by the four legions of the invasion army began to appear at a very early stage, the most popular type for imitation being the well-known Claudian copper as with reverse type fighting Minerva. Some of these copies are well-executed and of a style not much inferior to the prototype, suggesting that their local minting may have been officially sanctioned by the Roman government in order to make good a shortage of currency in the newly-conquered territory. Other examples are of much poorer style and execution and are frequently well below the normal weight of a Claudian as (usually between 10 and 11 grams). These copies must have been issued unofficially and provide evidence of the huge demand for this type of currency in a population which had never before experienced the benefits of having base metal coins available for small everyday transactions.

In the decades that followed, the boundaries of the Roman province of Britannia were continually pushed further north and west until, under the celebrated Flavian governor Gnaeus Julius Agricola, the Roman army even penetrated to northern Scotland (A.D. 83/4). A few years later, under Trajan, the northern frontier was established along the Tyne-Solway line, a barrier made permanent by the construction of Hadrian's Wall following the emperor's visit to the province in 122. For a brief period in the mid-2nd century the frontier was temporarily advanced to the Forth-Clyde line with the building of the Antonine Wall, though this seems to have been abandoned early in the reign of Marcus Aurelius (ca. 163) when the Hadrianic barrier was re-commissioned and became the permanent frontier. The security thus provided to the now-peaceful province in the south facilitated urban expansion and the development of commerce. The new prosperity brought a flood of Roman coinage into the island-province and it was no longer necessary for shortages to be made good by large scale local imitation.

Until the mid-3rd century the production of Roman coinage remained the prerogative of the mint in the capital, with only occasional issues from provincial centres to serve short-term local needs. But with the deepening political and economic crisis in the third quarter of the century there was a dramatic decentralization of minting operations, with permanent establishments being set up in many important cities in the western as well as the eastern provinces. Britain, however, still remained without an official mint at this time and in the dark days of the 270s, when the separatist Gallic Empire to which Britain belonged was close to collapse, large scale production of imitative antoniniani (commonly called 'barbarous radiates') occurred in the province. The integrity and prestige of the Empire was, to some extent, restored by a rapid succession of Illyrian 'soldier emperors', until the situation was finally stabilized by Diocletian (A.D. 284-305) who established the tetrarchy system under which governmental responsibility was shared by four rulers. By the end of the 3rd century Britain had been reorganized into a civil diocese of four provinces: it had already been subdivided into Britannia Superior and Britannia Inferior almost a hundred years before, under Septimius Severus or Caracalla.

It was left to the colourful and enigmatic usurper Carausius (A.D. 287-293) to establish mints in Britain. It was, of course, vital for him to do so as his dominion was mostly confined to the island-province. Londinium (London) was his principal mint, with a secondary establishment at a place usually signing itself 'C' (probably Camulodunum, modern Colchester). After the downfall of Carausius' murderer and successor Allectus (293-296) Britain was restored to the central government, an event commemorated by the celebrated gold medallion of Constantius I showing the Caesar riding alongside the Thames approaching the gateway of the city of Londinium. At this point the mysterious 'C' mint disappears from the picture. Londinium, on the other hand, retained its status as an official mint under Diocletian's tetrarchy and its successors down to A.D. 325, when it was closed by Constantine the Great who regarded it as superfluous to his needs. In nearly four decades of existence as a Roman mint Londinium had produced a varied and extensive coinage in the names of almost all the emperors, empresses and Caesars of the period. It was destined never again to be active during Roman times, unless the extremely rare gold and silver issues of the late 4th century usurper Magnus Maximus, signed AVG, AVGOB and AVGPS, are correctly attributed to Londinium under its late Roman name of Augusta.

The termination of Roman rule in the British provinces is traditionally dated to A.D. 410 when the emperor Honorius, in response to an appeal for aid from his British subjects, told them to arrange for their own defence as best they might ('Rescript of Honorius'). In reality, the end probably came quite gradually. As the machinery of government ground to a halt and the soldiers stopped receiving their pay there would have been a steady drift of population away from the semi-ruinous cities and military installations to the countryside, where they could better provide for themselves through farming. Under these conditions the need for coinage would have been drastically reduced, as a primitive economy based on barter would largely have replaced the complex monetary economy of the late Roman period. In any case the supply of coinage from the Continent would now have dried up. The few monetary transactions which still took place were made with worn-out coins from earlier periods augmented by local imitations, production of which in Britain had resumed in the mid-4th century. Such was the pitiful end of the long tradition of Roman coinage in the remote island-province of Britannia. More than two centuries of 'Dark Ages' were to elapse before England's new rulers, the Anglo-Saxons, commenced the issue of gold thrymsas, the designs of many of which were based on late Roman types.

As Rome's Imperial coinage provided the currency needs of this country over a period of almost four centuries no representative collection of British coins is complete without some examples of these important issues. The following listing is divided into four categories: 1. Regular Roman issues, all of which would have been legal tender in Britain after A.D. 43; 2. Issues with types referring specifically to the province of Britannia, usually in commemoration of military campaigns in the north; 3. Official Roman coinage struck in Britain; 4. Imitations of Roman coins produced in Britain, all but possibly some of the earliest being of unofficial origin. The reference 'R.R.C.' is to the listing of the type in Michael Crawford's *Roman Republican Coinage* (Cambridge, 1974); and 'R.I.C.' to *The Roman Imperial Coinage* (London, 1923-1994, in ten volumes).

For more detailed collectors' information on Roman coinage, including a more comprehensive listing of types, the reader is referred to *Roman Coins and their Values* by David R. Sear (4th revised edition). A complete catalogue of silver issues may be found in the 5 volumes of *Roman Silver Coins* (H.A. Seaby and C.E. King) which provides a quick and convenient reference and is especially aimed at the collector. Gilbert Askew's *The Coinage of Roman Britain* (2nd edition) concentrates on those issues which are particularly associated with the Roman province of Britannia, but does not provide valuations. A more recent work on this subject is R. Reece's *Coinage in Roman Britain*. Newly published is David R. Sear's *The History and Coinage of the Roman Imperators, 49–27 BC* which is devoted to the vital two decades of transition from Republic to Empire.

The standard works on the coinages of the Roman Republic and the Roman Empire have already been mentioned *(Roman Republican Coinage and Roman Imperial Coinage)*. These monumental publications are essential to the advanced collector and student and their importance cannot be overstated. The British Museum Catalogues (3 volumes of Republican, 6 volumes of Imperial) are also vital. They contain superb interpretive material in their introductions and are very fully illustrated. A similar work is Anne S. Robertson's *Roman Imperial Coins in the Hunter Coin Cabinet,* in 5 volumes (volume 4 is especially important for the later 3rd century coinage). For more general reading we may recommend J.P.C. Kent and M. & A. Hirmer's *Roman Coins,* undoubtedly the most lavishly illustrated book on the subject; C.H.V. Sutherland's *Roman Coins;* and R.A.G. Carson's *Coins of the Roman Empire*. Finally, for a most useful single-volume work on interpretation and background information we would suggest A *Dictionary of Ancient Roman Coins* by John Melville Jones.

1. REGULAR ROMAN ISSUES

A token selection of the types of Roman coins which might be found on Romano-British archaeological sites. Many of the rarer emperors and empresses have been omitted and the types listed often represent only one of hundreds of variant forms which might be encountered.

		F £	*VF* £
451	**THE REPUBLIC: P. Aelius Paetus** (moneyer), 138 B.C. AR *denarius*. Helmeted hd. of Roma r. Rev. The Dioscuri galloping r. R.R.C. 233/1 ...	20	50
	Although dating from long before the Roman conquest many Republican coins circulated well into the Imperial period and found their way to Britain where they are often represented in early hoards.		
452	**L. Thorius Balbus** (moneyer), 105 B.C. AR denarius. Hd. of Juno Sospita r., clad in goat's skin. Rev. Bull charging r. *R.R.C. 316/1*.......................	25	60
453	**Q. Antonius Balbus** (moneyer), 83-82 B.C. AR *denarius*. Laur. hd. of Jupiter r. Rev. Victory in quadriga r. *R.R.C. 364/1*.................................	20	55

454

456

454	**C. Calpurnius Piso** (moneyer), 67 B.C. AR *denarius*. Laur. hd. of Apollo r. Rev. Horseman galloping r., holding palm-branch. *R.R.C. 408/1a*.......	25	60
455	**Mn. Acilius Glabrio** (moneyer), 49 B.C. AR *denarius*. Laur. hd. of Salus r. Rev. Valetudo stg. l., holding snake and resting on column. *R.R.C. 442/1.*	20	55
456	**Julius Caesar** (dictator), visited Britain 55 and 54 B.C., died 44 B.C. AR *denarius*. CAESAR. Elephant r. Rev. Priestly emblems. *R.R.C. 443/1*....	75	150
456A	— Wreathed hd. of Caesar r. Rev. P. SEPVLLIVS MACER. Venus stg. l., holding Victory and sceptre. *R.R.C. 480/9*.	300	700
457	**Mark Antony** (triumvir), died 30 B.C. AR *denarius*. Galley r. Rev. LEG. II. Legionary eagle between two standards. *R.R.C. 544/14*..........................	50	125

458

459

458	**Octavian** (triumvir), named Augustus 27 B.C. AR *denarius*. Bare hd. of Octavian r. Rev. IMP. CAESAR. Trophy set on prow. *R.I.C. 265a*.........	90	200
459	**THE EMPIRE: Augustus,** 27 B.C.-A.D. 14. AR *denarius*. Rev. C. L. CAESARES AVGVSTI F COS DESIG PRINC IVVENT. The emperor's grandsons, Gaius and Lucius, stg. facing, with spears and shields. *R.I.C. 207.*	55	130
	Almost all the coins in the Roman Imperial series have a head or bust of the emperor, empress or prince as their obverse type. Therefore, in most instances only the reverses will be described in the following listings.		

		F £	VF £
460	Æ as. ROM. ET AVG. The altar of Lugdunum. *R.I.C. 230.*	50	125
460A	Æ quadrans. Obv. Anvil. Rev. Moneyers' inscription around large S. C. *R.I.C. 443.*	15	35
461	**Augustus and Agrippa,** general and designated heir of Augustus, died 12 B.C. Æ *dupondius*. Obv. Their hds. back to back. Rev. COL. NEM. Crocodile r., chained to palm-branch. *R.I.C. 159.* .... *See also no. 468.*	55	140
462	**Divus Augustus,** deified A.D. 14. Æ as. PROVIDENT S. C. Large altar. *R.I.C. 81.*	60	150
463	**Tiberius,** A.D. 14-37. AV *aureus*. PONTIF MAXIM. Livia (?) seated r., holding sceptre and branch. *R.I.C. 29.*	350	850

464

467

		F £	VF £
464	AR denarius. Similar. *R.I.C. 30.* .... *This type is commonly referred to as the 'Tribute Penny' of the Bible (Matthew 22, 17-21).*	70	150
464A	Æ *as*. Inscription around large S. C. *R.I.C. 44.*	55	140
465	**Livia,** wife of Augustus, mother of Tiberius. Æ *dupondius*. Obv. Veiled bust of Livia as Pietas r. Rev. Inscription of Drusus Caesar around large S. C. *R.I.C. 43.*	120	325
466	**Drusus,** son of Tiberius. Æ *as*. Inscription around large S. C. *R.I.C. 45.*	65	165
467	**Caligula,** A.D. 37-41. Æ *as*. VESTA S. C. Vesta seated l. *R.I.C. 38*......	85	225

468

		F £	VF £
468	**Agrippa,** grandfather of Caligula, died 12 B.C. Æ *as*. S. C. Neptune stg. l., holding dolphin and trident. *R.I.C. 58.* .... *See also no. 461 and under Category 4.*	50	150
469	**Germanicus,** father of Caligula, brother of Claudius, died A.D. 19. Æ *as*. Inscription of Caligula around large S. C. *R.I.C. 35.*	65	165
470	**Agrippina Senior,** mother of Caligula, died A.D. 33. Æ *sestertius*. S.P.Q.R. MEMORIAE AGRIPPINAE. Carpentum drawn l. by two mules. *R.I.C. 55.*	250	850

471

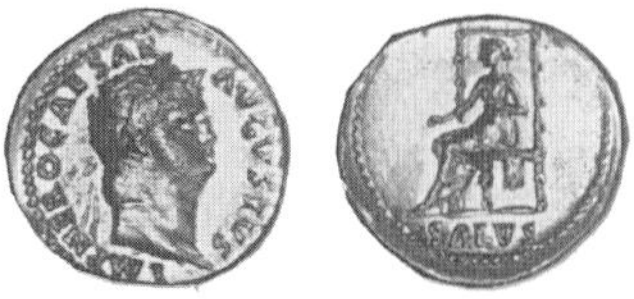

474

No.	Description	F £	VF £
471	**Claudius,** A.D. 41-54, initiated the conquest of Britain by his invasion in A.D. 43. Æ *as*. LIBERTAS AVGVSTA S. C. Libertas stg. r., holding pileus. *R.I.C. 113.*	55	140
471A	Æ *quadrans*. Obv. Hand holding scales. Rev. Inscription around large S. C. *R.I.C. 85.*	15	35
	See also under Categories 2 and 4.		
472	**Nero Claudius Drusus,** father of Claudius, died 9 B.C. Æ *sestertius*. TI. CLAVDIVS CAESAR AVG. P. M. TR .P. IMP. P. P. S. C. Claudius seated l. on curule chair amidst arms. *R.I.C. 109*	130	450
	See also under Category 4.		
473	**Antonia,** mother of Claudius, died A.D. 37. Æ *dupondius*. TI. CLAVDIVS CAESAR AVG P.M. TR. P. IMP. S. C. Claudius stg. l., holding simpulum. *R.I.C. 92.*	100	275
	See also under Category 4.		
474	**Nero,** 54-68, emperor at the time of Queen Boudicca's rebellion in Britain. **AV** *aureus*. SALVS. Salus seated l. *R.I.C. 66.*	450	1,050
475	AR *denarius*. IVPPITER CVSTOS. Jupiter seated l. *R.I.C. 53.*	85	250
476	Æ *sestertius*. ROMA S. C. Roma seated l., holding Victory and parazonium. *R.I.C. 274.*	100	350
476A	Æ as. S. C. Victory hovering l., holding shield inscribed S. P. Q. R. *R.I.C. 312.*	50	125
477	**Galba,** 68-69. AR *denarius*. S.P.Q.R. / OB / C.S. within oak-wreath. *R.I.C. 167.*	90	275
478	**Otho,** 69. AR *denarius*. SECVRITAS P. R. Securitas stg. l. *R.I.C. 10*	200	500
479	**Vitellius,** 69. AR denarius. CONCORDIA P. R. Concordia seated l. *R.I.C. 90.*	90	275
480	**Vespasian,** 69-79, commanded Legio II in the Claudian invasion of Britain (43) and appointed Agricola to governorship of the province in 77/8. **AV** *aureus*. ANNONA AVG. Annona seated l. *R.I.C. 131a*	500	1,200

481

No.	Description	F £	VF £
481	Æ *denarius*. VICTORIA AVGVSTI. Victory advancing r., crowning standard. *R.I.C. 52.*	22	65
481A	Æ *dupondius*. FELICITAS PVBLICA S. C. Felicitas stg. l. *R.I.C. 554*	40	100
482	**Titus,** 79-81 (Caesar 69-79). AR *denarius*. TR. P. IX. IMP. XV. COS. VIII. P. P. Thunderbolt on throne. *R.I.C. 23a*	40	120

483

485

No.	Description	F £	VF £
483	**Domitian,** 81-96 (Caesar 69-81), recalled Agricola in 83/4 and abandoned the conquest of northern Scotland (ca. 87). Æ *denarius*. IMP. XIX. COS. XIIII. CENS. P. P. P. Minerva stg. l., resting on spear. *R.I.C. 140*.	22	55
484	Æ *dupondius*. VIRTVTI AVGVSTI S. C. Virtus stg. r. *R.I.C. 393*..........	30	75
484A	Æ *as*. MONETA AVGVSTI S. C. Moneta stg. l. *R.I.C. 354b*.................	30	75
485	**Nerva,** 96-98. Æ denarius. AEQVITAS AVGVST. Aequitas stg. l. *R.I.C. 13*.	40	100
485A	Æ *as*. LIBERTAS PVBLICA S. C. Libertas stg. l. *R.I.C. 86*.	55	140
486	**Trajan,** 98-117, established the northern frontier in Britain along the Tyne-Solway line (ca. 100). *N aureus*. P. M. TR. P. COS. VI. P. P. S. P. Q. R. Genius stg. l., holding patera and corn-ears. *R.I.C. 347*.	400	900

487

490

No.	Description	F £	VF £
487	Æ *denarius*. COS. V. P. P. S. P. Q. R. OPTIMO PRINC. Military trophy. *R.I.C. 147*.	22	55
488	Æ *sestertius*. S. P. Q. R. OPTIMO PRINCIPI S. C. Spes walking l., holding flower. *R.I.C. 519*...	40	150
488A	Æ *dupondius*. SENATVS POPVLVSQVE ROMANVS S. C. Emperor advancing between two trophies. *R.I.C. 676*...	25	65
489	**Hadrian,** 117-138, visited Britain in 122 and initiated the construction of a fortified frontier line (Hadrian's Wall). *N aureus*. HISPANIA. Hispania reclining l. *R.I.C. 305*.	500	1,100
490	Æ d*enarius*. P. M. TR. P. COS. III. Roma stg. l., holding Victory and spear. *R.I.C. 76*.	25	60
491	Æ *sestertius*. COS. III. S. C. Neptune stg. r., holding dolphin and trident, foot on prow. *R.I.C. 632*..	50	175
491A	Æ *as*. FELICITATI AVG COS. III. P. P. S. C. Galley travelling l. over waves. *R.I.C. 719*.	40	100
	See also under Category 2.		
492	**Sabina,** wife of Hadrian. Æ *denarius*. IVNONI REGINAE. Juno stg. l. *R.I.C. 395a*.	40	100
493	**Aelius Caesar,** heir of Hadrian, 136-138. Æ *denarius*. CONCORD. TR. POT. COS. II. Concordia seated l. *R.I.C. 436*.	75	200
493A	Æ *as*. TR. POT. COS. II. S. C. Spes walking l., holding flower. *R.I.C. 1067*.	50	130

		F £	*VF* £
494	**Antoninus Pius,** 138-161, ordered the expansion of the Roman province to include southern Scotland and constructed the Antonine Wall on the Forth-Clyde line (beginning ca. 143). An uprising in northern Britain in the 150s results in a permanent withdrawal to the Hadrianic frontier early in the next reign. **Ꞛ** *aureus*. COS. IIII. Togate emperor stg. l., holding globe. *R.I.C. 233b.*	350	750
495	Ꞧ *denarius*. PIETATI AVG. COS. IIII. Pietas stg. l. between two children, holding two more in her arms. *R.I.C. 313c.*	20	50

496

		F £	*VF* £
496	Æ *sestertius*. SALVS AVG. S. C. Salus stg. l. at altar, feeding snake. *R.I.C. 635.*	32	120
496A	Æ *dupondius*. TR. POT. XX. COS. IIII. S. C. Providentia stg. l., pointing at globe at her feet and holding sceptre. *R.I.C. 2025.*	24	60
	See also under Categories 2 and 3.		
497	**Antoninus Pius and Marcus Aurelius Caesar**. Ꞧ *denarius*. Obv. Laur. hd. of Antoninus Pius r. Rev. AVRELIVS CAESAR AVG PII F. COS. Bare hd. of young Marcus Aurelius r. *R.I.C. 417a.*	50	120

498

501

		F £	*VF* £
498	**Divus Antoninus Pius,** deified 161. Ꞧ *denarius*. CONSECRATIO. Four-storeyed crematorium of Antoninus Pius. *R.I.C. 436.*	24	60
499	**Diva Faustina Senior,** wife of Antoninus Pius, deified 141. Ꞧ *denarius*. AETERNITAS. Aeternitas stg. l., holding globe and billowing veil. *R.I.C. 351.*	20	50
499A	Æ *sestertius*. AVGVSTA S. C. Ceres stg. l., holding two torches. *R.I.C. 1120.*	30	110
500	**Marcus Aurelius,** 161-180 (Caesar 139-161), re-established Hadrian's Wall as the permanent northern frontier of the province, ca. 163. **Ꞛ** *aureus*. PROV. DEOR. TR. P. XV. COS. III. Providentia stg. l., holding globe and cornucopiae. *R.I.C. 19*	400	900
501	Ꞧ *denarius*. PIETAS AVG. Priestly emblems. *R.I.C. 424a.*	24	60
501A	— SALVTI AVG. COS. III. Salus stg. l. at altar, feeding snake. *R.I.C. 222.*	20	55
502	Æ *sestertius*. CONCORD. AVGVSTOR. TR. P. XVI. COS. III. S. C. Marcus Aurelius and Lucius Verus stg. face to face, clasping hands. *R.I.C. 826.*	35	120
502A	Æ *as*. HONOS TR. POT. II. COS. II. S. C. Honos stg. r. *R.I.C. 1271a.*	30	75

		F £	VF £
503	**Divus Marcus Aurelius,** deified 180. Æ *denarius*. CONSECRATIO. Eagle stg. r. on altar. *R.I.C. 272.*	28	70

504

506A

		F £	VF £
504	**Faustina Junior,** daughter of Antoninus Pius, wife of Marcus Aurelius. Æ *denarius*. FECVNDITAS. Fecunditas stg. r., holding sceptre and child. *R.I.C. 677.*	20	50
504A	Æ *sestertius*. HILARITAS S. C. Hilaritas stg. l. *R.I.C. 1642.*	30	110
505	**Diva Faustina Junior,** deified 175. Æ *as*. S. C. Crescent and seven stars. *R.I.C. 1714.*	30	75
506	**Lucius Verus,** 161-169. Æ denarius. PAX TR. P. VI. IMP. IIII. COS. II. Pax stg. l. *R.I.C. 561.*	25	65
506A	Æ *dupondius*. TR. P. IIII. IMP. II. COS. II. S. C. Mars stg. r., resting on spear and shield. *R.I.C. 1387.*	30	75
507	**Lucilla,** daughter of Marcus Aurelius, wife of Lucius Verus. Æ *denarius*. IVNONI LVCINAE. Juno stg. l., holding child in swaddling clothes. *R.I.C. 771.*	25	65
507A	Æ *sestertius*. PIETAS S. C. Pietas stg. l., altar at feet. *R.I.C. 1756.*	35	120
508	**Commodus,** 177-192 (Caesar 175-177), major warfare on the British frontier early in the reign; situation restored by Ulpius Marcellus in 184/5, followed by unrest in the British legions. Æ *denarius*. LIB. AVG. IIII. TR. P. VI. IMP. IIII. COS. III. P. P. Liberalitas stg. l. *R.I.C. 22.*	20	50

509

511

		F £	VF £
509	Æ *sestertius*. IOVI VICTORI IMP. III. COS. II. P. P. S. C. Jupiter seated l. *R.I.C. 1612.*	35	110
509A	Æ *as*. ANN. AVG. TR. P. VII. IMP. IIII. COS. III. P. P. S. C. Annona stg. l., modius at feet. *R.I.C. 339* *See also under Category 2.*	24	60
510	**Crispina,** wife of Commodus. Æ *denarius*. CONCORDIA. Clasped hands. *R.I.C. 279.*	30	75
511	**Pertinax,** January-March 193, formerly governor of Britain, ca. 185-7. Æ *denarius*. PROVID. DEOR. COS. II. Providentia stg l., reaching up to star. *R.I.C. 11a.*	250	550

512

513A

No.	Description	F £	VF £
512	**Didius Julianus,** March-June 193. Æ *denarius*. CONCORD MILIT. Concordia Militum stg. l., holding standards. *R.I.C. 1*.	375	850
513	**Clodius Albinus,** 195-197 (Caesar 193-195), governor of Britain (from 191/2) at the time of his imperial proclamation by his troops. Æ *denarius*. MINER. PACIF. COS. II. Minerva stg. l. *R.I.C. 7*.	55	125
513A	— FIDES LEGION. COS. II. Clasped hands holding legionary eagle. *R.I.C. 20b*.	75	175

514

516

No.	Description	F £	VF £
514	**Septimius Severus,** 193-211, restored the frontier forts in northern Britain following the downfall of Clodius Albinus; later repaired Hadrian's Wall, and spent the years 208-11 in Britain campaigning in Scotland; divided Britannia into two provinces, Superior and Inferior; died at York, February 211. Æ *denarius*. VIRT AVGG. Roma stg. l., holding Victory, spear and shield. *R.I.C. 171a*.	15	35
514A	— P.M. TR. P. XVIII. COS. III. P. P. Jupiter stg. l. between two children. *R.I.C. 240*.	15	35
	See also under Category 2.		
515	**Julia Domna,** wife of Septimius Severus, mother of Caracalla and Geta, accompanied her husband and sons on the British expedition, 208-211, and probably resided in London during the northern campaigns. Æ *denarius*. VENERI VICTR. Venus stg. r., resting on column. *R.I.C. 536*.	15	40
515A	— VESTA. Vesta stg. l., holding palladium and sceptre. *R.I.C. 390*.	15	40
516	**Caracalla,** 198-217 (Caesar 196-198), accompanied his father and brother on the British expedition, 208-211, and led the final campaign in Scotland in 210 during Severus' illness; made frontier dispositions before returning to Rome and finalized his father's arrangements for the division of Britain into two provinces. Æ *antoninianus* (*double denarius,* introduced in 215). VENVS VICTRIX. Venus stg. l., holding Victory and resting on shield. *R.I.C. 311c*.	25	65
517	Æ *denarius*. PART. MAX. PONT. TR. P. IIII. Trophy with two captives at base. *R.I.C. 54b*.	15	40
517A	— P. M. TR. P. XV. COS. III. P. P. Hercules stg. l., holding olive-branch and club. *R.I.C. 192*	15	35
	See also under Category 2.		

		F £	*VF* £
518	**Plautilla,** wife of Caracalla. Æ *denarius*. PROPAGO IMPERI. Caracalla and Plautilla clasping hands. *R.I.C. 362.*	25	65

519

522A

		F £	*VF* £
519	**Geta,** 209-212 (Caesar 198-209), accompanied his father and brother on the British expedition, 208-211, and took charge of the civil administration in London during the northern campaigns. Æ *denarius*. PRINC. IVVENTVTIS. Prince stg. l. beside trophy, holding branch and spear. *R.I.C. 18.*	20	50
519A	— FORT RED TR. P. III. COS. II. Fortuna seated l. *R.I.C. 75*	25	65
	See also under Category 2.		
520	**Macrinus,** 217-218. Æ *denarius*. PROVIDENTIA DEORVM. Providentia stg. l., globe at feet. *R.I.C. 80.*	30	75
521	**Diadumenian,** 218 (Caesar 217-218). Æ *denarius*. PRINC. IVVENTVTIS. Prince stg. l., two standards behind. *R.I.C. 109.*	70	175
522	**Elagabalus,** 218-222. Æ *antoninianus*. MARS VICTOR. Mars advamcing r. *R.I.C. 122.*	22	55
522A	Æ *denarius*. P. M. TR. P. III. COS. III. P. P. Jupiter seated l., eagle at feet *R.I.C. 27.*	15	35
523	**Julia Paula**, first wife of Elagabalus. Æ *denarius*. CONCORDIA. Concordia seated l. *R.I.C. 211.*	40	100
524	**Aquilia Severa,** second wife of Elagabalus. Æ *denarius*. CONCORDIA. Concordia stg. l., altar at feet. *R.I.C. 226.*	60	150
525	**Julia Soaemias,** mother of Elagabalus. Æ *denarius*. VENVS CAELESTIS. Venus seated l., child at feet. *R.I.C. 243.*	30	75
526	**Julia Maesa,** grandmother of Elagabalus and Severus Alexander. Æ *denarius*. SAECVLI FELICITAS. Felicitas stg. l., altar at feet. *R.I.C. 271.*	22	55
527	**Severus Alexander,** 222-235 (Caesar 221-222). Æ *denarius*. PAX AETERNA AVG. Pax stg. l. *R.I.C. 165.*	15	35
527A	— P. M. TR. P. XIII. COS. III. P. P. Sol advancing l., holding whip. *R.I.C. 123.*	15	35

528

		F £	*VF* £
528	Æ *sestertius*. MARS VLTOR S. C. Mars advancing r., with spear and shield. *R.I.C. 635.*	25	75

		F £	*VF* £
529	**Orbiana,** wife of Severus Alexander. Æ *denarius*. CONCORDIA AVGG. Concordia seated l. *R.I.C. 319*.	70	175
530	**Julia Mamaea,** mother of Severus Alexander. Æ *denarius*. VESTA. Vesta stg. l. *R.I.C. 362*.	20	45
530A	Æ *sestertius*. FELICITAS PVBLICA S. C. Felicitas stg. facing, hd. l., resting on column. *R.I.C. 676*.	30	85

531

531	**Maximinus I,** 235-238. Æ *denarius*. PAX AVGVSTI. Pax stg. l. *R.I.C. 12*.	20	45
531A	Æ *sestertius*. SALVS AVGVSTI S. C. Salus seated l., feeding snake arising from altar. *R.I.C. 85*.	30	85
532	**Maximus Caesar,** son of Maximinus I. Æ *denarius*. PRINC IVVENTVTIS. Prince stg. l., two standards behind. *R.I.C. 3*.	50	125
533	**Gordian I Africanus,** March-April 238, governor of Britannia Inferior late in the reign of Caracalla. Æ *denarius*. P. M. TR. P. COS. P. P. Togate emperor stg. l. *R.I.C. 1*.	250	600
534	**Gordian II Africanus,** March-April 238. Æ *denarius*. VIRTVS AVGG. Virtus stg. l., with shield and spear. *R.I.C. 3*	250	600
535	**Balbinus,** April-July 238. Æ *antoninianus*. FIDES MVTVA AVGG. Clasped hands. *R.I.C. 11*.	75	175
535A	Æ *denarius*. PROVIDENTIA DEORVM. Providentia stg. l., globe at feet. *R.I.C. 7*.	50	125
536	**Pupienus,** April-July 238. Æ *antoninianus*. AMOR MVTVVS AVGG. Clasped hands. *R.I.C. 9a*.	75	175
536A	Æ *denarius*. PAX PVBLICA. Pax seated l. *R.I.C. 4*.	50	120
537	**Gordian III,** 238-244 (Caesar 238). Æ *antoninianus*. LAETITIA AVG. N. Laetitia stg. l. *R.I.C. 86*.	12	25
538	Æ *denarius*. DIANA LVCIFERA. Diana stg. r., holding torch. *R.I.C. 127*.	15	30

538A

538A	Æ *sestertius*. AETERNITATI AVG. S.C. Sol stg. l., holding globe. *R.I.C. 297a*.	22	65

539

No.		F £	VF £
539	**Philip I,** 244-249. Æ *antoninianus*. ROMAE AETERNAE. Roma seated l. *R.I.C. 65.*	12	25
539A	Æ *sestertius*. SECVRIT. ORBIS S. C. Securitas seated l. *R.I.C. 190.*	22	65
540	**Otacilia Severa,** wife of Philip I. Æ *antoninianus*. PIETAS AVGVSTAE. Pietas stg. l. *R.I.C. 125c.*	15	35
540A	Æ *sestertius*. CONCORDIA AVGG. S. C. Concordia seated l. *R.I.C. 203a.*	25	75
541	**Philip II,** 247-249 (Caesar 244-247). Æ *antoninianus*. PRINCIPI IVVENT. Prince stg. l., holding globe and spear. *R.I.C. 218d.*	15	35
541A	Æ *sestertius*. PAX AETERNA S. C. Pax stg. l. *R.I.C. 268c.*	25	75

542

543

No.		F £	VF £
542	**Trajan Decius,** 249-251. Æ *antoninianus*. DACIA. Dacia stg. l., holding staff with ass's hd. *R.I.C. 12b.*	12	30
542A	Æ *sestertius*. PANNONIAE S. C. The two Pannoniae stg., each holding standard. *R.I.C. 124a*	25	75
543	**Herennia Etruscilla,** wife of Trajan Decius. Æ *antoninianus*. PVDICITIA AVG. Pudicitia stg. l. *R.I.C. 58b*	15	35
544	**Herennius Etruscus,** 251 (Caesar 250-251). Æ *antoninianus*. PIETAS AVGG. Mercury stg. l., holding purse and caduceus. *R.I.C. 142b.*	25	65
545	**Hostilian,** 251 (Caesar 251). Æ *antoninianus*. PRINCIPI IVVENTVTIS. Apollo seated l., holding branch. *R.I.C. 180.*	35	85
546	**Trebonianus Gallus,** 251-253. Æ *antoninianus*. FELICITAS PVBLICA. Felicitas stg. l., resting on column. *R.I.C. 34A*	12	30
546A	Æ *sestertius*. SALVS AVGG S. C. Salus stg. r., feeding snake held in her arms. *R.I.C. 121a.*	25	75
547	**Volusian,** 251-253 (Caesar 251). Æ *antoninianus*. VIRTVS AVGG. Virtus stg. l. *R.I.C. 186.*	12	30
548	**Aemilian,** 253. Æ *antoninianus*. PACI AVG. Pax stg. l., resting on column. *R.I.C. 8.*	50	120
549	**Valerian,** 253-260. Billon antoninianus. FIDES MILITVM. Fides stg. r., holding two standards. *R.I.C. 241*	8	20
550	**Diva Mariniana,** wife of Valerian, deified 253. Billon *antoninianus*. CONSECRATIO. Empress seated on peacock flying r. *R.I.C. 6.*	45	110

		F £	*VF* £
551	**Gallienus,** 253-268, during whose reign Rome temporarily lost control over Britain when Postumus rebelled and established the independent Gallic Empire in 260. Billon *antoninianus*. VIRT GALLIENI AVG. Emperor advancing r., captive at feet. *R.I.C. 54*.	10	25

552

552	— DIANAE CONS. AVG. Doe l. *R.I.C. 176*.	8	20
552A	— SOLI INVICTO. Sol stg. l., holding globe. *R.I.C. 658*.	8	18
553	**Salonina,** wife of Gallienus. Billon *antoninianus*. VENVS FELIX. Venus seated l., child at feet. *R.I.C. 7*.	8	20
553A	— IVNONI CONS. AVG. Doe l. *R.I.C. 16*.	8	20
554	**Valerian Junior,** son of Gallienus, Caesar 256-258. Billon *antoninianus*. IOVI CRESCENTI. Infant Jupiter seated on goat r. *R.I.C. 13*.	15	35
555	**Divus Valerian Junior,** deified 258. Billon *antoninianus*. CONSECRATIO. Large altar. *R.I.C. 24*.	12	30
556	**Saloninus,** 260 (Caesar 258-260). Billon *antoninianus*. PIETAS AVG. Priestly emblems. *R.I.C. 9*	12	30
557	**Macrianus,** usurper in the East, 260-261. Billon *antoninianus*. SOL. INVICTO. Sol stg. l., holding globe. *R.I.C. 12*	35	85
558	**Quietus,** usurper in the East, 260-261. Billon *antoninianus*. INDVLGENTIAE AVG. Indulgentia seated l. *R.I.C. 5*.	35	85
559	**Postumus,** usurper in the West, 260-268, founder of the 'Gallic Empire' which temporarily detached Britain from the rule of the central government, a state of affairs which continued until Aurelian's defeat of Tetricus in 273. Billon *antoninianus*. HERC. DEVSONIENSI. Hercules stg. r. *R.I.C. 64*.	12	30

560

560	— MONETA AVG. Moneta stg. l. *R.I.C. 75*.	10	25
560A	Æ *sestertius*. FIDES MILITVM. Fides stg. l., holding two standards. *R.I.C. 128*.	50	140
561	**Laelianus,** usurper in the West, 268. Billon *antoninianus*. VICTORIA AVG. Victory advancing r. *R.I.C. 9*.	110	275
562	**Marius,** usurper in the West, 268. Billon *antoninianus*. CONCORDIA MILITVM. Clasped hands. *R.I.C. 7*.	35	85
563	**Victorinus**, usurper in the West, 268-270. Billon *antoninianus*. INVICTVS. Sol advancing l. *R.I.C. 114*.	8	20

		F £	*VF* £
564	**Tetricus,** usurper in the West, 270-273, defeated by Aurelian, thus ending the 'Gallic Empire' and the isolation of Britain from the authority of Rome. Billon *antoninianus*. LAETITIA AVGG. Laetitia stg. l. *R.I.C. 87*..........	8	20
	See also under Category 4.		
565	**Tetricus Junior,** son of Tetricus, Caesar 270-273. Billon *antoninianus*. SPES PVBLICA. Spes walking l., holding flower *R.I.C. 272*.................	8	20
	See also under Category 4.		
566	**Claudius II Gothicus,** 268-270. Billon *antoninianus*. IOVI STATORI. Jupiter stg. r. *R.I.C. 52*.	8	18
567	**Divus Claudius II,** deified 270. Billon *antoninianus*. CONSECRATIO. Large altar. *R.I.C. 261*............	8	20
	See also under Category 4.		
568	**Quintillus,** 270. Billon *antoninianus*. DIANA LVCIF. Diana stg. r., holding torch. *R.I.C. 49*............	18	45
569	**Aurelian,** 270-275, restored Britain to the rule of the central government through his defeat of Tetricus in 273; possibly began construction of the chain of 'Saxon Shore' forts on the eastern and southern coastlines. Billon *antoninianus*. ORIENS AVG. Sol stg. l. between two captives. *R.I.C. 63*.	10	25
569A	— RESTITVT. ORBIS. Female stg. r., presenting wreath to emperor stg. l. *R.I.C. 399*.	10	25
570	**Aurelian and Vabalathus,** ruler of Palmyra 267-272 and usurper in the East from 271. Billon *antoninianus*. Obv. Laur. bust of Vabalathus r. Rev. Rad. bust of Aurelian r. *R.I.C. 381*.	25	65

571

574A

		F £	*VF* £
571	**Severina,** wife of Aurelian. Billon *antoninianus*. PROVIDEN. DEOR. Concordia (or Fides) Militum stg. r., facing Sol stg. l. *R.I.C. 9*.	18	45
572	**Tacitus,** 275-276. Billon *antoninianus*. SECVRIT. PERP. Securitas stg. l., leaning on column. *R.I.C. 163*.	15	35
573	**Florian,** 276. Billon *antoninianus*. LAETITIA FVND. Laetitia stg. l. *R.I.C. 34*.	30	75
574	**Probus,** 276-282, suppressed governor's revolt in Britain and lifted restrictions on viticulture in Britain and Gaul. Billon *antoninianus*. ADVENTVS PROBI AVG. Emperor on horseback l., captive seated before. *R.I.C. 160*.	10	25
574A	— VICTORIA GERM. Trophy between two captives. *R.I.C. 222*.	15	40
575	**Carus,** 282-283. Billon *antoninianus*. PAX EXERCITI. Pax stg. l., holding olive-branch and standard. *R.I.C. 75*............	15	40
576	**Divus Carus,** deified 283. Billon *antoninianus*. CONSECRATIO. Eagle facing, hd. l. *R.I.C. 28*.	18	45
577	**Carinus,** 283-285 (Caesar 282-283). Billon *antoninianus*. SAECVLI FELICITAS. Emperor stg. r. *R.I.C. 214*.	12	30

		F £	VF £
578	**Magnia Urbica,** wife of Carinus. Billon *antoninianus*. VENVS VICTRIX. Venus stg. l., holding helmet, shield at feet. *R.I.C. 343*	60	150
579	**Numerian,** 283-284 (Caesar 282-283). Billon *antoninianus*. CLEMENTIA TEMP. Emperor stg. r., receiving globe from Jupiter stg. l. *R.I.C. 463*. ..	12	35
580	**Diocletian,** 284-305. Æ *argenteus*. VIRTVS MILITVM. The four tetrarchs sacrificing before gateway of military camp. *R.I.C. 27a (Rome)*.	100	250
581	Billon *antoninianus*. IOVI CONSERVAT AVGG. Jupiter stg. l. *R.I.C. 162*.	10	25
582	Æ *follis*. GENIO POPVLI ROMANI. Genius stg. l. R.I.C. 14a *(Alexandria)*.	10	30
582A	— (post-abdication coinage, after 305). PROVIDENTIA DEORVM QVIES AVGG. Quies and Providentia stg. facing each other. *R.I.C. 676a (Treveri)*. *See also under Category 3*.	22	65
583	**Maximian,** 286-305 and 306-308, failed in his attempts to suppress the usurpation of Carausius in Britain. Æ *argenteus*. VICTORIA SARMAT. The four tetrarchs sacrificing before gateway of military camp. *R.I.C. 37b (Rome)*.	100	250

584

		F £	VF £
584	Billon *antoninianus*. SALVS AVGG. Salus stg. r., feeding snake held in her arms. *R.I.C. 417*.	8	20
585	Æ *follis*. SAC. MON. VRB. AVGG. ET CAESS. NN. Moneta stg. l. *R.I.C. 105b (Rome)*.	12	35
585A	— (second reign). CONSERVATORES VRB SVAE. Roma seated in hexastyle temple. *R.I.C. 84b (Ticinum)*. *See also under Category 3*. *[For coins of the usurpers **Carausius** and **Allectus** see under Category 3]*	12	35
586	**Constantius I,** 305-306 (Caesar 293-305), invaded Britain 296 and defeated the usurper Allectus, thus restoring the island to the rule of the central government; Britain now divided into four provinces and the northern frontier defences reconstructed; died at York, July 306. Æ *argenteus*. PROVIDENTIA AVGG. The four tetrarchs sacrificing before gateway of military camp. *R.I.C. 11a (Rome)*	110	275

587

		F £	VF £
587	Æ *follis*. GENIO POPVLI ROMANI. Genius stg. l. *R.I.C. 26a (Aquileia)*.	12	35
587A	— SALVIS AVGG. ET CAESS. FEL. KART. Carthage stg. l., holding fruits. *R.I.C. 30a (Carthage)*. *See also under Category 3*.	15	40

588

		F £	VF £
588	**Galerius,** 305-311 (Caesar 293-305). A argenteus. VIRTVS MILITVM. The four tetrarchs sacrificing before gateway of military camp. *R.I.C. 15b (Ticinum).*	100	250
588A	— XC / VI in wreath. *R.I.C. 16b (Carthage)*	150	400
589	Æ *follis*. GENIO AVGG ET CAESARVM NN. Genius stg. l. *R.I.C. 11b (Cyzicus)*	12	35
589A	— GENIO IMPERATORIS. Genius stg. l. *R.I.C. 101a (Alexandria)*	8	25
	See also under Category 3.		
590	**Galeria Valeria,** wife of Galerius. Æ *follis*. VENERI VICTRICI. Venus stg. l. *R.I.C. 110 (Alexandria).*	35	85
591	**Severus II,** 306-307 (Caesar 305-306). Æ *follis*. FIDES MILITVM. Fides seated l. *R.I.C. 73 (Ticinum).*	35	85
	See also under Category 3.		
592	**Maximinus II,** 310-313 (Caesar 305-310). Æ *follis*. GENIO CAESARIS. Genius stg. l. *R.I.C. 64 (Alexandria)*	8	25
592A	— GENIO POP. ROM. Genius stg. l. *R.I.C. 845a (Treveri)*	8	20
	See also under Category 3.		

593

		F £	VF £
593	**Maxentius,** 306-312 (Caesar 306). Æ *follis*. CONSERV. VRB. SVAE. Roma seated in hexastyle temple. *R.I.C. 210 (Rome)*	10	30
594	**Romulus,** son of Maxentius, deified 309. Æ *quarter follis*. AETERNAE MEMORIAE. Temple with domed roof. *R.I.C. 58 (Ostia).*	35	85
595	**Licinius,** 308-324. Æ *follis*. GENIO AVGVSTI. Genius stg. l. *R.I.C. 198b (Siscia).*	8	20
595A	Æ 3. IOVI CONSERVATORI AVGG. Jupiter stg. l. *R.I.C. 24 (Nicomedia).*	8	20
	See also under Category 3.		
596	**Licinius Junior,** son of Licinius, Caesar 317-324. Æ 3. CAESARVM NOSTRORVM around wreath containing VOT. / V. *R.I.C. 92 (Thessalonica).*	8	22
597	**Constantine I, the Great,** 307-337 (Caesar 306-307), campaigned with his father Constantius I against the Picts in northern Britain, summer 306, and proclaimed emperor by the legions at York on Constantius' death in July; closed the London mint early in 325 ending almost four decades of operation. Æ *follis*. GENIO POP ROM. Genius stg. l. *R.I.C. 719b (Treveri).*	12	35
598	— SOLI INVICTO COMITI. Sol stg. l. *R.I.C. 307 (Lugdunum)*	6	18
598A	Æ 3. PROVIDENTIAE AVGG. Gateway of military camp. *R.I.C. 153 (Thessalonica).*	5	15

599

600

		F £	VF £
599	— VIRTVS EXERCIT. Trophy between two captives. *R.I.C. 280 (Treveri).*	12	30
599A	Æ 3/4. GLORIA EXERCITVS. Two soldiers stg. either side of two standards. *R.I.C. 518 (Treveri)*.	4	12
	See also under Category 3.		
600	**'Urbs Roma',** after 330. Æ 3/4. Obv. Helmeted bust of Roma l. Rev. She-wolf l., suckling twins. *R.I.C. 195 (Nicomedia).*	5	15

601

604

		F £	VF £
601	**'Constantinopolis',** after 330. Æ 3/4. Obv. Helmeted bust of Constantinopolis l. Rev. Victory stg. l., foot on prow. *R.I.C. 339 (Rome).*	5	15
602	**Fausta,** wife of Constantine I. Æ 3. SALVS REIPVBLICAE. Empress stg. l., holding two children. *R.I.C. 459 (Treveri)*.	18	45
	See also under Category 3.		
603	**Helena,** mother of Constantine I. Æ 3. SECVRITAS REIPVBLICE. Empress stg. l., holding branch. *R.I.C. 38 (Alexandria).*	18	40
603A	Æ 4 (posthumous issue, 337-340). PAX PVBLICA. Pax stg. l. *R.I.C. 78 (Treveri).*	10	25
	See also under Category 3.		
604	**Theodora,** second wife of Constantius I. Æ 4 (posthumous issue, 337-340). PIETAS ROMANA. Pietas stg. r., holding child. R.I.C. 43 (Treveri).	12	30
605	**Crispus,** eldest son of Constantine I, Caesar 317-326. Æ 3. CAESARVM NOSTRORVM around wreath containing VOT. / V. *R.I.C. 68 (Aquileia).*	8	20
	See also under Category 3.		
606	**Delmatius,** nephew of Constantine I, Caesar 335-337. Æ 3/4. GLORIA EXERCITVS. Two soldiers stg. either side of two standards. *R.I.C. 90 (Antioch)*.	18	45
607	**Hanniballianus,** nephew of Constantine I, Rex 335-337. Æ 4. SECVRITAS PVBLICA. River-god Euphrates reclining r. *R.I.C. 147 (Constantinople).*	100	250
608	**Constantine II,** 337-340 (Caesar 317-337). Æ 3. BEATA TRANQVILLITAS. Altar inscribed VOT / IS / XX. *R.I.C. 312 (Treveri).*	8	20
608A	Æ 3/4. GLORIA EXERCITVS. Two soldiers stg. either side of standard. *R.I.C. 392 (Rome).*	4	10
	See also under Category 3.		
609	**Constans,** 337-350 (Caesar 333-337), visited Britain in 343, the last reigning emperor to do so. Æ 2. FEL. TEMP. REPARATIO. Soldier r., dragging barbarian from hut beneath tree. *R.I.C. 103 (Aquileia).*	10	30

609A

611B

		F £	VF £
609A	— FEL. TEMP. REPARATIO. Emperor stg. l. on galley steered by Victory. *R.I.C. 219 (Treveri)*.	10	30
609B	Æ 4. VICTORIAE DD. AVGG. Q. NN. Two Victories stg. face to face. *R.I.C. 195 (Treveri)*.	4	10
610	**Constantius II,** 337-361 (Caesar 324-337). Æ 3/4. GLORIA EXERCITVS. Two soldiers stg. either side of two standards. *R.I.C. 85 (Cyzicus)*.	4	12
611	Æ *siliqua*. VOTIS / XXX. / MVLTIS / XXXX. in wreath. *R.I.C. 207 (Arelate)*.	25	60
611A	Æ 2. FEL. TEMP. REPARATIO. Emperor stg. l. on galley. *R.I.C. 218 (Treveri)*.	10	30
611B	Æ 3. FEL. TEMP. REPARATIO. Soldier advancing l., spearing fallen horseman. *R.I.C. 189 (Lugdunum)*.	5	15
	See also under Categories 3 and 4.		

612

616

612	**Magnentius,** usurper in the West, 350-353, temporarily detached Britain from the rule of the legitimate Constantinian dynasty. Æ 1. SALVS DD. NN. AVG. ET CAES. *Chi-Rho* Christian monogram between Alpha and Omega. *R.I.C. 34 (Ambianum)*.	75	175
612A	Æ 2. FELICITAS REIPVBLICE. Emperor stg. l., holding Victory and labarum. *R.I.C. 264 (Treveri)*.	15	40
	See also under Category 4.		
613	**Decentius,** brother of Magnentius, Caesar 351-353. Æ 2. VICTORIAE DD. NN. AVG. ET CAE. Two Victories supporting between them shield inscribed VOT. / V. / MVLT. / X. *R.I.C. 146 (Lugdunum)*.	20	50
	See also under Category 4.		
614	**Vetranio,** 'usurper' in the Balkans, 350. Æ 2. CONCORDIA MILITVM. Emperor stg. l., holding two labara. *R.I.C. 281 (Siscia)*.	50	125
615	**Constantius Gallus,** Caesar under Constantius II, 351-354. Æ 2. FEL. TEMP. REPARATIO. Soldier advancing l., spearing fallen horseman. *R.I.C. 94 (Cyzicus)*.	15	40
616	**Julian II,** 360-363 (Caesar 355-360). Æ *siliqua*. VOT. / X. / MVLT. / XX. in wreath. *R.I.C. 309 (Arelate)*.	25	60

		F £	VF £
617	Æ 1. SECVRITAS REIPVB. Bull stg. r. *R.I.C. 411 (Siscia)*....................	45	140
617A	Æ 3. VOT. / X. / MVLT. / XX. in wreath. *R.I.C. 108 (Sirmium)*............	8	25
618	**Jovian,** 363-364. Æ 3. VOT. / V. / MVLT. / X. in wreath. *R.I.C. 426 (Siscia)*.	12	35
619	**Valentinian I,** 364-375 (in the West), during whose reign the Roman province of Britannia was devastated by the simultaneous attack of hordes of invaders on several fronts (the 'Barbarian Conspiracy'); order eventually restored by Count Theodosius, father of the future emperor . **AV** *solidus*. RESTITVTOR REIPVBLICAE. Emperor stg. r., holding standard and Victory. *R.I.C. 2b (Antioch)*..	100	250
619A	Æ 3. GLORIA ROMANORVM. Emperor advancing r., dragging barbarian and holding labarum. *R.I.C. 14a (Siscia)*.	5	15

619B

		F £	VF £
619B	— SECVRITAS REIPVBLICAE. Victory advancing l. *R.I.C. 32a (Treveri)*.	5	15
620	**Valens,** 364-378 (in the East). AR *siliqua*. VRBS ROMA. Roma seated l. *R.I.C. 27e (Treveri)*...	25	60
620A	Æ 3. SECVRITAS REIPVBLICAE. Victory advancing l. *R.I.C. 42b (Constantinople)*..	5	15
621	**Procopius,** usurper in the East, 365-366. Æ 3. REPARATIO FEL. TEMP. Emperor stg. r., holding standard and shield. *R.I.C. 17a (Constantinople)*.	50	125
622	**Gratian,** 367-383 (in the West), overthrown by Magnus Maximus who had been proclaimed emperor by the army in Britain. AR *siliqua*. VRBS ROMA. Roma seated l. *R.I.C. 27f (Treveri)*..	25	65
623	**Valentinian II,** 375-392 (in the West). Æ 2. REPARATIO REIPVB. Emperor stg. l., raising kneeling female figure. *R.I.C. 20c (Arelate)*......	10	30
623A	Æ 4. SALVS REIPVBLICAE. Victory advancing l., dragging barbarian. *R.I.C. 20a (Alexandria)*...	4	12
624	**Theodosius I,** the Great, 379-395 (in the East), son of the Count Theodosius who had cleared Britain of barbarian invaders in the reign of Valentinian I; the Emperor Theodosiua twice restored Britain to the rule of the central government, by his defeat of the usurpers Magnus Maximus (in 388) and Eugenius (in 394). AR *siliqua*. CONCORDIA AVGGG. Constantinopolis enthroned facing, foot on prow. *R.I.C. 55a (Treveri)*.	30	75

624A

		F £	VF £
624A	— VIRTVS ROMANORVM. Roma enthroned facing. *R.I.C. (Aquileia) 28d*.	30	75
624B	Æ 2. VIRTVS EXERCIT. Emperor stg. r., foot on captive, holding labarum and globe. *R.I.C. 24b (Heraclea)*...	12	35

F VF
£ £

625 **Aelia Flaccilla,** wife of Theodosius I. Æ 2. SALVS REIPVBLICAE.
Victory seated r., inscribing Christian monogram on shield set on cippus.
R.I.C. 81 (Constantinople). 25 65

626

627

626 **Magnus Maximus,** usurper in the West, 383-388, proclaimed emperor
by the army in Britain, invaded Gaul, and overthrew the legitimate western
emperor Gratian; possibly reopened the London mint for a brief issue of
precious metal coinage (Rudyard Kipling presented a rather fanciful
version of his career in "Puck of Pook's Hill"). Ꭿ *siliqua*. VIRTVS
ROMANORVM. Roma enthroned facing. *R.I.C. 84b (Treveri).* 30 75
See also under Category 3.
627 **Flavius Victor,** son of Magnus Maximus, co-emperor 387-388. Æ 4.
SPES ROMANORVM. Gateway of military camp. *RIC 55b (Aquileia).* 40 100
628 **Eugenius,** usurper in the West, 392-394, recognized in Britain until his
defeat by Theodosius the Great. Ꭿ *siliqua*. VIRTVS ROMANORVM.
Roma seated l. on cuirass. *R.I.C. 106d (Treveri).* 120 275
629 **Arcadius,** 395-408 (in the East, co-emperor with his father Theodosius I
from 383). Ꭿ *solidus*. VICTORIA AVGGG. Emperor stg. r., foot on
captive, holding standard and Victory. *R.I.C. 1205 (Milan).* 90 225

629A

631

629A Æ 2. GLORIA ROMANORVM. Emperor stg. l., holding standard and
shield, captive at feet. *R.I.C. 41 (Antioch).* 15 40
630 **Honorius,** 395-423 (in the West, co-emperor with his father Theodosius I
and brother Arcadius from 393), this reign saw the end of Roman rule in
Britain following a succession of usurpations in the province, culminating
in that of Constantine III against whom the Britons rebelled in 409;
Honorius' celebrated 'Rescript' of the following year instructed the
provincials to look to their own defence as he was no longer able to assist
them. ***N*** *solidus*. VICTORIA AVGGG. Emperor stg. r., foot on captive,
holding standard and Victory. *R.I.C. 1287 (Ravenna).* 90 225
630A Ꭿ *siliqua*. VIRTVS ROMANORVM. Roma seated l. on cuirass.
R.I.C. 1228 (Milan). 35 85
631 **Constantine III,** usurper in the West, 407-411, proclaimed emperor by the
army in Britain, but his authority rejected by the Romano-Britons two years
later, thus effectively ending 366 years of Roman rule in Britain. Ꭿ *siliqua*.
VICTORIA AVGGG. Roma enthroned l. *R.I.C. 1532 (Treveri)* 125 300

		F £	*VF* £
632	**Valentinian III,** 425-455 (in the West), during whose reign the Saxon conquest of the former Roman province commenced, following the final unsuccessful appeal of the Romano-Britons for help addressed to the general Aetius in 446. ***AV*** *solidus*. VICTORIA AVGGG. Emperor stg. facing, foot on human-headed serpent. *R.I.C. 2010 (Ravenna)*.	125	300
632A	Æ 4. VOT. PVB. Gateway of military camp. *R.I.C. 2123 (Rome)*.	25	75

2. ISSUES WITH TYPES REFERRING SPECIFICALLY TO THE PROVINCE OF BRITANNIA

Struck in Rome, unless otherwise indicated. These usually commemorate military operations in the northern frontier region of the province or beyond.

633

635

		F £	*VF* £
633	**Claudius,** A.D. 41-54. AV aureus, celebrating the early stages of the Roman conquest of Britain which commenced in A.D. 43. DE BRITANN on architrave of triumphal arch. *R.I.C. 33*.	900	2250
634	*AR denarius*. Similar. *R.I.C. 34*	275	650
634A	*AR didrachm* of Caesarea in Cappadocia. DE BRITANNIS. Emperor in triumphal quadriga r. *R.I.C. 122*.	300	750
635	**Hadrian,** 117-138. Æ as, commemorating the restoration of order in the province following a serious uprising (or invasion) in the north, probably early in the governorship of Q. Pompeius Falco (118-122). BRITANNIA PONT. MAX. TR. POT. COS. III. S. C. Britannia seated facing on rock. *R.I.C. 577a*.	125	325
636	Æ *sestertius,* commemorating Hadrian's visit to the province in 122, when he planned and initiated the construction of the northern frontier system which bears his name. ADVENTVI AVG. BRITANNIAE S.C. Emperor and Britannia stg. either side of altar. *R.I.C. 882*.	*Extremely rare*	

637

637	— BRITANNIA S. C. Britannia seated facing, foot resting on rock. *R.I.C. 845*.	*Extremely rare*	

		F £	*VF* £
637A	Æ *dupondius* or as. *Similar. R.I.C. 846*	*Extremely rare*	
638	Æ *sestertius,* commemorating Hadrian's attention to the legionary garrison strength of the province, principally his transfer of *VI Victrix* from Germany in 122. EXERC. BRITANNICVS S. C. Emperor on horseback r., addressing gathering of troops. *R.I.C. 912.*	*Extremely rare*	
638A	— EXERC. BRITANNICVS S.C. Emperor stg. r. on tribunal, addressing gathering of troops. *R.I.C. 913.*	*Extremely rare*	
639	**Antoninus Pius,** 138-161. **AV** *aureus,* commemorating the conquests in Scotland by the governor Q. Lollius Urbicus (138/9-142/3) at which time construction of the Antonine Wall was begun. BRITAN. IMPERATOR II. Victory stg. l. on globe. *R.I.C. 113.*	600	1500

640

640	Æ *sestertius*. BRITANNIA S. C. Britannia seated l. on rock, holding standard. *R.I.C. 742*	400	1000
641	— BRITAN. IMPERATOR II. S. C. Helmeted Britannia seated l., foot on rock. *R.I.C. 743.*	450	1200
642	— BRITAN. IMPERATOR II. S. C. Britannia seated l. on globe above waves, holding standard. *R.I.C. 744.*	500	1400
643	— BRITAN. IMPERATOR II. S. C. Victory stg. l. on globe. *R.I.C. 719.*	175	450
643A	— BRITANNIA IMPERATOR II. S. C. Britannia seated l. on rock, holding standard. *R.I.C. 745.*	450	1200
644	Æ *as*. IMPERATOR II. S. C. Victory hovering l., holding shield inscribed BRI / TAN. *R.I.C. 732.*	90	225
645	Æ *dupondius,* commemorating the quelling of a serious uprising in the north, ca. 154/5, necessitating the evacuation of the recently constructed Antonine Wall in Scotland. BRITANNIA COS. IIII. S. C. Britannia seated l. on rock, shield and vexillum in background. *R.I.C. 930.*	75	185

No.	Description	F £	VF £
646	Æ *as*. Similar. *R.I.C. 934*. .... *Many specimens of this type are carelessly struck on inadequate flans. Moreover, they have been found in significant quantities on Romano-British sites, notably in Coventina's Well at Carrawburgh fort on Hadrian's Wall, raising the interesting possibility that they may have been issued from a temporary mint in Britain. The style of the engraving is quite regular, indicating that even if locally produced these coins would have been struck from normal Roman dies brought to Britain especially for this purpose. See under Category 3.*	60	150
647	**Commodus,** 177-192. *Æ sestertius,* commemorating the victories in Scotland of the governor Ulpius Marcellus in 184/5. These were in retribution for a major barbarian invasion several years earlier resulting in serious damage to Hadrian's Wall, which had been temporarily overrun, and the defeat and death of an unknown governor. BRITT. P. M. TR. P. VIIII. IMP. VII. COS. IIII. P. P. S. C. Britannia stg. l., holding curved sword and helmet. *R.I.C. 437*.	*Extremely rare*	

648

No.	Description	F £	VF £
648	— VICT. BRIT. P. M. TR. P. VIIII. (or X.) IMP. VII. COS. IIII. P. P. S. C. Victory seated r., about to inscribe shield. *R.I.C. 440, 452*	90	240

649

No.	Description	F £	VF £
649	**Septimius Severus,** 193-211. *AV aureus,* commemorating the success of the punitive Roman campaigns in Scotland during 209 and 210 culminating in the illness and death of Severus at York in Feb. 211. VICTORIAE BRIT. Victory advancing l. *R.I.C. 334*.	1200	3000
650	— VICTORIAE BRIT. Victory advancing r., leading child by hand. *R.I.C. 302*.	1400	3500
651	AR *denarius*. VICTORIAE BRIT. Victory advancing r. *R.I.C. 332*..........	35	75
651A	— VICTORIAE BRIT. Victory stg. facing beside palm-tree with shield attached. *R.I.C. 336*.	40	85
651B	— VICTORIAE BRIT. Victory stg. l. *R.I.C. 333*..................................	40	85
651C	— VICTORIAE BRIT. Victory seated l., holding shield. *R.I.C. 335*.	40	80

652

		F £	VF £
652	Æ *sestertius*. VICTORIAE BRITTANNICAE S. C. Two Victories placing shield on palm-tree with captives at base. *R.I.C. 818.*	300	750
653	— P. M. TR. P. XVIII. COS. III. P. P. S. C. Similar. *R.I.C. 796.*	150	375
654	Æ *dupondius*. VICT. BRIT. P. M. TR. P. XIX. COS. III. P. P. S. C. Victory stg. r. between two captives, holding vexillum. *R.I.C. 809.*	100	275
655	Æ *as*. VICTORIAE BRITTANNICAE S. C. Similar. *R.I.C. 837a.*	100	275
656	Billon *tetradrachm* of Alexandria in Egypt. NEIKH KATA BRET. Nike flying l. *Milne 2726*	*Extremely rare*	
657	**Caracalla,** 198-217. AV *aureus,* commemorating the victories achieved by the Romans in Scotland during the campaigns led jointly by Severus and Caracalla in 209, and by Caracalla alone the following year during his father's illness. VICTORIAE BRIT. Victory seated l., holding shield. *R.I.C. 174.*	1200	3000

658

659A

		F £	VF £
658	AR *denarius*. VICTORIAE BRIT. Victory advancing l. *R.I.C. 231*	40	80
658A	— VICTORIAE BRIT. Victory advancing r., holding trophy. *R.I.C. 231A.*	40	80
659	Æ *sestertius*. VICTORIAE BRITTANNICAE S. C. Victory stg. r., erecting trophy to r. of which Britannia stands facing, captive at feet. *R.I.C. 464.*	250	650
659A	— VICT. BRIT. TR. P. XIIII. COS. III. S.C. Similar. *Cf. R.I.C. 483c.*	225	550
660	Æ *dupondius*. VICTORIAE BRITTANNICAE S. C. Victory stg. r., inscribing shield set on palm-tree. *R.I.C. 467.*	100	275
661	Æ *as*. VICT. BRIT. TR. P. XIIII. COS. III. S. C. Similar. *R.I.C. 490*	100	250
662	**Geta,** 209-212. AR *denarius,* commemorating the victories achieved by his father and brother in Scotland in 209-10 while he and his mother were resident in London. VICTORIAE BRIT. Victory stg. l. *R.I.C. 92.*	40	85
662A	— VICTORIAE BRIT. Victory advancing r. *R.I.C. 91*	40	85

663

		F £	VF £
663	Æ *sestertius*. VICTORIAE BRITTANNICAE S. C. Victory seated r., inscribing shield set on knee. *R.I.C. 166*	250	650
663A	— VICT. BRIT. TR. P. III. COS. II. S. C. Similar. *R.I.C. 172b.*	225	550
664	Æ *as*. VICTORIAE BRITTANNICAE S. C. Victory seated l., balancing shield on knee. *R.I.C. 191a.*	100	275
665	Billon *tetradrachm* of Alexandria in Egypt. NEIKH KATA BRETAN. Nike advancing l. *B.M.C. (Alexandria) 1481.*	*Extremely rare*	

3. OFFICIAL ROMAN COINAGE STRUCK IN BRITAIN

The London mint, and the associated 'C' mint (possibly Colchester), were created by the usurper Carausius soon after his seizure of Britain in 287. Prior to this, in the mid-2nd century, there may have been minting of 'Britannia' asses of Antoninus Pius in the province using dies brought from Rome, though this has not been firmly established. After the downfall of the rebel British regime in 296 the minting establishment in London (though not the subsidiary mint) was retained by the tetrarchal government and the succeeding Constantinian administration. Early in 325, however, Constantine the Great closed the London mint after almost four decades of operation. A possible brief revival under the usurper Magnus Maximus has been postulated for gold and silver coins marked 'AVG', 'AVGOB' and 'AVGPS', though the attribution has not received universal acceptance.

		F £	VF £
666	**Antoninus Pius,** 138-161. Æ *as,* struck in northern Britain (?) in 155. BRITANNIA COS. IIII. S. C. Britannia seated l. on rock, shield and vexillum in background. *R.I.C. 930.*	50	125
	Many poorly struck examples of this type have been found on Romano-British sites, notably at Brocolitia (Carrawburgh) fort on Hadrian's Wall in Northumberland, where no fewer than 327 specimens were discovered in the great votive deposit in the well which formed part of the shrine of the water-nymph Coventina. There appears to be a very real possibility that many of these 'Britannia' asses had been issued from a temporary mint in Britain, most likely situated in the north. The dies, however, are quite regular, and would thus have been brought from Rome to the island province for the express purpose of supplementing the money supply at a time of crisis.		
667	**Carausius,** usurper in Britain and northwestern Gaul, A.D. 287-293. **AV** *aureus,* London. CONSERVAT. AVG. Jupiter stg. l., eagle at feet, ML in ex. *R.I.C. 1.*	5000	12500
668	**AR** *denarius,* London. EXPECTATE VENI. Britannia stg. r. and emperor l., clasping hands, RSR in ex. *R.I.C. 555.*	400	1000

669

672A

		F £	VF £
669	— RENOVAT. ROMANO. She-wolf r., suckling twins, RSR in ex. *R.I.C. 571.*	300	800
670	Billon *antoninianus,* London. COMES AVG. Victory stg. l., S—P in field, ML in ex. *R.I.C. 14.*	40	100
670A	— HILARITAS AVG. Hilaritas stg. l., B—E in field, MLXXI in ex. *R.I.C. 41.*	25	60
671	— LAETITIA AVG. Laetitia stg. l., F—O in field, ML in ex. *R.I.C. 50.*	25	60
671A	— LEG. II. AVG. Capricorn l., ML in ex. *R.I.C. 58.*	70	175
	Legio II Augusta was stationed at Isca (Caerleon in South Wales).		
672	— LEG. XX. V. V. Boar stg. r. *R.I.C. 82.*	70	175
	Legio XX Valeria Victrix was stationed at Deva (Chester in the northwest Midlands).		
672A	— PAX AVG. Pax stg. l., F—O in field, ML in ex. *R.I.C. 101.*	22	55
673	— Similar, but without mint mark. *R.I.C. 880*	20	50
673A	— PROVIDENT. AVG. Providentia stg. l., B—E in field, MLXXI in ex. *R.I.C. 149.*	25	60
674	— SALVS AVGGG. Salus stg. r., feeding snake held in her arms, S—P in field, ML in ex. *R.I.C. 164.*	25	65
	The reverse legends with triple-ending (AVGGG.) presumably are subsequent to Carausius' recognition by Diocletian and Maximian in 289 following the failure of the latter's attempt to dislodge the usurper from his island stronghold.		
674A	— TEMPORVM FELICITAS. Felicitas stg. l., B—E in field, ML in ex. *R.I.C. 172.*	20	60
675	— VIRTVS AVGGG. Mars (or Virtus) stg. r., holding spear and shield, S—P in field, MLXXI in ex. *R.I.C. 183.*	25	65
676	Billon *antoninianus,* Colchester (?). CONCORDIA MILIT. Emperor stg. r. and Concordia l., clasping hands, C in ex. *R.I.C. 205.*	50	120
676A	— EXPECTATE VENI. Britannia stg. r. and emperor l., clasping hands, MSC in ex. *R.I.C. 216.*	100	250
677	— FELICITAS AVG. Galley with mast and rowers, CXXI in ex. *R.I.C. 221.*	80	200
677A	— FORTVNA RAEDVX. Fortuna seated l., SPC in ex. *R.I.C. 237.*	40	100
678	— LAETITIA AVG. Laetitia stg. l., globe at feet, S—P in field, C in ex. *R.I.C. 255.*	25	60
678A	— MONETA AVG. Moneta stg. l., CXXI in ex. *R.I.C. 287.*	25	60
679	— ORIENS AVG. Sol stg. l., C in ex. *R.I.C. 293.*	30	75
679A	— PAX AVGGG. Pax stg. l., S—P in field, MC in ex. *R.I.C. 335.*	25	60

680

		F £	VF £
680	— PROVID. AVG. Providentia stg. l., S—P in field, C in ex. *R.I.C. 353.*	25	60
680A	— SALVS AVG. Salus stg. l. at altar, feeding snake, S—C in field, C in ex. *R.I.C. 396*	25	60
681	— SPES PVBLICA. Spes walking l., holding flower, S—P in field, C in ex. *R.I.C. 413*	25	60
681A	— VICTORIA AVG. Victory advancing l., captive at feet, MC in ex. *R.I.C. 429.*	30	75
682	**Carausius, Diocletian and Maximian,** after 289. Billon *antoninianus,* Colchester (?). Obv. CARAVSIVS ET FRATRES SVI. Conjoined busts of the three emperors l. Rev. PAX AVGGG. Pax stg. l., S—P in field, C in ex. *R.I.C. 1*	800	2000

682A

684A

682A	— MONETA AVGGG. Moneta stg. l., S—P in field, C in ex. *R.I.C. —.* *See also nos. 693-4 and 698-700 as well as regular Carausian types with the triple-ending 'AVGGG.' on reverse.*	1000	2500
683	**Allectus,** usurper in Britain, 293-296. **Ꜹ** *aureus,* London. ORIENS AVG. Sol stg. l. between two captives, ML in ex. *R.I.C. 4.*	7000	17500
684	Æ *antoninianus,* London. LAETITIA AVG. Laetitia stg. l., S—A in field, MSL in ex. *R.I.C. 22.*	25	65
684A	— PAX AVG. Pax stg. l., S—A in field, ML in ex. *R.I.C. 28.*	30	70
685	— PROVID. AVG. Providentia stg. l., holding globe and cornucopiae, S—P in field, ML in ex. *R.I.C. 36.*	30	75
685A	— SALVS AVG. Salus stg. r., feeding snake held in her arms, S—A in field, MSL in ex. *R.I.C. 42*	25	65
686	— TEMPOR. FELICITAS. Felicitas stg. l., S—A in field, ML in ex. *R.I.C. 47.*	25	60
686A	— VICTORIA AVG. Victory advancing l., S—P in field, ML in ex. *R.I.C. 48.*	25	60
687	Æ *antoninianus,* Colchester (?). AEQVITAS AVG. Aequitas stg. l., S—P in field, C in ex. *R.I.C. 63.*	25	65
687A	— FIDES MILITVM. Fides stg. l., holding two standards, S—P in field, C in ex. *R.I.C. 69*	25	65

688A

		F £	VF £
688	— LAETITIA AVG. Laetitia stg. l., S—P in field, CL in ex. *R.I.C. 79.* . *This form of mint mark has given rise to the alternative identification of this mint as Clausentum (Bitterne, Hants.)*	40	100
688A	— MONETA AVG. Moneta stg. l., S—P in field, C in ex. *R.I.C. 82.*	35	85
689	— PAX AVG. Pax stg. l., S—P in field, C in ex. *R.I.C. 86.*	30	70
689A	— PROVIDENTIA AVG. Providentia stg. l., globe at feet, S—P in field, C in ex. *R.I.C. 111*	25	65
690	— TEMPORVM FELIC. Felicitas stg. l., S—P in field, CL in ex. *R.I.C. 117.*	40	100
690A	— VIRTVS AVG. Mars stg. r., holding spear and shield, S—P in field, C in ex. *R.I.C. 121*	25	65
691	Æ *'quinarius'*, London. VIRTVS AVG. Galley l., QL in ex. *R.I.C. 55.* . *An experimental denomination issued only during this reign, the types of the so-called 'quinarius' would seem to indicate that it was in some way associated with the operations of the fleet upon which the survival of the rebel regime in Britain was totally dependent.*	25	65

692

693

692	Æ *'quinarius'*, Colchester (?). LAETITIA AVG. Galley r., QC in ex. *R.I.C. 124.*	25	65
692A	— VIRTVS AVG. Galley l., QC in ex. *R.I.C. 128.*	30	70
693	**Diocletian,** 284-305. Billon *antoninianus* of London, struck by Carausius between 289 and 293. PAX AVGGG. Pax stg. l., S—P in field, MLXXI in ex. *R.I.C. 9.*	35	85
694	Billon *antoninianus* of Colchester (?), same date. PROVID AVGGG. Providentia stg. l., globe at feet, S—P in field, C in ex. *R.I.C. 22.*	35	85

695

No.	Description	F £	VF £
695	Æ *follis,* London. GENIO POPVLI ROMANI. Genius stg. l., LON in ex. *R.I.C. 1a.*	100	250
	By the time the central government had recovered control of Britain in 296 the antoninianus had been replaced by the larger follis under Diocletian's sweeping currency reform. London was retained as an official imperial mint, but the secondary British establishment (at Colchester?) was now abandoned. Except for its initial issue in 297 (marked 'LON') the London mint under the tetrarchic government produced only unsigned folles throughout its first decade of operation. Perhaps Constantius did not wish to draw attention to his employment of a mint which had been the creation of a rebel regime.		

696

No.	Description	F £	VF £
696	— Similar, but without mint mark. *R.I.C. 6a*	10	25
697	— (post-abdication coinage, after 305). PROVIDENTIA DEORVM QVIES AVGG. Quies and Providentia stg. facing each other (no mint mark). *R.I.C. 77a.*	25	55
697A	— QVIES AVGG. Quies stg. l., holding branch and sceptre, PLN in ex. *R.I.C. 98.*	18	45
698	**Maximian,** 286-305 and 306-308. **AV** *aureus* of London, struck by Carausius between 289 and 293. SALVS AVGGG. Salus stg. r., feeding snake held in her arms, ML in ex. *R.I.C. 32.*	*Extremely rare*	
699	Billon *antoninianus* of London, same date. PROVIDENTIA AVGGG. Providentia stg. l., S—P in field, MLXXI in ex. *R.I.C. 37.*	35	85
700	Billon *antoninianus* of Colchester (?), same date. PAX AVGGG. Pax stg. l., S—P in field, C in ex. *R.I.C. 42*	35	85
701	Æ *follis,* London. GENIO POPVLI ROMANI. Genius stg. l., LON in ex. *R.I.C. 2.*	100	250
702	— Similar, but without mint mark. *R.I.C. 23b*	10	25
703	— (post-abdication coinage, after 305). PROVIDENTIA DEORVM QVIES AVGG. Quies and Providentia stg. facing each other (no mint mark). *R.I.C. 77b.*	25	55

704

		F £	VF £
704	— (second reign). GENIO POP. ROM. Genius stg. l., PLN in ex. *R.I.C. 90.*	15	35
704A	— HERCVLI CONSERVATORI. Hercules stg. l., resting on club, PLN in ex. *R.I.C. 91*	25	65
705	**Constantius I,** 305-306 (Caesar 293-305). Æ *follis,* London (as Caesar). GENIO POPVLI ROMANI. Genius stg. l., LON in ex. *R.I.C. 4a.*	110	275

706

		F £	VF £
706	— Similar, but without mint mark. *R.I.C. 30*	12	30
707	— (as Augustus). Similar. *R.I.C. 52a.*	15	40
708	**Divus Constantius I,** deified 306. Æ *follis,* London. MEMORIA FELIX. Altar flanked by eagles, PLN in ex. *R.I.C. 110*	18	45
709	**Galerius,** 305-311 (Caesar 293-305). Æ *follis,* London (as Caesar). GENIO POPVLI ROMANI. Genius stg. l., LON in ex. *R.I.C. 4b.*	110	275
710	— Similar, but without mint mark. *R.I.C. 15*	10	25
711	— (as Augustus). Similar. *R.I.C. 42.*	12	30
711A	— GENIO POP. ROM. Genius stg. l., PLN in ex. *R.I.C. 86.*	18	45
712	**Severus II,** 306-307 (Caesar 305-306). Æ *follis,* London (as Caesar). GENIO POPVLI ROMANI. Genius stg. l. (no mint mark). *R.I.C. 58a*	35	85
713	— (as Augustus). Similar. *R.I.C. 52c*	35	85
714	**Maximinus II,** 310-313 (Caesar 305-310). Æ *follis,* London (as Caesar). GENIO POPVLI ROMANI. Genius stg. l. (no mint mark). *R.I.C. 57.*	15	40
715	— GENIO POP. ROM. Genius stg. l., PLN in ex. *R.I.C. 89a.*	15	40
716	— (as Augustus). Similar, but with star in r. field. *R.I.C. 209b*	12	30
717	**Licinius,** 308-324. Æ *follis,* London. GENIO POP. ROM. Genius stg. l., star in r. field, PLN in ex. *R.I.C. 209c.*	12	30
717A	— Similar, but with S—F in field. *R.I.C. 3.*	8	20
718	— SOLI INVICTO COMITI. Sol stg. l., holding globe, S—P in field, MSL in ex. *R.I.C. 79.*	10	25
719	**Constantine I, the Great,** 307-337 (Caesar 306-307). Æ *follis,* London (as Caesar). GENIO POPVLI ROMANI. Genius stg. l. (no mint mark). *R.I.C. 72.*	25	65
719A	— GENIO POP. ROM. Genius stg. l., PLN in ex. *R.I.C. 88b*	15	35

		F £	*VF* £
720	— PRINCIPI IVVENTVTIS. Prince stg. l., holding standards, PLN in ex. *R.I.C. 97.*	25	60
721	— (as Augustus). ADVENTVS AVG. Emperor on horseback l., captive on ground before, star in r. field, PLN in ex. *R.I.C. 133*	22	55

722

722	— COMITI AVGG. NN. Sol stg. l., holding globe and whip, same mint mark. *R.I.C. 155.*	18	45
723	— CONCORD. MILIT. Concordia stg. l., holding standards, same mint mark. *R.I.C. 195.*	15	40
724	— MARTI CONSERVATORI. Mars. stg. r., holding spear and shield, star in l. field, PLN in ex. *R.I.C. 254.*	15	35
724A	— SOLI INVICTO COMITI. Sol stg. l., holding globe, S—F in field, MLL in ex. *R.I.C. 27.*	8	20
725	Æ 3, London. VICTORIAE LAETAE PRINC. PERP. Two Victories supporting shield, inscribed VOT. / P. R., over altar, PLN in ex. *R.I.C. 159.*	10	25
726	— VIRTVS EXERCIT. Vexillum, inscribed VOT. / XX., between two captives, PLN in ex. R.I.C. 191.	10	25
727	— BEAT. TRANQLITAS. Altar, inscribed VOT / IS / XX., surmounted by globe and three stars, PLON in ex. *R.I.C. 267.*	8	20
727A	— SARMATIA DEVICTA. Victory advancing r., trampling captive, PLON and crescent in ex. *R.I.C. 289.*	18	45
728	— PROVIDENTIAE AVGG. Gateway of military camp, PLON in ex. *R.I.C. 293.*	8	20
729	**Fausta,** wife of Constantine I. Æ 3, London. SALVS REIPVBLICAE. Empress stg. l., holding two children, PLON in ex. *R.I.C. 300.*	60	150
730	**Helena,** mother of Constantine I. Æ 3, London. SECVRITAS REIPVBLICE. Empress stg. l., holding branch, PLON in ex. *R.I.C. 299.*	60	150
731	**Crispus,** eldest son of Constantine I, Caesar 317-326. Æ 3, London. SOLI INVICTO COMITI. Sol stg. l., holding globe, crescent in l. field, PLN in ex. *R.I.C. 144*	12	30
731A	— VIRTVS EXERCIT. Vexillum, inscribed VOT. / XX., between two captives, PLN in ex. *R.I.C. 194*	12	30
732	— BEATA TRANQVILLITAS. Altar, inscribed VOT / IS / XX., surmounted by globe and three stars, P—A in field, PLON in ex. *R.I.C. 211.*	10	25
733	— CAESARVM NOSTRORVM around wreath containing VOT. / X., PLON and crescent in ex. *R.I.C. 291.*	10	25

734

737A

		F £	VF £
734	— PROVIDENTIAE CAESS. Gateway of military camp, PLON in ex. *R.I.C. 295.*	10	25
735	**Constantine II,** 337-340 (Caesar 317-337). Æ 3, London (as Caesar). CLARITAS REIPVBLICAE. Sol stg. l., holding globe, crescent in l. field, PLN in ex. *R.I.C. 131*	12	30
736	— VICTORIAE LAETAE PRINC. PERP. Two Victories supporting shield, inscribed VOT. / P. R., over altar ornamented with wreath, PLN in ex. *R.I.C. 182.*	12	30
737	— VIRTVS EXERCIT. Vexillum, inscribed VOT. / XX., between two captives, PLON in ex. *R.I.C. 190*	12	30
737A	— BEATA TRANQVILLITAS. Altar, inscribed VOT / IS / XX., surmounted by globe and three stars, PLON in ex. *R.I.C. 236.*	10	25
738	— CAESARVM NOSTRORVM around wreath containing VOT. / X., PLON and crescent in ex. *R.I.C. 292.*	10	25
738A	— PROVIDENTIAE CAESS. Gateway of military camp, PLON in ex. *R.I.C. 296.*	10	25
739	**Constantius II,** 337-361 (Caesar 324-337). Æ 3, London (as Caesar). PROVIDENTIAE CAESS. Gateway of military camp, PLON in ex. *R.I.C. 298.*	25	60
740	**Magnus Maximus,** usurper in the West, 383-388. **AV** *solidus,* London (?). RESTITVTOR REIPVBLICAE. Emperor stg. r., holding labarum and Victory, AVG in ex. *R.I.C. 1.*	*Unique*	

The attribution to London of this rare series has not been firmly established, though Maximus was certainly proclaimed emperor in Britain and it is well attested that the principal city of the British provinces bore the name 'Augusta' in the late Roman period (Ammianus Marcellinus XXVII, 8, 7; XXVIII, 3, 7).

741

		F £	VF £
741	— VICTORIA AVGG. Two emperors enthroned facing, Victory hovering in background between them, AVGOB in ex. *R.I.C. 2b.*	5000	10000

Maximus appears to have struck a similar type in the name of the eastern emperor Theodosius I (cf. R.I.C. 2a), though it is presently known only from a silver-gilt specimen preserved in the British Museum.

		F £	VF £
742	Æ *siliqua,* London (?). VOT. / V. / MVLT. / X. within wreath, AVG below. *R.I.C. 4.*	850	2000
742A	– VICTORIA AVGG. Victory advancing l., AVGPS in ex. *R.I.C. 3.*	750	1750

4. IMITATIONS OF ROMAN COINS PRODUCED IN BRITAIN

At certain periods during the three and a half centuries of its occupation Roman Britain seems to have been the source of much local imitation of the official imported coinage. This began soon after the Claudian invasion in A.D. 43 when significant quantities of sestertii, dupondii and asses (especially the last) were produced in the newly conquered territory, as evidenced by the frequency of their occurrence in archaeological finds. The technical excellence of many of these 'copies', together with the surprising extent of their minting, would seem to indicate that some, at least, of these coins were produced with official sanction in order to make good an unexpected deficiency in the currency supply. Others are much poorer and well below weight, representing the 'unofficial' branch of this operation, some of it probably emanating from territory as yet unconquered. As conditions in the new province settled down rapid Romanization and urbanization of British society brought a general increase in wealth, and with it a much greater volume of currency flowing into the country. Local imitation now virtually ceased, except for the occasional activities of criminal counterfeiters, and this state of affairs lasted down to the great political crisis and financial collapse of the second half of the 3rd century. At this point large scale minting of imitations of the debased antoniniani of the late 260s and early 270s began in Britain and in the other northwestern provinces, all of which had been serioulsy affected by the political dislocation of this turbulent era. This class of imitations is usually referred to as 'barbarous radiates', the emperor's spiky crown being a constant and conspicuous feature of the obverses. Most frequently copied were the antoniniani of the Gallic rulers Tetricus Senior and Tetricus Junior (ca. 270-273) and the posthumous issues of Claudius Gothicus (died 270). The quality of the 'barbarous radiates' is variable in the extreme, some exhibiting what appears to be a revival of Celtic art forms, others so tiny that it is virtually impossible to see anything of the design. Their production appears to have ended abruptly with Aurelian's reconquest of the western provinces in 273. A similar phenomenon, though on a lesser scale, occurred in the middle decades of the following century when normal life in Britain was again disrupted, not only by usurpation but additionally by foreign invasion. With supplies of currency from the Continent temporarily disrupted local imitation, particularly of the 'Æ 2' and 'Æ 3' issues of Constantius II and the usurper Magnentius, began in earnest. How long this continued is difficult to determine as life in the island province was now subject to increasingly frequent episodes of dislocation. By now urban life in Britain was in serious decline and when Roman rule ended early in the 5th century, bringing a total cessation of currency supplies, the catastrophic decline in monetary commerce in the former provinces rendered it no longer necessary for the deficiency to be made good.

		F £	VF £
743	**Agrippa,** died 12 B.C. Æ as, of irregular British mintage, imitating the Roman issue made under Agrippa's grandson Caligula, A.D. 37-41. S. C. Neptune stg. l., holding dolphin and trident.	40	100
	The large official issue of Agrippa asses was made shortly before the Claudian invasion of Britain in A.D. 43 and would thus have comprised a significant proportion of the 'aes' in circulation at this time. In consequence, it would soon have become familiar to the new provincials providing an ideal prototype for imitation.		
744	**Claudius,** 41-54. Æ *sestertius,* of irregular British mintage. SPES AVGVSTA S. C. Spes walking l., holding flower.	75	250
745	Æ *dupondius,* of irregular British mintage. CERES AVGVSTA S. C. Ceres enthroned l., holding corn- ears and torch.	35	100

746

		F £	VF £
746	Æ *as,* of irregular British mintage. S. C. Minerva advancing r., brandishing spear and holding shield.......... *This is by far the commonest of the Claudian imitations and the prototypes must have represented the bulk of the aes coinage carried by the legions at the time of the invasion. The martial type may well have been specially selected as a suitable theme for the initial import of coinage into the newly conquered territory.*	30	85
747	**Nero Claudius Drusus,** father of Claudius, died 9 B.C. Æ *sestertius,* of irregular British mintage. TI. CLAVDIVS CAESAR AVG. P. M. TR .P. IMP. S. C. Claudius seated l. on curule chair amidst arms.......... *This type was issued by Claudius half a century after his father's death and would thus have been prominently represented in the initial wave of coinage imported into the new province.*	85	300
748	**Antonia,** mother of Claudius, died A.D. 37. Æ *dupondius,* of irregular British mintage. TI. CLAVDIVS CAESAR AVG P.M. TR. P. IMP. P. P. S. C. Claudius stg. l., holding simpulum.......... *Another Claudian issue for a deceased parent, this represents one of only two dupondius types struck during this reign and would have entered Britain in significant quantities at the time of the invasion in A.D. 43.*	60	175

749A

749B

749C

749	**'Barbarous radiates',** ca. 270-273. British and Continental imitations of billon *antoniniani,* principally of Divus Claudius II (A), Tetricus Senior (B) and Tetricus Junior (C). The inscriptions are usually blundered and the types sometimes unrecognizable. British mintage can only be established by provenance..........	5	10

		F £	*VF* £
750	**Barbarous 4th century,** mostly of the second half of the century, and principally imitated from 'Æ 2' and 'Æ 3' issues of the later Constantinian period, notably those of Constantius II ('soldier spearing fallen horseman' type), and the usurpers Magnentius and Decentius ('two Victories' type). The copies, especially those of Magnentius and Decentius, are often of excellent style and execution, though the legends frequently contain small errors. Those of Constantius II are sometimes very barbarous and poorly struck, occasionallyover regular issues of the earlier Constantinian period. Again, the likelihood of British mintage can only be established by provenance.	5-8	10-15

Grading of Hammered Coins

As the name suggests, hammered coins were struck by hand with a hammer. This can lead to the coin being struck off centre, double struck, weak in the design, suffer cracks or flan defects. It is important to take these factors into account when assessing the grade of this series. Value is considerably reduced if the coin is holed, pierced, plugged or mounted.

Extremely Fine
Design and legends sharp and clear.

Very Fine
Design and legends still clear but with slight evidence of wear and/or minor damage.

Fine
Showing quite a lot of wear but still with design and legends distinguishable.

Anglo-Saxon 'Porcupine' Sceat

Gold Noble

Silver Crown

EARLY & MIDDLE ANGLO-SAXON KINGDOMS & MINTS (C.650-973)

EARLY ANGLO-SAXON PERIOD, *c.* 600-*c.* 775

The withdrawal of Roman forces from Britain early in the 5th century A.D. and the gradual decline of central administration resulted in a rapid deterioration of the money supply. The arrival of Teutonic raiders and settlers hastened the decay of urban commercial life and it was probably not until late in the 6th century that renewed political, cultural and commercial links with the kingdom of the Merovingian Franks led to the appearance of small quantities of Merovingian gold *tremisses* (one-third solidus) in England. A purse containing such pieces was found in the Sutton Hoo ship-burial. Native Anglo-Saxon gold *thrymsas* were minted from about the 630s, initially in the style of their continental prototypes or copied from obsolete Roman coinage and later being made in pure Anglo-Saxon style. By the middle of the 7th century the gold coinage was being increasingly debased with silver, and gold had been superseded entirely by about 675.

These silver coins, contemporary with the *deniers or denarii* of the Merovingian Franks, are the first English pennies, though they are commonly known today as *sceattas* (a term more correctly translated as 'treasure' or 'wealth'). They provide important material for the student of Anglo-Saxon art.

Though the earliest sceattas are a transition from the gold thrymsa coinage, coins of new style were soon developed which were also copied by the Frisians of the Low Countries. Early coins appear to have a standard weight of 20 grains (1.29 gms) and are of good silver content, though the quality deteriorates early in the 8th century. These coins exist in a large number of varied types, and as well as the official issues there are mules and other varieties which are probably contemporary imitations. Many of the sceattas were issued during the reign of Aethelbald of Mercia, but as few bear inscriptions it is only in recent years that research has permitted their correct dating and the attribution of certain types to specific areas. Some silver sceattas of groups II and III and most types of groups IV to X were issued during the period (A.D. 716-757) when Aethelbald, King of Mercia, was overlord of the southern English. Though a definitive classification has not yet been developed, the arrangement given below follows the latest work on the series: this list is not exhaustive.

This section has been catalogued in line with research published by Dr D. M. Metcalf. Wherever possible the catalogue number previously in use has been retained. Where it has been necessary to allocate a new and different number, the 'old' S. number is listed, in brackets, at the end of the entry. New entries are given a new number. The primary sceattas are followed by the secondary sceattas and, finally, the continental sceattas. This is not chronologically correct but has been adopted for ease of reference and identification. The reference 'B.M.C.' is to the type given in *British Museum Catalogue: Anglo-Saxon Coins.* Other works of reference include:

North, J. J. *English Hammered Coinage*, Vol. 1, *c.* 650-1272 (1994).
Metcalf, D.M. *Thrymsas and Sceattas in the Ashmolean Museum,* Vols I-III.
Rigold, S. E. 'The two primary series of sceattas', *B.N.J.*, xxx (1960).
Sutherland, C. H. V. *Anglo-Saxon Gold Coinage in the light of the Crondall Hoard* (1948).

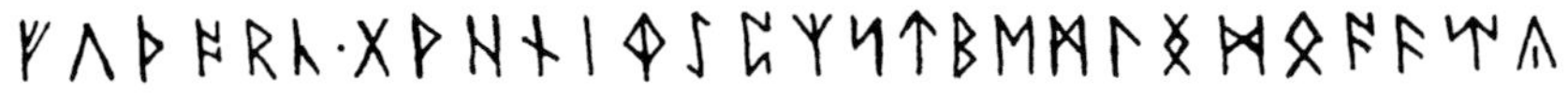

f u th o r k . z w h n i j ih p x s t b e m l ng d oe a Æ ea y

Early Anglo-Saxon Runes

GOLD

		F £	*VF* £
A.	**Early pieces, of uncertain monetary status**		
751	Thrymsa. Name and portrait of Bishop Leudard (chaplain to Queen Bertha of Kent). R. Cross. *(S.751)*	*Extremely rare*	
752	Solidus. Imitating solidi of Roman rulers. Blundered legends, some with runes. *(S.757)*	*Extremely rare*	

753

754

755

B. Crondall types, *c*.620 – *c*.645

Twelve different types, which are almost certainly English, were found in the Crondall hoard of 1828. All are thrysmas, containing 70-40% gold.

		F £	*VF* £
753	'Witmen' type. Bust r. with trident. R. Cross. Legend normally blundered. *M. 1-21 (S.767)*	750	1750
754	London-derived type. Head r. with pseudo-legend. R. Cross. Pseudo-legend. *M. 22-32 (S.765)*	900	2250
755	'Licius' type. Elegant imitation of Roman triens. Bust l. R. VOT XX. *M. 33-41 (S.762)*	1200	3000

756

757

758

		F £	*VF* £
756	'LEMC' type. Head l. R. Maltese cross with letters L, E, M, C in angles, or cross on steps. *M. 42-9 (S.753)*	900	2250
757	'LONDINIV' type. Facing bust, crosslets l. and r. R. Tall cross, LONDVNIV and pseudo-legend around. *M. 51-7 (S.764)*	1000	2750
758	— similar, but bust r. AVDVARLD REGES. R. Tall cross, LONDENV. Usually garbled. *M. 50 (S.771)*	1250	3000

759

762

		F £	*VF* £
759	Other crude types, usually with head or bust, R. Cross. *M. 58-72 (S.775)*	550	1250

C. Ultra-Crondall types, *c*.620 – 655?

Thrymsas not represented in the Crondall hoard, but probably of the same date range.

		F £	*VF* £
760	'Benutigo' type. Bust r., blundered legend. R. Cross on steps, runic legend (Benutigoii?) *(S.756)*	950	2650
761	'Wuneetton' type. Bust r., cross before. R. Cross. Blundered legend (WVNEETON or similar). *M. 77 (S.768)*	900	2500
762	'York' type. Kite-shaped shield enclosing cross, crosslets to l. and r., squared pattern beneath. R. Cross. Blundered (runic?) legend. *M. 76 (S.769)*	1350	3500

D. Post-Crondall types, *c*.655 – *c*.675

Pale gold types, visibly debased and sometimes almost silvery, containing 35-10% gold.

		F £	*VF* £
764	'Crispus' type. Helmeted bust, r. CRISPUS NOB CAES. R. Cross and XX in wreath, runic legend De Lundonia (?). *N.7 (S.761)*	1250	3250
765	'Concordia' type. Radiate bust r. R. Clasped hands. *N.5 (S.759)*	1200	3000
766	'Oath-taking' type. Bust r. or l. with hand placed against cross. R. Lyre-shaped object, or eight-rayed symbol. *N.6 (S.760)*	1000	2750

767

770/3

771/4

		F £	*VF* £
767	'Two emperors' type. Helmeted bust r. R. Bust of angel with wings above two facing heads. *M. 79-80 (S.763)*	800	1750
768	'Pada', Type Ia Helmeted bust r. R. Runic Pada on panel. *M.p.73. (S.777)*	850	2000
768A	— Type Ib. Similar. R. Standard TTXX, Pada in runes in legend. *M. 81*	700	1600
769	— Type IIa. Diademed bust r. R. Pada in runes in field, blundered legend around, *M.p.73. (S.773)*	575	1250
770	— Type III. Diademed bust r. R. Cross with annulet in angles. R. Runic Pada in legend. *M.p.73. (S.773)*	625	1350
771	'Varimundus', Type A. Diademed bust r. holding sceptre. R. Cross, with CA in lower angles. VARIMVNDVS MONE. *M.p.82 (S.780)*	850	2000
772	— Type B. Similar. R. Small cross in double circle of dots. *M. 84*	700	1750

SILVER

A. Early transitional types by thrymsa moneyers, *c*.675-685

773	'Pada', Type III. As 770, but silver. *M. 82. (S.779)*	375	850
774	'Varimundus', Type B. As 772, but silver. *M. 85-7. (S.780)*	400	900

B. Primary Sceattas, *c*.680 – *c*.710

Minted in various regions of England.

775

776

777

775	Series A, Radiate bust r., TIC. R. Standard, TOTII. *B.M.C.2a M. 89-94. (S.781)*	50	150
776	Series BX. Diad. bust r., VANTAVMA or similar. R. Bird r. above cross on steps. *B.M.C. 26. M. 97-9. (S.782)*	65	170
777	— BI. Similar but diad. head r. within serpent circle. R. Bird r. on cross. *B.M.C. 27a.. M. 100-106. (S.783)*	45	115
777A	— BII. Similar but simplified legend VAVAVA. R. Crosslet beside bird. *M. 113-6. (S.784)*	50	140

778

779

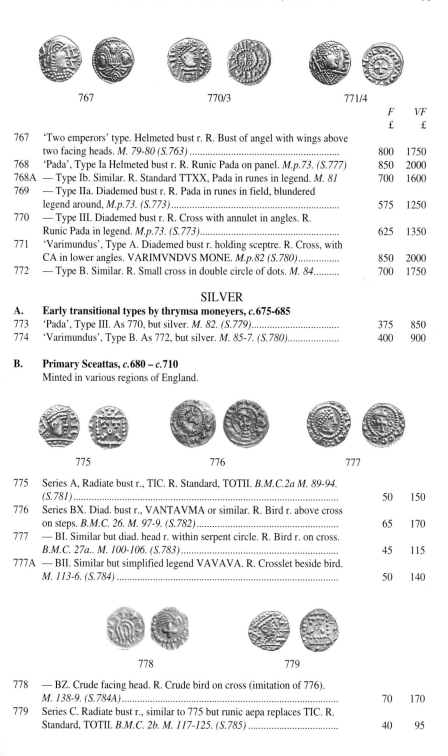

778	— BZ. Crude facing head. R. Crude bird on cross (imitation of 776). *M. 138-9. (S.784A)*	70	170
779	Series C. Radiate bust r., similar to 775 but runic aepa replaces TIC. R. Standard, TOTII. *B.M.C. 2b. M. 117-125. (S.785)*	40	95

780

782

		F £	*VF* £
780	King Aethelred of Mercia? (674-704). 'Porcupine'. R. Aethiliraed on runes in two lines. *M. 134-5. (S.837)*	125	300
781	Series F. Bust r., with broad-rimmed hat, blundered legend. R. Small cross on steps, annulets around. *M. 136-7. (S.839A)*	55	125
782	Series Z. Facing head with moustaches. R. Long-legged dog r. with head lowered. *M. 140-2. (S.817)*	150	425
782A	Series Z-related. Crude animal r., perhaps copy of 782. R. Crude cross-crosslet design *M. 143-4.*	130	375

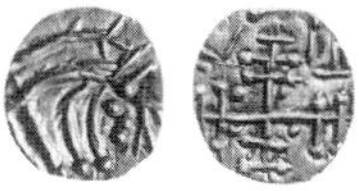
782A

784

791

783	'Vernus' type. Porcupine-related head r., VER before. R. Standard. *M. 146-8.*	70	160
784	'Saroaldo' type. Unusual bust r. R. Saltire and pellets in square, SAROALDO legend around. *M. 151-3.*	100	250
785	Series W. Half or full-length facing figure holding two crosses. R. Cross crosslet on saltire. *M. 155. (S.807A)*	110	325

C. Secondary Sceattas, c.710-760

Minted in all the main regions of southern and eastern England, but especially in the south-east and the Thames basin.

791	Series J, Type 85. Large head r. R. Bird on cross. *M. 293-5.*	50	120
791A	— Type 36. Bust r., cross in front. R. One large and one small bird r. *M. 301-2. (S.801)*	75	225

792

793

797

792	— Type 37. Two heads face-to-face. R. Four birds clockwise round cross. *M. 296-300.*	60	160
792A	— Type 72. Similar. R. Bird r., looking back. *M. 303.*	80	230
793	Series U, Type 23b. Standing figure r. holds two crosses. R. Pecking bird. *M. 445-51*	90	260
794	Series K, Type 42. Bust r. with bird, cross or flower. R. Hound 1., plant behind. *M. 311-3*	100	325
795	— Type 20. Bust r. with chalice. R. Standing figure holds cross and hawk. *M. 314-18.*	70	175
796	— Type 32a. Bust r. with cross. R. Wolf curled head to tail. *M. 309.*	110	350
797	— — Similar. R. Wolf-headed serpent. *M. 310*	75	200
798	— Type 32b. Similar. but R. Wolf-serpent within torque. *M. 307-8.*	90	275

		F £	*VF* £
799	— Type 33. Bust r., cross in front. R. Wolf's head with long tongue, l. or r. *M. 306.*	110	350

800

801

802

803

800	'Archer' type. Kneeling archer r. R. Bird on branch r., head turned back. *M. 349. (S.800A)*	350	900
801	'Carip' group. Bust r., CARIP. R. Pecking bird, wolf-serpent, or standing figure. *M. 336-40.*	150	450
802	Series O, Type 38. Bust r. in cable border. R. Bird r. in torque. *M. 373-5.*	85	240
803	— Type 21. Similar, but bust l. R. Standing figure with two crosses. *M. 376*	150	450

804

805

806

804	'Triquetras' eclectic group. Facing bust, man and crosses, winged figure, or bird and branch. R. Interlace pattern. *M.p.425.*	140	425
805	Series H, Type 39. Pecking bird. R. Round shield with bosses. *M. 283-4.*	80	200
806	— Type 49. 'Wodan' head, annulets around. R. Pecking bird. *M. 285-8.*	85	225
807	— Type 48. Whorl of 3 wolf heads. R. Round shield with bosses. *M. 289-92.*	80	200

808

809A
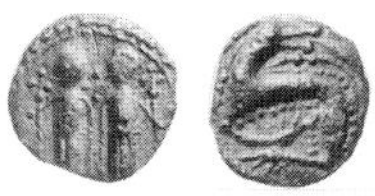
810

808	Series G. Bust r., cross before. R. Standard with 3 or 4 X's. *(Minted in Northern France?) M. 267-70.*	50	135
809	— crude copies, some with bird or bird on cross. *M. 271-4.*	40	95
809A	Series M. Prancing dog l. or r. R. Spiral branch. *M. 363-6. (S.836c.)*	90	275
810	Series N. Two standing figures. R. Monster looking back r. or l. *M. 368-72.*	65	185

811
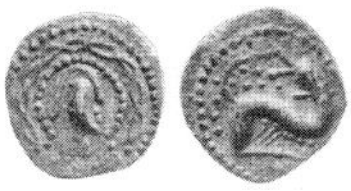
813

815

811	Series O, Type 40. Standing figure holds two crosses. R. As last. *M. 379-81.*	70	200
812	— Type 43. Interlace shield. R. As last. *M.p.482.*	110	350
813	— Type 57. Bust r. in cable border. R. Monster looking back l. *M. 377..*	120	375
814	'Animal mask' group. Facing animal (lion?) mask. R. Bird, figure, monster or cross. *M. 354-6. (S.814v).*	250	725
815	Series V. Wolf and twins. R. Bird in vine. *M. 453.*	135	400

816

818

822

		F £	*VF* £
816	Series T. Diad. bust r., +LEL. R. 'Porcupine' l. *M. 442-4.*	95	275
818	Series L, Type 12. Bust r., LVNDONIA. R. Standing figure holds two crosses. *M. 319-22.*	110	350
820	— Type 13. Similar. R. Seated figure holds hawk and cross. *M.p.409.*	200	600
821	— Type 14. Similar, but bust l. R. Celtic cross. *M.p.427.*	125	400
822	— Type 15. Bust r. with cross, no legend. R. Standing figure holds two crosses. *M. 323-6.*	75	235
825	— Type 16. Bust r. with floral scroll. R. Standing figure holds branch and cross, or two branches. *M. 329-30.*	95	275
827	— Type 18. Bust r. with cross. R. Standing figure holds cross and bird. *M. 331-3.*	70	210
828	— Type 19. Similar, but bust l. *M. 335.*	90	265
828A	— Type 34. Bust r. with cross or sceptre. R. Celtic cross. *M. 345-6. (S.800)*	110	350
828B	Series L-related. Bust r. rosettes in field. R. Standing figure holds two crosses. *M. 347.*	135	425

829

831

832

		F £	*VF* £
829	Type 22. Victory standing with wreath. R. Winged figure, or standing figure holding two crosses. *M. 350-1.*	175	525
830	Type 23e. Standing figure holds two crosses. R. Whorl of 3 wolf heads. *M. 359-62.*	85	240
831	Series S. Female centaur. R. Whorl of 4 wolf heads. *M. 438-41.*	75	210
832	Series R. Bust r. or l. Epa, Wigraed, Spi, etc in runes. R. Standard. *M. 391-428.*	40	90

833

834A

836

		F £	*VF* £
832B	Series Q(R), Type 73. Crude radiate bust r. or l. R. Quadruped r. *M. 388.*	85	240
833	'Saltire Standard' types. Bust l. or r. with cross, two standing figures, or double croix ancree. R. Saltire and pellets in square. *M. 432-5.*	70	180
834	'Monita Scorum' type. Small bird looking back, MONITA SCORUM. R. Standard with saltire of annulets. *M.p.436.*	275	750
834A	— Bust r., MONITA SCORUM. R. 'porcupine' l., figure with two crosses, or triquetra. *M. 348.*	325	900
835	Type 70. Saltire-standard. R. Standard. *M. 436-7.*	45	100
836	Series Q, Types QII-IVd Bird l. or r. R. Quadruped l. or r. *M. 386-7.*	95	275
836A	— Type QIVe Quadruped both sides. *M.p.501*	110	325
836B	— Type QIe Bust r. with cross. R. Walking bird l. *M. 383.*	120	350

		F £	*VF* £
836C	— Type QIf Standing figure with two crosses. R. Walking bird l. *M. 384.*	140	425
836D	— Type QIg Facing head. R. Long-legged quadruped looking back. *M.p.492.*	185	550

844

844A

844	Type 30. Facing 'Wodan' head. R. Two standing figures, or standard. *M. 429-31.*	140	450
844A	— Type 53. 'Porcupine', similar to 787. R. Stepped cross, annulet at centre. *Mint? M. 258-62.*	80	185

C. Continental Sceattas, *c.*695-*c.*740

Most are from the Rhine area, or Frisia

786

786	Series E. Porcupine-like figure, body with annulet at one end, triangle at other. R. 'Standard' with four pellets around central annulet. *Dorestad. M. 209-11.*	30	65

787

789

790

787	— Similar, with triangular fore-leg. R. 'Standard' with four lines and central annulet. *M. 200-5.*	30	60
788	— Similar, with parallel lines in curve of body. R. 'Standard' with VICO. *M. 194-8.*	30	65
789	— Figure developed into plumed bird. R. Standard. *M. 190-3.*	35	90
790	Later issues. R. 'Standard' 'Porcupine'. Innumerable varieties. *M. 214-53.*	25	50
832A	Type 10. Bust r., AEPA or APA. R. Porcupine modified into profile face. *Mint? M.p.248.*	175	350
838	'Porcupine' R. Small cross, S E D E in angles. *Mint? M. 263.*	185	550

839

840

843

839	Series D, Type 2c. Bust r., pseudo-runes. R. Plain cross with pellets in angles. *Domburg? M. 158-80.*	35	80
840	— Type 8. Standard. R. As 839. *M. 183-6.*	30	70
841	'Maastricht' Type. Crude head l. R. Quatrefoil interlace. *M. 265-6*	150	450
843	Series X. Facing 'Wodan' head. R. Monster l. *Ribe, Jutland, M. 275-81.*	95	250
843A	— cruder copies. *English, M. 282.*	125	375

KINGS OF NORTHUMBRIA AND BISHOPS OF YORK

The issues associated with pre-Viking Northumbria encompass a late seventh-century emission of gold, the following series of silver sceattas and the subsequent styca coinage. On the fringe of the later are two special issues, Eanred's penny and Wigmund's *solidus,* for neither of which is there yet evidence of use within the kingdom.

The Stycas developed in two phases, becoming a robust currency of small-denomination coins which seem to have been of great practical use. Production must have ceased early in Osberht's reign, although the old money may have continued in circulation until the Viking capture of York in 867. The official styca coinage, however, does appear to have been overwhelmed by irregular issues, which may reflect a period of civil war during the years *c.* 843 to *c.* 855.

The separation of kings and archbishops is no longer regarded as appropriate and the classification is chronological. In the spelling of names *U* for *W* would be appropriate in the Northumbrian context. *W* is based on West Saxon practice, but is used here on grounds of familiarity.

		F £	*VF* £
762	**AV thrymsa,** *temp.* Ecgfrith (?) (670-85). Building wih tower and window. R. Indeterminate legend around cross (*see also under Early Anglo-Saxon Period, Ultra-Crondall types)*	1350	3500

Æ sceattas (a). Regal issues

		F £	*VF* £
846	**Aldfrith** (685-705). Pellet in annulet. R. Canine, lying 1., stylized tree	275	650
847	**Eadberht** (737-758). Small cross (mainly). R. Stylized stag, to 1. or r (852).	90	225
848	**Aethelwald Moll** (759-765). (A possible, though disputed, issue is known)		

849

852

		F £	*VF* £
849	**Alchred** (765-774). Small cross. R. Stylized stag to 1. or r. (853)	185	400
850	**Aethelred I** (first reign, 774-779/80). R. Stylized stag to 1. or r. (854)	225	550
851	**Aelfwald I** (779/80-788). R. Stylized stag to 1. or r. (855)	200	500

Æ sceattas (b). Joint issues, by kings and archbishops

		F £	*VF* £
852	**Eadberht** with **Abp. Ecgberht** (737-758). Small cross. R. Mitred figure holding two crosses (866)	150	450
853	**Aethelwald Moll** with **Abp. Ecgberht** (759-765). Cross each side (866A)	425	975
854	**Alchred** with **Abp. Ecgberht** (765-766). Cross each side (867)	250	700
855	**Aethelred I,** with **Abp. Eanbald I** (*c.* 779-780). Various motifs.	125	375

Stycas Phase Ia. Issues in base silver, for kings and archbishop separately, c. 790-830, with moneyers named

		F £	*VF* £
856	**Aethelred I** (second reign, 789-796). R. CUDHEARD, or others (858).	95	240
857	– R. 'Shrine', CUDCILS	325	750

858

		F £	*VF* £
858	**Eardwulf** (first reign, 796-806). R. Small cross, CUDHEARD (858A)..	600	1250
859	**Aelfwald II** (806-808). R. Small cross, CUDHEARD (856)	190	450
860	**Eanred** (810-841 (total reign)). R. CUDHEARD, or others (859)	40	90

860

865

861	**Abp. Eanbald II** (796-835 (total tenure)). R. EADWULF or EDILWEARD (868)	75	200
861A	**Eanred,** *c.* 830. Æ *penny.* Bust right. R. Cross, part moline part crosslet....	*Extremely rare*	

861

863A

870

Stycas Phase Ib. Early issues in copper alloy, *c.* 830-835, with moneyers named

862	**Eanred.** R DAEGBERCT, EADUINI, HEARDWULF or HERRED (860) 40		15
863	**Abp. Eanbald II** R EADWULF, or EDILWEARD (869)......................	65	150
863A	**Abp. Wigmund** (837-849/50). *AV solidus.* Facing bust. R. Cross in wreath (870)	*Extremely Rare*	

Stycas Phase II. Later issues in copper alloy, *c.* 837-*c.*855, with moneyers named

864	**Eanred.** R MONNE or others (860)...	15	40
865	**Aethelred II** (first reign, 841-843/4). R. MONNE or others (861)..........	15	35
866	– R. Hound 1., LEOFDEGN (862)	150	425
867	**Redwulf** (843/4). R. MONNE or others (863)	35	90
868	**Aethelred II** (second reign, 843/4-849/50). R. EARDWULF or others (864)	15	35
869	**Osberht** (849/50-867). R. WINIBERHT or others (865)........................	40	100
870	**Abp. Wigmund** (837-849/50). R. EDILVEARD or others (871)...........	20	45
871	**Abp. Wulfhere** (849/50-900). R. WULFRED (872)	65	150
872	**Irregular Issues** (*c.*843/4-*c.*855). Various types; legends often mere nonsense.	15	30

Pirie E.J.E. Coins of the Kingdom of Northumbria c.700-867. 1996

In the kingdom of the Franks a reformed coinage of good quality *deniers* struck on broad flans had been introduced by Pepin in 755 and continued by his son Charlemagne and his descendants. A new coinage of *pennies* of similar size and weighing about 20 grains (1.3 gms) was introduced into England, probably by Offa, the powerful king of Mercia, about 755/780, though early pennies also exist of two little known kings of Kent, Heaberht and Ecgberht, of about the same period.

The silver penny (*Lat.* 'denarius', hence the *d.* of our *£ s. d.*) remained virtually the sole denomination of English coinage for almost five centuries, with the rare exception of occasional gold coins and somewhat less rare silver halfpence. The penny reached a weight of 24 grains, i.e., a 'pennyweight' during the reign of Alfred the Great. Silver pennies of this period normally bear the ruler's name, though not always his portrait, and the name of the moneyer responsible for their manufacture.

Pennies were issued by various rulers of the Heptarchy for the kingdoms of Kent, Mercia, East Anglia and Wessex by the Danish settlers in the Danelaw and the Hiberno-Norse kings of York, and also by the Archbishops of Canterbury and a Bishop of London. Under Eadgar, who became the sole ruler of England, a uniform coinage was instituted throughout the country, and it was he who set the pattern for the 'reformed' coinage of the later Anglo-Saxon and Norman period.

Halfpence were issued by most rulers from Alfred to Eadgar between 871-973 for S. England, and although all are rare today, it is probable that reasonable quantities were made.

Nos. 873-1387 are all silver pennies except where stated.

NB. Many pennies of the early part of this period have chipped flans and prices should be reduced accordingly.

KINGS OF KENT

		F £	*VF* £
873	**Heaberht** (*c.* 765). Monogram for REX. R. Five annulets, each containing a pellet, joined to form a cross	*Extremely rare*	
874	**Ecgberht** (*c.* 780). Similar. R. Varied	850	2250

875

877

875	**Eadberht Praen.** Type 1. (796-798). As illustration. R. Varied	950	2750
875A	— Type 2. (*c.* 798). His name around , in centre, R. Moneyer's name in angles of a tribrach	1000	2850
876	**Cuthred** (798-807). *Canterbury.* Various types without portrait	375	850
877	— — Portrait. R. Cross and wedges or A	475	1100

878

881

878	**Anonymous** (*c.* 822-823). *Canterbury.* As illustration or 'Baldred' style head	675	1750
879	**Baldred** (*c.* 823-825). *Canterbury.* diademed head r. R. DRUR CITS within inner circle	875	2400

		F £	*VF* £
880	— Cross each side	625	1650
881	*Rochester.* Bust r. R. Cross moline or wheel design	750	1900

ARCHBISHOPS OF CANTERBURY

882

881A	**Jaenberht** (765-792). New type (early). Under Ecgberht II of Kent (?). (before *c.* 780 ?) His name around small cross of pellets in centre. R. PONTIFEX in three lines	950	3000
882	Under Offa of Mercia (*c.* 780-792) His name around central ornament or cross and wedges. R. OFFA REX in two lines	750	2000
883	— His name in three lines. R. OFFA or OFFA REX between the limbs of Celtic cross	850	2250
884	**Aethelheard** (el. 792, cons. 793, d. 805). With Offa as overlord. First issue (792-?), with title *Pontifex*	850	2000

885

887

885	— Second issue (?-796), with title *Archiepiscopus*	750	1850
885A	— Third issue (*c.* 796-798), with title *Archiepiscopus.* His name and AR around EP in centre. R. Moneyer's name, EADGAR or CIOLHARD	850	2250
886	— With Coenwulf as overlord. (798-800 ?) Fourth Issue. As last. R. King's name in the angles of a tribrach	800	2000
886A	— Fifth issue (*c.* 798-805?). As last R. Coenwulf's name around $\overline{\text{M}}$ in centre	650	1450
887	**Wulfred** (805-832). group I (805-*c.* 810). As illustration. R. Crosslet, alpha-omega	650	1600
888	— Group II (*c.* 810). As last. R. DOROVERNIA C monogram	550	1400
889	— Group III (pre- 823). Bust extends to edge of coin. R. As last	475	1200
890	— Groups IV and V (*c.* 822-823). Anonymous under Ecgberht. Moneyer's name in place of the Archbishop's. R. DOROBERNIA CIVITAS in three or five lines	575	1500
891	— Group VI (*c.* 823-825). Baldred type. Crude portrait. R. DRVR CITS in two lines	800	2250
892	— Group VII (*c.* 832). Second monogram (Ecgberht) type. Crude portrait r., PLFRED. R. DORIB C. Monogram as 1035	725	2000

893

894

		F £	*VF* £
893	**Ceolnoth** (833-870). Group I with name CIALNOD. Tonsured bust facing. R. Varied	375	850
894	— Group II. Similar but CEOLNOD. R. Types of Aethelwulf of Wessex	375	850
895	— Group III. Diad. bust r. R. Moneyer's name in and between lunettes .	525	1250

896

898

896	**Aethelred** (870-889). Bust r. R. As illustration or with long cross with lozenge panel	1250	3750
897	— Cross pattee. R. ELF / STAN	950	2750
898	**Plegmund** (890-914). DORO in circle. R. As illustration above, various moneyers	425	1000
899	— Similar, but title EPISC, and XDF in centre	450	1100
900	— Small cross pattee. R. Somewhat as last	350	850
901	— Crosses moline and pommee on *obv.*	550	1350
901A	— Halfpenny. As 900	975	3000

KINGS OF MERCIA

Until 825 Canterbury was the principal mint of the Kings of Mercia and some moneyers also struck coins for the Kings of Kent and Archbishops of Canterbury.

GOLD

902

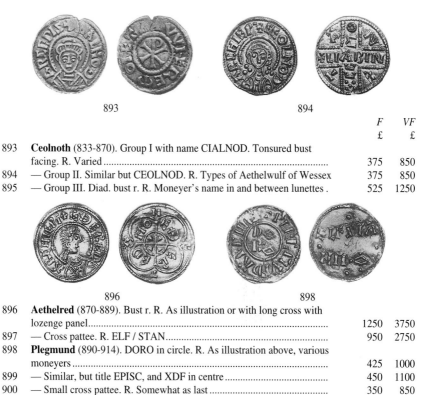

903

902	**Offa** (757-796). Gold *dinar*. Copy of Arabic dinar of Caliph Al Mansur, dated 157 A.H. (A.D. 774), with OFFA REX added on *rev.*	*Extremely rare*
903	Gold *penny*. Bust r., moneyer's name. R. Standing figure, moneyer's name	*Extremely rare*

A copy of a solidus with a diademed bust appears to read CIOLHEARD and is probably Mercian of this or the following reign.

SILVER

904

905

905

		F £	*VF* £
904	Light Coinage. (*c.* 780?-792) *London and Canterbury.* Various types without portraits. Small flans	350	775
905	— (*c.* 780?-792) *London and Canterbury.* Various types with portraits. Small flans.	650	1600
906	— East Anglia. Various types with portraits. R. Some with runic letters, small flans	750	1850

908

909

		F £	*VF* £
907	— — Various types without portraits. R. often with runic letters, small flans	450	1000
908	Heavy Coinage. (*c.* 792-796) *London, Canterbury and East Anglia.* Various types without portraits, large flans.	425	950
909	**Cynethryth** (wife of Offa). Coins as light coinage of Offa. As illustration	1000	3000
910	— *O. As rev.* of last. R. EOBA on leaves of quatrefoil	850	2000
911	**Eadberht** (Bishop of London, died 787/789). EADBERHT EP in three lines or aDBERHT in two lines within a beaded rectangle, EP below. R. Name of Offa	900	2400
912	**Coenwulf** (796-821). Group I (796-805). *London.* Without portrait. His name in three lines. R. Varied	450	1000
913	— *Canterbury.* Name around ϻ as illus. below. R. Moneyer's name in two lines	500	1250

914

915

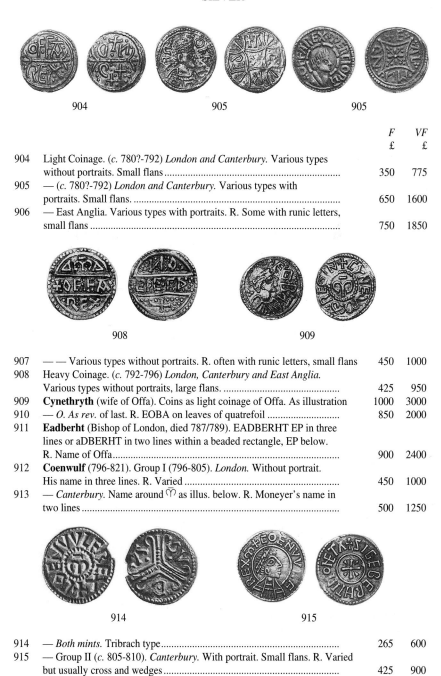

		F £	*VF* £
914	— *Both mints.* Tribrach type	265	600
915	— Group II (*c.* 805-810). *Canterbury.* With portrait. Small flans. R. Varied but usually cross and wedges	425	900

		F £	*VF* £
916	— Groups III and IV (*c.* 810-820). *Canterbury*. Similar but larger flans. R. Varied	375	850
917	— *Rochester.* Large diad. bust of coarse style. R. Varied. (Moneyers: Dun, Ealhstan)	500	1250
918	— *London.* With portrait generally of Roman style. R. Crosslet	450	1000
919	— *E. Anglia.* Crude diad. bust r. R. Moneyer's name LVL on leaves in arms of cross	325	700
920	— — *O.* as last. R. Various types	375	900

921

929

921	**Ceolwulf I** (821-823). *Canterbury.* Group I. Bust r. R. Varied. (Moneyers: Oba, Sigestef)	700	1750
922	— — Group II. Crosslet. R. Varied	625	1450
923	— — Group III. Tall cross with MERCIORŪ. R. Crosslet. SIGESTEF DOROBERNIA	750	1850
924	— *Rochester.* Group I. Bust r. R. Varied	750	1850
925	— — Group IIA. As last but head r.	750	1850
926	— — Group IIB. Ecclesiastical issue by Bp. of Rochester. With mint name, DOROBREBIA, but no moneyer	900	2250
927	— *East Anglia.* Crude style and lettering with barbarous portrait. R. Varied	525	1200
928	**Beornwulf** (823-825). Bust r. R. Moneyer's name in three lines	750	1850
929	— R. Cross crosslet in centre	700	1750
930	Crude copy of 928 but moneyer's name in two lines with crosses between	950	2500
931	**Ludica** (825-827). Bust r. R. Moneyer's name in three lines as 928	2100	5250

932

933

932	— Similar. R. Moneyer's name around cross crosslet in centre, as 929	2250	5500
933	**Wiglaf,** first reign (827-829). Crude head r. R. Crosslet	1750	4500

934

935

No.	Description	F £	VF £
934	Second reign (830-840). Cross and pellets, or [monogram] R. Moneyer's name in three lines or between lunettes of pellets	1350	3500
935	**Berhtwulf** (840-852). Various types with bust	650	1650
936	— without bust	700	1700
937	As before. R. IAETHELWLF REX. cross pommee over cross pattée (crude die copying on obverse of Aethelwulf of Wessex)	900	2250

938

939

940

941

No.	Description	F £	VF £
938	**Burgred** (852-874). *B.M.C. type A.* Bust r. R. Moneyer's name in and between lunettes	85	180
939	— — B. Similar but lunettes broken in centre of curve	175	450
940	— — C. Similar but lunettes broken in angles	90	200
941	— — D. Similar but legend divided by two lines with a crook at each end	90	180
942	— — E. As last, but m above and below	425	1000
943	**Ceolwulf II** (874-*c.* 880). Bust r. R. Two emperors seated. Victory above.	*Extremely rare*	

944

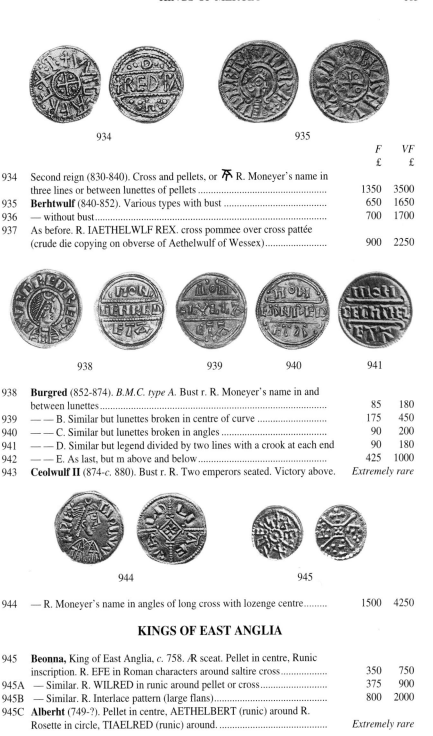

945

No.	Description	F £	VF £
944	— R. Moneyer's name in angles of long cross with lozenge centre	1500	4250

KINGS OF EAST ANGLIA

No.	Description	F £	VF £
945	**Beonna,** King of East Anglia, *c.* 758. Æ sceat. Pellet in centre, Runic inscription. R. EFE in Roman characters around saltire cross	350	750
945A	— Similar. R. WILRED in runic around pellet or cross	375	900
945B	— Similar. R. Interlace pattern (large flans)	800	2000
945C	**Alberht** (749-?). Pellet in centre, AETHELBERT (runic) around R. Rosette in circle, TIAELRED (runic) around.	*Extremely rare*	

946

		F £	VF £
946	**Aethelberht** (d. 794). As illustration	*Extremely rare*	
947	**Eadwald** (*c.* 798). King's name in three lines. R. Moneyer's name in quatrefoil or around cross	675	1750
947A	— King's name around cross or ꟿ in centre. R. Moneyer's name in quatrefoil	800	1850

948

951

		F	VF
948	**Aethelstan I** (*c.* 825-840). Bust r. or l. R. Crosslet or star	675	1750
949	Bust r. R. Moneyer's name in three or four lines	675	1750
950	Alpha or A. R. Varied	250	600
951	*O.* and *rev.* Cross with or without wedges or pellets in angles	275	650
952	— Similar, with king's name both sides	425	950
952A	Name around ship in centre. R. Moneyer Eadgar, around cross of pellets or in two lines (Possibly the earliest of his coins.)	1350	4500

953

954

		F	VF
953	**Aethelweard** (*c.* 840-*c.* 855), A. Omega or cross and crescents. R. Cross with pellets or wedges	375	750
954	**Edmund** (855-870). Alpha or A. R. Cross with pellets or wedges	150	365
955	— *O.* Varied. R. Similar	150	365

For the St. Edmund coins and the Danish issues struck in East Anglia bearing the name of Aethelred I, see Danish East Anglia.

Danish East Anglia, *c.* 885-915

957

		F £	*VF* £
956	**Aethelstan II** (878-890), originally named Guthrum? Cross pattee. R. Moneyer's name in two lines	825	2000
957	**Oswald** (unknown except from his coins). Alpha or A. R. Cross pattee..	1350	3750
958	— Copy of Carolinigian 'temple' type. R Cross and pellets	1350	3750
959	**Aethelred I.** (*c.*870) As last, with name of Aethelred I. R. As last, or cross-crosslet	1200	3000
959A	— As 954	900	2500
960	**St. Edmund,** memorial coinage, Æ *penny,* type as illus. below, various legends of good style	70	160

961

962

961	— Similar, but barbarous or semi-barbarous legends	65	145
962	*Halfpenny.* Similar	300	700

963

966

963	**St. Martin of Lincoln.** As illustration	1350	3750
964	**Alfred.** (Viking imitations, usually of very barbarous workmanship.) Bust r. R. *Londonia* monogram	450	1250
965	— Similar, but *Lincolla* monogram	650	1800
966	— Small cross, as Alfred group II *(Br. 6),* various legends, some read REX DORO	175	375
967	— Similar. R. 'St. Edmund type' A in centre	375	850
968	— Two emperors seated. R. As 964. (Previously attributed to Halfdene.)	*Extremely rare*	
969	*Halfpenny.* As 964 and 965	275	600

970

		F £	VF £
970	— As 966	250	525

DANELAW, *c.* 898-915

971

975

971	**Alfred** (Imitations). ELFRED between ORSNA and FORDA. R. Moneyer's name in two lines (occasionally divided by horizontal long cross)	300	650
972	— *Halfpenny.* Similar, of very crude appearance	375	900
973	**Alfred/Plegmund.** *Obv.* ELFRED REX PLEGN	525	1250
974	**Plegmund.** Danish copy of 900	300	650
975	**Earl Sihtric.** Type as 971. SCELDFOR between GVNDI BERTVS. R SITRIC COMES in two lines	1450	4000

Viking Coinage of York?

References are to 'The Classification of Northumbrian Viking Coins in the Cuerdale hoard', by C. S. S. Lyon and B. H. I. H. Stewart, in Numismatic Chronicle, 1964, p. 281 ff.

975A	**Guthfrith.** GU DE F. RE Small cross. R. Moneyer's name in two lines.	*Extremely rare*	
976	**Siefred.** C. SIEFRE DIIS REX in two lines. R. EBRAICE CIVITAS (or contractions), small cross. *L. & S. Ia, Ie, Ii*	175	475
977	— Cross on steps between. R. As last. *L. & S. If, Ij*	250	650
978	— Long cross. R. As last. *L. & S. Ik*	250	650
979	SIEFREDVS REX, cross crosslet within legend. R. As last. *L. & S. Ih*	135	300

980

984

980	SIEVERT REX, cross crosslet to edge of coin. R. As last. *L. & S. Ic, Ig, Im*	140	325
981	— Cross on steps between. R. As last. *L. & S. Il*	225	550
982	— Patriarchal cross. R. DNS DS REX, small cross. *L. & S. Va*	200	450
983	— — R. MIRABILIA FECIT, small cross. *L. & S. VIb*	225	550
984	REX, at ends of cross crosslet. R. SIEFREDVS, small cross. *L. & S. IIIa, b*	150	350

		F £	VF £
985	— Long cross. R. As last. *L. & S. IIIc*	150	325
986	*Halfpenny.* Types as 977, *L. & S. Ib; 980, Ic; and 983, VIb*	425	900
987	**Cnut.** CNVT REX, cross crosslet to edge of coin. R. EBRAICE CIVITAS, small cross. *L. & S. Io, Iq*	150	350
988	— — R. CVNNETTI, small cross. *L. & S. IIc*	140	300
989	— Long cross. R. EBRAICE CIVITAS, small cross. *L. & S. Id, In, Ir*....	90	200
990	— — R. CVNNETTI, small cross. *L. & S. IIa, IId*	80	170
991	— Patriarchal cross. R. EBRAICE CIVITAS, small cross. *L. & S. Ip, Is*	75	165
992	— — R.— *Karolus* monogram in centre. *L. & S . It*	550	1450

993

995

993	— — R. CVNNETTI, small cross. *L. & S. IIb, IIe*	75	150
994	*Halfpenny.* Types as 987, *L. & S. Iq; 989, Id; 991, Is; 992, Iu; 993, IIb and e*	300	650
995	As 992, but CVNNETTI around *Karolus* monogram. *L. & S. IIf*	275	625
996	**Cnut and/or Siefred.** CNVT REX, patriarchal cross. R. SIEFREDVS, small cross. *L. & S. IIId*	130	275
997	— — R. DNS DS REX, small cross. *L. & S. Vc.*	225	550

998

998	— — R. MIRABILIA FECIT. *L. & S. VId*	110	225
999	EBRAICE C, patriarchal cross. R. DNS DS REX, small cross. *L. & S. Vb*	165	400

1000

1002

1000	— — R. MIRABILIA FECIT. *L. & S. VIc*	110	235
1001	DNS DS REX in two lines. R. ALVALDVS, small cross. *L. & S. IVa*....	600	1350
1002	DNS DS O REX, similar. R. MIRABILIA FECIT. *L. & S. VIa*	250	575
1003	*Halfpenny.* As last. *L. & S. VIa*	425	950
1004	**'Cnut'.** Name blundered around cross pattée with extended limbs. R. QVENTOVICI around small cross. *L. & S. VII*	275	600

		F £	VF £
1005	*Halfpenny*. Similar. *L. & S. VII*	450	975
	Possibly not Northumbrian; the reverse copied from the Carolingian coins of Quentovic, N. France.		

York, early tenth century issues

1006

1009

1006	**St. Peter coinage.** Early issues. SCI PETRI MO in two lines. R. Cross pattee	160	350
1007	— similar. R. 'Karolus' monogram	750	1750
1008	*Halfpenny.* Similar. R. Cross pattee	525	1200
1009	**Regnald** (blundered types). RAIENALT, head to l. or r. R. EARICE CT, 'Karolus' monogram	1450	4250

1010

1010	— Open hand. R. Similar	1000	2750
1011	— Hammer. R. Bow and arrow	1500	4000
1012	Anonymous R. Sword	1300	3500

ENGLISH COINS OF THE HIBERNO-NORSE VIKINGS

Early period, *c.* 919-925

1013	**Sihtric** (921-927). SITRIC REX, sword. R. Cross, hammer or T	1200	3250
1014	**St. Peter coinage.** Late issues SCI PETRI MO, sword and hammer. R. EBORACEI, cross and pellets	525	1250

1015

1016

1015	— Similar. R. Voided hammer	450	950
1016	— Similar. R. Solid hammer	620	1400
	St. Peter coins with blundered legends are rather cheaper.		

Later period, 939-954 (after the battle of Brunanburh). Mostly struck at York.

No.	Description	*F* £	*VF* £
1017	**Anlaf Guthfrithsson,** 939-941. Flower type. Small cross, ANLAF REX TO D. R. Flower above moneyer's name	1500	4500
1018	**Olaf Guthfrithsson.** Circumscription type, with small cross each side, ANLAF CVNVNC, M in field on reverse *(Derby)*	1350	3750
1018A	— Two line type. ONLAF REX. Large letter both sides *(Lincoln?)*	1350	3750

1019

1020

No.	Description	*F* £	*VF* £
1019	— Raven type. As illustration, ANLAF CVNVNC	1350	3250
1020	**Olaf Sihtricsson,** first reign, 941-944. Triquetra type. As illus., CVNVNC. R. Danish standard	1450	4000
1021	— Circumscription type (a). Small cross each side, CVNVNC	1200	3000
1022	— Cross moline type, CVNVN C. R. Small cross	1250	3250
1023	— Two line type. Small cross. R. ONLAF REX. R. Name in two lines	1250	3250
1024	**Regnald Guthfrithsson,** 943-944. Triquetra type. As 1020. REGNALD CVNVNC	1500	4250

1025

1030

No.	Description	*F* £	*VF* £
1025	— Cross moline type. As 1022, but REGNALD CVNVNC	1400	4000
1026	**Sihtric Sihtricsson,** *c.* 942. Triquetra type. As 1020, SITRIC CVNVNC	1400	4000
1027	— Circumscription type. Small cross each side	1350	3750
1027A	**Anonymous?** Two line type. Small cross ELTANGERHT. R. RERNART in two lines	1250	3250
1028	**Eric Blood-axe,** first reign, 948. Two line type. Small cross, ERICVC REX A; ERIC REX AL; or ERIC REX EFOR. R. Name in two lines	1650	5000
1029	**Olaf Sihtricsson,** second reign, 948-952. Circumscription type (b). Small cross each side. ONLAF REX	1250	3250
1029A	— Flower type. small cross ANLAF REX R. Flower above moneyer's name	1500	4250
1029B	— Two line type. Small cross, ONLAF REX. R. Moneyer's name in two lines	1250	3250
1030	**Eric Blood-axe,** second reign, 952-954. Sword type. ERIC REX in two lines, sword between. R. Small cross	1850	5250

Later, KINGS OF ALL ENGLAND FROM 959

All are silver pennies unless otherwise stated

BEORHTRIC, 786-802

Beorhtric was dependent on Offa of Mercia and married a daughter of Offa.

1031

		F £	*VF* £
1031	As illustration	*Extremely rare*	
1032	Alpha and omega in centre. R. Omega in centre	*Extremely rare*	

ECGBERHT, 802-839

King of Wessex only, 802-825; then also of Kent, Sussex, Surrey, Essex and East Anglia, 825-839, and of Mercia also, 829-830.

1033	*Canterbury.* Group I. Diad. hd. r. within inner circle. R. Various	750	2200
1034	— II. Non-portrait types. R. Various	525	1350

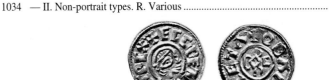

1035

1035	— III. Bust r. breaking inner circle. R. DORIB C	600	1650
1036	*London.* Cross potent. R. LVN / DONIA / CIVIT	900	2750
1037	— — R. REDMVND MONE around TA	750	2200
1038	*Rochester,* royal mint. Non-portrait types with king's name ECGBEO RHT	575	1450
1039	— — Portrait types, ECGBEORHT	725	1850
1040	*Rochester,* bishop's mint. Bust r. R. SCS ANDREAS (APOSTOLVS)...	800	2500
1041	*Winchester.* SAXON monogram or SAXONIORVM in three lines. R. Cross	650	1650

Son of Ecgberht; sub-King of Essex, Kent, Surrey and Sussex, 825-839; King of all southern England, 839-855; King of Essex, Kent and Sussex only, 855-858. No coins are known of his son Aethelbald who ruled over Wessex proper, 855-860.

1043

1045

		F	VF
		£	£
1042	*Canterbury.* Phase I (839-c. 843). Head within inner circle. R. Various. *Br. 3*	275	675
1043	— — Larger bust breaking inner circle. R. A. *Br. 1 and 2*	300	700
1044	— — Cross and wedges. R. SAXONIORVM in three lines in centre. *Br. 10*	250	600
1045	— — Similar, but OCCINDENTALIVM in place of moneyer. *Br. 11*	275	625
1046	— Phase II (*c.* 843-848?). Cross and wedges. R. Various, but chiefly a form of cross or a large A. *Br. 4*	235	525
1047	— — New portrait, somewhat as 1043. R. As last. *Br. 7*	300	725
1048	— — Smaller portrait. R. As last, with *Chi/Rho* monogram. *Br. 7*	325	750

1049

1051

1049	— Phase III (*c.* 848/851-*c.* 855). DORIB in centre. R. CANT mon. *Br. 5*	250	550
1050	— — CANT mon. R. CAN M in angles of cross. *Br. 6*	325	750
1051	— Phase IV (*c.* 855-859). Type as Aethelberht. New neat style bust R. Large voided long cross. *Br. 8*	250	550
1052	*Winchester.* SAXON mon. R. Cross and wedges. *Br. 9*	375	850

Son of Aethelwulf; sub-King of Kent, Essex and Sussex, 858-860; King of all southern England, 860-865/6.

1053

		F	VF
		£	£
1053	As illustration above	225	500
1054	*O*. Similar, R. Cross fleury over quatrefoil	500	1250

AETHELRED I, 865/866-871

Son of Aethelwulf; succeeded his brother Aethelberht.

1055

1055	As illustration	275	600
1056	Similar, but moneyer's name in four lines	525	1250

For another coin with the name Aethelred see 959 under Viking coinages.

Brother and successor to Aethelred, Alfred had to contend with invading Danish armies for much of his reign. In 878 he and Guthrum the Dane divided the country, with Alfred holding all England south and west of Watling Street. Alfred occupied London in 886.

Types with portraits

1057

1058

		F £	VF £
1057	Bust r. R. As Aethelred I. *Br. 1* (*name often* AELBRED)	275	625
1058	— R. Long cross with lozenge centre, as 944, *Br. 5*	950	3000
1059	— R. Two seated figures, as 943. *Br. 2*	*Extremely rare*	
1060	— R. As Archbp. Aethered; cross within large quatrefoil. *Br. 3*	*Extremely rare*	

1061

1062

1061	*London.* Bust. r. R. LONDONIA monogram	625	1600
	Copies made of tin at the Wembley Exhibition are common		
1062	— R. Similar, but with moneyer's name added	725	1700
1063	— *Halfpenny.* Bust r. or rarely l. R. LONDONIA monogram as 1061	325	725
1064	*Gloucester.* R. Æ GLEAPA in angles of three limbed cross	*Extremely rare*	

Types without portraits

1065	King's name on limbs of cross, trefoils in angles. R. Moneyer's name in quatrefoil. *Br. 4.*	*Extremely rare*	

1066

1069

1066	Cross pattée. R. Moneyer's name in two lines. *Br. 6*	275	550
1067	— As last, but neater style, as Edw, the Elder	285	575
1068	— *Halfpenny.* As 1066	300	650
1069	*Canterbury.* As last but DORO added on *obv. Br. 6a*	325	675
1070	*Exeter?* King name in four lines. R. EXA vertical	1850	5000
1071	*Winchester?* Similar to last, but PIN	2000	5500
1071A	*Oxford.* Elfred between OHSNA and FORDA. R. Moneyer's name in two lines (much commoner as a Viking Imitation see 971)	600	1350
1072	'Offering penny'. Very large and heavy. AELFRED REX SAXORVM in four lines. R. ELIMO in two lines i.e. (*Elimosina,* alms)	*Extremely rare*	

For other pieces bearing the name of Alfred see under the Viking coinages.

Edward, the son of Alfred, aided by his sister Aethelflaed 'Lady of the Mericians', annexed all England south of the Humber and built many new fortified boroughs to protect the kingdom.

1074

1078

Rare types

		F £	VF £
1073	*Br. 1. Bath?* R. BA	1250	3250
1074	— *2. Canterbury.* Cross moline in pommee. R. Moneyer's name	750	1800
1075	— *3. Chester?* Small cross. R. Minster	1000	2750
1076	— *4.* — Small cross. R. Moneyer's name in single line	650	1500
1077	— *5.* — R. Two stars	800	2000

1081

1082

1078	— *6.* — R. Flower above central line, name below	950	2750
1079	— *7.* — R. Floral design with name across field	1000	2750
1080	— *8.* — R. Bird holding twig	1500	5250
1081	— *9.* — R. Hand of Providence, several varieties	1250	3750
1082	— *10.* — R. City gate of Roman style	1200	3000
1083	— *11.* — R. Anglo-Saxon burg	1000	2750

Ordinary types

1084

1087

1084	*Br. 12.* Bust l. R. Moneyer's name in two lines	350	925
1085	— — As last, but in *gold*	*Extremely rare*	
1086	— *12a.* Similar, but bust r. of crude style	525	1200
1087	— *13.* Small cross. R. Similar (to 1084)	135	300
1088	*Halfpenny.* Similar to last	600	1250
1088A	— — R. Hand of Providence	900	2500

Aethelstan, the eldest son of Eadward, decreed that money should be coined only in a borough, that every borough should have one moneyer and that some of the more important boroughs should have more than one moneyer.

1089

		F £	VF £
1089	**Main issues.** Small cross. R. Moneyer's name in two lines	145	350
1090	Diad. bust r. R. As last	550	1450
1091	— R. Small cross	525	1350
1092	Small cross both sides	225	525

1093

1094

		F £	VF £
1093	— Similar, but mint name added	175	375
1094	Crowned bust r. As illustration. R. Small cross	350	850
1095	— Similar, but mint name added	325	800
1096	**Local Issues.** *N. Mercian mints.* Star between two pellets. R. As 1089	625	1650
1097	— Small cross. R. Floral ornaments above and below moneyer's name	725	2000
1098	— Rosette of pellets each side	225	525
1099	— Small cross one side, rosette on the other side	250	550

1100

1104

		F £	VF £
1100	*N.E. mints.* Small cross. R. Tower over moneyer's name	900	2650
1101	Similar, but mint name added	950	2750
1102	— Bust in high relief r. or l. R. Small cross	500	1200
1103	— Bust r. in high relief. R. Cross-crosslet	500	1200
1104	'Helmeted' bust or head r. R. As last or small cross	525	1350
1104A	Halfpenny, small cross. R. Moneyer's name in two lines	600	1350

Eadmund, the brother of Aethelstan, extended his realm over the Norse kingdom of York.

1105

1107

		F £	VF £
1105	Small cross, rosette or annulet. R. Moneyer's name in two lines with crosses or rosettes between	145	350
1106	Crowned bust r. R. Small cross	400	950
1107	Similar, but with mint name	400	950
1108	Small cross either side, or rosette on one side	225	525
1109	Cross of five pellets. R. Moneyer's name in two lines	225	500
1110	Small cross. R. Flower above name	850	2350
1111	'Helmeted' bust r. R. Cross-crosslet	625	1500

1111

1112

1112	*Halfpenny.* small cross, R. Moneyer's name in two lines or one line between rosettes	575	1250
1112A	— Flower. R. As 1105	700	1750

EADRED, 946-955

Eadred was another of the sons of Eadward. He lost the kingdom of York to Eric Bloodaxe.

1113

1115

1113	As illustration. R. Moneyer's name in two lines	135	275
1114	— Similar, but mint name after REX	350	900
1115	Crowned bust r. As illustration	325	750
1116	— R. Similar, with mint name added	375	925

		F £	VF £
1117	Rosette. R. As 1113	200	450
1118	Small cross. R. Rosette	225	475
1119	— R. Flower enclosing moneyer's name. *B.M.C. II*	950	2500
1120	*Halfpenny.* Similar to 1113	475	1000

HOWEL DDA, d. 949/950

Grandson of Rhodri Mawr, Howel succeeded to the kingdom of Dyfed *c.* 904, to Seisyllog *c.* 920 and became King of Gwynedd and all Wales, 942.

1121

1121 HOPÆL REX, small cross or rosette. R. Moneyer's name in two lines. *Extremely rare*

EADWIG, 955-959

Elder son of Eadmund, Eadwig lost Mercia and Northumbria to his brother Eadgar in 957.

1122

1123

		F £	VF £
1122	*Br. 1.* Type as illustration	185	400
1123	— — Similar, but mint name in place of crosses	350	800
1124	— *2.* As 1122, but moneyer's name in one line	675	1600
1125	— *3.* Similar. R. Floral design	950	2500
1126	— *4.* Similar. R. Rosette or small cross	300	675
1127	— *5.* Bust r. R. Small cross	1500	4750

1128

		F £	VF £
1128	*Halfpenny.* Small cross. R. Flower above moneyer's name	800	2000
1128A	— Similar. R. PIN (Winchester) across field	975	2500
1128B	— Star. R. Moneyer's name in two lines	750	1650

King in Mercia and Northumbria from 957; King of all England 959-975.

It is now possible on the basis of the lettering to divide up the majority of Eadgar's coins into issues from the following regions: N.E. England, N.W. England, York, East Anglia, Midlands, S.E. England, Southern England, and S.W. England. (See 'Anglo-Saxon Coins', ed. R. H. M. Dolley.)

1129

1135

		F £	VF £
1129	*Br I.* Small cross. R. Moneyer's name in two lines, crosses between, trefoils top and bottom	100	225
1130	— — R. Similar, but rosettes top and bottom (a N.W. variety)	120	250
1131	— — R. Similar, but annulets between	120	275
1132	— — R. Similar, but mint name between (a late N.W. type)	165	425
1133	— *2.* — R. Floral design	850	2250
1134	— *4.* Small cross either side	110	225
1135	— — Similar, with mint name	165	375
1136	— — Rosette either side	125	275
1137	— — Similar, with mint name	250	550
1138	— *5.* Large bust to r. R. Small cross	450	1100
1139	— — Similar, with mint name	550	1200
1140	*Halfpenny.* (8.5 grains.) *Br. 3.* Small cross. R. Flower above name	800	1850
1140A	— — R. Mint name around cross (Chichester)	950	2500
1140B	— Bust r. R. 'Londonia' monogram	475	950

For Eadgar 'reform' issues see overleaf

In 973 Eadgar introduced a new coinage. A royal portrait now became a regular feature and the reverses normally have a cruciform pattern with the name of the mint in addition to that of the moneyer. Most fortified towns of burghal status were allowed a mint, the number of moneyers varying according to their size and importance: some royal manors also had a mint and some moneyers were allowed to certain ecclesiastical authorities. In all some seventy mints were active about the middle of the 11th century (see list of mints pp. 127-8).

The control of the currency was retained firmly in the hands of the central government, unlike the situation in France and the Empire where feudal barons and bishops controlled their own coinage. Coinage types were changed at intervals to enable the Exchequer to raise revenue from new dies and periodic demonetization of old coin types helped to maintain the currency in a good state. No halfpence were minted during this period. During the latter part of this era, full pennies were sheared into 'halfpennies' and 'farthings'. They are far rarer than later 'cut' coins.

Eadgar, 959-975 *continued*

1141

		F £	*VF* £
1141	**Penny.** Type 6. Small bust l. R. Small cross, name of moneyer and mint.	525	1100

EDWARD THE MARTYR, 975-978

Son of Eadgar and Aethelflaed, Eadward was murdered at Corfe castle, reputedly on the orders of his stepmother Aelfthryth.

1142

1142	Type as illustration above	625	1350

LATE ANGLO-SAXON MINTS (973-1066)

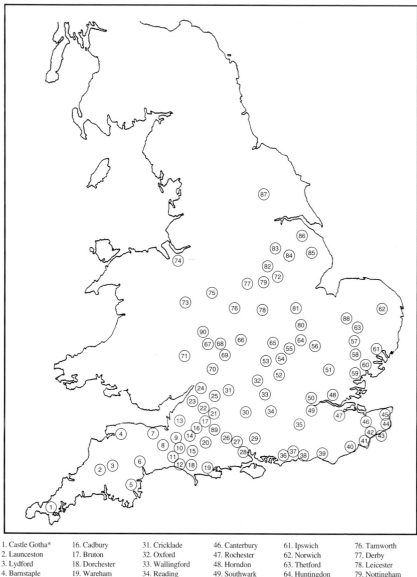

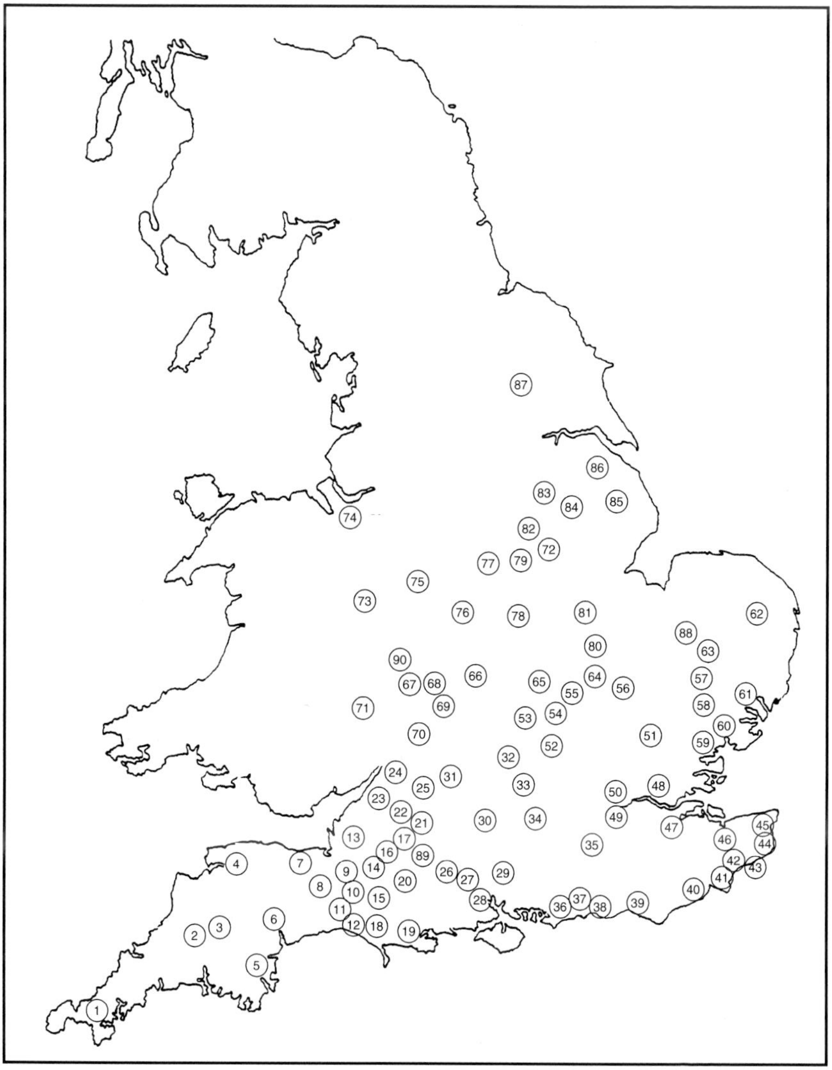

1. Castle Gotha*
2. Launceston
3. Lydford
4. Barnstaple
5. Totnes
6. Exeter
7. Watchet
8. Taunton
9. Langport
10. Petherton
11. Crewkerne
12. Bridport
13. Axbridge
14. Ilchester
15. Miborne Port
16. Cadbury
17. Bruton
18. Dorchester
19. Wareham
20. Shaftesbury
21. Warminster
22. Bath
23. Bristol
24. Berkeley
25. Malmesbury
26. Wilton
27. Salisbury
28. Southampton
29. Winchester
30. Bedwyn
31. Cricklade
32. Oxford
33. Wallingford
34. Reading
35. Guildford
36. Chichester
37. Cissbury
38. Steyning
39. Lewes
40. Hastings
41. Romney
42. Lympne
43. Hythe
44. Dover
45. Sandwich
46. Canterbury
47. Rochester
48. Horndon
49. Southwark
50. London
51. Hertford
52. Aylesbury
53. Buckingham
54. Newport Pagnell*
55. Bedford
56. Cambridge
57. Bury St Edmunds
58. Sudbury
59. Maldon
60. Colchester
61. Ipswich
62. Norwich
63. Thetford
64. Huntingdon
65. Northampton
66. Warwick
67. Worcester
68. Pershore
69. Winchcombe
70. Gloucester
71. Hereford
72. Grantham*
73. Shrewsbury
74. Chester
75. Stafford
76. Tamworth
77. Derby
78. Leicester
79. Nottingham
80. Peterborough
81. Stamford
82. Newark
83. Torksey
84. Lincoln
85. Horncastle
86. Caistor
87. York
88. Wilton. Norfolk*
89. Frome*
90. Droitwich

**Possible location of uncertain mint*

He was the son of Eadgar and Aelfthryth. His reign was greatly disturbed by incursions of Danish fleets and armies which massive payments of money failed to curb. He was known as 'The Unready', from UNREDE, meaning 'without counsel', ie. he was without good advice.

1143

1144

		F £	*VF* £
1143	First small cross type. Style of 1142, usually backless dress, 3 pellets in front, *Br. 1; B.M.C. I*	325	800
1144	First Hand type. Bust r., no sceptre. R. Hand of Providence. *Br. 2; B.M.C. IIa*	85	190
1145	— Similar, but bust to l. *B.M.C. IIb*	400	950

1146

1147

1146	Second Hand type, with sceptre. *B.M.C. IId*	85	180
1147	Benediction type. *O.* As last. R. Hand giving Benediction. *B.M.C. IIf*	650	1500

1148

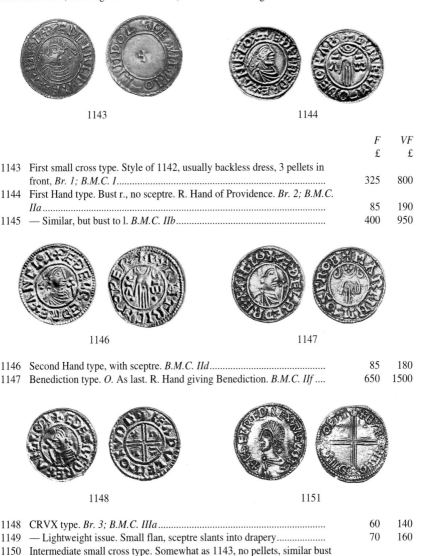

1151

1148	CRVX type. *Br. 3; B.M.C. IIIa*	60	140
1149	— Lightweight issue. Small flan, sceptre slants into drapery	70	160
1150	Intermediate small cross type. Somewhat as 1143, no pellets, similar bust to CRVX type (1148) but no sceptre	625	1650
1151	Long cross type. *Br. 5; B.M.C. IVa*	70	150

1152

		F	VF
		£	£
1152	Helmet type. *Br. 4; B.M.C. VIII*	80	175
1153	— — Similar, but struck in **gold**	*Extremely rare*	

1154

1156

		F	VF
1154	Last small cross type. As 1143, but different style	55	120
1154A	Similar, but bust r.	175	475
1155	— Similar, but bust to edge of coin. *B.M.C. Id*	275	650
1156	Agnus Dei type. *c.* 1009. *Br. 6; B.M.C. X*	2750	7500

Son of Swegn Forkbeard, King of Denmark, Cnut was acclaimed King by the Danish fleet in England in 1014 but was forced to leave. He returned in 1015 and in 1016 agreed on a division of the country with Eadmund Ironsides, the son of Aethelred. No coins of Eadmund are known and on his death in November 1016 Cnut secured all England, marrying Emma of Normandy, widow of Aethelred.

Main types

1157

1158

1159

1160

		F £	VF £
1157	Quatrefoil type. *Br. 2; B.M.C. VIII*	55	120
1158	Helmet type. *Br. 3; B.M.C. XIV*	45	95
1159	Short cross type. *Br. 4; B.M.C. XVI*	45	90
1159A	— Similar, but with banner in place of sceptre	600	1500
1160	Jewel cross type. *Br. 6; B.M.C. XX.* Type as 1163	300	750

This type is now considered to be a posthumous issue struck under the auspices of his widow, Aelgifu Emma.

HAROLD I, 1035-1040

Harold, the son of Cnut and Aelgifu of Northampton, initially acted as regent for his half-brother Harthacnut on Cnut's death, was then recognised as King in Mercia and the north, and King throughout England in 1037.

1163

1165

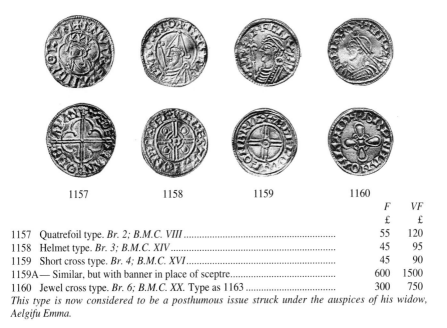

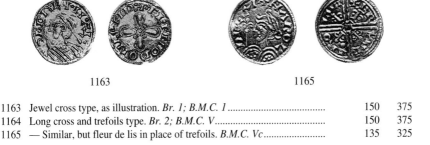

		F £	VF £
1163	Jewel cross type, as illustration. *Br. 1; B.M.C. I*	150	375
1164	Long cross and trefoils type. *Br. 2; B.M.C. V*	150	375
1165	— Similar, but fleur de lis in place of trefoils. *B.M.C. Vc*	135	325

He was heir to Cnut but lost the throne to his half-brother Harold owing to his absence in Denmark. On Harold's death he recovered his English realm.

		F	*VF*
		£	£
1166	**Early period, 1036.** Jewel cross type, as 1163; bust l. *Br. 1; B.M.C. I* ...	675	1750

1167

1168

1167	— Similar, but bust r. *B.M.C. Ia*	625	1500
1168	**Restoration, 1040-1042.** Arm and sceptre type, with name Harthacnut. *Br. 2; B.M.C. II*	550	1300

1169

1170

1169	— Similar, but with name 'Cnut'	275	550
1170	**Danish types,** of various designs, some of English type mostly struck at Lund, Denmark (now Sweden)	150	375

EDWARD THE CONFESSOR, 1042-1066

Edward was the son of Aethelred II and Emma of Normandy. A number of new mints were opened during his reign.

1171

1173

1170A	Arm and Sceptre type. B.M.C. iiic	700	1650
1171	PACX type, cross extends to edge of coin. *Br. 4; B.M.C. IV*	125	260
1172	— Similar, but cross ends at legend. *B.M.C. IVa*	135	300
1173	Radiate type. *Br. 2; B.M.C. I*	65	135

1174

1175

		F	*VF*
		£	£
1174	Trefoil quadrilateral type. *Br. 1; B.M.C. III*	70	150
1175	Short cross type, small flans. *Br. 3; B.M.C. II*	60	120

1176

1179

1176	Expanding cross type; light issue (18 grs.). *Br. 5; B.M.C. V*	75	160
1177	— — Heavy issue (27 grs.)	70	150
1178	— — Similar, but struck in **gold**	*Extremely rare*	
1179	Helmet type. *Br. 6; B.M.C. VII*	75	160
1180	— — Similar but bust l.	425	950

1181

1182

1181	Sovereign type. *Br. 7; B.M.C. IX*	85	190
1182	Hammer cross type. *Br. 8; B.M.C. XI*	70	150

1183

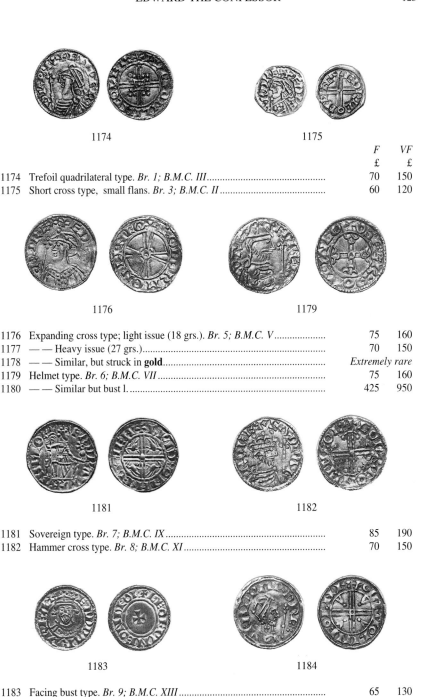

1184

1183	Facing bust type. *Br. 9; B.M.C. XIII*	65	130
1184	Pyramids type. *Br. 10; B.M.C. XV*	80	165

1185

		F	VF
		£	£
1185	Transitional Pyramids type. *B.M.C. XIV*	750	2000

Most York coins of this reign have an annulet in one quarter of the reverse.

HAROLD II, 1066

Harold was the son of Godwin Earl of Wessex. He was the brother-in-law of Edward the Confessor and was recognised as King on Edward's death. He defeated and killed Harald of Norway who invaded the north, but was himself defeated and killed at the Battle of Hastings by William of Normandy.

1186

1187

1186	Bust l. with sceptre. R. PAX across centre of *rev. B.M.C. I*	350	775
1187	Similar, but without sceptre. *B.M.C. Ia*	425	950
1188	Bust r. with sceptre *B.M.C. 1b*	700	1750

ANGLO-SAXON, NORMAN AND EARLY PLANTAGENET MINTS

In Anglo-Saxon times coins were struck at a large number of towns. The place of mintage is normally given on all coins from the last quarter of the 10th century onwards, and generally the name of the person responsible (e.g. BRVNIC ON LVND). Below we give a list of the mints, showing the reigns (Baronial of Stephen's reign omitted), of which coins have been found. After the town names we give one or two of the spellings as found on the coins, although often they appear in an abbreviated or extended form. On the coins the Anglo-Saxon and Norman w is like a P or T and the th is Ð. We have abbreviated the kings' names, etc.:

Alf	—	Alfred the Great	Wi	—	William I
EE	—	Edward the Elder	Wii	—	William II
A'stan	—	Aethelstan	He	—	Henry I
EM	—	Edward the Martyr	St	—	Stephen (regular issues)
Ae	—	Aethelred II	M	—	Matilda
Cn	—	Cnut	HA	—	Henry of Anjou
Hi	—	Harold I	WG	—	William of Gloucester
Ht	—	Harthacnut	T	—	'Tealby' coinage
ECfr	—	Edward the Confessor	SC	—	Short cross coinage
Hii	—	Harold II	LC	—	Long cross coinage

Abergavenny (FANI), Wi.
Axbridge (ACXEPO, AGEPOR) Ae, Cn, Ht.
Aylesbury (AEGEL) Ae, Cn, ECfr.
Barnstaple (BEARDA, BARDI), Edwig, Ae-Hi, ECfr, Wi, He.
Bath (BADAN) EE-Edmund, Edwig-ECfr, Wi, He, St.
Bedford (BEDANF, BEDEF) Edwig-T.
Bedwyn (BEDE CIN) ECfr, Wi.
Berkeley (BEORC) ECfr, Wi.
Bramber ? (BRAN) St.
Bridport (BRIPVT, BRIDI) A'stan, Ae, Cn, Ht, ECfr, Wi.
Bristol (BRICSTO) Ae-T, M. HA, LC.
Bruton (BRIVT) Ae-Cn, ECfr
Buckingham (BVCIN) EM-Hi, ECfr.
Bury St. Edmunds (EDMVN, SEDM, SANTEA) A'stan?, ECfr, Wi, He-LC.
Cadbury CADANB) Ae, Cn
Caistor (CASTR) EM, Ae, Cn.
Cambridge (GRANTE) Edgar-He.
Canterbury (DORO, CAENT, CANTOR, CANT CAR) Alf, A'stan, Edgar-LC.
Cardiff (CAIRDI, CARDI, CARITI) Wi, He, St, M.
Carlisle (CAR, CARDI, EDEN) He-LC.
Castle Gotha ? (GEOÐA, IOÐA) Ae-Ht.
Castle Rising (RISINGE) St.
Chester (LEIGECES, LEGECE, CESTRE) A'stan, Edgar-T.
Chichester (CISSAN CIV, CICES, CICST) A'stan, Edgar-St, SC
Chippenham ? (CIPEN) St.
Christchurch, see Twynham.
Cissbury (SIÐEST) Ae, Cn.
Colchester (COLEAC, COLECES) Ae-Hi, ECfr-T.
Crewkerne (CRVCERN) Ae, Cn.
Cricklade (CROCGL, CRIC, CREC) Ae-Wii.
Derby (DEOR, DIORBI, DERBI) A'stan, Edgar-ECfr, Wi-St.
Dorchester (DORCE, DORECES) Ae-ECfr, Wi-He, WG.
Dover (DOFER) A'stan, Edgar-St.
Droitwich (PICC, PICNEH) ECfr. Hii.
Dunwich (DVNE) St.
Durham (DVRE, DVRHAN) Wi, St-LC.
Exeter (EAXANC, EXEC, XECST) Alf, A'stan, Edwig-LC.
Eye (EI, EIE) St.
Frome ? (FRO) Cn-ECfr.
Gloucester (GLEA C EC, GLE C , G C) Alf, A'stan, Edgar-St, HA, T, LC.
Grantham (GRE) Ae
Guildford (GILDEF) EM-Cn, Ht-Wii.
Hastings (HAESTIN) Ae-St.
Hedon, near Hull (HEDVN) St.
Hereford (HEREFOR) A'stan, Ae-St, HA, T, LC.
Hertford (HEORTF) A'stan, Edwig-Hi, ECfr, Wi, Wii.
Horncastle ? (HORN) EM, Ae.
Horndon ? (HORNIDVNE) ECfr.
Huntingdon (HVNTEN) Edwig-St.
Hythe (HIÐEN) Cn, ECfr, Wi, Wii.
Ilchester (IVELCE, GIFELCST, GIVELC) Edgar, E M-He, T, LC.
Ipswich (GIPES C IC) Edgar-SC.
Kings Lynn (LENN, LENE) SC.
Langport (LANCPOR) A'stan, Cn, Hi, ECfr.
Launceston (LANSTF, SANCTI STEFANI) Ae, Wi, Wii, St. T.
Leicester (LIGER, LIHER, LEHRE) A'stan, Edgar-T.
Lewes (LAEPES) A'stan, Edgar-T.
Lichfield (LIHFL) SC.
Lincoln (LINCOLNE, NICOLE) Edgar-LC.
London (LVNDENE) Alf-LC.
Lydford (LYDAN) EM-Hi, ECfr.
Lympne (LIMEN) A'stan, Edgar-Cn.
Maldon (MAELDVN, MAELI) A'stan, Ae-Hi, ECfr, Wii.
Malmesbury (MALD, MEALDMES) Ae-Wii, HA.
Marlborough (MAERLEB) Wi, Wii.
Milbourne Port (MYLE) Ae, Cn.
Newark (NEPIR, NIPOR) Edwig, Eadgar, Ae, Cn.
Newcastle (NEWEC, NIVCA) St, T, LC.
Newport (NIPAN, NIPEP) Edgar, ECfr.
Northampton (HAMTVN, NORHANT) Edwig, Edgar-Wi, He-LC.
Norwich (NORPIC) A'stan-LC.
Nottingham (SNOTINC) A'stan, Ae-St.
Oxford (OXNAFOR, OXENEF) Alf A'stan, Edmund, Edred, Edgar-St, M, T-LC.
Pembroke (PAN, PAIN) He-T.
Pershore (PERESC) ECfr.

Peterborough (MEDE, BVR) Ae, Cn, Wi.
Petherton (PEDÐR) ECfr.
Pevensey (PEFNESE, PEVEN) Wi, Wii, St.
Reading (READIN) ECfr.
Rhuddlan (RVDILI, RVLA) Wi, SC.
Rochester (ROFEC) A'stan, Edgar-He, SC.
Romney (RVME, RVMNE) Ae-Hi, ECfr-He.
Rye (RIE) St.
Salisbury (SAEREB, SALEB) Ae-ECfr, Wi- T.
Sandwich (SANPIC) ECfr, Wi-St.
Shaftesbury (SCEFTESB, SCEFITI) A'stan, Ae-St.
Shrewsbury (SCROBES, SALOP) A'stan, Edgar-LC.
Southampton (HAMWIC, HAMTVN) A'stan, Edwig-Cn.
Southwark (SVDGE, SVD C EEORC) Ae-St.
Stafford (STAFF, STAEF) A'stan, Ae-Hi, ECfr, Wi, Wii, St, T.
Stamford (STANFOR) Edgar-St.
Steyning (STAENIG) Cn-Wii.
Sudbury (SVDBI, SVB) Ae, Cn, ECfr, Wi- St.
Swansea (SWENSEI) HA?
Tamworth (TOMPEARÐGE, TAMPRÐ) A'stan, Edwig-Hi, ECfr, Wi-St.
Taunton (TANTVNE) Ae, Cn, Ht-St.
Thetford (ÐEOTFOR,, TETFOR) Edgar-T.
Torksey (TORC, TVRC) EM-Cn.
Totnes (DARENT VRB, TOTANES, TOTNESE) A'stan, Edwig-Cn, Wii.
Twynham, now Christchurch (TPIN, TVEHAM) Wi, He.
Wallingford (PELING, PALLIG) A'stan, Edgar-He, T, LC.
Wareham (PERHAM) A'stan, Ae, Cn, Ht-St, M, WG.
Warminster (PORIME) Ae-Hi, ECfr.
Warwick (PAERING, PERPIC) A'stan, Edgar-St.
Watchet (PECEDPORT, PICEDI) Ae-ECfr, Wi-St.
Wilton (PILTVNE) Edgar-LC.
Winchcombe (PINCELE, PINCL) Edgar-Cn, Ht-Wi.
Winchester (PINTONIA, PINCEST) Alf-A'stan, Edwig -LC.
Worcester (PIHRAC, PIHREC) EM, Ae-Hi, ECfr-Sc.
York (EBORACI, EOFERPIC) A'stan, Edmund, Edgar-LC

The location of the following is uncertain.
AESTHE *(? Hastings)* Ae.
DERNE, DYR *(E. Anglian mint East Dereham?)* ECfr.
DEVITVN *(? Welsh Marches* or *St. Davids)* Wi.
MAINT, Wi.
WEARDBYRIG *(? Warborough)* A'stan, Edgar.
BRYGIN *(? Bridgnorth*, but die-links with NIPAN and with *Shaftesbury)* Ae.
EANBYRIG, Cn.
ORSNAFORDA *(Danelaw imitation)*
'WILTV' *(?Wilton, Norfolk)* Ae

EDWARDIAN AND LATER MINTS

Aberystwyth: Chas. I.
Aberystwyth: -Furnace: Chas. I.
Ashby de la Zouche: Chas. I.
Berwick-on-Tweed: Edw. I-Edw. III.
Birmingham, Heaton: Vic., Geo. V.
Birmingham, King's Norton: Geo. V.
Birmingham, Soho: Geo. III.
Bombay, India (branch mint): Geo. V.
Bridgnorth: Chas. I.
Bristol: Edw. I, Edw. IV, Hen. VI rest., Hen. VIII-Edw. VI, Chas. I, Wm. III.
Bury St. Edmunds: Edw. I-Edw. III.
Calais: Edw. III-Hen. IV, Hen. VI.
Canterbury: Edw. I-Edw. III, Edw. IV, Hen. VII-Edw. VI.
Carlisle: Chas. I.
Chester: Edw. I, Chas. I, Wm. III.
Colchester: Chas. I.
Coventry: Edw. IV.
Durham: Edw. I-Edw. IV, Rich. III-Hen. VIII.
Exeter: Edw. I, Chas. I, Wm. III.
Hartlebury Castle, Worcs.: Chas. I.
Hereford: Chas. I.
Kingston-upon-Hull: Edw. I.
Lincoln: Edw. I.
Llantrisant: Eliz. II (decimal coinage).
London, Tower: Edw. I-Geo. III.
London, Tower Hill: Geo. III-Eliz. II.
London, Durham House: Hen. VIII (posth.)-Edw. VI.
Melbourne, Australia (branch mint): Vic.-Geo. V.
Newark: Chas. I.
Newcastle-upon-Tyne: Edw. I.
Norwich: Edw. IV, Wm. III.
Ottowa, Canada (branch mint): Edw. VII-Geo. V.
Oxford: Chas I.
Perth, Australia (branch mint): Vic.-Geo. V.
Pontefract: Chas. I.
Pretoria, South Africa (branch mint): Geo. V.
Reading: Edw. III.
Scarborough: Chas. I.
Shrewsbury: Chas. I.
Southwark: Hen. VIII-Edw. VI.
Sydney, Australia (branch mint): Vic.-Geo. V.
Tournai, Belgium: Hen. VIII.
Truro: Chas. I.
Welsh Marches: Chas I
Worcester: Chas I.
York: Edw. I, Edw. III-Edw. IV, Rich. III-Edw. VI, Chas. I, Wm. III.

NORMAN MINTS (WILLIAM I TO HENRY I)

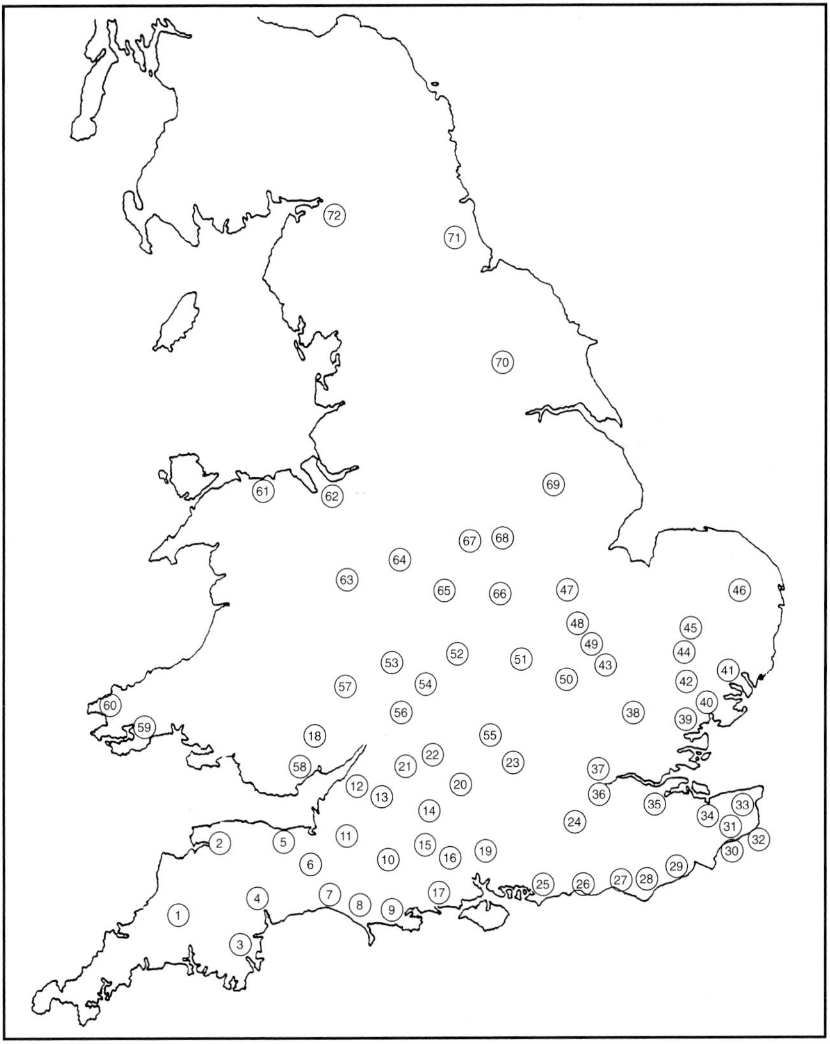

1. Launceston
2. Barnstaple
3. Totnes
4. Exeter
5. Watchet
6. Taunton
7. Bridport
8. Dorchester
9. Wareham
10. Shaftesbury
11. Ilchester
12. Bristol
13. Bath
14. Marlborough
15. Wilton
16. Salisbury
17. Chirstchurch
18. Abergavenny*
19. Winchester
20. Bedwyn
21. Malmesbury
22. Cricklade
23. Wallingford
24. Guildford
25. Chichester
26. Steyning
27. Lewes
28. Pevensey
29. Hastings
30. Romney
31. Hythe
32. Dover
33. Sandwich
34. Canterbury
35. Rochester
36. Southwark
37. London
38. Hertford
39. Maldon
40. Colchester
41. Ipswich
42. Sudbury
43. Cambridge
44. Bury
45. Thetford
46. Norwich
47. Stamford
48. Peterborough
49. Huntingdon
50. Bedford
51. Northampton
52. Warwick
53. Worcester
54. Winchcombe
55. Oxford
56. Gloucester
57. Hereford
58. Cardiff
59. Pembroke
60. St Davids*
61. Rhuddlan
62. Chester
63. Shrewsbury
64. Stafford
65. Tamworth
66. Leicester
67. Derby
68. Nottingham
69. Lincoln
70. York
71. Durham
72. Carlisle

* Possible location of uncertain mint

There were no major changes in the coinages following the Norman conquest. The controls and periodic changes of the type made in the previous reigns were continued. Nearly seventy mints were operating during the reign of William I; these had been reduced to about fifty-five by the middle of the 12th century and, under Henry II, first to thirty and later to eleven. By the second half of the 13th century the issue of coinage had been centralized at London and Canterbury, with the exception of two ecclesiastical mints. Of the thirteen types with the name PILLEMVS, PILLELM, etc. (William), the first eight have been attributed to the Conqueror and the remaining five to his son William Rufus. Cut 'halfpennies' and 'farthings' were still made in this period and are scarce until the later issues of Henry I and Stephen.

From William I to Edward II inclusive all are silver pennies unless otherwise stated.

WILLIAM I, 1066-1087

William Duke of Normandy was the cousin of Edward the Confessor. After securing the throne of England he had to suppress several rebellions.

1250

1251

		F £	VF £
1250	*Penny*. Profile left type. *Br. I*	175	475

1252

1253

		F £	VF £
1251	Bonnet type. *Br. II*	120	260
1252	Canopy type. *Br. III*	225	525

1254

1255

		F £	VF £
1253	Two sceptres type. *Br. IV*	145	350
1254	Two stars type. *Br. V*	110	250
1255	Sword type. *Br. VI*	210	500

1256

1257

		F	VF
		£	£
1256	Profile right type. *Br VII*	275	650
1257	PAXS type. *Br. VIII*	95	190

WILLIAM II, 1087-1100

William Rufus was the second son of William I, his elder brother Robert succeeded to the Dukedom of Normandy. He was killed while hunting in the New Forest.

1258

1259

1258	Penny. Profile type. *Br. 1*	350	800
1259	Cross in quatrefoil type. *Br. 2*	325	700

1260

1261

1260	Cross voided type. *Br. 3*	325	700
1261	Cross pattée and fleury type. *Br. 4*	350	750

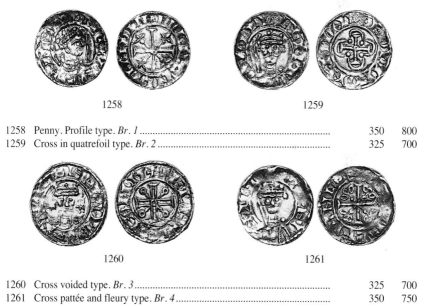

1262

1262	Cross fleury and piles type. *Br. 5*	375	850

Fifteen types were minted during this reign. In 1106-7 provision was made for minting round halfpence again, none having been struck since the time of Eadgar, but relatively few can have been made. The standard of coinage manufacture was now beginning to deteriorate badly. Many genuine coins were being cut to see if they were plated counterfeits and there was a reluctance by the public to accept such damaged pieces. About 1107-8 an extraordinary decision was taken to order the official mutilation of all new coins by snicking the edges, thus ensuring that cut coins had to be accepted. Pennies of types VII to XII (Nos. 1268-1273) usually have a cut in the flan that sometimes penetrated over a third of the way across the coin.

At Christmas 1124 the famous 'Assize of the Moneyers' was held at Winchester when all the moneyers in England were called to account for their activities and a number are said to have been mutilated for issuing coins of inferior quality.

The dates and the order of Henry's issues have been modified several times since Brooke. The main changes are as follows: BMC 11 preceded 10 and BMC 9 follows 6. The order of BMC 7 and 8 remains uncertain. The issues were not made for equal periods of time, as BMC 15 began in early 1125. The contemporary chronicles mention the round halfpenny (and farthings) and the order to snick whole coins under 1107 or 1108. The halfpennies are now dated to agree with these references when BMC 6 and 9 pennies were current. A few pennies of BMC 6 are snicked as are most of the halfpennies. Snicks continue to be used on coins of BMC 13 and 14, thought the cut is smaller and only a quarter to a half of the coins are snicked. [Brooke 1916; Archibald and Conté SNC 1990; Blackburn RNS 1990.]

1263

1263A

		F	*VF*
		£	£
1263	**Penny.** *Br*. I. Annulets type	300	700
1263A	— II. Profile l. R. Cross fleury	200	475

1264

1265

1264	— III. PAX type	185	450
1265	— IV. Facing bust. R. Five annulets and four piles	225	575

1266

1267

1266	— V. — R. Voided cross with fleur in each angle	425	950
1267	— VI. Pointing bust and stars type	550	1450

1268

		F	VF
		£	£
1268	*Br*. VII. Facing bust. R. Quatrefoil with piles	200	525

1269

1270

		F	VF
1269	— VIII. Large bust 1. R. Cross with annulet in each angle	750	2250
1270	— IX. Facing bust. R. Cross in quatrefoil	400	950

1271

1272

		F	VF
1271	— X. Small facing bust in circle. R. Cross fleury	125	300
1272	— XI. Very large bust l. R. 'Double inscription' around small cross pattee	350	850

1273

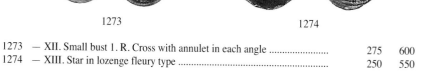

1274

		F	VF
1273	— XII. Small bust 1. R. Cross with annulet in each angle	275	600
1274	— XIII. Star in lozenge fleury type	250	550

MINTS OF STEPHEN AND THE ANARCHY

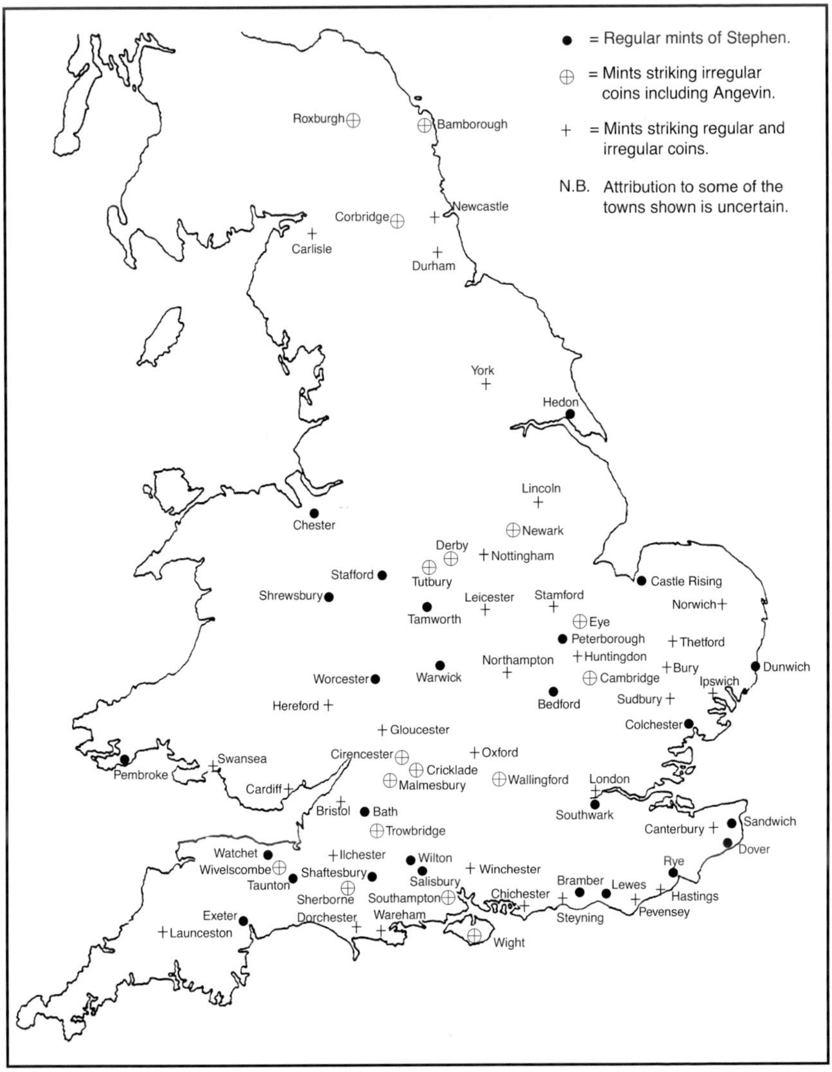

1275

1276

		F	VF
		£	£
1275	Br. XIV. Pellets in quatrefoil type	140	375
1276	— XV. Quadrilateral on cross fleury type	100	240

1277

1277	*Halfpenny*. Facing head. R. Cross potent with pellets in angles	950	2500
1277A	— As above R. Struck from a penny die of type IX	1750	5250

STEPHEN, 1135-1154
and the Civil War and Anarchy, 1138-1153

Stephen of Blois, Count of Boulogne and a nephew of Henry I, hastily crossed the Channel on his uncle's death and secured the throne for himself, despite Henry's wishes that his daughter Matilda should succeed him. She was the widow of the German emperor Henry V, and was then married to Geoffrey, Count of Anjou. Two years later Matilda arrived in England to claim the throne, supported by her half-brother Robert of Gloucester.

During the protracted civil war that ensued Matilda and later her son, Henry of Anjou, set up an alternative court at Bristol and held much of the west of England, striking coins at mints under their control. Many irregular coins were struck during this troubled period, some by barons in their own name. Particularly curious are the coins from the Midlands and E. Anglia which have Stephen's head defaced, now believed to have been issued during the Interdict of 1148. In 1153, following the death of Stephen's son, Eustace, a treaty between the two factions allowed for the succession of Matilda's son Henry and a uniform coinage was once more established throughout the kingdom.

B.M.C. Norman Kings, 2 vols. (1916). *M.—* Mack, R. P., 'Stephen and the Anarchy 1135-54', *BNJ, XXXV* (1966), pp. 38-112.

Regular regal issuess

1278

1280

		F £	VF £
1278	**Penny.** Cross moline (Watford) type. Bust r., with sceptre. R. Cross moline with lis in angles. *B.M.C. I; M. 3-42*	125	300
1279	— Similar, but obv. reads PERERIC or PERERICM. *M. 43-50*	325	750
1280	Voided cross type. Facing bust with sceptre. R. Voided cross pattée with mullets in angles. *East and South-east mints only. B.M.C. II; M. 53-66*	135	350

1281

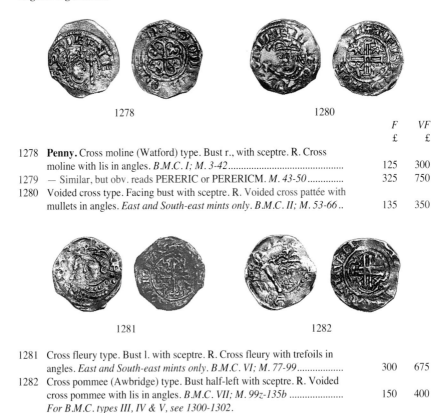

1282

1281	Cross fleury type. Bust l. with sceptre. R. Cross fleury with trefoils in angles. *East and South-east mints only. B.M.C. VI; M. 77-99*	300	675
1282	Cross pommee (Awbridge) type. Bust half-left with sceptre. R. Voided cross pommee with lis in angles. *B.M.C. VII; M. 99z-135b*	150	400

For B.M.C. types III, IV & V, see 1300-1302.

LOCAL AND IRREGULAR ISSUES OF THE CIVIL WAR

A. Coins struck from erased or defaced dies (interdict of 1148)

1283

		F £	VF £
1283	As 1278, with king's bust defaced with long cross. *East Anglian Mints. M. 137-147*	475	1000
1284	— Similar, but king's bust defaced with small cross. *Nottingham. M. 149*	425	950
1285	— Similar, but sceptre defaced with bar or cross. *Nottingham, Lincoln and Stamford. M. 148 and 150-154*	400	850
1286	— Similar, but king's name erased. *Nottingham. M. 157*	325	700
1286A	— Other defacements	400	850

B. South-Eastern variant

1287	As 1278, but king holds mace instead of sceptre. *Canterbury. M. 158*	800	2250

C. Eastern variants

1288

1288	As 1278, but roundels in centre or on limbs of cross or in angles. *Suffolk mints. M. 159-168*	525	1200
1288A	As 1278, but star before sceptre and annulets at tips of *fleurs on reverse. Suffolk mints. M. 188*	600	1350
1289	As 1278, but thick plain cross with pellet at end of limbs, lis in angles. *Lincoln. M. 169-173*	525	1250
1290	— Similar, but thick plain cross superimposed on cross moline. *M. 174.*	600	1350
1290A	As 1278. R. Quadrilateral over voided cross. *M. 176*	800	2000
1290B	As 1278. R. Long cross to edge of coin, fleurs outwards in angles. *Lincoln. M. 186-187*	800	2000

		F £	VF £

D. Southern variants

		F £	VF £
1291	As 1278, but with large rosette of pellets at end of obverse legend. *M. 184-185*	550	1250
1292	— Similar, but star at end of obverse legend. *M. 187y*	475	1000
1293	Crowned bust r. or l. with rosette of pellets before face in place of sceptre. R. As 1280, but plain instead of voided cross. *M. 181-183*	650	1500

1291

1295

		F £	VF £
1295	As 1278, but usually collar of annulets. R. Voided cross moline with annulet at centre. *Southampton. M. 207-212*	225	525

E. Midland variants

1296

		F £	VF £
1296	As 1278, but cross moline on reverse has fleured extensions into legend. *Leicester. M. 177-178*	700	1650
1297	As 1278 but crude work. R. Voided cross with lis outwards in angles. *Tutbury. M. 179*	750	1750

1298

1300

		F £	VF £
1298	Somewhat similar. R. Voided cross with martlets in angles. *Derby. M. 175*	1250	3000
1299	As 1278. R. Plain cross with T-cross in each angle. *M. 180*	800	2000
1300	Facing bust with three annulets on crown. R. Cross pattée, fleurs inwards in angles. *Northampton or Huntingdon (?). B.M.C. III; M. 67-71*	950	2500

1301

1302

		F £	VF £
1301	Facing bust with three fleurs on crown. R. Lozenge fleury, annulets in angles. *Lincoln or Nottingham. B.M.C. IV; M. 72-75*	1000	2750
1302	Bust half-right with sceptre. R. Lozenge with pellet centre, fleurs inwards in angles. *Leicester. B.M.C. V; M. 76*	1250	3000
1303	**Robert,** Earl of Leicester(?). As 1280, but reading ROBERTVS. *M. 269*	1500	4500

F. North-east and Scottish border variants

1304	As 1278, but star before sceptre and annulets at tips of fleurs on reverse. *M. 188*	650	1350
1305	As 1278, but a voided cross extending to outer circle of reverse. *M. 189-192*	700	1650
1306	As 1278, but crude style, with Stephen's name. *M. 276-279 and 281-282*	425	850
1307	— Similar. R. Cross crosslet with cross-pattée and crescent in angles. *M. 288*	900	2500
1308	David I (K. of Scotland). As 1305, but with name DAVID REX. *M. 280*	1250	3000
1309	**Henry** (Earl of Northumberland, son of K. David). hENRIC ERL. As 1278. *M. 283-285*	1250	3000
1310	— Similar. R. Cross fleury. *M. 286-287*	1000	2750
1311	— As 1307, but with name NENCI : COM on obverse. *M. 289*	1250	3250

G. 'Ornamented' series. *So-called 'York Group' but probably minted in Northern France*

1312	As 1278, with obverse inscription NSEPEFETI, STEFINEI or RODBDS. R. WISĐ. GNETA, etc., with ornament(s) in legend (sometimes retrograde). *M. 215-216 and 227*	1250	3250

1313

1315

1313	Flag type. As 1278, but king holds lance with pennant, star to r. R. As 1278, mostly with four ornaments in legend. *M. 217*	800	1750
1313A	— Similar, but with eight ornaments in reverse inscription. *M. 217*	800	1750
1314	As 1278, but STIEN and ornaments, sceptre is topped by pellet in lozenge. R. Cross fleury over plain cross, ornaments in place of inscription. *M. 218*	1000	2750
1314A	King stg. facing, holding sceptre and long standard with triple-tailed pennon. R. Cross pattee, crescents and quatrefoils in angles, pellets around, ornaments in legend	1750	5250
1315	**Stephen and Queen Matilda.** Two standing figures holding sceptre, as illustration. R. Ornaments in place of inscription. *M. 220*	1500	4500

1316

1320

		F £	VF £
1316	**Eustace.** EVSTACIVS, knight stg. r. holding sword. R. Cross in quatrefoil, EBORACI EDTS (or EBORACI TDEFL). *M. 221-222*	1450	4000
1317	— Similar, but ThOMHS FILIuS VIF. *M. 223*	1450	4000
1318	— Similar, but mixed letters and ornaments in *rev*. legend. *M. 224*	1300	3500
1319	[EVSTA] CII . FII . IOANIS, lion passant r, collonnade (or key?) below. R. Cross moline with cross-headed sceptres in angles, mixed letters and ornaments in legend. *M. 225*	1450	4000
1320	Lion rampant r., looped object below, EISTAOhIVS. R. Cross fleury with lis in angles, mostly, ornaments in legend. *M. 226*	1300	3500

1321

1322

		F £	VF £
1321	**Rodbert.** Knight on horse r., RODBЄRTVS IESTV (?). R. As 1314. *M. 228*	2000	5250
1322	**Bishop Henry.** Crowned bust r., crozier and star to r., HЄNRICVS ЄPC. R. Somewhat as last, STЄPhANVS RЄX. M. 229	2250	6000

H. Uncertain issues

		F £	VF £
1323	Crowned bust r. with sceptre, -NEΓ:. R. Cross pattée with annulets in angles (as Hen. I type XIII). *M. 272*	650	1350
1324	Crowned facing bust with sceptre, star to r. (as Hen. I type XIV). R. As last. *M. 274 Extr*	1000	2750
1325	Other types	600	1250

1326

		F £	VF £
1326	**Matilda,** Dowager Empress, Countess of Anjou (in England 1139-1148). As 1278, but cruder style, MATILDI IMP. etc. *M. 230-240*	800	2000
1326A	Obv. similar. R. Cross pattee over cross fleury (Cardiff hoard)	800	2000
1326B	Similar, but triple pellets or plumes at end of cross (Cardiff hoard)	900	2200
1326C	**Henry of Neubourg,** Bust r., R. As 1276A or 1278	1750	4000

		F £	*VF* £
1327	**Duke Henry,** son of Matilda and Geoffrey of Anjou, Duke of Normandy from 1150 (in England 1147-1149-1150 and 1153-1154). As 1278 but hENRICVS, etc. *M. 241-245*	1350	3500
1327A	As 1295 but hENRIC. *M. 246*	1350	3500
1327B	As 1326B, but hENNENNVS R, etc	1400	3750
1328	Obverse as 1278. R. Cross crosslet in quatrefoil. *M. 254*	1400	3750
1329	Crowned bust r. with sceptre. R. Cross fleury over quadrilateral fleury. *M. 248-253*	1400	3750

1330

1331

1330	Crowned facing bust, star each side. R. Cross botonnée over a quadrilateral pommée. *M. 255-258*	1500	4000
1331	Obverse as 1330. R. Voided cross botonnée over a quadrilateral pommée. *M. 259-261*	1500	4000
1331A	**Robert, Earl of Gloucester,** 1143-7, Lion. r. R. Cross fleury	1350	3500
1332	**William,** Earl of Gloucester (succeeded his father, Earl Robert, in 1147). Type as Henry of Anjou, no. 1329. *M. 262*	1500	4000
1333	Type as Henry of Anjou, no. 1330. *M. 263*	1600	4250
1334	Type as Henry of Anjou, no. 1331. *M. 264-268*	1600	4250
1334A	— Lion. R. Cross fleury	1250	3250
1335	**Brian Fitzcount,** Lord of Wallingford (?). Type as Henry of Anjou, no. 1330. *M. 270*	2500	7500
1336	**Patrick,** Earl of Salisbury (?). Helmeted bust r. holding sword, star behind. R. As Henry of Anjou, no. 1329. *M. 271*	3000	7500

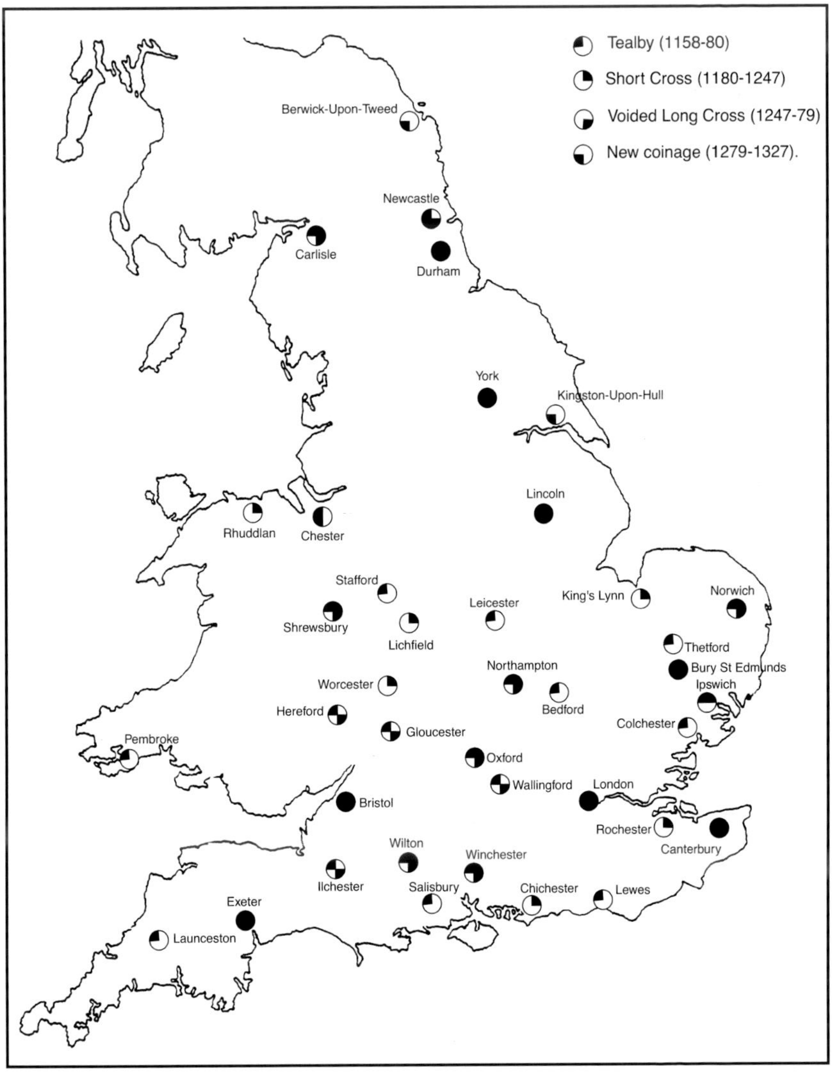
Tealby (1158-80)
Short Cross (1180-1247)
Voided Long Cross (1247-79)
New coinage (1279-1327).
Berwick-Upon-Tweed
Newcastle
Carlisle
Durham
York
Kingston-Upon-Hull
Lincoln
Rhuddlan
Chester
Stafford
Leicester
King's Lynn
Norwich
Shrewsbury
Lichfield
Thetford
Northampton
Bury St Edmunds
Ipswich
Worcester
Bedford
Hereford
Gloucester
Colchester
Pembroke
Oxford
Wallingford
London
Bristol
Rochester
Canterbury
Wilton
Winchester
Ilchester
Salisbury
Chichester
Lewes
Exeter
Launceston

HENRY II, 1154-1189

Cross-and-crosslets ('Tealby') Coinage, 1158-1180

Coins of Stephen's last type continued to be minted until 1158. Then a new coinage bearing Henry's name replaced the currency of the previous reign which contained a high proportion of irregular and sub-standard pennies. The new Cross and Crosslets issue is more commonly referred to as the 'Tealby' coinage, as over 5000 of these pennies were discovered at Tealby, Lincolnshire, in 1807. Thirty mints were employed in this re-coinage, but once the re-minting had been completed not more than a dozen mints were kept open. The issue remained virtually unchanged for twenty-two years apart from minor variations in the king's portrait. The coins tend to be poorly struck on irregular plans.

Cut coins occur with varying degrees of frequency during this issue, according to the type and local area.

The price quoted for coins in this section allows for the usual poor quality strike.

1337A

B

C

Penny

		F £	*VF* £
1337	Class A. No hair	60	135
1338	— B. Similar but mantle varies	70	165
1339	— C. Decorated collar, curl of hair	65	150

D

E

F

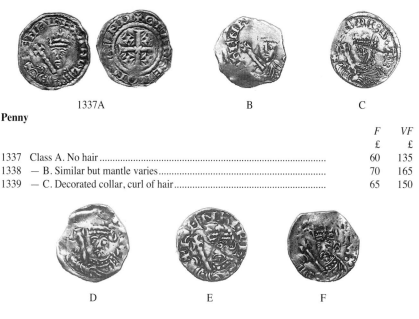

1340	— D. Decoration continues along shoulder	65	150
1341	— E. Similar bust, but shoulder not decorated	70	165
1342	— F. Hair in long ringlet to r. of bust	70	170

Mints and classes of the Cross-and-Crosslets coinage

Approximate dates for the various classes are as follows:

A 1158-1161, B and C 1161-1165, D 1165-1168, E 1168-1170 and F 1170-1180.

Bedford	A - - - - -	Ilchester	A B C D - F	Pembroke	A - - - - -
Bristol	A B C D E F	Ipswich	- B C D E F	Salisbury	A - - - - -
Bury St. Edmunds	A B C D E F	Launceston	A - - - - -	Shrewsbury	A - - - - -
Canterbury	A B C D E F	Leicester	A - - - - -	Stafford	A - C - - -
Carlisle	A - C D E F	Lewes	- - - - ? F	Thetford	A - C D - F
Chester	A - - D - -	Lincoln	A B C D E F	Wallingford	A - - - - -
Colchester	A - C - E -	London	A B C D E F	Wilton	A - - - - -
Durham	A B C - - -	Newcastle	A - C D E F	Winchester	A - C D ? -
Exeter	A B C D - -	Northampton	A - C ? - -	York	A - C D - -
Gloucester	A - - - - -	Norwich	A B C D - F		
Hereford	A - C - - -	Oxford	A - - D E -		

The publishers would like to thank Prof. Jeffrey Mass for re-organising and updating the short cross series. All illustrations have kindly been supplied by Prof. Mass.

'Short Cross' coinage of Henry II (1180-1189)

In 1180 a coinage of new type, known as the Short Cross coinage, replaced the Tealby issue. The new coinage is remarkable in that it covers not only the latter part of the reign of Henry II, but also the reigns of his sons Richard and John and on into the reign of his grandson Henry III, and the entire issue bears the name 'hENRICVS'. There are no English coins with the names of Richard or John. The Short Cross coins can be divided chronologically into various classes: ten mints were operating under Henry II and tables of mints, moneyers and classes are given for each reign.

1a 1a var. 1b 1c

		F £	VF £
1343	Class 1a. Small face, square E, and/or C, and/or round M, irregular number of curls	110	275
1343A	Class 1a var. Small face, seriffed X, round E and C, square M, irregular number of curls	70	165
1344	1b. Fine portrait, curls 2 left and 5 right, stop before REX on most coins	30	80
1345	1c. Portrait less finely shaped, irregular number of curls, normally no stop before REX	30	80

RICHARD I, 1189-1199

Pennies of Short Cross type continued to be issued throughout the reign, all bearing the name hENRICVS. The coins of class 4, which have very crude portraits, continued to be issued in the early years of the next reign. The only coins bearing Richard's name are from his territories of Aquitaine and Poitou in western France.

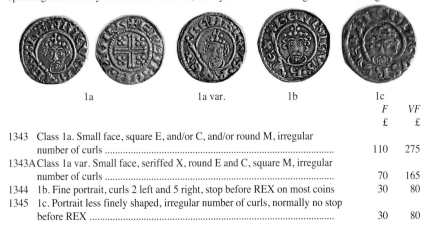

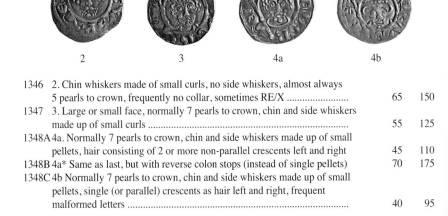

2 3 4a 4b

		F £	VF £
1346	2. Chin whiskers made of small curls, no side whiskers, almost always 5 pearls to crown, frequently no collar, sometimes RE/X	65	150
1347	3. Large or small face, normally 7 pearls to crown, chin and side whiskers made up of small curls	55	125
1348A	4a. Normally 7 pearls to crown, chin and side whiskers made up of small pellets, hair consisting of 2 or more non-parallel crescents left and right	45	110
1348B	4a* Same as last, but with reverse colon stops (instead of single pellets)	70	175
1348C	4b Normally 7 pearls to crown, chin and side whiskers made up of small pellets, single (or parallel) crescents as hair left and right, frequent malformed letters	40	95

'Short Cross' coinage *continued*. All with name hЄNRICVS

The Short Cross coins of class 4 continued during the early years of John's reign, but in 1205 a re-coinage was initiated and new Short Cross coins of better style replaced the older issues. Coins of classes 5a and 5b were issued in the re-coinage in which sixteen mints were employed. Only ten of these mints were still working by the end of class 5. The only coins to bear John's name are the pennies, halfpence and farthings issues for Ireland.

4c

5a1

5a2

5b

5c

6a

		F £	*VF* £
1349	4c. Reversed S, square face at bottom, 5 pearls to crown, normally single crescents as hair left and right	65	150
1350A	5a1 Reversed or regular S, irregular curved lines as hair (or circular curls containing no pellets), cross pattee as initial mark on reverse, *London and Canterbury* only	75	175
1350B	5a2 Reversed S, circular curls left and right (2 or 3 each side) containing single pellets, cross pomme as initial mark on reverse	50	120
1350C	5a/5b or 5b/5a	40	100
1351	5b. Regular S, circular pelleted curls, cross pattee as initial mark on reverse	30	75
1352	5c. Slightly rounder portrait, letter X in the form of a St. Andrew's cross	30	70
1353	6a. Smaller portrait, with smaller letter X composed of thin strokes or, later, short wedges	35	80

'Short Cross' coinage *continued* (1216-47)

The Short Cross coinage continued for a further thirty years during which time the style of portraiture and workmanship deteriorated. By the 1220s minting had been concentrated at London and Canterbury, one exception being the mint of the Abbot of Bury St. Edmunds.

Halfpenny and farthing dies are recorded early in this issue; a few halfpennies and now farthings have been discovered. See nos 1357 D-E.

6b 6c 6c orn. 6x 6d

		F	*VF*
		£	£
1354	6b. Very tall lettering and long rectangular face	25	55
1355	6c. Lettering now shorter, face narrow and triangular	25	55
1355A	6c. orn. Various letters now ornamental in design, curls 3/3 left and right	50	125
1355B	6x. Canterbury mint only, RE/X, curls 2/2, nostril pellets outside nose...	100	275
1355C	6d. Face less distinct in shape, N's containing a pellet along the crossbar	35	80

7a 7b 7c

1356A	7a. Small compact face, letter A with top coming to a point under crossbar	15	40
1356B	7b. Letter A with square top, M appears as H	15	40
1356C	7c. Degraded portrait, letter A and M as in 7b, large lettering	15	35

8a 8b 8c

1357A	8a. New portrait; letter X in shape of curule; cross pattee as initial mark on reverse (early style), or cross pommee (late style)	50	135
1357B	8b. Degraded portrait, wedge-shaped X, cross pomme as initial mark	25	65
1357C	8c. Degraded portrait, cross pomme X, cross pomme as initial mark	25	60
1357D	Round halfpenny in style of class 7, initial mark in shape of up-turned crescent, London mint only	750	1750
1357E	Round farthing in style of class 7, initial mark in shape of up-turned crescent, London mint only	800	1850

1357D

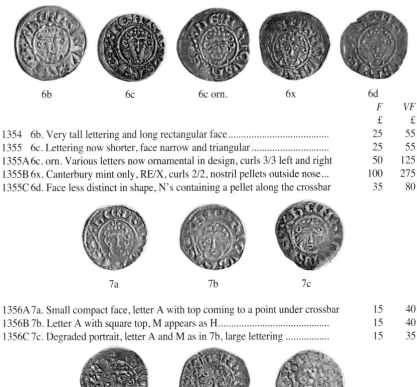

1357E

Moneyer tables for the short cross coinage

		Fine
Henry II:		
London: Aimer (1a-b), Alain (1a-b), Alain V (1a-b), Alward (1b), Davi (1b-c), Fil Aimer (1a-b), Gefrei (1c), Gilebert (1c), Godard (1b), Henri (1a-b), Henri Pi (1a), Iefrei (1a-b), Iohan (1a-b), Osber (1b), Pieres (1a-c), Pieres M (1a-b), Randvl (1a-b), Ravl (1b-c), Reinald (1a-b), Willelm (1a-b)	*From*	30
Carlisle: Alain (1b-c)	*From*	70
Exeter: Asketil (1a-b), Iordan (1a-b), Osber (1a-b), Ravl (1b), Ricard (1b-c), Roger (1a-c)	*From*	65
Lincoln: Edmvnd (1b-c), Girard (1b), Hvgo (1b), Lefwine (1b-c), Rodbert (1b), Walter (1b), Will. D.F. (1b), Willelm (1b-c)	*From*	50
Northampton: Filip (1a-b), Hvgo (1a-b), Ravl (1a-c), Reinald (1a-c), Simvn (1b), Walter (1a-c), Willelm (1a-b)	*From*	35
Oxford: Asketil (1b), Iefrei (1b), Owein (1b-c), Ricard (1b-c), Rodbert (1b), Rodbt. F. B. (1b), Sagar (1b)	*From*	60
Wilton: Osber (1a-b), Rodbert (1a-b)	*From*	65
Winchester: Adam (1a-c), Clement (1a-b), Gocelm (1a-c), Henri (1a), Osber (1a-b), Reinier (1b), Rodbert (1a-b)	*From*	35
Worcester: Edrich (1b), Godwine (1b-c), Osber (1b-c), Oslac (1b)	*From*	60
York: Alain (1a-b), Efrard (1a-c), Gerard (1a-b), Hvgo (1a-c), Hunfrei (1a-b), Isac (1a-b), Tvrkil (1a-c), Willelm (1a-b)	*From*	35
Richard I		
London: Aimer (2-4a), Fvlke (4a-b), Henri (4a-b), Ravl (2), Ricard (2-4b), Stivene (2-4b), Willelm (2-4b)	*From*	40
Canterbury: Goldwine (3-4b), Hernavd (4b), Hve (4b), Ioan (4b), Meinir (2-4b), Reinald/Reinavd (2-4b), Roberd (2-4b), Samvel (4b), Simon (4b), Vlard (2-4b)	*From*	40
Carlisle: Alein (3-4b)	*From*	90
Durham: Adam (4a), Alein (4a-b), Pires (4b)	*From*	100
Exeter: Ricard (3)	*From*	95
Lichfield: Ioan (2)	*Extremely rare*	
Lincoln: Edmvnd (2), Lefwine (2), Willelm (2)	*From*	75
Northampton: Giferei (4a), Roberd (3), Waltir (3)	*From*	80
Northampton or Norwich: Randvl (4a-b), Willelm (4a-b)	*From*	70
Shrewsbury: Ive (4a-b), Reinald/Reinavd (4a-b), Willem (4a)	*From*	165
Winchester: Adam (3), Gocelm (3), Osbern (3-4a), Pires (4a), Willelm (3-4a)	*From*	55
Worcester: Osbern (2)	*From*	200
York: Davi (4a-b), Efrard/Everard (2-4b), Hvgo/Hve (2-4a), Nicole (4a-b), Tvrkil (2-4a)	*From*	50
John		
London: Abel (5c-6a), Adam (5b-c), Beneit (5b-c), Fvlke (4c-5b), Henri (4c-5b/5a), Ilger (5b-6a), Ravf (5c-6a), Rener (5a/b-5c), Ricard (4c-5b), Ricard B (5b-c), Ricard T (5a/b-5b), Walter (5c-6a), Willelm (4c-5b), Willelm B (5a/b-5c), Willelm L (5b-c), Willelm T (5b-c)	*From*	30
Canterbury: Goldwine (4c-5c), Hernavd/Arnavd (4c-5c), Hve (4c-5c), Iohan (4c-5c), Iohan B (5b-c), Iohan M (5b-c), Roberd (4c-5c), Samvel (4c-5c), Simon (4c-5c)	*From*	30
Bury St Edmunds: Fvlke (5b-c)	*From*	65
Carlisle: Tomas (5b)	*From*	80
Chichester: Pieres (5b/a-5b), Ravf (5b/a-5b), Simon (5b/a-5b), Willelm (5b)	*From*	50
Durham: Pieres (5a-6a)	*From*	60
Exeter: Gileberd (5a-b), Iohan (5a-b), Ricard (5a-b)	*From*	50

Ipswich: Alisandre (5b-c), Iohan (5b-c)	*From*	40
Kings Lynn: Iohan (5b), Nicole (5b), Willelm (5b)	*From*	100
Lincoln: Alain (5a), Andrev (5a-5c), Hve (5a/b-5c), Iohan (5a), Ravf (5a/b-5b), Ricard (5a-5b/a), Tomas (5a/b-5b)	*From*	30
Northampton: Adam (5b-c), Roberd (5b), Roberd T (5b)	*From*	40
Northampton or Norwich: Randvl (4c)	*From*	80
Norwich: Gifrei (5a/b-5c), Iohan (5a-c), Renald/Renavd (5a-c)	*From*	40
Oxford: Ailwine (5b), Henri (5b), Miles (5b)	*From*	50
Rochester: Alisandre (5b), Hvnfrei (5b)	*From*	80
Winchester: Adam (5a-c), Andrev (5b-c), Bartelme (5b-c), Henri (5a), Iohan (5a-c), Lvkas (5b-c), Miles (5a-c), Ravf (5b-c), Ricard (5a-b)	*From*	30
York: Davi (4c-5b), Nicole (4c-5c), Renavd (5b), Tomas (5a/b-5b)	*From*	35

Henry III

London: Abel (6b-7a), Adam (7b-c), Elis (7a-b), Giffrei (7b-c), Ilger (6b-7b), Ledvlf (7b-c), Nichole (7c-8c), Ravf (6b-7b), Ricard (7b), Terri (7a-b), Walter (6b-c)	*From*	20
Canterbury: Arnold (6c/6x, 6x), Henri (6b-6c/d, 7a-c), Hivn/Ivn (6b-7b), Iohan (6b-7c, 8b-c), Ioan Chic (7b-c), Ioan F. R. (7b-c), Nichole (7c, 8b-c), Osmvnd (7b-c), Robert (6b, 7b-c), Robert Vi (7c), Roger (6b-7b), Roger of R (7a-b), Salemvn (6x, 7a-b), Samvel (6b-d, 7a), Simon (6b-d, 7a-b), Tomas (6d, 7a-b), Walter (6b-7a), Willem (7b-c, 8b-c), Willem Ta (7b-c)	*From*	20
Bury St Edmunds: Iohan (7c-8c), Norman (7a-b), Ravf (6c-d, 7a), Simvnd (7b-c), Willelm (7a)	*From*	30
Durham: Pieres (7a)	*From*	80
Winchester: Henri (6c)	*From*	85
York: Iohan (6c), Peres (6c), Tomas (6c), Wilam (6c)	*From*	85

Irregular Local Issue		
Rhuddlan (in chronological order)	*From*	75
Group I (c. 1180 – pre 1205) Halli, Tomas, Simond		
Group II (c.1205 – 1215) Simond, Henricus		

Rhuddlan

'Long Cross' coinage (1247-72)

By the middle of Henry's reign the coinage in circulation was in a poor state, being worn and clipped. In 1247 a fresh coinage was ordered, the new pennies having the reverse cross extended to the edge of the coin to help safeguard the coins against clipping. The earliest of these coins have no mint or moneyers' names. A number of provincial mints were opened for producing sufficient of the Long Cross coins, but these were closed again in 1250, only the royal mints of London and Canterbury and the ecclesiastical mints of Durham and Bury St. Edmunds remained open.

In 1257, following the introduction of new gold coinages by the Italian cities of Brindisi (1232), Florence (1252) and Genoa (1253), Henry III issued a gold coinage in England. This was a gold 'Penny' valued at 20 silver pence and twice the weight of the silver penny. The coinage was not a success, being undervalued, and it ceased to be minted after a few years; few coins have survived.

Cut halfpennies and farthings are common for this period, with a greater concentration in the early part. They are up to 100 times commoner than in late Anglo-Saxon times.

Without sceptre

Ia

Ib

		F £	*VF* £
1358	Class Ia. hЄNRICVS: RЄX. R. ANGLIЄ TЄRCI	250	650
1359	Ib. hЄNRICVS REX. ANG. R. LIE TЄRCI LON *(London),* CAN *(Canterbury)* (rare) or AED *(Bury St. Edmunds)* (very rare) *from*	35	80
1360	— — I/II mule	30	70

II

IIIb

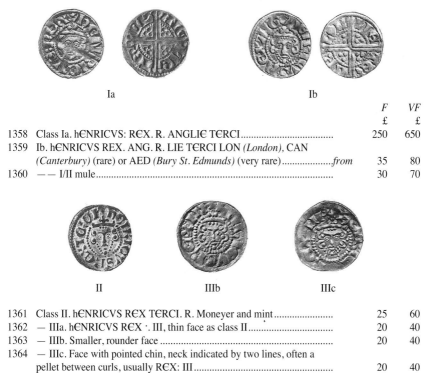

IIIc

		F £	*VF* £
1361	Class II. hЄNRICVS RЄX TЄRCI. R. Moneyer and mint	25	60
1362	— IIIa. hЄNRICVS RЄX ·. III, thin face as class II	20	40
1363	— IIIb. Smaller, rounder face	20	40
1364	— IIIc. Face with pointed chin, neck indicated by two lines, often a pellet between curls, usually RЄX: III	20	40

With sceptre

IVa

IVb

Va

Vb

		F	VF
		£	£
1365	Class IVa. Similar to last, but with sceptre	60	125
1366	— IVb. Similar, but new crown with half-fleurs and large central fleur..	75	175
1367	— Va. With class IV bust, crown as IVa or IVb, round eyes, from now on legend begins at 10 o'clock. Ball-tailed R.	20	35
1368	— Vb. Narrower face, wedge-tailed R, round eyes	15	35
1369	— Vc. Shorter, broader face with almond-shaped eyes	15	35

Vd

Ve

Vf

Vg

Vh

1370	— Vd. Portrait of quite different style; new crown with true-shaped fleur	45	110
1371	— Ve. Similar, with jewelled or beaded crown	95	275
1372	— Vf. New style larger face, double-banded crown	20	40
1373	— Vg. Single band to crown, low central fleur, curule chair shaped X ...	15	30
1374	— Vh. Crude copy of Vg, with pellets in lieu of fleur	30	75
1375	— Vi. Similar to last, but triple line of pellets for beard	175	475

Vi

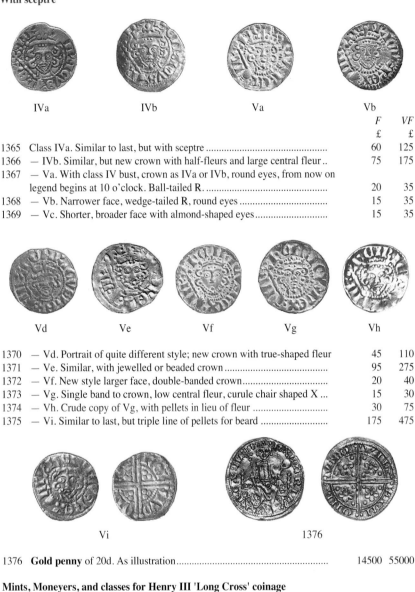

1376

1376	**Gold penny** of 20d. As illustration	14500	55000

Mints, Moneyers, and classes for Henry III 'Long Cross' coinage

		Fine
London: Davi or David (IIIc-Vf), Henri (IIIa-Vd, f, g), Ion, Ioh, Iohs or Iohan (Vc-g), Nicole (Ib/II mule, II-Vc), Renaud (Vg-i), Ricard (IIIc-Vg), Robert (Vg), Thomas (Vg), Walter (Vc-g), Willem (Vc-g and gold penny)	*from*	15
Bristol: Elis (IIIa, b, c), Henri (IIIb) , Iacob (IIIa, b, c), Roger (IIIa, b, c), Walter (IIIb, c)	*from*	22
Bury St. Edmunds: Ion or Iohs (II-Va, Vg, h, i), Randulf (Va-f), Renaud (Vg), Stephane (Vg)	*from*	20

		Fine
Canterbury: Alein (Vg, h), Ambroci (Vg), Gilbert (II-Vd/c mule, Vf, g), Ion, Ioh, Iohs, or Iohanes (IIIe-Vd, f, g), Nicole or Nichole (Ib/II mule, II-Vh), Ricard (Vg, h), Robert (Vc-h), Walter (Vc-h), Willem or Willeme (Ib/II mule, II-Vd, f, g)	*from*	15
Carlisle: Adam (IIIa, b), Ion (IIIa, b), Robert (IIIa, b), Willem (IIIa, b)	*from*	45
Durham: Philip (IIIb), Ricard (V, b, c), Roger (Vg), Willem (Vg)	*from*	60
Exeter: Ion (II-IIIc), Philip (II-IIIc), Robert (II-IIIc), Walter (II-IIIb)................	*from*	30
Gloucester: Ion (II-IIIc), Lucas (II-IIIc), Ricard (II-IIIc), Roger (II-IIIc)	*from*	30
Hereford: Henri (IIIa, b), Ricard (IIIa, b, c), Roger (IIIa, b, c), Walter (IIIa, b, c)	*from*	40
Ilchester: Huge (IIIa, b, c), Ierveis (IIIa, b, c), Randulf (IIIa, b, c), Stephe (IIIa, b, c)..........	*from*	65
Lincoln: Ion (II-IIIc), Ricard (II-IIIc), Walter (II-IIIc), Willem (II-IIIc)............	*from*	25
Newcastle: Adam (IIIa, b), Henri (IIIa, b, c), Ion (IIIa, b, c), Roger (IIIa, b, c) ..	*from*	22
Northampton: Lucas (II-IIIb), Philip (II-IIIc), Tomas (II-IIIc), Willem (II-IIIc)	*from*	25
Norwich: Huge (II-IIIc), Iacob (II-II Ic), Ion (II-IIIc), Willem (II-IIIc)	*from*	30
Oxford: Adam (II-IIIc), Gefrei (II-IIIc), Henri (II-IIIc), Willem (II-IIIc)	*from*	30
Shrewsbury: Lorens (IIIa, b, c), Nicole (IIIa, b, c), Peris (IIIa, b, c), Ricard (IIIa, b, c)	*from*	40
Wallingford: Alisandre (IIIa, b), Clement (IIIa, b), Ricard (IIIa, b), Robert (IIIa, b)	*from*	60
Wilton: Huge (IIIb, c), Ion (IIIa, b, c), Willem (IIIa, b, c)	*from*	35
Winchester: Huge (II-IIIc), Iordan (II-IIIc), Nicole (II-IIIc), Willem (II-IIIc)	*from*	22
York: Alain (II-IIIb), Ieremie (II-IIIb), Ion (II-IIIc), Rener (II-IIIc), Tomas (IIIb, c)	*from*	25

EDWARD I, 1272-1307

'Long Cross' coinage (1272-79). With name hЄNRICVS

The earliest group of Edward's Long Cross coins are of very crude style and known only of Durham and Bury St. Edmunds. Then, for the last class of the type, pennies of much improved style were issued at London, Durham and Bury, but in 1279 the Long Cross coinage was abandoned and a completely new coinage substituted.

Cut halfpennies and farthings also occur for this issue, and within this context are not especially rare.

VI

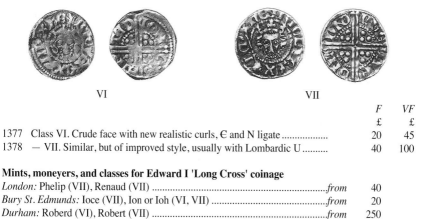

VII

		F	VF
		£	£
1377	Class VI. Crude face with new realistic curls, Є and N ligate	20	45
1378	— VII. Similar, but of improved style, usually with Lombardic U	40	100

Mints, moneyers, and classes for Edward I 'Long Cross' coinage

London: Phelip (VII), Renaud (VII)	*from*	40
Bury St. Edmunds: Ioce (VII), Ion or Ioh (VI, VII)	*from*	20
Durham: Roberd (VI), Robert (VII)	*from*	250

The publishers would like to thank Jeffrey North for re-organising and updating the coinage of Edward I and II and early silver of Edward III.

New Coinage (from 1279).

A major re-coinage was embarked upon in 1279 which introduced new denominations. In addition to the penny, halfpence and farthings were also minted and, for the first time, a fourpenny piece called a 'Groat' (from the French *Gros*).

As mint administration was now very much centralized, the practice of including the moneyer's name in the coinage was abandoned (except for a few years at Bury St. Edmunds). Several provincial mints assisted with the re-coinage during 1279-81, then minting was again restricted to London, Canterbury, Durham and Bury.

The provincial mints were again employed for a subsidiary re-coinage in 1299-1302 in order to remint lightweight coins and the many illegal *esterlings* (foreign copies of the English pennies, mainly from the Low Countries), which were usually of poorer quality than the English coins.

1379

		F	*VF*
		£	£
1379	**Groat.** (=4d.; wt. 89 grs.). Type as illustration but several minor varieties *Extant specimens often show traces of having been mounted on the obverse and gilded on the reverse; such coins are worth less.*	950	3750

1a

1b

1c

1380	**Penny.** *London.* Class 1a. Crown with plain band, ЄDW RЄX; Lombardic n on *obv;* pellet 'barred' S on rev. A with sloping top	225	650
1381	— 1b. — ЄD RЄX; no drapery on bust, Roman N	650	2000
1382	— Ic. — ЄDW RЄX; Roman N, normal or reversed; small lettering	20	45
1383	— Id. — ЄDW R;—; large lettering and face	20	45

1d(1384)

2a

2b

1384	— — — Annulet below bust (for the Abbot of Reading)	100	265
1385	— 2a. Crown with band shaped to ornaments; usually broken left petal to central fleur portraits as ld. N usually reversed	15	40
1386	— 2b. — tall bust; long neck; N reversed	15	35

3a 3b 3c

		F £	VF £
1387	— 3a. Crescent-shaped contraction marks; pearls in crown, drapery is foreshortened circle with hook ends	25	65
1388	— 3b. — — drapery is segment of a circle, pearls in crown	20	40
1389	— 3c. — normal crown; drapery in one piece, hollowed in centre	15	35

3e 3f 3g 4a

		F £	VF £
1390	— 3d. — — drapery in two pieces, broad face	15	30
1391	— 3e. — long narrow face (Northern mints)	20	35
1392	— 3f. — broad face, large nose, rougher work, late S first used	30	70
1393	— 3g. — Spread crown small neat bust, narrow face	15	30

4b 4c 4d 4e

		F £	VF £
1394	— 4a. Comma-shaped contraction mark, late S always used, C and Є open	15	35
1395	— 4b. Similar, but face and hair shorter	15	30
1396	— 4c. Larger face with more copious hair; nick to band of crown	20	50
1397	— 4d. Pellet at beginning of *obv.* and *rev.* inscription	15	30
1398	— 4e. Three pellets on breast, ropy hair, pellet in *rev.* legend (no pellets on Bury or Durham)	15	35

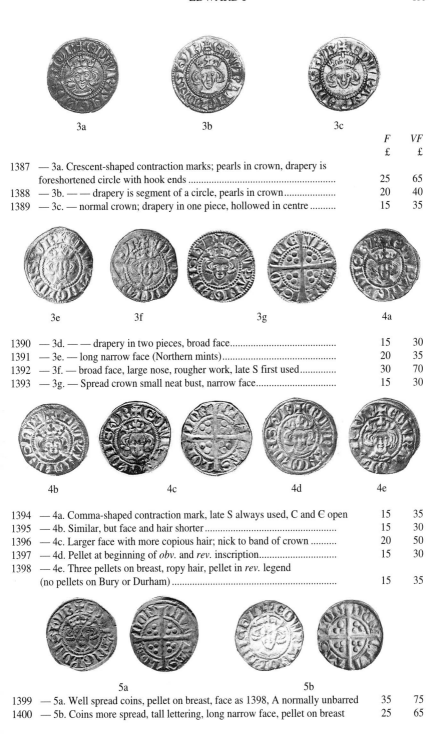

5a 5b

		F £	VF £
1399	— 5a. Well spread coins, pellet on breast, face as 1398, A normally unbarred	35	75
1400	— 5b. Coins more spread, tall lettering, long narrow face, pellet on breast	25	65

6a

6b

7a

7b

		F £	VF £
1401	— 6a. Smaller coins, smaller lettering with closed E (from now on) initial cross almost plain, crown with wide fleurs, crude appearance.......	70	175
1402	— 6b. Initial cross well pattee	40	95
1403	— 7a. Rose on breast (except Bury), short hair; almond-shaped eyes, double barred N..	35	80

8b

8c

		F £	VF £
1404	— 7b. Rose on breast (London only) longer hair, new crown.................	50	120
1405	— 8a. Crown resembling 7b with central fleur usually broken...............	20	45
1406	— 8b. Similar to 1405 with wider drapery, top-tilted S	25	55
1406A	— 8c — — Crown with very arched band	30	65

9a

9b

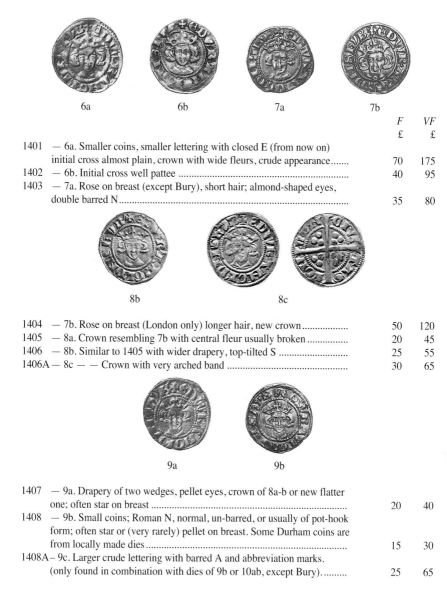

		F £	VF £
1407	— 9a. Drapery of two wedges, pellet eyes, crown of 8a-b or new flatter one; often star on breast	20	40
1408	— 9b. Small coins; Roman N, normal, un-barred, or usually of pot-hook form; often star or (very rarely) pellet on breast. Some Durham coins are from locally made dies	15	30
1408A	– 9c. Larger crude lettering with barred A and abbreviation marks. (only found in combination with dies of 9b or 10ab, except Bury).	25	65

10ab

		F £	VF £
1409	— 10ab. ЄDWARD. Bifoliate crown (converted 9b or new taller one). Narrow incurved lettering.	15	35
1409A	— 10ab. Similar with annulet on breast or a pellet each side of head and on breast	65	150
1409B	— 10ab. ЄDWAR (rarely ЄDWR). Similar to 1409. A few early coins have the trifoliate crown of 9b.	15	35

10cf1 10cf2

Crown 1 Crown 2 Crown 3 Crown 4 Crown 5

		F £	VF £
1410	— 10cf1. Crown 1 (Axe-shaped central fleur, wedge-shaped petals). ЄDWA from now on. Stub-tailed. R	15	30
1411	— 10cf2. Crown 2 (Well-shaped central lis, no spearheads). Spreading hair.	15	30

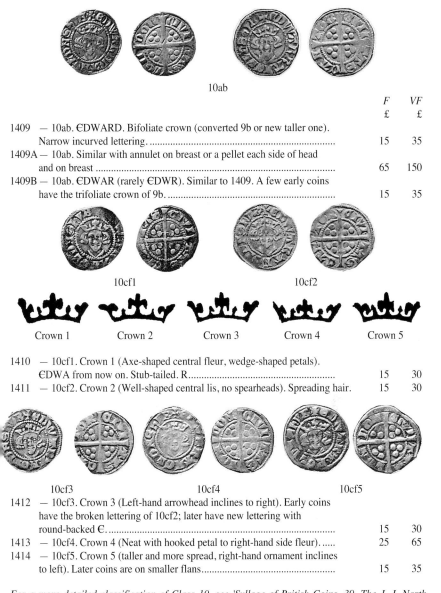

10cf3 10cf4 10cf5

		F £	VF £
1412	— 10cf3. Crown 3 (Left-hand arrowhead inclines to right). Early coins have the broken lettering of 10cf2; later have new lettering with round-backed Є.	15	30
1413	— 10cf4. Crown 4 (Neat with hooked petal to right-hand side fleur).	25	65
1414	— 10cf5. Crown 5 (taller and more spread, right-hand ornament inclines to left). Later coins are on smaller flans	15	35

For a more detailed classification of Class 10, see 'Sylloge of British Coins, 39, The J. J. North Collection, Edwardian English Silver Coins 1279-1351', The Classification of Class 10, c. 1301-10, by C. Wood.

Prices are for full flan, well struck coins.
The prices for the above types are for London. For coins of the other mints see following pages; types are in brackets, prices are for the commonest type of each mint.

Berwick Type 1 | Type II | Type III | Type IV

		F	*VF*
		£	£
1415	*Berwick-on-Tweed.* (Blunt types I-IV) Local dies ... *from*	20	45
1416	*Bristol.* (2; 3b; c, d; 3f, g; 9b) ... *from*	15	35
1417	*Bury St. Edmunds.* Robert de Hadelie (3c, d, g; 4a, b, c) ... *from*	40	90
1418	— Villa Sci Edmundi (4e; 5b; 6b; 7a; 8ab, 9a – 10 cf 5) ... *from*	20	50
1419	*Canterbury.* (2; 3b-g; 4; 5; 7a; 7b; 9;10) ... *from*	15	30
1420	*Chester.* (3g; 9b) ... *from*	35	80
1421	*Durham.* Plain cross mm (9b; 10ab; 10cf 2-3; 10cf 5) ... *from*	20	45
1422	— Bishop de Insula (2; 3b, c, e, g; 4a) ... *from*	20	45
1423	— Bishop Bec (4b-e; 5b; 6b; 7b; 9a, 9b, 10) with *mm.* cross moline ... *from*	20	45
1424	— — (4b) cross moline in one angle of *rev.* ...	150	450
1425	*Exeter.* (9b) ...	40	100
1426	*Kingston-upon-Hull.* (9b) ...	40	100
1427	*Lincoln.* (3c, d, f, g) ... *from*	15	30
1428	*Newcastle-upon-Tyne.* (3e; 9b; 10ab) ... *from*	20	45
1429	*York.* Royal mint (2; 3b, c, d, e, f; 9b) ... *from*	15	30
1430	— Archbishop's mint (3e, f; 9b). R. Quatrefoil in centre ... *from*	15	35
1431	**Halfpenny,** *London.* Class 3b. ЄDWR ANGL DNS hYB, drapery composed of curved line with wedges above ...	30	80
1432	— 3c Drapery composed of two wedges ...	20	40

1434A 1433

1433	— 3g. New wide crown, thick-waisted S, drapery as 3b ...	20	45
1433A	— — 4c. Narrower crown, drapery of two unequal wedges ...	25	60
1433B	— — Similar, pellet before LON ...	35	75
1434	— 4e. Single-peice collar with (usually) three pellets on breast ...	40	90
1434A	— 6. Small face with short hair, large coarse crown, closed Є ...	40	90
1435	— 7. Larger face with square jaw, open Є, usually double-barred N ...	35	85
1436	— 8. Similar, new crown with straight sides ...	30	75
1437	— 10. ЄDWAR R ANGL DNS hYB, bifoliate or trifoliate crown, new waisted letters ...	30	65

The above prices are for London; halfpence of the mints given below were also struck.

		F £	VF £
1438	*Berwick-on-Tweed*. (Blunt types I, II and III) *from*	50	135
1439	*Bristol*. Class 3c, 3g, 4c *from*	25	60
1440	*Lincoln*. Class 3c	35	75
1441	*Newcastle*. Class 3e, single pellet in each angle of *rev*.	45	120
1442	*York*. Class 3b	30	70

1443A

1445

		F £	VF £
1443	**Farthing,** *London*. Class 1a. Base silver issue (6.65 grains), ЄDWARDVS RЄX. bifoliate crown with no intermediate jewels, inner circle. R. LONDONIЄNSIS, (rarely LONDRIЄNSIS),	30	90
1443A	— 1c. Similar trifoliate crown	25	75
1444	— 2. Smaller face, trifoliate crown with intermediate jewels	20	50
1445	— 3c. New tapering face, wide at top, crown with curved band.	20	45
1445A	— 3de. Sterling silver issue (5.51 grains.) Є R ANGLIЄ bust (usually) to bottom of coin, no inner circle. R. LONDONIЄNSIS	25	60
1446	— 3g. Similar, new wide crown with curving side fleurs	15	35
1446A	— 4de. Similar to 3de. R. CIVITAS LONDON	30	80
1446B	— 5. Similar, crude wide crown.	30	80
1447	— 6-7. New large face with wide cheeks, pellet or almond eyes	35	90
1448	— 8. Similar, small rounded face, tall crude crown	25	70
1449	— 9a. Є R ANGL DN, small tapering face, (a variety has the face of class 6-7)	25	70
1449A	— 9b. Small ugly face, usually wide crown with outwards-sloping sides. .	35	90
1450	— 10 ЄDWARDVS REX (-, A, AN or ANG,) large bust within inner circle	12	30

Type 1450 often appears on oval flans.

It is now thought that the order of London Halfpennies is class 4de, 6-7, 5, 9a, 8, 9b

1446

1452

		F £	VF £
1451	*Berwick-on-Tweed*. (Blunt type I, IIIb)	100	300
1452	*Bristol*. Class 2, 3c, 3de	30	75
1453	*Lincoln*. Class 3de	35	80
1453A	*Newcastle*. Class 3de, R NOVI CASTRI	175	450
1454	*York*. Class 2, 3c, 3de	40	100

For further information see Farthings and Halfpennies, Edward I and II, Paul and Bente R Wither's, 2001

The coinage of this reign differs only in minor details from that of Edward I. No groats were issued in the years *c*. 1282-1351.

11a

12a

13

14

15a

15b

15c

		F £	*VF* £
1455	**Penny,** *London*. Class 11a. Broken spear-head or pearl on l. side of crown; long narrow face, straight-sided N; round back to C and Є	15	40
1456	— 11b. — Є with angular back (till 15b), N with well-marked serifs (late)	15	40
1457	— 11c. — — A of special form	45	110
1458	— 12a. Central fleur of crown formed of three wedges; thick cross mm.	25	55
1458A	— 12b — Crown with diamond-shaped petals and cruciform central fleur; cross of four wedges mm	35	100
1458B	— 12c — Crown with heart-shaped petals; cross patte mm	40	100
1459	— 13. Central fleur of crown as Greek double axe	20	50
1460	— 14. Crown with tall central fleur; large smiling face with leering eyes	15	45
1461	— 15a. Small flat crown with both spear-heads usually bent to l.; face of 14	20	50
1462	— 15b. — very similar, but smaller face	15	45
1463	— 15c. — large face, large Є	20	50

Berwick Type V

Type VI

Type VII

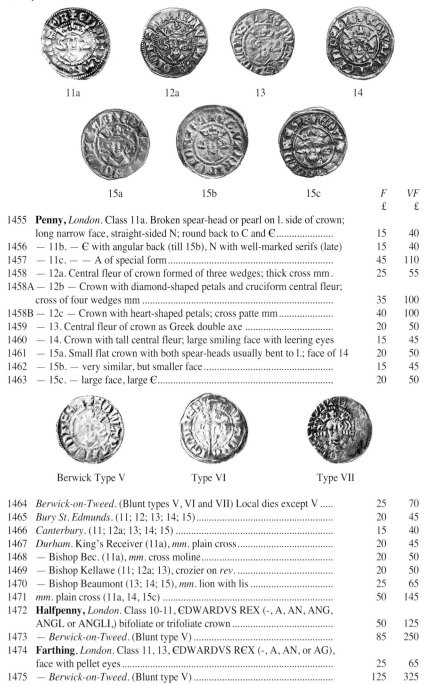

		F £	*VF* £
1464	*Berwick-on-Tweed*. (Blunt types V, VI and VII) Local dies except V	25	70
1465	*Bury St. Edmunds*. (11; 12; 13; 14; 15)	20	45
1466	*Canterbury*. (11; 12a; 13; 14; 15)	15	40
1467	*Durham*. King's Receiver (11a), *mm*. plain cross	20	45
1468	— Bishop Bec. (11a), *mm*. cross moline	20	50
1469	— Bishop Kellawe (11; 12a; 13), crozier on *rev*.	20	50
1470	— Bishop Beaumont (13; 14; 15), *mm*. lion with lis	25	65
1471	*mm*. plain cross (11a, 14, 15c)	50	145
1472	**Halfpenny,** *London*. Class 10-11, ЄDWARDVS REX (-, A, AN, ANG, ANGL or ANGLI,) bifoliate or trifoliate crown	50	125
1473	— *Berwick-on-Tweed*. (Blunt type V)	85	250
1474	**Farthing**, *London*. Class 11, 13, ЄDWARDVS RЄX (-, A, AN, or AG), face with pellet eyes	25	65
1475	— *Berwick-on-Tweed*. (Blunt type V)	125	325

During Edward's early years small quantities of silver coin were minted following the standard of the previous two reigns, but in 1335 halfpence and farthings were produced which were well below the .925 Sterling silver standard. In 1344 an impressive gold coinage was introduced comprising the Florin or Double Leopard valued at six shillings, and its half and quarter, the Leopard and the Helm. The design of the Florin was based on the contemporary gold of Philip de Valois of France.

The first gold coinage was not successful and it was replaced later the same year by a heavier coinage, the Noble, valued at 6s. 8d, i.e., 80 pence, half a mark or one third of a pound, together with its fractions. The Noble was lowered in weight in two stages over the next few years, being stabilized at 120 grains in 1351. With the signing of the Treaty of Bretigni in 1360 Edward's title to the Kingdom of France was omitted from the coinage, but it was resumed again in 1369.

In 1344 the silver coinage had been re-established at the old sterling standard, but the penny was reduced in weight to just over 20 grains and in 1351 to 18 grains. Groats were minted again in 1351 and were issued regularly henceforth until the reign of Elizabeth.

Subsequent to the treaty with France which gave England a cross-channel trading base at Calais, a mint was opened there in 1363 for minting gold and silver coins of English type. In addition to coins of the regular English mints, the Abbot of Reading also minted silver pence, halfpence and farthings with a scallop shell in one quarter of the reverse while coins from Berwick display one or two boars' or bears' heads.

There is evidence of re-use of dies at later periods, e.g. 3rd coinage halfpennies.

For further study of the English Hammered Gold Coinage see: Sylloge of Coins of the British Isles, 47, the Herbert Schneider Collection Volume One, by Peter Woodhead. 1996.

Mintmarks

6 1 2 3 74 4 5 7a

1334-51	Cross pattée (6)	1356	Crown (74)
1351-2	Cross 1 (1)	1356-61	Cross 3 (4)
1351-7	Crozier on cross end (76a, *Durham*)	1361-9	Cross potent (5)
1352-3	Cross 1 broken (2)	1369-77	Cross pattée (6)
1354-5	Cross 2 (3)		Plain cross (7a)

The figures in brackets refer to the plate of mintmarks in Appendix III.

GOLD

Third coinage, 1344-51
First period, 1344

1476

1477

1478

		F £	VF £
1476	**Florin** or **Double Leopard.** (=6s.; wt. 108 grs.). King enthroned beneath canopy; crowned leopard's head each side. R. Cross in quatrefoil...........	*Extremely rare*	
1477	**Half-florin** or **Leopard.** Leopard sejant with banner l. R. Somewhat as last	*Extremely rare*	
1478	**Quarter-florin** or **Helm.** Helmet on fleured field. R. Floriate cross	*Extremely rare*	

Second period, 1344-46

1479

1479	**Noble** (=6s. 8d., wt. 138.46 grs.). King stg. facing in ship with sword and shield. R. L in centre of royal cross in tressure..	*Extremely rare*	
1479A	Half-noble. Similar..	*Extremely rare*	
1480	**Quarter-noble.** Shield in tressure. R. As last..	1000	2750

Third period, 1346-51

1481	**Noble** (wt. 128.59 grs.). As 1479, but Є in centre; large letters	850	2000
1482	**Half-noble.** Similar..	1250	3250
1483	**Quarter-noble.** As 1480, but Є in centre	275	650

Fourth coinage, 1351-77
Reference: L. A. Lawrence, *The Coinage of Edward III from 1351.*
Pre-treaty period, 1351-61. With French title.

1484	**Noble** (wt. 120 grs.), series B (1351). Open Є and C, Roman M; *mm.* cross 1 (1)..	425	1000
1485	— — *rev.* of series A (1351). Round lettering, Lombardic M and N; closed inverted Є in centre	450	1050

		F	VF
		£	£
1486	C (1351-1352). Closed Є and C, Lombardic M; *mm.* cross 1 (1)	350	800
1487	D (1352-1353). *O.* of series C. R. *Mm.* cross 1 broken (2)	750	2000

1488

1498

1488	E (1354-1355). Broken letters, V often has a nick in r. limb; *mm.* cross 2 (3)	375	850
1489	F (1356). *Mm.* crown (74)	475	1100
1490	G (1356-1361). *Mm.* cross 3 (4). Many varieties	350	725
1491	**Half-noble,** B. As noble with *rev.* of series A, but closed Є in centre not inverted	325	725
1492	C. *O.* as noble. *Rev.* as last	375	850
1493	E. As noble	525	1350
1494	G. As noble. Many varieties	300	625
1495	**Quarter-noble,** B. Pellet below shield. R. Closed Є in centre	175	375
1496	C. *O.* of series B. *Rev.* details as noble	250	550
1497	E. *O.* as last. *Rev.* details as noble, pellet in centre	225	475
1498	G. *Mm.* cross 3 (4). Many varieties	160	325

Transitional treaty period, 1361. French title omitted, replaced by that of Aquitaine on the noble and (rarely) on the half-noble, but not on the quarter-noble; irregular sized letters; *mm.* cross potent (5).

1499

1499	**Noble.** R. Pellets or annulets at corners of central panel	400	925

1500

1503

		F	*VF*
		£	£
1500	**Half-noble.** Similar	225	500
1501	**Quarter-noble.** Similar. Many varieties. Pellet and rarely Є in centre	175	325

Treaty period, 1361-69. Omits FRANC, new letters, usually curule-shaped X; *mm.* cross potent(5).

1502	**Noble.** *London.* Saltire or nothing before ЄDWARD	375	825
1503	— Annulet before ЄDWARD (with, rarely, crescent on forecastle)	350	800
1504	*Calais.* C in centre of *rev.*, flag at stern of ship	400	850
1505	— — without flag	400	850

1506

1508

1506	**Half-noble.** *London.* Saltire before ЄDWARD	250	525
1507	— Annulet before ЄDWARD	250	550
1508	*Calais.* C in centre of *rev.*, flag at stern of ship	400	900
1509	— — without flag	450	1000
1510	**Quarter-noble.** *London.* As 1498. R. Lis in centre	145	300
1511	— — annulet before ЄDWARD	150	325
1512	*Calais.* R. Annulet in centre	165	375
1513	— — cross in circle over shield	165	375
1514	— R. Quatrefoil in centre; cross over shield	200	475
1515	— — crescent over shield	275	600

Post-treaty period, 1369-1377. French title resumed.

1516	**Noble.** *London.* Annulet before ЄD. R. Treaty period die	525	1250
1517	— — — crescent on forecastle	450	975
1518	— — post-treaty letters. R. Є and pellet in centre	425	900
1519	— — — R. Є and saltire in centre	475	1000
1520	*Calais.* Flag at stern. R. Є in centre	450	950

1521

		F	VF
		£	£
1521	— — *Rev*. as 1518, with Є and pellet in centre	425	900
1522	— As 1520, but without flag. R. Є in centre	450	975
1523	**Half-noble.** *London*. *O*. Treaty die. *Rev*. as 1518	800	1850
1524	*Calais*. Without AQT, flag at stern. R. Є in centre	650	1400
1525	— — R. Treaty die with C in centre	675	1450

SILVER

First coinage, 1327-35 (.925 fineness)

1526

1530

1526	**Penny.** *London*. As Edw. II; class XVd with Lombardic n's	300	650
1527	*Bury St. Edmunds*. Similar	400	1000
1528	*Canterbury; mm*. cross pattée with pellet centre	250	525
1529	— — three extra pellets in one quarter	250	475
1530	*Durham*. R. Small crown in centre	375	850
1531	*York*. As 1526, but quatrefoil in centre of *rev;* three extra pellets in TAS quarter	225	475
1532	— — — pellet in each quarter of *mm*.	250	500
1534	— — — Roman N's on *obv*	250	500
1535	*Berwick* (1333-1342, Blunt type VIII). Bear's head in one quarter of *rev*.	375	900
1536	**Halfpenny.** *London*. Indistinguishable from EDWARD II (cf. 1472)	50	125
1537	*Berwick* (Bl. VIII). Bear's head in one or two quarters	50	125
1538	**Farthing.** *London*. Indistinguishable from those of EDWARD II (cf. 1474)	25	65
1539	*Berwick* (Bl. VIII). As 1537	45	110

1535

1537

1540

Second coinage, 1335-43 (.833 fineness)

No.	Description	*F* £	*VF* £
1540	**Halfpenny.** *London*. ЄDWARDVS RЄX AN(G). Six-pointed star after AN and before LON. Bifoliate or trifoliate crown	15	40
1540A	— — New tall crown. Star of eight or six points after ANG and DON and before CIVI or none on rev.	15	40
1541	*Reading*. Escallop in one quarter, star before or after mint	225	525
1542	**Farthing.** *London*. A (N), six-pointed star after A (rarely omitted) and before LON, flat crown	25	75
1542A	— ANG, star after ANG and before LON or after DON, tall crown	30	80

Third or florin coinage, 1344-51. Bust with bushy hair. (.925 fine, 20 grs.)

1543

1544

Reverses: I. Lombardic N. II. Roman N. III. Reversed N. IV. Reversed Double-barred N.

No.	Description	*F* £	*VF* £
1543	**Penny**. *London*. Class 1. ЄDW, Lombardic N. Rev. I	15	50
1544	— — Class 2, ЄDWA, Lombardic N. Rev. I, II.	15	45
1545	— — Class 3. ЄDW. Roman N. Rev. I, II, III.	15	45
1546	— — Class 4. ЄDW. Reversed N. Rev. I, II, II, IV (doubtful)	15	45
1546A	— Unusual types designated A to E.	40	100
1547	— Canterbury. Class 2. as 1544. Rev. I.	50	135
1548	— — Class 4. as 1546 Rev. I.	40	125
1549	*Durham,* Sede Vacante (1345). A, ЄDW R. R. No marks	35	85
1550	— — B, similar, ЄDWAR R	50	125
1551	— Bp. Hatfield. C, similar, but pellet in centre of *rev*.	35	90
1552	— — — Crozier on *rev*	40	100
1553	— — — — with pellet in centre of *rev*.	50	125
1554	— — D, ЄDWARDVS RЄX AIn, crozier on *rev*.	75	225

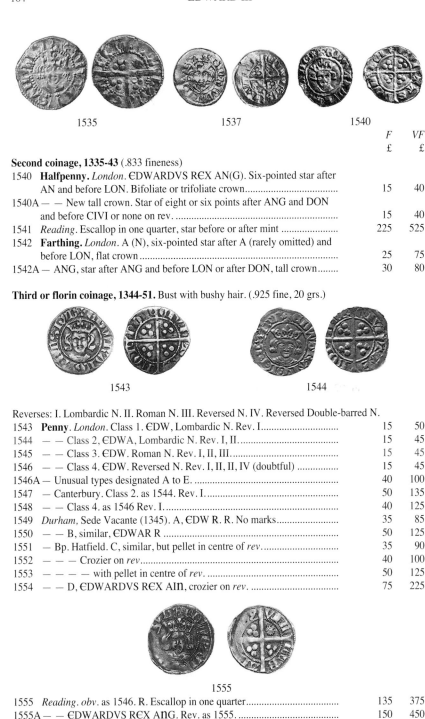

1555

No.	Description	*F* £	*VF* £
1555	*Reading*. *obv*. as 1546. R. Escallop in one quarter	135	375
1555A	— — ЄDWARDVS RЄX AnG. Rev. as 1555.	150	450
1556	*York*. *obv*. as 1546. R. Quatrefoil in centre	20	55

		F £	VF £
1557	**Halfpenny.** *London.* ЄDWARDVS RЄX	15	30
1558	— — ЄDWARDVS RЄX An.	15	35
1559	— — as 1558 with pellet or small saltire each side of crown and/or in one reverse quarter	25	60
1560	— *Reading*. as 1557. Rev. Escallop in one quarter	225	500
1561	— — as 1558. Rev. as 1560	225	525
1562	**Farthing.** *London.* ЄDWARDVS RЄX	25	60
1562A	*Reading*. As S.1562. Rev. as 1560.	275	625
1562B	— — ЄDWARDVS RЄX An. Rev. as 1560	300	650

Fourth coinage, 1351-77

Reference: L. A. Lawrence, *The Coinage of Edward III from 1351.*

A large variety of mules exist between styles and issue.

Pre-treaty period, 1351-61. With French title.

1563

1567

1563	**Groat** (=4d., 72 grs.). *London,* series B (1351). Roman M, open C and Є; *mm.* cross 1	150	425
1564	— — — crown in each quarter	*Extremely rare*	
1565	— C (1351-2). Lombardic m, closed C and Є, R with wedge-shaped tail; *mm.* cross 1	35	100
1566	— D (1352-3). R with normal tail; *mm.* cross 1 or cross 1 broken (2)	60	170
1567	— E (1354-5). Broken letters, V often with nick in r. limb; *mm.* cross 2 (3)	40	110
1568	— — — lis on breast	45	145
1569	— F (1356). *Mm.* crown (74)	55	165

1570

1572

1570	— G (1356-61). Usually with annulet in one quarter and sometimes under bust, *mm.* cross 3 (4). Many varieties	40	110
1571	*York,* series D. As London	125	300
1572	— E. As London	50	140

1573

1574

		F £	VF £
1573	**Halfgroat.** *London,* series B. As groat	80	225
1574	— C. As groat	20	55
1575	— D. As groat	25	65
1576	— E. As groat	25	65
1577	— F. As groat	30	75
1578	— G. As groat	25	65
1579	— — — annulet below bust	35	85
1580	*York,* series D. As groat	60	150
1581	— E. As groat	40	100
1582	— — — lis on breast	50	145
1583	**Penny.** *London*. Series A (1351). Round letters, Lombardic m and n, annulet in each quarter; *mm.* cross pattee	65	175

1584

1587

1591

		F £	VF £
1584	— C. Details as groat, but annulet in each quarter	15	35
1585	— D. Details as groat, but annulet in each quarter	15	45
1586	— E. Sometimes annulet in each quarter	15	40
1587	— F. Details as groat	20	50
1588	— G. Details as groat	15	40
1589	— — — annulet below bust	20	45
1590	— — — saltire in one quarter	30	85
1591	*Durham,* Bp. Hatfield. Series A. As 1583, but extra pellet in each quarter, VIL LA crozier DVRR€M	85	225
1592	— C. Details as groat. R. Crozier, CIVITAS DVN€LMI€	20	50
1593	— D — — —	25	65
1594	— E — — —	30	70
1595	— F — R. Crozier, CIVITAS DVR€M€	25	65
1596	— G — — —	25	60
1597	— — — — — annulet below bust	30	70
1598	— — — — — saltire in one quarter	35	90
1599	— — — — — annulet on each shoulder	35	80
1600	— — — — — trefoil of pellets on breast	35	80
1601	— — — R. Crozier, CIVITAS DVR€LMI€	40	100

		F £	VF £
1602	*York*, Royal Mint. Series D	25	65
1603	— — E	20	45
1604	— Archb. Thoresby. Series D. R. Quatrefoil in centre	30	70
1605	— — G —	20	45
1606	— — — annulet or saltire on breast	30	70
1607	**Halfpenny.** *London*. Series E. ЄDWARDVS RЄX An	75	200
1608	— G, but with *obv*. of F (*mm*. crown). Annulet in one quarter	100	325
1609	**Farthing.** *London*. Series E. ЄDWARDVS RЄX	80	200
1609A	— — Series G. Annulet in one quarter	90	225

Transitional treaty period, 1361. French title omitted, irregular sized letters; *mm*. cross potent (5).

1610	**Groat.** *London*. Annulet each side of crown	225	600

1611

1612

1611	**Halfgroat.** Similar, but only seven arches to tressure	100	275
1612	**Penny,** *London*. Omits RЄX, annulet in two upper qtrs. of *mm*	60	150
1613	*York*, Archb. Thoresby. Similar, but quatrefoil enclosing pellet in centre of *rev*.	50	135
1614	*Durham*. Bp. Hatfield. Similar. R. Crozier, CIVITAS DORЄLMЄ	50	135
1615	**Halfpenny.** Two pellets over *mm*., ЄDWARDVS RЄX An	65	175

Treaty period, 1361-69. French title omitted, new letters, usually 'Treaty' X, rarely curule chair X *mm*. cross potent (5).

1616	**Groat,** *London*. Many varieties	60	160
1617	— Annulet before ЄDWARD	70	175
1618	— Annulet on breast	100	250

1617

1619

1619	*Calais*. As last	125	350

1621

1635

		F £	VF £
1620	**Halfgroat,** *London*. As groat	35	85
1621	— — Annulet before ЄDWARDVS	35	85
1622	— — Annulet on breast	50	135
1623	*Calais*. As last	100	250
1624	**Penny,** *London*. ЄDWARD AnGL R, etc	25	70
1625	— — — pellet before ЄDWARD	25	70
1626	*Calais*. R. VILLA CALЄSIE	125	300
1627	*Durham*. R. CIVITAS DVnЄLMIS	50	125
1628	— R. Crozier, CIVITAS DVRЄMЄ	45	110
1629	*York,* Archb. Thoresby. Quatrefoil in centre of *rev.,* ЄDWARDVS DЄI G RЄX An	35	100
1630	— — — ЄDWARDVS RЄX AnGLI	30	70
1631	— — — — quatrefoil before ЄD and on breast	30	80
1632	— — — — annulet before ЄD	30	80
1633	— — — ЄDWARD AnGL R DnS HYB	35	90
1634	**Halfpenny.** ЄDWARDVS RЄX An, pellet stops	25	70
1635	— Pellet before ЄD, annulet stops	30	80
1636	**Farthing.** ЄDWARDVS RЄX, pellet stops	90	225

Post-treaty period, 1369-77. French title resumed, X like St. Andrew's cross; *mm*. 5, 6, 7a.

1637

1639

1637	**Groat.** Various readings, *mm*. cross pattee	85	250
1638	— — row of pellets across breast (chain mail)	200	575
1639	— row of annulets below bust (chain mail); *mm*. cross potent with four pellets	225	600
1640	**Halfgroat.** Various readings	100	275

1640A

		F	VF
		£	£
1640A	— Thin portrait of Richard II	125	375
1641	— row of pellets one side of breast (chain mail)	150	475
1642	**Penny,** *London*. No marks on breast	40	110
1643	— Pellet or annulet on breast	45	125
1644	— Cross or quatrefoil on breast	35	100
1645	*Durham,* Bp. Hatfield. *Mm.* 7a, CIVITAS DVnOLM, crozier	45	125
1646	— — — — annulet on breast	50	135
1647	— — — — lis on breast	40	110
1648	*York*. Archb. Thoresby or Neville. R. Quatrefoil in centre	30	80
1649	— — — lis on breast	35	95
1650	— — — annulet on breast	30	90
1651	— — — cross on breast	40	110

1652

1652	**Farthing.** €DWARD R€X ANGL, large head without neck	125	300

There was no change in the weight standard of the coinage during this reign and the coins evolve from early issues resembling those of Edward III to late issues similar to those of Henry IV.

There is no overall, systematic classification of the coins of Richard II but a coherent scheme for the gold coinage has been worked out and is published in the Schneider Sylloge (SCBI 47). This classification has been adopted here.

Reference: *Silver coinages of Richard II, Henry IV and V.* (B.N.J. 1959-60 and 1963).

Mintmark: cross pattée (6) 

GOLD

		F £	*VF* £
1653	**Noble,** *London*. Style of Edw. III. IA. Lis over sail (1654)	575	1250

1654

1658

		F £	*VF* £
1654	— IB. Annulet over sail (1655)	475	950
1655	French title omitted. IIA. Crude style, saltire over sail. IIB. Fine style, trefoil over sail. IIC. Porcine style, no mark over sail (1656, 58)	500	1000
1656	French title resumed. IIIA. Fine style, no marks (1656)	525	1100
1657	— IIIB. Lis on rudder. IIIC. Trefoil by shield (1656, 1658)	625	1350
1658	Henry IV style. IVA. Escallop on rudder. IVB. Crescent on rudder (1658)	850	2000
1659	*Calais*. Mule with *obv*. of Edw. III (1659)	650	1400
1660	Style of Edw. III. IB. Voided quatrefoil over sail (1660)	600	1250

1661

1662

		F £	*VF* £
1661	French title omitted. IIA. Crude style, no marks. IIB. Fine style, trefoil over sail. IIC. Porcine style, no marks (1661, 63)	525	1050
1662	French title resumed. IIIA. Fine style, no marks (1661)	550	1200
1663	— IIIB. Lion on rudder. IIIC. Two pellets by shield (1662)	700	1500
1664	**Half-noble,** *London*. With altered *obv*. of Edw. III. Usually muled with *rev*. or altered *rev*. of Edw. III (1664)	650	1500

1665

1673

		F	*VF*
		£	£
1665	Style of Edw. III. IB. No marks or saltire over sail (1665)	600	1250
1666	French title omitted. IIA. New style, no marks (1665)	650	1400
1667	French title resumed. IIIA. No marks. IIIB. Lion on rudder (1666)	650	1400
1668	Henry IV style. IVB. Crescent on rudder (1667)	750	1750
1669	*Calais*. Mule with *obv*. or *rev*. of Edw. III (1668)	950	2500
1670	Style of Edw. III. IB. Quatrefoil over sail (1669)	900	2250
1671	Late style. French title. IIIA. No marks. IIIB. Saltire by rudder (1671)	900	2250
1672	**Quarter-noble,** *London*. IA. R in centre of *rev*. (1672)	350	625
1673	IB Lis in centre of *rev*. (1673)	325	550
1674	— lis or cross over shield (1677)	350	650

1675

1677

1675	IIIA. Pellet in centre of *rev*. (1673)	325	550
1676	IIIB. Trefoil of annulets over shield or trefoils in spandrels (1676)	325	725
1677	IVA. Escallop over shield (1675)	325	650

SILVER

1679

1682

1678	**Groat.** I. Style of Edw. III, F *(i.e. et)* before FRANC, etc.	250	800
1679	II. New lettering, retrograde Z before FRANC, etc.	200	625
1680	III. Bust with bushy hair, 'fishtail' serifs to letters	300	900
1681	IV. New style bust and crown, crescent on breast	950	3000
1682	**Halfgroat.** II. New lettering; with or without French title	175	450
1683	III. As 1680	250	650
1684	— — with *obv*. die of Edw. III (1640A)	300	825

No.	Description	F £	VF £
1685	IV. As 1681, but no crescent	500	1350
1686	**Penny,** *London*. I Lettering as 1678, RICARDVS RЄX AnGLIЄ	225	650
1688	— II. As 1679, Z FRAnC lis on breast	225	650

1689

1692

No.	Description	F £	VF £
1689	— III. As 1680, RICARD RЄX AnGLIЄ, fish-tail letters	250	700
1690	*York*. I. Early style, usually with cross or lis on breast, quatrefoil in centre of *rev*	50	150
1691	— II. New bust and letters, no marks on breast	60	160
1692	— Local dies. Pellet above each shoulder, cross on breast, REX AnGLIE or AnGILIE	50	140
1693	— — — RЄX DNS ЄB	85	275
1694	— — — RЄX AnG FRAnC	85	250
1695	— III. As 1680, RЄX AnGL Z FRAnC (scallop after TAS)	60	170
1696	— IV. Very bushy hair, new letters, R. R in centre of quatrefoil	225	575
1697	*Durham*. Cross or lis on breast, DVnOLM	125	450

1698

1699

1701

1704

No.	Description	F £	VF £
1698	**Halfpenny.** Early style. LONDON, saltire or annulet (rare) on breast	50	135
1699	Intermediate style. LOnDOn, no marks on breast	25	80
1700	Type III. Late style. Similar, but fishtail letters	30	85
1700A	Type IV. Short, stubby lettering	35	90
1701	**Farthing.** Small bust and letters	100	250
1703	Similar but no neck	85	200
1704	Rose in each angle of *rev*. instead of pellets	135	375
1704A	Large head with broad face as Henry IV	150	400

HENRY IV, 1399-1413

In 1412 the standard weights of the coinage were reduced, the noble by 12 grains and the penny by 3 grains, partly because there was a scarcity of bullion and partly to provide revenue for the king, as Parliament had not renewed the royal subsidies. As in France, the royal arms were altered, three fleur-de-lis taking the place of the four or more lis previously displayed.

Mintmark: cross pattée (6)

GOLD

Heavy coinage, 1399-1412

1707

1705

		F £	*VF* £
1705	**Noble** (120 grs.), *London.* Old arms with four lis in French quarters; crescent or annulet on rudder	3750	9000
1706	— New arms with three lis; crescent, pellet or no marks on rudder	3750	9000
1707	*Calais.* Flag at stern, old arms; crown on or to l. of rudder	4500	11000

1708

1710

		F £	*VF* £
1708	— — new arms; crown or saltire on rudder	4250	10500
1709	**Half-noble,** *London.* Old arms	3000	7500
1710	— new arms	2750	6500
1711	*Calais.* New arms	3250	8000
1712	**Quarter-noble,** *London.* Crescent over old arms	850	2250
1713	— — — new arms	800	2000
1714	*Calais.* New arms. R. *Mm.* crown	1200	3000

1715

Light coinage, 1412-13

		F £	*VF* £
1715	**Noble** (108 grs.). Trefoil, or trefoil and annulet, on side of ship. R. Trefoil in one quarter	950	2250
1716	**Half-noble.** Similar, but always with annulet	2000	5000

1717

1717	**Quarter-noble.** Trefoils, or trefoils and annulets beside shield, lis above. R. Lis in centre	375	825

SILVER

Heavy coinage, 1399-1412

1718

1722

1723

1718	**Halfgroat** (36 grs.). Star on breast	1000	2500
1718A	— Muled with Edw. III (1640A) *obv.*	700	1650
1719	**Penny,** *London.* Similar, early bust with long neck	500	1350
1720	— later bust with shorter neck, no star	500	1350
1722	*York* Bust with broad face, round chin	300	800
1723	**Halfpenny.** Early small bust	125	325
1724	— later large bust, with rounded shoulders,	135	350
1725	**Farthing.** Face without neck	600	1450

Light coinage, 1412-13

1728

1731

1737

		F £	VF £
1726	**Groat** (60 grs.). I. Pellet to l., annulet to r. of crown; altered die of Richard II	1500	4500
1727	New dies; II. Annulet to l., pellet to r. of crown, 8 or 10 arches to tressure	1350	4000
1728	— III. Similar but 9 arches to tressure	1250	3750
1729	**Halfgroat.** Pellet to l., annulet to r. of crown	500	1250
1730	Annulet to l., pellet to r. of crown	425	950
1731	**Penny,** *London.* Annulet and pellet by crown; trefoil on breast and before CIVI	375	825
1732	— — annulet or slipped trefoil before LON	400	850
1733	— Pellet and annulet by crown	450	1000
1734	*York.* Annulet on breast. R. Quatrefoil in centre	150	500
1735	*Durham.* Trefoil on breast, DVnOLM	135	475
1736	**Halfpenny.** Struck from heavy dies	125	325
1737	New dies; annulets by crown or neck, or no marks	135	375
1738	**Farthing.** Face, no bust; ?trefoil after RЄX	525	1250

There was no change of importance in the coinage of this reign. There was, however, a considerable development in the use of privy marks which distinguished various issues, except for the last issue of the reign when most marks were removed. The Calais mint, which had closed in 1411, did not re-open until early in the next reign.

Mintmarks

Cross pattee (4)

Pierced cross with pellet centre (20)

Pierced cross (18).

GOLD

		F £	*VF* £
1739	**Noble.** A. Quatrefoil over sail and in second quarter of *rev.* Short broad letters, no other marks	950	2750
1740	— B. Ordinary letters; similar, or with annulet on rudder	550	1250
1741	— C. Mullet by sword arm, annulet on rudder	475	1000

1742

1742	— — — broken annulet on side of ship	425	850
1743	—D. Mullet and annulet by sword arm, trefoil by shield, broken annulet on ship	450	975

1744

1744	— E. Mullet, or mullet and annulet by sword arm, trefoil by shield, pellet by sword point and in one quarter, annulet on side of ship	450	950
1745	— — Similar, but trefoil on ship instead of by shield	525	1200
1746	— F. Similar, but no pellet at sword point, trefoil in one quarter	550	1250
1747	— G. No marks; annulet stops, except for mullet after first word	675	1500
1748	**Half-noble.** B. As noble; Hen. IV *rev.* die	1250	3000
1749	— C. Broken annulet on ship, quatrefoil below sail	550	1250

No.	Description	F £	VF £
1750	— — Mullet over shield, broken annulet on *rev.*	425	850
1751	— F. Similar, but no annulet on ship, usually trefoil by shield	650	1450

1752

1756

No.	Description	F £	VF £
1752	— F/E. As last, but pellet in 1st and annulet in 2nd quarter	650	1450
1753	— G. As noble, but quatrefoil over sail, mullet sometimes omitted after first word of *rev.*	500	1100
1754	**Quarter-noble.** A. Lis over shield and in centre of *rev.* Short broad letters; quatrefoil and annulet beside shield, stars at corners of centre on *rev.*	500	1250
1755	— C. Ordinary letters; quatrefoil to l., quat. and mullet to r. of shield	275	575
1756	— — — annulet to l., mullet to r. of shield	225	475
1757	— F. Ordinary letters; trefoil to l., mullet to r. of shield	250	550
1758	— G. — no marks, except mullet after first word	250	525

SILVER

No.	Description	F £	VF £
1759	**Groat.** A. Short broad letters; 'emaciated' bust	550	1500

1759

No.	Description	F £	VF £
1760	— — muled with Hen. IV *obv*	750	2000
1761	— — muled with Hen .IV *rev*	650	1650

1762

1765

No.	Description	F £	VF £
1762	B. Ordinary letters; 'scowling' bust	225	525
1762A	— — mullet in centre of breast	250	650
1762B	— — mullet to r. of breast	300	750
1763	— — muled with Hen. IV	400	1100
1764	C. Normal bust	150	425
1765	— — mullet on r. shoulder	90	200

		F £	VF £
1766	— — R muled with Hen. IV	375	1000
1767	G. Normal bust; no marks	175	475
1768	**Halfgroat.** A. As groat, but usually with annulet and pellet by crown	425	1000
1769	B. Ordinary letters; no marks	275	675
1770	— — muled with Hen. IV *obv.*	275	675
1771	C. Tall neck, broken annulet to l. of crown	75	200
1772	— — — mullet on r. shoulder	85	250

1773

1774

		F £	VF £
1773	— — — mullet in centre of breast	75	200
1774	F. Annulet and trefoil by crown, mullet on breast	95	275
1775	G. New neat bust: no marks.	80	225
1776	**Penny.** *London.* A. Letters, bust and marks as 1768	200	525
1777	— Altered Hen. IV *obv.* with mullet added to l. of crown	275	750

1778

1791

		F £	VF £
1778	— C. Tall neck, mullet and broken annulet by crown	20	65
1779	— D. Similar, but whole annulet	25	85
1780	— F. Mullet and trefoil by crown	30	95
1781	— G. New neat bust, no marks, DI GRA	30	100
1782	*Durham.* C. As 1778 but quatrefoil at end of legend	35	90
1783	— D. As 1779	30	90
1784	— G. Similar, but new bust. R. Annulet in one qtr.	35	100
1785	*York.* C. As 1778, but quatrefoil in centre of *rev.*	20	60
1786	— D. Similar, but whole annulet by crown	25	70
1787	— E. As last, but pellet above mullet	40	110
1788	— F. Mullet and trefoil by crown	20	60
1789	— — Trefoil over mullet to l., annulet to r. of crown	40	100
1790	— G. Mullet and trefoil by crown (London dies)	30	80
1791	— — Mullet and lis by crown, annulet in one qtr. (usually local dies)	30	80
1792	**Halfpenny.** A. Emaciated bust, annulets by crown	100	275
1793	— altered dies of Hen. IV	120	300
1794	C. Ordinary bust, broken annulets by crown	15	45
1795	D. Annulets, sometimes broken, by hair	15	45

1796

1798

		F	VF
		£	£
1796	F. Annulet and trefoil by crown	15	50
1797	G. New bust; no marks, (usually muled with Henry VI annulet *rev.*)	40	100
1798	**Farthing.** G. Small face with neck	110	325

The supply of gold began to dwindle early in the reign, which accounts for the rarity of gold after 1426. The Calais mint was reopened in 1424 and for some years a large amount of coin was struck there. It soon stopped minting gold; the mint was finally closed in 1440. A royal mint at York was opened for a short time in 1423/4.

Marks used to denote various issues become more prominent in this reign and can be used to date coins to within a year or so.

Reference: C. A. Whitton Heavy Coinage of Henry VI. (B.N.J. 1938-41).

Mintmarks

136 7a 105 18 133 8 9 15

1422-7	Incurved pierced cross (136)
1422-3	Lis (105, York)
1422-60	Plain cross (7a, intermittently Lis (105, on gold)
1422-27	Pierced cross (18)
1460	Lis (105, on rev. of some groats)
1422-34	Cross pommée (133)
1427-34	Cross patonce (8)
	Cross fleury (9)
1434-35	Voided cross (15)
1435-60	Cross fleury (9)

For Restoration mintmarks see page 196.

GOLD

1799

		F	*VF*
	Annulet issue, 1422-7	£	£
1799	**Noble.** *London.* Annulet by sword arm, and in one spandrel on *rev.;* trefoil stops on *obv.* with lis after hЄnRIC, annulets on *rev.*, with mullet after IhC	400	825
1800	— Similar, but *obv.* from Henry V die	750	1850
1801	— As 1799, but Flemish imitative coinage	300	575
1802	*Calais.* As 1799, but flag at stern and C in centre of *rev*	500	1000

1803

		F	VF
		£	£
1803	— — with h in centre of *rev.*	475	950
1804	*York.* As London, but with lis over stern	525	1100

1805

1805	**Half-noble.** *London.* As 1799	250	550
1806	— Similar, but *obv.* from Henry V die	600	1300
1807	*Calais.* As noble, with C in centre of *rev.*	525	1200
1808	— — with h in centre of *rev.*	500	1100
1809	***York.*** As noble	550	1250
1810	**Quarter-noble.** *London.* Lis over shield; *mm.* large lis	150	325
1811	— — — trefoil below shield	175	375
1812	— — — pellet below shield	200	425
1813	*Calais.* Three lis over shield; *mm.* large lis	250	550

1814

1819

1814	— Similar but three lis around shield	225	475
1815	— As 1810, but much smaller *mm.*	175	400
1816	*York.* Two lis over shield	225	475

		F £	VF £

Rosette-mascle issue, 1427-30

		F	VF
1817	**Noble.** *London.* Lis by sword arm and in *rev.* field; stops, rosettes, or rosettes and mascles	700	1650
1818	*Calais.* Similar, with flag at stern	950	2200
1819	**Half-noble.** *London.* Lis in *rev.* field; stops, rosettes and mascles	1000	2500
1820	*Calais.* Similar, flag at stern; stops, rosettes	1200	3000
1821	**Quarter-noble.** *London.* As 1810; stops, as noble	450	950
1822	— without lis over shield	475	1000
1823	*Calais.* Lis over shield, rosettes r. and l., and rosette stops	575	1250

Pinecone-mascle issue, 1430-4

1824

		F	VF
1824	**Noble.** *London.* Stops, pinecones and mascles	650	1500
1825	**Half-noble.** *London. O.* Rosette-mascle die. R. As last	1350	4000
1826	**Quarter-noble.** As 1810, but pinecone and mascle stops	625	1400

Leaf-mascle issue, 1434-5

		F	VF
1827	**Noble.** Leaf in waves; stops, saltires with two mascles and one leaf	1500	4500
1828	**Half-noble.** (Fishpool hoard and Reigate hoard)	1450	4500
1829	**Quarter-noble.** As 1810; stops, saltire and mascle; leaf on inner circle of *rev.*	750	1650

Leaf-trefoil issue, 1435-8

		F	VF
1830	**Noble.** Stops, leaves and trefoils	1500	4500
1830A	**Half-noble.**	1650	5000
1831	**Quarter-noble.** Similar	750	1750

Trefoil issue, 1438-43

		F	VF
1832	**Noble.** Trefoil to left of shield and in *rev.* legend	1500	4500

Leaf-pellet issue, 1445-54

		F	VF
1833	**Noble.** Annulet, lis and leaf below shield	1500	4500

Cross-pellet issue, 1454-60

		F	VF
1834	**Noble.** Mascle at end of *obv.* legend	2000	5500

Muling exists in Henry VI coins spanning two or three issues. Full flan coins in the smaller denominations are difficult to find.

SILVER

Annulet issue, 1422-7

1836

1838

		F £	VF £
1835	**Groat.** *London.* Annulet in two quarters of *rev.*	30	95
1836	*Calais.* Annulets at neck. R. Similar	25	65
1837	— — no annulets on *rev.*	65	170
1838	*York.* Lis either side of neck. R. As 1835	675	1750
1839	**Halfgroat.** *London.* As groat	35	100

1840

1843

1840	*Calais.* As 1836	20	50
1841	— — no annulets on *rev.*	35	100
1842	— — only one annulet on *rev.* (mule with annulet-trefoil *rev.*)	45	125

1845

1849

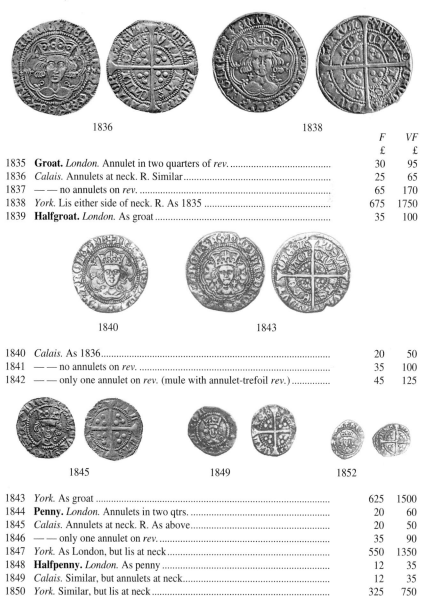

1852

1843	*York.* As groat	625	1500
1844	**Penny.** *London.* Annulets in two qtrs.	20	60
1845	*Calais.* Annulets at neck. R. As above	20	50
1846	— — only one annulet on *rev.*	35	90
1847	*York.* As London, but lis at neck	550	1350
1848	**Halfpenny.** *London.* As penny	12	35
1849	*Calais.* Similar, but annulets at neck	12	35
1850	*York.* Similar, but lis at neck	325	750
1851	**Farthing.** *London.* As penny, but *mm.* cross pommée	85	200
1852	*Calais.* Similar, but annulets at neck	125	350
1852A	*York.* Similar, but lis at neck	450	950

		F £	VF £

Annulet-trefoil sub-issue

		F	VF
1854	**Groat.** *Calais,* as 1836 but trefoil to l. of crown.	40	120
1855	**Halfgroat.** *Calais.* Similar, but usually with ann. or rosette mascle *rev.*.	50	150
1856	**Penny.** *Calais.* Similar	45	125
1857	— — only one annulet on *rev*	65	175

Rosette-mascle issue, 1427-30. All with rosettes (early) or rosettes and mascles somewhere in the legends.

		F	VF
1858	**Groat.** *London.*	45	135

1859

1861

		F	VF
1859	*Calais*	30	70
1860	— mascle in two spandrels (as illus. 1863)	40	95
1861	**Halfgroat.** *London.*	60	150
1862	*Calais*	25	65

1863

1872

		F	VF
1863	— mascle in two spandrels, as illustrated	30	80
1864	**Penny.** *London.*	75	225
1865	*Calais*	30	85
1866	*York.* Archb. Kemp. Crosses by hair, no rosette	25	65
1867	— — Saltires by hair, no rosette	30	80
1868	— — Mullets by crown	25	65
1869	*Durham,* Bp. Langley. Large star to l. of crown, no rosette, DVnOLMI	45	120
1870	**Halfpenny,** *London*	15	40
1871	*Calais*	15	40
1872	**Farthing,** *London*	110	300
1873	*Calais. Mm.* cross pommee	135	425

Pinecone-mascle issue, 1430-4. All with pinecones and mascles in legends.

1874

1876/7

1879

		F £	VF £
1874	**Groat,** London	30	75
1875	*Calais*	30	70
1876	**Halfgroat,** *London*	35	100
1877	*Calais*	25	65
1878	**Penny,** *London*	40	100
1879	*Calais*	30	70
1880	*York,* Archb. Kemp. Mullet by crown, quatrefoil in centre of *rev.*	25	70
1881	— — rosette on breast, no quatrefoil	25	70
1882	— — mullet on breast, no quatrefoil	30	75
1883	*Durham,* Bp. Langley. DVnOLMI	35	100

1884

1888

		F £	VF £
1884	**Halfpenny,** *London*	12	35
1885	*Calais*	15	40
1886	**Farthing,** *London*	110	300
1887	*Calais. Mm.* cross pommée	135	400

Full flan coins are difficult to find in the smaller denominations.

Leaf-mascle issue, 1434-5. Usually with a mascle in the legend and a leaf somewhere in the design.

		F £	VF £
1888	**Groat.** *London.* Leaf below bust, all appear to read DOnDOn	150	425
1889	— — *rev.* of last or next coinage	100	250
1890	*Calais.* Leaf below bust, and usually below MЄVM	85	200
1891	**Halfgroat.** *London.* Leaf under bust, pellet under TAS and DON	125	300

1892

1897

		F £	VF £
1892	*Calais.* Leaf below bust, and sometimes on *rev.*	85	225
1893	**Penny.** *London.* Leaf on breast, no stops on *rev.*	50	125
1894	*Calais.* Leaf on breast and below SIЄ	60	140
1895	**Halfpenny.** *London.* Leaf on breast and on *rev.*	25	65
1896	*Calais.* Leaf on breast and below SIЄ	65	150

Leaf-trefoil issue, 1435-8. Mostly with leaves and trefoil of pellets in the legends.

		F £	VF £
1897	**Groat.** *London.* Leaf on breast	50	145
1898	— without leaf on breast	50	140
1899	*Calais.* Leaf on breast	375	950
1900	**Halfgroat.** *London.* Leaf on breast; *mm.* plain cross	45	120
1901	— *O. mm.* cross fleury; leaf on breast	45	120
1902	— — without leaf on breast	50	125
1902A	*Calais.* leaf on breast, mule with leaf mascle *rev.*	90	250
1903	**Penny.** *London.* Leaf on breast	45	125
1903A	*Calais.* Similar	275	650
1904	*Durham,* Bp. Neville. Leaf on breast. R. Rings in centre, no stops, DVnOLM	100	250
1905	**Halfpenny.** *London.* Leaf on breast	20	45
1906	— without leaf on breast	20	50
1906A	*Calais.* leaf on breast, mule with leaf mascle rev.	100	250
1907	**Farthing.** *London.* Leaf on breast; stops, trefoil and saltire on *obv.*	125	325

Trefoil issue, 1438-43. Trefoil of pellets either side of neck and in legend, leaf on breast.

1909

1911A

		F £	VF £
1908	**Groat.** *London.* Sometimes a leaf before LON.	60	165
1909	— Fleurs in spandrels, sometimes extra pellet in two qtrs.	100	275
1910	— Trefoils in place of fleurs at shoulders, none by neck, sometimes extra pellets	80	200
1911	*Calais*	175	450
1911A	**Halfgroat,** *London* Similar, but trefoil after DEUM and sometimes after POSUI Mule only with leaf trefoil *obv.*	125	325
1911B	— *Calais Obv.* Similar to 1911, mule with leaf mascle *rev.*	275	700
1912	**Halfpenny,** *London*	20	50

Trefoil pellet issue, 1443-5

1912

1913

1915

1917

		F £	*VF* £
1913	**Groat.** Trefoils by neck, pellets by crown, small leaf on breast; sometimes extra pellet in two quarters	95	240

Leaf-pellet issue, 1445-54. Leaf on breast, pellet each side of crown, except where stated.

1914	**Groat.** AnGL; extra pellet in two quarters	50	135
1915	*Similar,* but AnGLI	45	120
1916	— — trefoil in *obv.* legend	60	165
1917	Leaf on neck, fleur on breast, often extra pellet in two quarters	45	120
1918	As last, but two extra pellets by hair	125	375
1919	**Halfgroat.** As 1914 *mm.*Cross patonce	50	135
1920	Similar, but *mm.* plain cross, some times no leaf on breast, no stops	45	125
1921	**Penny.** *London.* Usually extra pellets in two quarters	40	95
1922	— — pellets by crown omitted	45	100
1923	— — trefoil in legend	50	125
1924	*York,* Archb. Booth. R. Quatrefoil and pellet in centre	30	90
1925	— — two extra pellets by hair (local dies)	30	85
1926	*Durham,* Bp. Neville. Trefoil in *obv.* legend. R. Two rings in centre of cross	50	140

1927

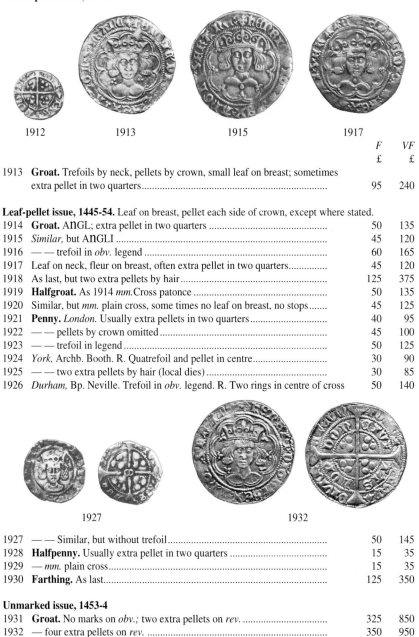

1932

1927	— — Similar, but without trefoil	50	145
1928	**Halfpenny.** Usually extra pellet in two quarters	15	35
1929	— *mm.* plain cross	15	35
1930	**Farthing.** As last	125	350

Unmarked issue, 1453-4

1931	**Groat.** No marks on *obv.;* two extra pellets on *rev.*	325	850
1932	— four extra pellets on *rev.*	350	950
1933	**Halfgroat.** As 1931	200	525

Cross-pellet issue, 1454-60

No.	Description	F £	VF £
1934	**Groat.** Saltire either side of neck, pellets by crown, leaf and fleur on breast, extra pellets on *rev.*	275	675
1935	Saltire on neck, no leaf, pellets by crown, usually mullets in legend; extra pellets on *rev.*	70	200

1935

1940

No.	Description	F £	VF £
1936	— Similar, but mascles in place of mullets on *obv.*	75	210
1937	— — pellets by hair instead of by crown	125	350
1938	**Halfgroat.** Saltire on neck, pellets by crown and on *rev.,* mullets in legend	200	525
1939	**Penny.** *London.* Saltire on neck, pellets by crown and on *rev.,* mascle(s), or mullet and mascle in legend	175	475
1940	*York,* Archb. Wm. Booth. Saltires by neck, usually leaf on breast, pellets by crown. R. Cross in quatrefoil in centre.	25	75
1941	*Durham,* Bp. Laurence Booth. Saltire and B or B only at neck, pellets by crown. R. Rings in centre	50	140
1942	**Halfpenny.** Saltires by neck, usually two extra pellets on *rev.*	45	120
1943	Similar, but saltire on neck, sometimes mullet after hENRIC	25	60
1944	**Farthing**. Saltire on neck, usually pellets by crown and on *rev.,* but known without either.	150	425

Lis-pellet issue, 1456-60

1945

No.	Description	F £	VF £
1945	**Groat.** Lis on neck; pellets by crown. R. Extra pellets	175	525

EDWARD IV, First Reign, 1461-70

In order to increase the supply of bullion to the mint the weight of the penny was reduced to 12 grains in 1464, and the current value of the noble was raised to 8s. 4d. Later, in 1465, a new gold coin was issued, the Ryal or 'Rose Noble', weighing 120 grains and having a value of 10s. However, as 6s. 8d. had become the standard professional fee the old noble was missed, and a new coin was issued to take its place, the Angel of 80 grains.

Royal mints were opened at Canterbury and York to help with the re-coinage, and other mints were set up at Bristol, Coventry and Norwich, though they were not open for long.

Reference: C. E. Blunt and C. A Whitton, *The Coinage of Edward IV and Henry VI (Restored),* B.N.J. 1945-7.

Mintmarks

105 9 7a 33 99 28 74 11

1461-4	Lis (105)	1467-70	Lis (105, *York*)	
	Cross fleury (9)	1467-8	Crown (74)	(often
	Plain cross (7a)		Sun (28)	combined)
1464-5	Rose (33 and 34)	1468-9	Crown (74)	(sometimes
1464-7	Pall (99, *Canterbury*)		Rose (33)	combined)
1465-6	Sun (28)	1469-70	Long cross	
1466-7	Crown (74)		fitchee (l.c.f) (11)	(often
			Sun (28)	combined)

GOLD

Heavy coinage, 1461-4

		F £	*VF* £
1946	**Noble** (=6s. 8d., wt. 108 grs.). Normal type, but *obv.* legend commences at top left, lis below shield; *mm.*-/lis (Spink's sale May 1993)	2000	5500
1947	— Quatrefoil below sword arm; *mm.* rose/lis	2250	6250
1948	— R. Roses in two spandrels; *mm.* rose	2500	7000
1949	**Quarter-noble**	*Extremely rare*	

1946

1950

		F £	VF £
	Light coinage, 1464-70		
1950	**Ryal** or rose-noble (=10s., wt. 120 grs.), *London.* As illustration. Large fleurs in spandrels; *mm.* 33-74	375	850
1951	— — Small trefoils in spandrels; *mm.* 74-11	375	850

1952

		F £	VF £
1952	— Flemish imitative coinage (mostly 16th cent. on a large flan)	300	600
1953	*Bristol.* B in waves, large fleurs; *mm.* sun, crown	425	925
1954	— — small fleurs in spandrels; *mm.* sun, crown	450	950
1955	*Coventry.* C in waves; *mm.* sun	800	2000
1956	*Norwich.* n in waves; *mm.* sun, rose	900	2250
1957	*York.* Є in waves, large fleurs in spandrels, *mm.* sun, lis	425	950
1958	— — small fleurs, *mm.* sun. lis	475	1100
1959	**Half-ryal.** *London.* As 1950	285	650
1960	*Bristol.* B in waves; *mm.* sun, sun/crown	475	1000
1961	*Coventry.* C in waves; *mm.* sun	1750	5000
1962	*Norwich.* n in waves; *mm.* rose	1600	4250

1963

1965

		F £	VF £
1963	*York.* Є in waves; *mm.* 28, 105, 33/105	325	700
1963A	Similar but lis instead of Є in waves (probably York)	400	900
1964	**Quarter-ryal.** Shield in tressure of eight arcs, rose above. R. Somewhat as half ryal; *mm.* sun/rose	675	1500
1965	Shield in quatrefoil, R. Є above, rose on l., sun on r.; *mm.* 33/28-74/33..	210	450
1966	— — sun on l., rose on r.; *mm.* 74-11	225	475

1967

		F £	VF £
1967	**Angel** (=6s. 8d., wt. 80 grs.). St. Michael spearing dragon. R. Ship, rays of sun at masthead, large rose and sun beside mast; *mm.*-/33	2750	7000
1968	— — small rose and sun at mast; *mm.*-/74	3000	8000

SILVER

Heavy coinage, 1461-4

1969	**Groat** (60 grs.). Group I, lis on neck, pellets by crown; *mm.* 9, 7a, 105, 9/105	125	325
1970	— Lis on breast, no pellets; *mm.* plain cross, 7a/105	135	350
1971	— — with pellets at crown; *mm.* plain cross	145	375

1972

1972	II, quatrefoils by neck, crescent on breast; *mm.* rose	110	280
1973	III, similar but trefoil on breast; *mm.* rose	120	300
1974	— — — eye in *rev.* inner legend, *mm.* rose	95	225
1975	— Similar, but no quatrefoils by bust	150	400
1976	— — Similar, but no trefoil on breast	150	375
1977	IV, annulets by neck, eye after TAS; *mm.* rose	175	525

1973

1978

1978	**Halfgroat.** I, lis on breast, pellets by crown and extra pellets in two qtrs.; *mm.* 9, 7a	350	850

		F £	VF £
1979	II, quatrefoils at neck, crescent on breast; *mm.* rose	250	550
1980	III, similar, but trefoil on breast, eye on rev.; *mm.* rose	250	525
1981	— Similar, but no mark on breast	250	525
1982	IV, annulets by neck, sometimes eye on *rev.; mm.* rose	275	600
1983	**Penny** (15 grs.), *London.* I, marks as 1978, but mascle after RЄX; *mm.* plain cross	300	725
1984	II, quatrefoils by neck; *mm.* rose	275	600

1985

1985	III, similar, but eye after TAS; *mm.* rose	225	475
1986	IV, annulets by neck; *mm.* rose	275	625
1987	*York,* Archb. Booth. Quatrefoils by bust, voided quatrefoil in centre of *rev.; mm.* rose	125	275
1988	*Durham. O.* of Hen. VI. R. DVnOLIn	135	300
	Some of the Durham pennies from local dies may belong to the heavy coinage period, but if so they are indistinguishable from the light coins.		
1989	**Halfpenny.** I, as 1983, but no mascle	90	225
1990	II, quatrefoils by bust; *mm.* rose	50	110
1991	— saltires by bust; *mm.* rose	40	95
1992	III, no marks by bust; *mm.* rose	40	95
1993	IV, annulets by bust; *mm.* rose	45	110
1994	**Farthing.** I, pellets by crown, extra pellets on rev., with or without lis on breast	250	600
1994A	II. saltires by bust; *mm.* rose	275	650
1994B	III, no marks by bust; *mm.* rose	225	550

Light coinage, 1464-70. There is a great variety of groats and we give only a selection. Some have pellets in one quarter of the reverse, or trefoils over the crown; early coins have fleurs on the cusps of the tressure, then trefoils or no marks on the cusps, while the late coins have only trefoils.

1995	**Groat** (48 grs.), *London.* Annulets at neck, eye after TAS; *mm.* 33 (struck from heavy dies, IV)	80	210
1996	— — — Similar, but new dies, eye after TAS or DOn	85	225
1997	— Quatrefoils at neck, eye; rose (heavy dies, III)	65	160
1998	— — — Similar, but new dies, eye in *rev.* legend	70	170
1999	— No marks at neck, eye; *mm* rose	125	325

2000

2002

Light coinage, silver, *continued.*

		F	*VF*
		£	£
2000	— Quatrefoils at neck, no eye; *mm.* 33, 74, 28, 74/28, 74/33, 11/28	35	105
2001	— — — rose or quatrefoil on breast; *mm.* 33, 74/28	40	120
2002	— No marks at neck; *mm.* 28, 74, 11/28, 11	50	145
2003	— Trefoils or crosses at neck; *mm.* 11/33, 11/28, 11	45	125
2004	*Bristol.* B on breast, quatrefoils at neck; *mm.* 28/33, 28, 28/74, 74, 74/28	45	125
2005	— — trefoils at neck; *mm.* sun	75	200
2006	— — no marks at neck; *mm.* sun	110	325
2007	— Without B, quatrefoils at neck; *mm.* sun	110	325
Bristol is variously rendered as BRESTOLL, BRISTOLL, BRESTOW, BRISTOW.			
2008	*Coventry.* C on breast, quatrefoils at neck, COVETRE; *mm.* 28/33, 28	80	200
2009	— — Local dies, similar; *mm.* rose	125	325
2010	— — — as last, but no C or quatrefoils	125	325
2011	Norwich. n on breast, quatrefoils at neck, nORWIC or nORVIC, *mm.* 28/33, 28	65	160
2012	*York.* € on breast, quatrefoils at neck, €BORACI; *mm.* 28, 105/74, 105, 105/28	45	120
2013	— Similar, but without € on breast, *mm.* lis	70	185
2014	— € on breast, trefoils at neck; *mm.* 105/28, 105	50	145
2015	**Halfgroat.** *London.* Annulets by neck (heavy dies); *mm.* 33	225	500
2016	— Quatrefoils by neck; *mm.* 33/-, 28/-, 74, 74/28	40	120
2017	— Saltires by neck; *mm.* 74, 74/28	50	145
2018	— Trefoils by neck; *mm.* 74, 74/28, 11/28	50	145
2019	— No marks by neck; *mm.* 11/28	85	225
2020	— *Bristol.* Saltires or crosses by neck; *mm.* 33/28, 28, 74, 74/-	125	325
2021	— Quatrefoils by neck; *mm.* 28/-, 74, 74/-	125	300
2022	— Trefoils by neck; *mm.* crown	150	350
2023	— No marks by neck; *mm.* 74/28	160	400
2024	*Canterbury,* Archb. Bourchier (1464-7). Knot below bust; quatrefoils by neck; *mm.* 99/-, 99, 99/33, 99/28	25	70
2025	— — — quatrefoils omitted *mm.* 99	25	70
2026	— — — saltires by neck; *mm.* 99/-, 99/28	25	75
2026A	— — — trefoils by neck; *mm.* 99	30	95

2027

2030

		F £	*VF* £
2027	— — — wedges by hair and/or neck; *mm.* 99, 99/–, 99/33, 99/28	30	85
2028	— — As 2024 or 2025, but no knot	30	90
2029	— Royal mint (1467-9). Quatrefoils by neck; *mm.* 74, 74/-	25	70
2030	— — Saltires by neck; *mm.* 74/-, 74	30	80
2031	— — Trefoils by neck; *mm.* 74, 74/-, 74/28, 33	25	65
2032	— No marks by neck; *mm.* sun	60	150
2033	*Coventry.* Crosses by neck; *mm.* sun	600	1600
2034	*Norwich.* Quatrefoils or saltires by neck; *mm.* sun	550	1450
2035	*York.* Quatrefoils by neck; *mm.* sun, lis, lis/-	65	165
2036	— Saltires by neck; *mm.* lis	60	160
2037	— Trefoils by neck; *mm.* lis, lis/-	65	175
2038	— Є on breast, quatrefoils by neck; *mm.* lis/-	65	175
2039	**Penny** (12 grs.), *London.* Annulets by neck (heavy dies); *mm.* rose	150	425
2040	— Quatrefoils by neck; *mm.* 74, sun. crown	30	75
2041	— Trefoil and quatrefoil by neck; *mm.* crown	35	100
2042	— Saltires by neck; *mm.* crown	35	90
2043	— Trefoils by neck; *mm.* crown, ll	35	90
2044	— No marks by neck; *mm.* ll	110	300
2045	*Bristol.* Crosses, quatrefoils or saltires by neck, BRISTOW; *mm.* crown	125	375
2046	— Quatrefoils by neck; BRI(trefoil)STOLL	135	400
2047	— Trefoil to r. of neck BRISTOLL	145	425
2048	*Canterbury,* Archb. Bourchier. Quatrefoils or saltires by neck, knot on breast; *mm.* pall	60	150
2049	— — Similar, but no marks by neck	60	150
2050	— — As 2048, but no knot	65	165
2051	— — Crosses by neck, no knot	65	165
2052	— Royal mint. Quatrefoils by neck; *mm.* crown	150	450
2053	— *Durham,* King's Receiver (1462-4). Local dies, mostly with rose in centre of rev.; *mm.* 7a, 33	25	70
2054	— Bp. Lawrence Booth (1465-70). B and D by neck, B on *rev.; mm.* 33	30	90
2055	— — Quatrefoil and B by neck; *mm.* sun	25	75
2056	— — B and quatrefoil by neck; *mm.* crown	30	95
2057	— — D and quatrefoil by neck; *mm.* crown	30	90
2058	— — Quatrefoils by neck; *mm.* crown	25	80
2059	— — Trefoils by neck; *mm.* crown	25	80
2060	— Lis by neck; *mm.* crown	25	75
2061	*York,* Sede Vacante (1464-5). Quatrefoils at neck, no quatrefoil in centre of *rev.; mm.* sun, rose	45	125
2062	— Archb. Neville (1465-70). Local dies, G and key by neck, quatrefoil on *rev.; mm.* sun, plain cross	25	70

2063

2068

		F	VF
		£	£
2063	— — London-made dies, similar; *mm.* 28, 105, 11	25	75
2064	— — Similar, but no marks by neck; *mm.* large lis	35	100
2065	— — — Quatrefoils by neck; *mm.* large lis	30	85
2066	— — — Trefoils by neck; *mm.* large lis	25	70
2067	**Halfpenny,** *London.* Saltires by neck; *mm.* 34, 28, 74	20	65
2068	— Trefoils by neck; *mm.* 28, 74, 11	20	55
2069	— No marks by neck; *mm.* 11	40	110
2070	*Bristol.* Crosses by neck; *mm.* crown	95	225
2071	— Trefoils by neck; *mm.* crown	85	200
2072	*Canterbury.* Archb. Bourchier. No marks; *mm.* pall	75	175
2072A	— — — Trefoils by neck, *mm.* pall	75	175
2073	— Royal mint. Saltires by neck; *mm.* crown	60	125
2074	— — Trefoils by neck; *mm.* crown	50	120
2074A	*Norwich.* Quatrefoils by neck., *mm.* Sun	200	525
2075	*York.* Royal mint. Saltires by neck; *mm.* lis/-, sun/-	60	125
2076	— — Trefoils by neck; *mm.* lis/-	50	110
2077	**Farthing,** *London.* ЄDWARD DI GRA RЄX, no marks at neck, *mm.* rose	225	575
2077A	— Trefoils by neck, *mm.* crown	275	650

Full flan coins are difficult to find in the smaller denominations.

The coinage of this short restoration follows closely that of the previous reign. Only angel gold was issued, the ryal being discontinued. Many of the coins have the king's name reading hENRICV—another distinguishing feature is an R that looks like a B.

Mintmarks

Cross pattée (6)
Restoration cross (13)
Trefoil (44 and 45)
Rose (33, Bristol)
Lis (105)
Short cross fitchée (12)

GOLD

2078

		F	*VF*
		£	£
2078	**Angel,** *London.* As illus. but no B; *mm.* -/6, 13, -/105, none	750	2000
2079	*Bristol.* B in waves; *mm.* -/13, none	975	2750
2080	**Half-angel,** *London.* As 2078; *mm.* -/6, -/13, -/105	1500	3750
2081	*Bristol.* B in waves; *mm.* -/13	2000	5250

SILVER

2082

2084

2082	**Groat,** *London.* Usual type; *mm.* 6, 6/13, 6/105, 13, 13/6, 13/105, 13 /12	110	300
2083	*Bristol.* B on breast; *mm.* 13, 13/33, 13/44, 44, 44/13, 44/33, 44/12	165	500
2084	*York.* C on breast; *mm.* lis, lis/sun	125	350
2085	**Halfgroat,** *London.* As 2082; *mm.* 13, 13/-	150	400
2086	*York.* C on breast; *mm.* lis	350	850
2087	**Penny,** *London.* Usual type; *mm.* 6, 13, 12	250	625

		F	*VF*
		£	£
2087A	*Bristol.* Similar; *mm.* 12	450	1000
2088	*York.* G and key by neck; *mm.* lis	175	450
2089	**Halfpenny,** *London.* As 2087; *mm.* 12, 13,	75	175
2090	*Bristol.* Similar; *mm.* cross	275	625

EDWARD IV, Second Reign, 1471-83

The Angel and its half were the only gold denominations issued during this reign. The main types and weight standards remained the same as those of the light coinage of Edward's first reign. The use of the 'initial mark' as a mintmark to denote the date of issue was now firmly established.

Mintmarks

33 105 12 55 44 55 28 56 17

30 37 6 18 19 20 31 11 38

1471-83	Rose (33, *York & Durham*)
	Lis (105, *York*)
1471	Short cross fitchee (12)
1471-2	Annulet (large, 55)
	Trefoil (44)
	Rose (33, *Bristol*)
1471-3	Pansy (30, *Durham*)
1472-3	Annulet (small, 55)
	Sun (28, *Bristol*)
1473-7	Pellet in annulet (56)
	Cross and four pellets (17)
	Cross in circle (37)
1473-7	Cross pattée (6)
	Pierced cross 1 (18)
1477-80	Pierced cross and pellet (19)
	Pierced cross 2 (18)
	Pierced cross, central pellet (20)
	Rose (33, *Canterbury*)
1480-3	Heraldic cinquefoil (31)
	Long cross fitchee (11, *Canterbury*)
1483	Halved sun and rose (38) (Listed under Ed. IV/V.)

GOLD

2091

2093

		F	*VF*
		£	£
2091	**Angel.** *London.* Type as illus.; *mm.* 12, 55, 56, 17, 18, 19, 31	300	650
2092	*Bristol.* B in waves; *mm.* small annulet	1350	3250
2093	**Half-angel.** As illus.; *mm.* 55, cross in circle, 19, 20/19, 31	275	550

		F £	VF £
2094	King's name and title on rev.; *mm.* 12/-	350	750
2095	King's name and the title both sides; *mm.* 55/-	375	850

SILVER

2096

2101

2096	**Groat,** *London.* Trefoils on cusps, no marks by bust; *mm.* 12-37	40	110
2097	— — roses by bust; *mm.* pellet in annulet	70	200
2098	— Fleurs on cusps; no marks by bust; *mm.* 18-20	40	110
2099	— — pellets by bust; *mm.* pierced cross	65	190
2100	— — rose on breast; *mm.* 31	45	120
2101	*Bristol.* B on breast no marks by bust; *mm.* 33, 33/55, 28/55, 55, 55/-, 28	85	250
2102	*York.* € on breast no marks by bust; *mm.* lis	90	265
2103	**Halfgroat,** *London.* As 2096; *mm.* 12-31	45	120
2104	*Bristol.* B on breast; *mm.* 33/12	275	675
2105	*Canterbury* (Royal mint). As 2103; *mm.* 33, 11, 11/31, 31	30	85

2106

2106	— C on breast; *mm.* rose	25	75
2107	— — R. C in centre; *mm.* rose	25	75
2108	— — R. Rose in centre; *mm.* rose	25	80
2109	*York.* No. € on breast; *mm.* lis	100	275
2110	**Penny,** *London.* No marks by bust; *mm.* 12-31	30	100
2111	*Bristol.* Similar; *mm.* rose	200	525
2112	*Canterbury* (Royal). Similar; *mm.* 33, 11	50	150
2113	— C on breast; *mm.* rose	75	200
2114	*Durham,* Bp. Booth (1471-6). No marks by neck; *mm.* 12, 44	20	65

2115

2116

2115	— — D in centre of *rev.;* B and trefoil by neck; *mm.* 44, 33, 56	20	65
2116	— — — two lis at neck; *mm.* rose	25	70
2117	— — — crosses over crown, and on breast; *mm.* rose	25	70

		F £	VF £
2118	— — — crosses over crown, V under CIVI; *mm.* rose, pansy	25	70
2119	— — — B to l. of crown, V on breast and under CIVI	20	65
2120	— — — As last but crosses at shoulders	20	65
2121	— Sede Vacante (1476). R. D in centre; *mm.* rose	30	85
2122	— Bp. Dudley (1476-83). V to r. of neck; as last	25	70

2123

2125

2134

		F £	VF £
2123	— — D and V by neck; as last, but *mm.* 31	20	65
	Nos. 2117-2123 are from locally-made dies.		
2124	*York,* Archb. Neville (1471-2). Quatrefoils by neck. R. Quatrefoil; *mm.* 12 (over lis)	60	150
2125	— — Similar, but G and key by neck; *mm.* 12 (over lis)	20	60
2126	— Neville suspended (1472-5). As last, but no quatrefoil in centre of *rev.*	35	90
2126A	— — no marks by bust, similar; *mm.* annulet	50	140
2127	— — No marks by neck, quatrefoil on *rev.; mm.* 55, cross in circle, 33 .	20	60
2128	— — Similar but Є and rose by neck; *mm.* rose	20	60
2129	— Archb. Neville restored (1475-6). As last, but G and rose	25	70
2130	— — Similar, but G and key by bust	20	60
2131	— Sede Vacante (1476). As 2127, but rose on breast; *mm.* rose	25	75
2132	— Archb. Lawrence Booth (1476-80). B and key by bust, quatrefoil on *rev.; mm.* 33, 31	20	60
2133	— Sede Vacante (1480). Similar, but no quatrefoil on rev.; *mm.* rose	25	75
2134	— Archb. Rotherham (1480-3). T and slanting key by neck, quatrefoil on *rev.; mm.* 33	20	65
2135	— — — Similar, but star on breast	50	125
2136	— — — Star on breast and to r. of crown	50	135
2137	**Halfpenny**, *London.* No marks by neck; *mm.* 12-31	20	50
2138	— Pellets at neck; *mm.* pierced cross	35	110
2139	*Canterbury* (Royal). C on breast and in centre of *rev.; mm.* rose	75	175
2140	— C on breast only; *mm.* rose	65	150
2141	— Without C either side; *mm.* 11	65	150
2142	*Durham,* Bp. Booth. No marks by neck. R. DЄRΛ̄M, D in centre; *mm.* rose	125	300
2142A	— — Lis either side of neck. R. D or no mark in centre	150	350
2142B	— — B to l. of crown, crosses at shoulders. R. D. in centre; *mm.* rose	150	350
2143	— — — Bp. Dudley V to l. of neck; as last	135	325

Full flan coins are very difficult to find in the small denominations.

On 12th February, 1483, the prolific cinquefoil coinage of Edward IV came to an end and an indenture between the king and the new master of the mint, Bartholomew Reed, saw the introduction of the sun and rose mintmark.

Edward IV died on 9th April, 1483, but the sun and rose coinage continued, essentially unaltered, through the short reign of Edward V and into the reign of Richard III, ending with the indenture of 20th July, 1483, with Robert Brackenbury, who had been Richard's ducal treasurer, and the introduction of the boar's head mintmark.

New dies prepared after the accession of Richard III on 26th June, 1483, bear his name but coins of the sun and rose coinage struck under Edward IV and Edward V can only be distinguished by arranging the dies in sequence. This is possible for the angels (Schneider Sylloge, SCBI 47, p.41) but has not yet been achieved for the silver coinage.

Mintmark: Halved sun and rose. 

	F £	*VF* £
2144 **Angel.** Type As 2091, reading EDWARD DEI GRA (Edward IV)	1000	2750
2144A— Similar but reading EDWARD DI GRA (Edward V)	4500	12500

2145

2145 **Half-angel.** As 2093 (probably Edward IV)	1850	4500

2146

2146A

2146 **Groat.** *London,* pellet below bust, reading EDWARD or EDVARD	475	1250
2146A— — No pellet below, reading EDWARD or EDWRD	525	1350
2147 **Penny.** *London* As 2110	625	1500
2148 **Halfpenny.** *London* As 2137	125	325

Richard's ruthless seizure of the crown left a core of bitter opposition which coalesced around Henry Tudor, earl of Richmond who had found asylum in Brittany. At Bosworth on 22 August, 1485, Richard was killed on the battlefield and the War of the Roses ended.

Richard's coinage follows the pattern of previous reigns. The portrait on the silver denominations remains stylised, though increasingly distinctive. It can be divided into three types according to mintmark. Type 1, the first sun and rose coinage, lasted 24 days to 20th July 1483. Type 2, the boar's head coinage, was issued until about June 1484. Type 3, the second sun and rose coinage, was struck until the end of the reign (Schneider Sylloge, SCBI 47, pp. 41-2).

It is evident that coin dies were stored in a 'loose-box' system which led to extensive muling between types. As an interim measure, after the indenture of 20th July, 1483, at least eleven existing sun and rose obverse dies, both gold and silver, were overpunched with the boar's head mark. The seven overpunched groat dies included four Edward IV/V dies, then still in use, and three dies of Richard III type 1.

Mintmarks

SR1 BH1 BH2 SR2 SR3 105 33

Halved sun and rose, 1, 2 and 3.
Boar's head, 1 (62) 2 (63).
Lis (105, *Durham*)
Rose only (33).

GOLD

		F £	*VF* £
2149	**Angel.** 1. Reading RICARD. R. R and rose by mast; *mm.* sun and rose 1 (2156)	1250	2750

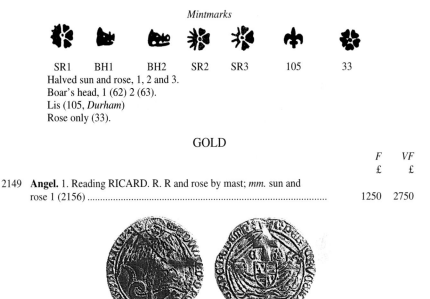

2150

2150	— 2a. Reading EDWARD. R. E and rose or R and rose by mast; *mm.* boar's head 1 over sun and rose 1/sun and rose 1 (2149)	3250	8500
2151	— 2b. Reading RICARD. R. R and rose by mast; mm. boar's head 1 over sun and rose 1/sun and rose 1, boar's head 1, boar's head 2 (often muled) (2156)	1100	2650

2152 2153

No.	Description	F £	VF £
2152	— 3. Reading RICARD or RICAD; *mm.* sun and rose 2 (2156)	1000	2500
2153	**Half-angel.** 2b. R. R and rose by mast; *mm.* boar's head 1 (2158)	2500	6000

SILVER

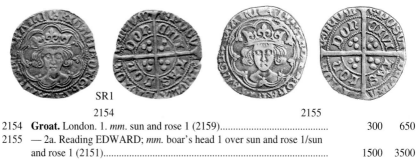

SR1

2154 2155

No.	Description	F £	VF £
2154	**Groat.** London. 1. *mm.* sun and rose 1 (2159)	300	650
2155	— 2a. Reading EDWARD; *mm.* boar's head 1 over sun and rose 1/sun and rose 1 (2151)	1500	3500

BH2/1

SR2

2156 2158

No.	Description	F £	VF £
2156	— 2b. Reading RICARD; *mm.* boar's head 1 over sun and rose 1/sun and rose 1, boar's head 1, boar's head 2 (often muled) (2159)	350	750
2157	— 3. *mm.* sun and rose 2, sun and rose 3 (2159)	300	625
2158	— — Pellet below bust, *mm.* sun and rose 2, sun and rose 3 (2160)	325	725
2159	York. 3. *mm.* sun and rose 2/- (2161)	700	1650
2160	**Halfgroat.** *London.* 2a. Reading EDWARD; *mm.* boar's head 1 over sun and rose 1/- (the *mm.* is indistinct) (2152)	1250	3500

2160 2161

No.	Description	F £	VF £
2161	— 2b. Reading RICARD; *mm.* boar's head 2/- (2164)	700	1650

		F £	*VF* £
2162	— 3. *mm.* sun and rose 2, sun and rose 2/-	425	950
2163	— — Pellet below bust; *mm.* sun and rose 2	525	1250

2164

2164	**Penny.** *London.* 2a. Reading EDWARD; *mm.* boar's head 1 over sun and rose 1/- (2153)	1000	3250
2165	— 2b. Reading RICARD; *mm.* boar's head 1/-	900	2500

2166

2166	*York.* Archb. Rotherham. T and upright key at neck. R. Quatrefoil in centre; *mm.* boar's head 1/- (2168)	165	425
2167	— — *mm.* rose/-	150	400
2168	— No marks at neck; *mm.* sun and rose 2/- (2166)	200	500

2169

2171

2169	*Durham.* Bp. Sherwood. S on breast. R. D in centre; *mm.* lis/-	110	300
2170	**Halfpenny.** *London.* 2b. No marks by neck; *mm.* boar's head 1/- (2171)	125	375
2171	— 3. *mm.* sun and rose 2/- (2170)	100	275
2171A	**Farthing.** *London.* 3. *mm.* sun and rose 2/-	750	1850

HENRY VII, 1485-1509

For the first four years of his reign Henry's coins differ only in name and mintmark from those of his predecessors, but in 1489 radical changes were made in the coinage. Though the pound sterling had been a denomination of account for centuries, a pound coin had never been minted. Now a magnificent gold pound was issued, and, from the design of the king enthroned in majesty, was called a 'Sovereign'. A small simplified version of the Sovereign portrait was at the same time introduced on the silver pence. The reverse of the gold 'Sovereign' had the royal arms set in the centre of a Tudor rose. A few years later the angel was restyled and St. Michael, who is depicted about to thrust Satan into the Pit with a cross-topped lance, is no longer a feathered figure but is clad in armour of Renaissance style. A gold ryal of ten shillings was also minted again for a brief period.

The other major innovation was the introduction of the shilling in the opening years of the 16th century. It is remarkable for the very fine profile portrait of the king which replaces the representational image of a monarch that had served on the coinage for the past couple of centuries. This new portrait was also used on groats and halfgroats but not on the smaller denominations.

Mintmarks

1485-7	Halved sun and rose (39)
	Lis upon sun and rose (41)
	Lis upon half rose (40)
	Lis-rose dimidiated (42)
	Rose (33, *York*)
1487	Lis (105)
	Cross fitchée (11)
1487-8	Rose (33)
	Plain cross (7a, *Durham*)
1488-9	No marks
1489-93	Cinquefoil (31)
	Crozier (76b, *Durham*)
1492	Cross fitchée (11, gold only)
1493-5	Escallop (78)
	Dragon (118, gold only)
	Lis (105, *Canterbury and York*
	Tun (123, *Canterbury*)
1495-8	Pansy (30)
	Tun (123, *Canterbury*)
	Lis (105, York)
1498-9	Crowned leopard's head (91)
	Lis issuant from rose (43)
	Tun (123, *Canterbury*)
1499-1502	Anchor (57)
1502-4	Greyhound's head (85)
	Lis (105, profile issue only)
	Martlet (94, *York*)
1504-5	Cross-crosslet (21)
1504-9	Martlet (94, (*York, Canterbury*)
	Rose (33, *York* and *Canterbury*)
1505-9	Pheon (53)

GOLD

		F £	VF £
2172	**Sovereign** (20s; wt. 240 gr.). Group I. Large figure of king sitting on backless throne. R. Large shield crowned on large Tudor rose. *mm*. 31 ..	*Extremely rare*	
2173	— Group II. Somewhat similar but throne has narrow back, lis in background. R. Large Tudor rose bearing small shield. *mm*. -/11	*Extremely rare*	

2174

		F £	VF £
2174	— III. King on high-backed very ornamental throne, with greyhound and dragon on side pillars. R. Shield on Tudor rose; *mm*. dragon	8500	18500
2175	— IV. Similar but throne with high canopy breaking legend and broad seat, *mm*. 105/118, (also with no *obv*. i.c. *mm*. 105/118, very rare)	7500	17250
2176	— Narrow throne with a portcullis below the king's feet (like Henry VIII); *mm*. 105/21, 105/53	7000	15000
2177	**Double-sovereign** and **Treble-sovereign** from same dies as 2176. These piedforts were probably intended as presentation pieces *mm*. 105/21, 105/53	*Extremely rare*	

2178

		F £	VF £
2178	**Ryal** (10s.). As illustration: *mm*. -/11	7000	20000
2179	**Angel** (6s. 8d). I. Angel of old type with one foot on dragon. R. PЄR CRVCЄM. etc., *mm*. 39, 40, (also muled both ways)..............................	625	1500
2179A	— With Irish title, and legend over angel head. mm. 33/-........................	675	1600
2180	— — Name altered from RICARD? and h on *rev*. from R. mm. 41/39, 41/40, 41/-, 39/?	650	1600

2181

2183

2187

		F £	VF £
2181	II. As 2179, but *mm.* none. 31/-.	425	975
2181A	II/III mule. *mm.* 31/78, R. PER CRUC or AVTЄM TRAnS	450	1000
2182	As 2181. R. IhC AVTЄM TRAnSIЄnS etc.; *mm.* none, 31/-	525	1250
2183	III. New dies, angel with both feet on dragons; (large straight lettering) *mm.* 78-85 except 91 (many mules exist)	350	700
2183A	— Angel with very small wings. *mm.* escallop	475	1050
2184	— — R. IhC AVTЄM TRAnSIЄnS, etc.; *mm.* escallop	450	1000
2185	IV. Small square lettering; *mm.* 85 (also muled with 2183)	325	650
2186	— Tall thin lettering; *mm.* 21 (also muled with 2185 obv.)	325	650
2187	V. Large crook-shaped abbreviation after hЄnRIC; *mm.* 21 and 53 (combinations and mules exist)	300	625
2188	**Half-angel or angelet.** I. *Mm.* 39, 41, (old dies RIII altered)	650	1500
2189	III. Angel with both feet on dragon: *mm.* 30, 57/30, -/85 30/85	350	750
2190	IV. Small square lettering; *mm.* rose	375	850
2191	— *Obv.* as last. R. Tall thin lettering; *mm.* 33/21	350	800
2192	V. As angel; *mm.* pheon	250	500

SILVER

Facing bust issues. Including 'Sovereign' type pennies.

2193	**Groat.** I. Open crown; *mm.* 40 (rose on bust), 39-42 and none (combinations)	80	240

2194

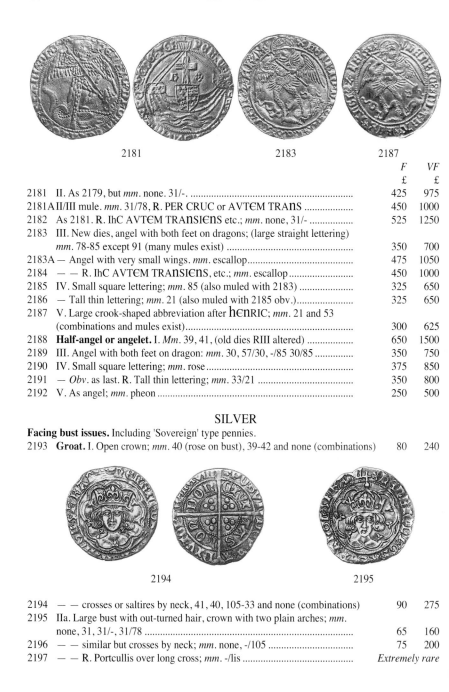

2195

2194	— — crosses or saltires by neck, 41, 40, 105-33 and none (combinations)	90	275
2195	IIa. Large bust with out-turned hair, crown with two plain arches; *mm.* none, 31, 31/-, 31/78	65	160
2196	— — similar but crosses by neck; *mm.* none, -/105	75	200
2197	— — R. Portcullis over long cross; *mm.* -/lis	*Extremely rare*	

2198

2199

2201

No.	Description	*F* £	*VF* £
2198	**Groat.** IIIa. Bust as IIa. Crown with two jewelled arches, *mm.* 31	200	475
2198A	IIIb. Similar, but new bust with realistic hair *mm.* 78, 30	50	140
2199	IIIc. Bust as IIIb, but crown with one plain and one jewelled arch, *mm.* 30-21 and none	45	125
2199A	IIId. As last, but plainer letters. mm 57, 85, 33 and none	50	140
2200	IVa. Wide single arch crown; arch is single or double bar with 4 crockets; *mm.* 85, 85/33, 21	65	175
2201	IVb. — Similar, but arch is double bar with 6 uprights or crockets as jewels; *mm.* 85, 21/85, 21	60	150
2202	**Halfgroat,** *London.* I. Open crown, tressure unbroken; *mm.* 40/-, 40/39 (R. III mule)	300	750
2203	— IIIa. Double arched crown, rosettes on tressure; mm. escallop	150	325
2204	— IIIb. Similar, nothing on tressure. R. Lozenge panel in centre; *mm.* lis	35	85
2205	— — Similar, but also with lis on breast; mm. lis	40	100
2206	— IIIc. Unarched crown with tressure broken. R. Lozenge panel in centre; *mm.* lis	30	75
2206A	— — — Similar but smaller dies and much smaller lettering	35	80

2207

2211

No.	Description	*F* £	*VF* £
2207	*Canterbury,* Archb. Morton. I. Open crown, crosses by neck. R. M in centre; *mm.* tun/-	40	95
2208	— — II. Similar, but double-arched crown; no *mm.*	40	90
2209	III King and Archb. jointly. As last but without M; (a) early lettering, trefoil stops; *mm.* lis, tun and lis/lis	30	80
2210	— — (b) ornate lettering, rosette stops; *mm.* tun, lis in combinations	25	70
2211	— — (c) — saltire or no stops; *mm.* 123, 123 & 30/123	25	65
2212	*York,* Royal mint. (a) Double-arched crown, lis on breast (rarely omitted). R. Lozenge panel in centre; *mm.* lis	50	125
2213	— — (b) Similar, but unarched crown, tressure broken, *mm.* lis.	35	90

2214 2221 2226

		F £	VF £
2214	— Archb. Savage. (a) Double-arched crown, keys at neck, no tressure; ornate lettering; *mm.* martlet	30	80
2215	— — (b) Similar, but fleured tressure, small square lettering; *mm.* martlet	30	85
2216	— — (c) As last, but tall thin lettering; *mm.* martlet	30	85
2217	— As last but no keys; *mm.* martlet	50	125
2218	**Penny.** Old type. London; *mm.* 40/-	175	475
2219	— — — crosses by bust, mm. small cross (obv.)	225	575
2220	— *Canterbury,* Archb. Morton. Open crown, *mm.* tun/- R. M in centre ..	200	500
2221	— — King and Archb. jointly, arched crown; *mm.* tun, tun/-	60	160
2222	— *Durham,* Bp. Sherwood. S on breast. R. D in centre; *mm.* 7a/-	50	135
2223	— *York,* Archb. Rotherham. With or without cross on breast, *mm.* 33/-, T and cross or key at neck. R. h in centre	40	110
2224	— — — T and trefoil at neck. R. Quatrefoil in centre and two extra pellets; *mm.* 39/-	40	100
2225	'Sovereign' type. *London*. Early lettering, no stops, no pillars to throne; no *mm.*	80	250
2226	— — — single pillar on king's right side, trefoil stops; no *mm.* or 31/- ..	40	100
2227	— — Ornate letters, rosette stops, single pillar; *mm.* lis (can be muled with above)	50	125
2228	— — saltire stops or none, two pillars; *mm.* none, -/30	45	95
2229	— — Similar, but small square lettering; no *mm.*	45	95
2230	— — Similar, but lettering as profile groats two double pillars; *mm.* 21, 53, none (sometimes on one side only)	45	95

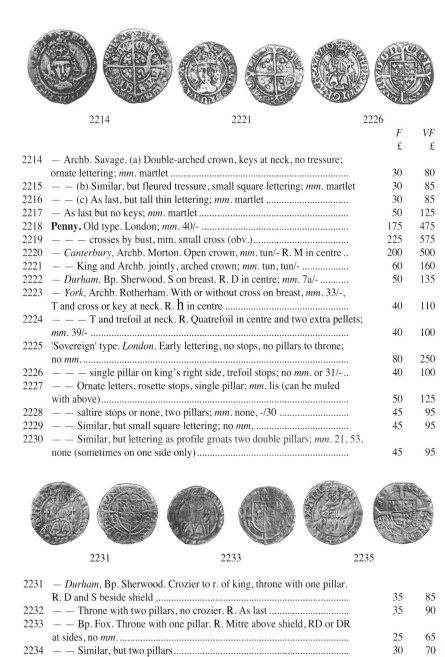

2231 2233 2235

		F £	VF £
2231	— *Durham,* Bp. Sherwood. Crozier to r. of king, throne with one pillar. R. D and S beside shield	35	85
2232	— — Throne with two pillars, no crozier. R. As last	35	90
2233	— — Bp. Fox. Throne with one pillar. R. Mitre above shield, RD or DR at sides, no *mm.*	25	65
2234	— — Similar, but two pillars	30	70

		F £	VF £
2235	*York,* Archb. Rotherham. Keys below shield; early lettering, trefoil stops, no pillars to throne, no *mm*	35	75
2236	— — — single pillar	30	65
2237	— — — — ornate lettering, rosette or no stops,	35	75
2238	— — — two pillars sometimes with crosses between legs of throne	30	70
2239	**Halfpenny,** *London*. I. Open crown; *mm*. 40, 42	45	125
2240	— — — trefoils at neck; no *mm*., rose	65	145
2241	— — — crosses at neck; *mm*. rose, cross fitchée	45	125
2242	— II. Double arched crown; *mm*. cinquefoil, none	25	65
2243	— — — saltires at neck; no *mm*.	30	70
2244	— IIIa. Crown with single arch, ornate lettering; no *mm*., pansy	20	50
2244A	— IIIb. Similar but with rosette stops; *mm*. none, rose, lis	35	75

2245

2248

2245	— IIIc. Much smaller portrait; *mm*. pheon, lis, none	20	50
2246	*Canterbury,* Archb. Morton. I. Open crown, crosses by neck; R. M in centre	75	185
2247	— — II. Similar, but arched crown, saltires by bust; *mm*. profile eye (82)	70	175
2247A	— — — no marks at neck	65	150
2248	— III. King and Archb. Arched crown; *mm*. lis, none	50	120

2249

2250

2249	*York,* Archb. Savage. Arched crown, key below bust to l or r. *mm*. martlet	65	150
2250	**Farthing,** *London*. hENRIC DI GRA REX (A), arched crown	135	425

*No.s 2239-49 have *mm*. on *obv*. only.

Profile issue

2251	Testoon (ls.). Type as groat. hENRIC (VS); *mm*. lis	5000	9500
2252	— hENRIC VII; *mm*. lis	5250	10000

2253

2253	— hENRIC SEPTIM; *mm*. lis	6000	12500

2254

2258

		F £	*VF* £
2254	**Groat,** *Tentative issue* (contemporary with full-face groats). Double band to crown, hEnRIC VII; *mm*. none, 105/-, -/105: 105/85, 105, 85, 21	140	375
2255	— — — tressure on *obv.; mm*. cross-crosslet	2500	6250
2256	— — hEnRIC (VS); *mm*. 105, -/105, 105/ 85, none	375	1000
2257	— — hEnRIC SEPTIM; *mm*. -/105	2650	6500
2258	*Regular issue*. Triple band to crown; *mm*. 21, 53 (both *mm*.s may occur on *obv*. or *rev*. or both)	75	200
2259	**Halfgroat,** *London*. As last; *mm*. 105, 53/105, 105/53, 53	80	225
2260	— — no numeral after King's name, no *mm*., -/lis	400	950

2261

2262

2261	*Canterbury,* King and Archb. As London, but *mm*. 94, 33, 94/33	60	150
2262	*York,* Archb. Bainbridge. As London, but two keys below shield; *mm*. 94, 33, 33/94	50	140
2262A	— Similar but no keys; *mm*. rose	75	185

2263

2263	— — XB beside shield; *mm*. rose/martlet	325	750
2263A	— — Similar but two keys below shield *mm*. rose(?)/martlet	350	800

Henry VIII is held in ill-regard by numismatists as being the author of the debasement of England's gold and silver coinage; but there were also other important numismatic innovations during his reign. For the first sixteen years the coinage closely followed the pattern of the previous issues, even to the extent of retaining the portrait of Henry VII on the larger silver coins.

In 1526, in an effort to prevent the drain of gold to continental Europe, the value of English gold was increased by 10%, the sovereign to 22s. 0d. and the angel to 7s. 4d., and a new coin valued at 4s. 6d.—the Crown of the Rose—was introduced as a competitor to the French *écu au soleil*. The new crown was not a success and within a few months it was replaced by the Crown of the Double Rose valued at 5s but made of gold of only 22 carat fineness, the first time gold had been minted below the standard 23c. At the same time the sovereign was again revalued to 22s. 6d. and the angel to 7s. 6d., with a new coin, the George Noble, valued at 6s. 8d. (one-third pound).

The royal cyphers on some of the gold crowns and half-crowns combine the initial of Henry with those of his queens: Katherine of Aragon, Anne Boleyn and Jane Seymour. The architect of this coinage reform was the chancellor, Cardinal Thomas Wolsey, who besides his other changes had minted at York a groat bearing his initials and cardinal's hat in addition to the other denominations normally authorized for the ecclesiastical mints.

When open debasement of the coinage began in 1544 to help finance Henry's wars, the right to coin of the archbishops of Canterbury and York and of the bishop of Durham was not confirmed. Instead, a second royal mint was opened in the Tower as in subsequent years were six others, at Southwark, York, Canterbury, Bristol, Dublin and Durham House in the Strand. Gold, which fell to 23c. in 1544, 22c. in 1545, and 20c. in 1546 was much less debased than silver which declined to 9oz 2dwt. in 1544, 6oz 2dwt. in 1545 and 4oz 2dwt. in 1546. At this last standard the blanched silver surface of the coins soon wore away to reveal the copper alloy beneath which earned for Henry the nickname 'Old Coppernose'.

Mintmarks

1509-26 Pheon (53)
Castle (69)
Castle with H (70, gold)
Portcullis crowned (108)
Rose (33, *Canterbury*)
Martlet (94, *Canterbury*)
Pomegranate (73, but broader, *Cant.*)
Cross fitchée (11, *Cant.*)
Lis (105, *Canterbury, Durham*)

1526-44 Rose (33)
Lis (105)

1509-14 Martlet (94, *York*)

1509-23 Radiant star (22, *Durham & York*)

1513-18 Crowned T (135, Tournai)

1514-26 Star (23, *York & Durham*)
Pansy (30, *York*)
Escallop (78, *York*)
Voided cross (15, *York*)

1523-26 Spur rowel (24, *Durham*)

1526-32 Cross patonce (8, *Cant.*)
T (114, *Canterbury*)

	Sunburst 110)
	Arrow (52)
	Pheon (53)
	Lis (106)
	Star (23, *Durham*)
1526-9	Crescent (72a, *Durham*)
	Trefoil (44 variety, *Durham*)
	Flower of eight petals and circle centre (*Durham*)
1526-30	Cross (7a, sometimes slightly voided, *York*)
	Acorn (65a, *York*)
	Uncertain mark (121, *Canterbury*)
1529-44	Radiant star (22, *Durham*)
1530-44	Key (90, *York*)
1533-44	Catherine wheel (36, *Canterbury*)
1544-7	Lis (105 and 106)
	Pellet in annulet (56)
	S (Southwark)
	Є or E (Southwark)
1546-7	WS monogram (116, *Bristol*)

GOLD

First coinage, 1509-26

		F £	*VF* £
2264	**Sovereign** (20s.). Similar to last sov. of Hen. VII; *mm*. 108	3500	9250
2264A	**Ryal** (10s.) King in ship holding sword and shield. R. Similar to 1950, *mm*.-/108	*Extremely rare*	
2265	**Angel** (6s. 8d.). As Hen. VIII, but hЄnRIC? VIII DI GRA RЄX, etc.; *mm*. 53, 69, 70, 70/69, 108, R. May omit h and rose, or rose only; *mm*. 69, 108	275	650
2266	**Half-angel.** Similar (sometimes without VIII), *mm*. 69, 70, 108/33, 108	250	550

2265

Second coinage, 1526-44

2267

		F £	*VF* £
2267	**Sovereign** (22s. 6d.). As 2264, R. single or double tressure *mm*. 110, 105, 105/52	3250	7500
2268	**Angel** (7s. 6d.). As 2265, hЄnRIC VIII D(I) G(RA) R(ЄX) etc,; *mm*. 110, 105	525	1200
2269	**Half-angel.** Similar; *mm*. lis	700	1650

2270

2272

No.	Description	F £	VF £
2270	**George-noble** (6s. 8d.). As illustration; *mm*. rose	3250	8250
2270A	— Similar, but more modern ship with three masts, without initials hR. R. St. George brandishing sword behind head.	5500	14000
2271	**Half-George-noble.** Similar to 2270 *mm* rose, lis	*Extremely rare*	
2272	**Crown of the rose** (4s. 6d., 23 c. 3 $\frac{1}{2}$ gr.). As illustration; *mm*. rose, two legend varieties	5500	13500
2273	**Crown of the double-rose** (5s., 22 c). Double-rose crowned, hK (Henry and Katherine of Aragon) both crowned in field. R. Shield crowned; *mm*. rose	300	625
2274	— hK both sides; *mm*. rose/lis, lis, arrow	300	650
2275*	— hK/hA or hA/hK; *mm*. arrow	750	1750
2276*	— hR/hK or hI/hR; *mm*. arrow	650	1500
2277	— hA (Anne Boleyn); *mm*. arrow	700	1600
2278	— hA/hR; *mm*. arrow	750	1750

2279

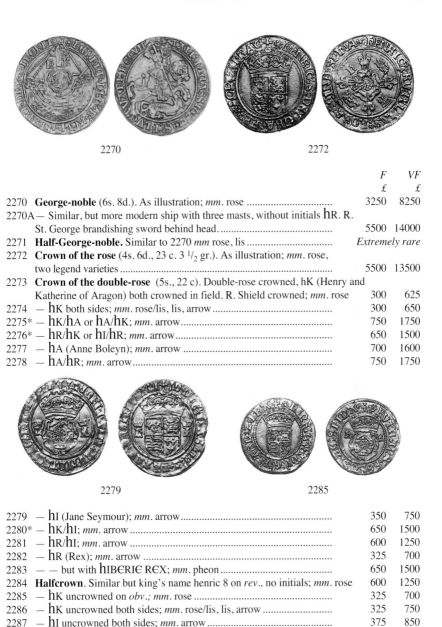

2285

No.	Description	F £	VF £
2279	— hI (Jane Seymour); *mm*. arrow	350	750
2280*	— hK/hI; *mm*. arrow	650	1500
2281	— hR/hI; *mm*. arrow	600	1250
2282	— hR (Rex); *mm*. arrow	325	700
2283	— — but with hIBERIC REX; *mm*. pheon	650	1500
2284	**Halfcrown**. Similar but king's name henric 8 on *rev*., no initials; *mm*. rose	600	1250
2285	— hK uncrowned on *obv.; mm*. rose	325	700
2286	— hK uncrowned both sides; *mm*. rose/lis, lis, arrow	325	750
2287	— hI uncrowned both sides; *mm*. arrow	375	850
2288	— hR uncrowned both sides; hIB REX; *mm*. pheon	450	1000

*The hK initials may on later coins refer to Katherine Howard (Henry's fifth wife).

Third coinage, 1544-7

2291

No.	Description	F £	VF £
2289	**Sovereign,** I (20s., Wt. 200 gr., 23 c.). As illustration but king with larger face and larger design; *mm*. lis	4500	12000
2290	II (20s., wt. 200 or 192 grs., 23, 22 or 20 ct.). *Tower*. As illustration; *mm*. lis, pellet in annulet/lis	1850	4250
2291	— *Southwark*. Similar; *mm*. S, Є/S	1750	4000
2292	— — Similar but Є below shield; *mm*. S/Є	2250	5250
2293	— *Bristol*. As London but *mm*. WS/-	2500	6250

2294

No.	Description	F £	VF £
2294	**Half-sovereign** (wt. 100 or 96 gr.), *Tower*. As illus.; *mm*. lis, pellet in annulet	375	750
2295	— Similar, but with annulet on inner circle (either or both sides)	350	800
2296	*Southwark*. *Mm*. S	375	850
2297	— Є below shield; *mm*. S, Є, S/Є, Є/S, (known without sceptre; *mm*. S)	350	800
2298	*Bristol*. Lombardic lettering; *mm*. WS, WS/-	650	1500
2299	**Angel** (8s., 23 c). Annulet by angel's head and on ship, hЄnRIC' 8; *mm*. lis	300	625
2300	— Similar, but annulet one side only or none	300	650
2301	**Half-angel.** Annulet on ship; *mm*. lis	325	650
2302	— No annulet on ship; *mm*. lis	325	700

2303

2304

No.	Description	F £	VF £
2303	— Three annulets on ship; *mm*. lis	375	850
2304	**Quarter-angel** Angel wears armour; *mm*. lis	275	600
2304A	— Angel wears tunic; *mm*. lis	275	625

		F £	VF £
2305	**Crown,** *London*. Similar to 2283, but hENRIC' 8 ; Lombardic lettering; mm . 56	275	600
2306	— without RVTILANS; *mm*. 56	300	650
2307	— — — with annulet on inner circle	300	650
2307A	— King's name omitted. DEI GRA both sides, *mm*. 56	475	1000
2308	— *Southwark*. As 2306; *mm*. S, Є, E/S, Є/-, E/Є	375	750
2309	*Bristol*. hЄNRIC VIII. ROSA etc. R. D G, etc.; *mm*.-/WS	275	600
2310	— Similar but hЄNRIC(VS) 8 R. DЄI) G(RA); *mm*. -/WS, WS	300	625
2311	**Halfcrown,** *London*. Similar to 2288; *mm*. 56, 56/-	250	500
2312	— — with annulet on inner circle *mm*. 56	250	525
2313	*Southwark*. As 2311; *mm*. S	275	600
2314	— *O*. hЄNRIC 8 ROSA SINЄ SPIN. R. DЄI GRA, etc.; *mm*. Є	300	625
2315	*Bristol*. *O*. RVTILAN S, etc. R. hЄNRIC 8; *mm*. WS/-	350	700

For other gold coins in Henry's name see page 218-19.

SILVER

First coinage, 1509-26

2316

2327

2316	**Groat.** Portrait of Hen. VII. *London mm*. 53, 69, 108, 108 over 135...	75	200
2317	— *Tournai; mm*. crowned T. R. CIVITAS TORNACЄN*	325	900
2318	**Halfgroat.** Portrait of Hen. VII. London; *mm*. 108, 108/-	85	250
2319	— *Canterbury,* Archb. Warham. POSVI *rev*.; *mm*. rose	100	275
2320	— — — WA above shield; *mm*. martlet	65	165
2321	— — — WA beside shield; *mm*. cross fitchee	65	165
2322	— — CIVITAS CANTOR *rev*., similar; *mm*. 73, 105, 11/105	45	120
2323	— *York,* POSVI *rev*., Archb. Bainbridge (1508-14). Keys below shield; *mm*. martlet	60	150
2324	— — — XB beside shield no keys; *mm*. martlet	60	150
2325	— — — Archb. Wolsey (1514-30). Keys and cardinal's hat below shield; *mm*. 94, 22	125	325
2326	— — CIVITAS ЄBORACI *rev*. Similar; *mm*. 22, 23, 30, 78, 15, 15/78	45	125
2327	— — As last with TW beside shield; *mm*. voided cross	80	200
2327A	— *Tournai*. As 2317	800	2250

*Other non-portrait groats and half-groats exist of this mint, captured during an invasion of France in 1513. (Restored to France in 1518.)

2332

2335

2336

		F	*VF*
		£	£
2328	**Penny,** 'Sovereign' type, *London; mm.* 69, 108 /-	45	120
2329	— *Canterbury*. WA above shield; *mm.* martlet	95	275
2330	— — — WA beside shield; *mm.* 73/-	70	175
2331	— *Durham,* Bp. Ruthall (1509-23). TD above shield; *mm.* lis	35	85
2332	— — — TD beside shield; *mm.* lis, radiant star	35	85
2333	— — Bp. Wolsey (1523-9). DW beside shield, cardinal's hat below; *mm.* spur rowel	150	425
2334	**Halfpenny.** Facing bust, hЄnRIC DI GRA RЄX (AGL). *London; mm.* 69, 108/-	20	60
2335	— *Canterbury*. WA beside bust; *mm.* 73/-, 11	65	160
2335A	— *York*. Key below bust, *mm.* star, escallop	90	250
2336	**Farthing.** *mm.* 108/-, hЄnRIC DI GRA RЄX, portcullis. R. CIVITAS LOnDON, rose in centre of long cross	275	650

Second coinage, 1526-44

2337

2337D

2337E

2337	**Groat.** His own young portrait. *London;* Laker bust A, large renaissance-style bust, crown arch breaking inner circle. Roman/Roman lettering, roses in cross-ends; *mm.* rose	325	950
2337A	— — Roman/Lombardic lettering, saltires in cross-ends; *mm.* rose	200	475
2337B	— — Lombardic/Lombardic lettering, roses in cross-ends; *mm.* rose	225	600
2337C	— — Lombardic/Lombardic lettering, saltires in cross-ends; *mm.* rose	135	350
2337D	— Laker bust B, smaller face with pointed nose, crown arch does not break inner circle. Lombardic lettering; *mm.* rose	70	200
2337E	— Laker bust D, larger squarer face with roman nose, fluffy hair, crown arch does not break inner circle. Lombardic lettering; *mm.* 33, 105, 110, 52, 53 (sometimes muled)	50	135
2338	— — with Irish title HIB; reads hЄnRIC 8; *mm.* 53, 105, 53/105, 105/53,	275	750
2339	— *York*, Archb. Wolsey. TW beside shield, cardinal's hat below; *mm.* voided cross, acorn, muled (both ways)	75	200
2340	— — — omits TW; *mm.* voided cross	250	650

2342

2343

2348

		F £	*VF* £
2341	**Halfgroat.** *London;* type as groats, Lombardic lettering both sides. *mm.* rose to arrow or none (sometimes muled)	35	95
2341A	— — Mainly Roman letters on obv. or on both sides, *mm.* rose	125	375
2342	As 2341 with Irish title HIB; *mm.* pheon	375	950
2343	— *Canterbury*, Archb. Warham (—1532). R. CIVITAS CANTOR, WA beside shield; *mm.* 121, 121/-, 121/33, 8, 8/T, T	35	100
2344	— — — nothing by shield; *mm.* 121/-	50	135
2345	— — Archb. Cranmer (1533—). TC beside shield; *mm.* 36, 36/-	30	100
2346	— *York,* Archb. Wolsey (—1530). R. CIVITAS ЄBORACI, TW beside shield, hat below; *mm.* 15/-, 15	45	125
2347	— — Sede Vacante (1530/1). No marks; *mm.* key	60	150
2348	— — Archb. Lee (1531-44). EL or LE beside shield; *mm.* key	35	100
2349	**Penny.** 'Sovereign' type h . D . G . ROSA SINЄ SPINA, *London; mm.* rose to arrow (*obv.* only), *mm.* lis both sides	30	80

2350

2359

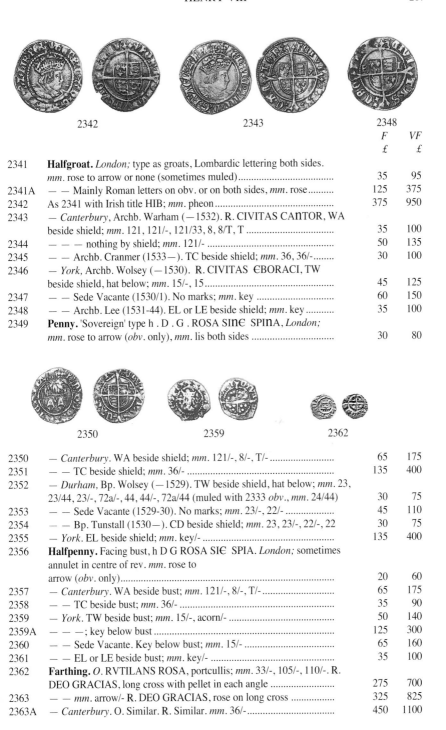

2362

		F £	*VF* £
2350	— *Canterbury*. WA beside shield; *mm.* 121/-, 8/-, T/-	65	175
2351	— — TC beside shield; *mm.* 36/-	135	400
2352	— *Durham,* Bp. Wolsey (—1529). TW beside shield, hat below; *mm.* 23, 23/44, 23/-, 72a/-, 44, 44/-, 72a/44 (muled with 2333 *obv.*, *mm.* 24/44)	30	75
2353	— — Sede Vacante (1529-30). No marks; *mm.* 23/-, 22/-	45	110
2354	— — Bp. Tunstall (1530—). CD beside shield; *mm.* 23, 23/-, 22/-, 22	30	75
2355	— *York*. EL beside shield; *mm.* key/-	135	400
2356	**Halfpenny.** Facing bust, h D G ROSA SIЄ SPIA. *London;* sometimes annulet in centre of rev. *mm.* rose to arrow (*obv.* only)	20	60
2357	— *Canterbury*. WA beside bust; *mm.* 121/-, 8/-, T/-	65	175
2358	— — TC beside bust; *mm.* 36/-	35	90
2359	— *York*. TW beside bust; *mm.* 15/-, acorn/-	50	140
2359A	— — —; key below bust	125	300
2360	— — Sede Vacante. Key below bust; *mm.* 15/-	65	160
2361	— — EL or LE beside bust; *mm.* key/-	35	100
2362	**Farthing.** *O.* RVTILANS ROSA, portcullis; *mm.* 33/-, 105/-, 110/-. R. DEO GRACIAS, long cross with pellet in each angle	275	700
2363	— — *mm.* arrow/- R. DEO GRACIAS, rose on long cross	325	825
2363A	— *Canterbury*. O. Similar. R. Similar. *mm.* 36/-	450	1100

2364

2368

Third coinage, 1544-7 (Silver progressively debased. 9oz (2dwt), 6oz (2dwt) 4oz (2dwt)).

		F £	VF £
2364	**Testoon.** *Tower*. hENRIC'. VIII, etc. R. Crowned rose between h and R.POSVI, etc.; *mm*. lis, lis and 56, lis/two lis	650	2250
2365	— hENRIC 8, *mm*. 105 and 56, 105/56, 105 and 56/56, 56	525	1750
2366	— — annulet on inner circle of rev. or both sides; *mm*. pellet in annulet	600	2000
2367	— *Southwark*. As 2365. R. CIVITAS LONDON; *mm*. S, Є, S/Є, Є/S	625	2100
2368	— *Bristol*. *mm*.-/WS monogram. (Tower or local dies.)	650	2250

2384

Bust 1

Bust 2

Bust 3

		F £	VF £
2369	**Groat.** *Tower*. As ill. above, busts 1, 2, 3; *mm*. lis/-, lis	65	200
2369A	Bust 1, R. As second coinage; i.e. saltires in forks; *mm*. lis	85	275
2370	Bust 2 or 3 annulet on inner circle, both sides or rev. only	75	240
2371	*Southwark*. As 2367, busts 1, 2, 3, 4; no *mm*. or lis/-; S or S and Є or Є in forks	65	200
2372	*Bristol*. *Mm*.-/WS monogram, Bristol bust and Tower bust 2 or 3	70	210
2373	*Canterbury*. Busts 1, 2, (2 var); no *mm*, or lis/–	75	210
2374	*York*. Busts 1 var., 2, 3, no *mm*.	70	200
2375	**Halfgroat.** *Tower*. As 2365, bust 1; *mm*. lis, none	60	175
2376	*Southwark*. As 2367, bust 1; no *mm*.; S or Є and S in forks	100	275
2377	*Bristol*. *Mm*.-/WS monogram	60	175
2378	*Canterbury*. Bust 1; no *mm*.	40	110
2379	*York*. Bust 1; no *mm*.	50	145
2380	**Penny.** *Tower*. Facing bust; no *mm*. or lis/-	30	100
2381	*Southwark*. Facing bust; *mm*. S/-, Є/-, -/Є	90	250
2382	*Bristol*. Facing bust; no *mm*. (Tower dies or local but truncated at neck)	40	125
2383	*Canterbury*. Facing bust; no *mm*	30	100
2384	*York*. Facing bust; no *mm*.	30	100
2385	**Halfpenny.** *Tower*. Facing bust; pellet in annulet in *rev*. centre, no *mm*. or lis/-	65	175
2386	*Bristol*. Facing bust; no *mm*.	70	175
2387	*Canterbury*. Facing bust; no *mm*., (some read H 8)	40	110
2388	*York*. Facing bust; no *mm*.	30	90
2388A	**Farthing** *obv*. Rose. R. Cross and pellets	500	1250

These coins were struck during the reign of Edward VI but bear the name and portrait of Henry VIII, except in the case of the half-sovereigns which bear the youthful head of Edward.

Mintmarks

56 105 52 K E 116

66 115 33 122 t 94

GOLD

		F £	*VF* £
2389	**Sovereign** (20 c), *London*. As no. 2290, but Roman lettering; *mm*. lis	2500	6000
2390	— *Bristol*. Similar but *mm*. WS	2750	6500

2391

2391A

2391	**Half-sovereign.** As 2294, but with youthful portrait with sceptre. *Tower*; *mm*. 52, 105, 94 (various combinations)	325	725
2391A	— Similar but no sceptre; *mm*. 52, 52/56	375	850
2392	— — — K below shield; *mm*.-/K, none,. E/-	325	750
2393	— — — grapple below shield; *mm*. 122, none, 122/-, -/122	350	800
2394	— *Southwark*. *Mm*. E, E/-, -/E, Є /E. Usually Є or E (sometimes retrograde) below shield (sceptre omitted; *mm*. -/E)	325	725
2394A	— — — R. As 2296; *mm*.-/S	425	950

2395

		F £	*VF* £
2395	**Crown.** Similar to 2305. *London; mm.* 52, 52/-, -/K, 122, 94,	300	675
2396	— Similar but transposed legends without numeral; *mm.* -/arrow	375	850
2396A	— As 2395, but omitting RVTILANS; *mm.* arrow	350	750
2396B	Similar, but RVTILANS both sides; *mm.* arrow	400	900
2397	— *Southwark.* Similar to 2396; *mm.* E	400	900
2398	— — King's name on *obv.*; *mm.* E/-, -/E	375	850
2399	**Halfcrown.** Similar to 2311. *London; mm.* 52, K/-, 122/-, 94, -/52	300	700
2399A	As last but E over h on *rev.*, *mm.* 56/52	450	950
2399B	As 2399 but RVTILANS etc. on both sides, *mm.* arrow	375	800
2400	— *Southwark. mm.* E, E/-, -/E	300	700

SILVER

AR (4oz .333)

2401	**Testoon.** *Tower.* As 2365 with lozenge stops one side; -/56, 56	950	3750

Bust 4

Bust 5

Bust 6

Some of the Bristol testoons, groats and halfgroats with WS monogram were struck after the death of Henry VIII but cannot easily be distinguished from those struck during his reign.

2403	**Groat.** *Tower.* Busts 4, 5, 6 (and, rarely, 2). R. POSVI, etc.; *mm.* 105-94 and none (frequently muled)	65	185
2404	— *Southwark.* Busts 4, 5, 6. R. CIVITAS LONDON; no *mm.* -/E; lis/-, -/lis, K/E; roses or crescents or S and Є in forks, or rarely annulets ...	60	170
2405	— *Durham House.* Bust 6. R. REDDE CVIQUE QVOD SVVM EST; *mm.* bow	135	425
2406	— *Bristol. mm.* WS on *rev.* Bristol bust B, Tower bust 2 and 3	75	225
2407	— — *mm.* TC on *rev.* Similar, Bristol bust B	85	250
2408	— *Canterbury.* Busts 5, 6; no *mm.* or rose/-	65	190
2409	— *York.* Busts 4, 5, 6; no *mm.* or lis/-, -/lis	65	180

		F £	VF £
2410	**Halfgroat.** Bust 1. *Tower*. POSVI, etc.; *mm*. 52, 52/-, 52/K , -/K, 52/122, 122, -/122	60	185

2411

		F £	VF £
2411	— *Southwark*. CIVITAS LONDON; *mm*. E, -/E, none, 52/E, K/E	50	150
2412	— *Durham House*. R. REDD, etc.; *mm*. bow, -/bow	300	750
2413	— *Bristol*. *Mm*. WS on *rev*.	60	175
2414	— — *mm*. TC on *rev*.	65	185
2415	— *Canterbury*. No *mm*. or t/-, -/t,	30	110
2416	— *York*. No *mm*., bust 1 and three quarter facing	45	145

2418

2422

2427

		F £	VF £
2417	**Penny.** *Tower*. CIVI TAS LONDON. Facing bust; *mm*. 52/-, -/52, -/K, 122/-, -/122, none	30	90
2418	— — three-quarter bust; no *mm*.	35	110
2419	— *Southwark*. As 2417; *mm*. E, -/E	40	125
2420	— *Durham House*. As groat but shorter legend; *mm*. -/bow	450	950
2421	— *Bristol*. Facing busts, as 2382 but showing more body, no *mm*.	50	165
2422	— *Canterbury*. Similar to 2417	30	90
2423	— — three-quarters facing bust; no *mm*	35	110
2424	— *York*. Facing bust; no *mm*.	30	95
2425	— — three-quarters facing bust; no *mm*	40	125
2426	**Halfpenny.** *Tower*. 52?, none	20	80
2427	— *Canterbury*. No *mm*., sometimes reads H8	35	110
2428	— *York*. No *mm*.	25	80

Coinage in his own name

The 4 oz. 2.5dwt coins of Henry VIII and those issued under Edward in 1547 and 1548 caused much disquiet, yet at the same time government was prevented by continuing financial necessity from abandoning debasement. A stratagem was devised which entailed increasing the fineness of silver coins, thereby making them appear sound, while at the same time reducing their weight in proportion so that in practice they contained no more silver than hitherto. The first issue, ordered on 24 January 1549, at 8 oz.2 dwt. fine produced a shilling which, at 60 gr., was so light that it was rapidly discredited and had to be replaced in April by another at 6 oz. 2 dwt. Weighing 80 gr., these later shillings proved acceptable.

Between April and August 1551 the issue of silver coins was the worst ever – 3 oz. 2dwt. fine at 72s per lb. before retrenchment came in August, first by a 50% devaluation of base silver coin and then by the issue of a fine standard at 11oz. 1dwt. 'out of the fire'. This was the equivalent of 11oz.3dwt. commixture, and means that since sterling was only 11oz. 2dwt., this issue, which contained four new denominations – the crown, halfcrown, sixpence and threepence – was in effect the finest ever issued under the Tudors.

Some base 'pence' were struck in parallel with the fine silver, but at the devalued rate, they and the corresponding 'halfpence' were used as halfpence and farthings respectively.

The first dates on English coinage appear in this reign, first as Roman numerals and then on the fine issue crowns and halfcrowns of 1551-3, in Arabic numerals.

Mintmarks

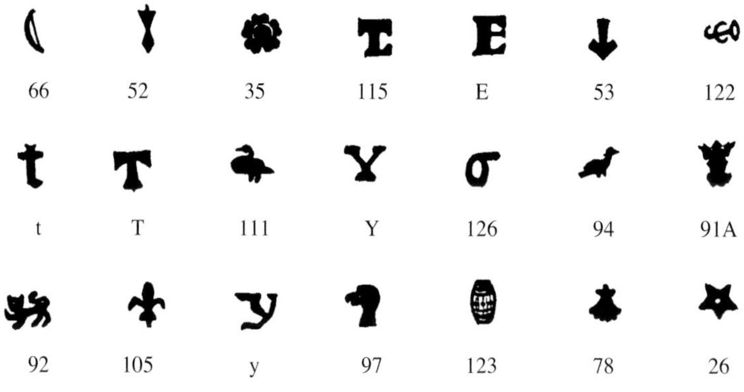

1548-9	Bow (66, *Durham House*)	1550	Martlet (94)
1549	Arrow (52)	1550	Leopard's head (91A)
	Grapple (122)	1550-1	Lion (92)
	Rose (35, *Canterbury*)		Lis (105, *Southwark*)
	TC monogram (115, *Bristol*)		Rose (33)
	Roman E (*Southwark*)	1551	Y or y (117, *Southwark*)
	Pheon (53)		Ostrich's head (97, gold only)
	t or T (*Canterbury*)	1551-3	Tun (123)
1549-50	Swan (111)		Escallop (78)
	Roman Y (*Southwark*)	1552-3	Pierced mullet (26, *York*)
1549-50	6 (126 gold only)		

GOLD

First period, Apr. 1547-Jan. 1549

2429

2431

		F £	VF £
2429	**Half-sovereign** (20 c). As 2391, but reading EDWARD 6. Tower; *mm.* arrow	725	1750
2430	— *Southwark* (Sometimes with E or Є below shield); *mm.* E	650	1500
2431	**Crown.** RVTILANS, etc., crowned rose between ER both crowned. R. EDWARD 6, etc., crowned shield between ER both crowned; *mm.* arrow, E over arrow/-	2250	6000
2431A	— *Obv.* as last. R. As 2305, *mm.* 52/56	2000	5000
2432	**Halfcrown.** Similar to 2431, but initials not crowned; *mm.* arrow	1650	4500

Second period, Jan. 1549-Apr. 1550

2433

2433	**Sovereign** (22 ct). As illustration; *mm.* arrow, –/arrow, Y,	2250	5250
2434	**Half-sovereign.** Uncrowned bust. *London.* TIMOR etc., MDXLIX on *obv. mm.* arrow	2500	6000

2435

2435	— — SCVTVM, etc., as illustration; *mm.* arrow, **6,** Y	700	1750

		F £	VF £
2436	— *Durham House*. Uncrowned, 1/2 length bust with MDXLVIII at end of *obv*. legend; *mm*. bow; SCVTVM etc.	3750	9500
2437	— Normal, uncrowned bust. LVCERNA, etc., on *obv*.; *mm*. bow	3250	8000

2438

2441

2438	— Crowned bust. *London*. EDWARD VI, etc. R. SCVTVM, etc.; *mm*. 52, 122, 111/52, 111, Y, 94	650	1650
2439	— *Durham House*. Crowned, half-length bust; *mm*. bow	3500	9000
2440	— — King's name on *obv*. and *rev*.; *mm*. bow (mule of 2439/37)	3250	8500
2441	**Crown.** Uncrowned bust, as 2435; *mm*. *6*, Y, 52/-, Y/-	875	2000
2442	— Crowned bust, as 2438; *mm*. 52, 122, 111, Y (usually *obv*. only)	825	1850
2443	**Halfcrown.** Uncrowned bust; R. As 2441, *mm*. arrow, Y, Y/-, 52/-	950	2500
2444	— Crowned bust, as illus. above; *mm*. 52, 52/111, 111, 122, Y, Y/-	800	1800
2445	— Similar, but king's name on *rev*., *mm*. 52, 122	825	1850

Third period, 1550-3

2446	**'Fine' sovereign** (30s.). King on throne; *mm*. 97, 123	9000	22500
2447	**Double sovereign.** From the same dies, *mm*. 97	*Extremely rare*	

2444

2448

2448	**Angel** (10s.). As illustration; *mm*. 97, 123	3500	9000
2449	**Half-angel.** Similar, *mm*. 97	*Extremely rare*	
2450	**Sovereign**. (=20s.). Half-length figure of king r., crowned and holding sword and orb. R. Crowned shield with supporters; *mm*. y, tun	1350	3500

2450

2451

		F £	VF £
2451	**Half-sovereign**. As illustration above; *mm*. y, tun	750	1750
2452	**Crown**. Similar, but *rev*. SCVTVM etc., *mm*. y, tun	850	2000
2453	**Halfcrown**. Similar, *mm*. tun, y	925	2500

**Small denominations often occur creased or straightened.*

SILVER

First period, Apr. 1547-Jan. 1549

2454

		F £	VF £
2454	**Groat.** Crowned bust r. *Tower*. R. Shield over cross, POSVI, etc.; *mm*. arrow	575	1650
2455	— As last, but EDOARD 6, *mm*. arrow	950	2250
2456	— *Southwark*. *Obv*. as 2454. R. CIVITAS LONDON; *mm*.-/E or none, somethimes S in forks	550	1600
2457	**Halfgroat**. *Tower*. *Obv*. as 2454; *mm*. arrow	450	1000
2458	*Southwark*. As 2456; *mm*. arrow, E	425	950

2459

2460

		F £	VF £
2459	*Canterbury*. Similar. No *mm*., reads EDOARD or EDWARD (rare)	225	550
2460	**Penny**. *Tower*. As halfgroat, but E.D.G. etc. R. CIVITAS LONDON; *mm*. arrow	275	850
2461	— *Southwark*. As last, but *mm*. -/E.	350	1000
2462	*Bristol*. Similar, but reads ED6DG or E6DG no *mm*.	225	750
2463	**Halfpenny**. *Tower*. *O*. As 2460, *mm*. E (?). R. Cross and pellets	325	900
2464	— *Bristol*. Similar, no *mm*. but reads E6DG or EDG	300	850

Second period, Jan. 1549-Apr. 1550

At all mints except Bristol, the earliest shillings of 1549 were issued at only 60 grains but of 8 oz. 2 dwt standard. This weight and size were soon increased to 80 grains., (S.2466 onwards), but the fineness was reduced to 6 oz. 2 dwt so the silver content remained the same. Dies, mm G were prepared for a coinage of 80gr shillings at York, but were not used. Coins from the *mm* are found suitably overmarked, from other mints, S.2466-8. The shilling bust types are set out in *J. Bispham 'The Base Silver Shillings of Edward VI; BNJ 1985*.

Bust 1

2465A

Bust 2

		F £	*VF* £
60 gr; 8oz. 2 dwt.			
2465	**Shilling**. *Tower*. Broad bust with large crown. *Obv*. TIMOR etc. MDXLIX. R. Small, oval garnished shield dividing ER. EDWARD VI etc., *mm*. 52, no *mm*; Bust 1, *mm*, –/52, Bust 2	175	675
2465A	*Southwark*. As last, Bust 1, *mm*. Y, EY/Y	165	625
2465B	*Canterbury*. As last, Bust 1, *mm*. -/rose	275	950
2465C	*Durham House*. Bust with elaborate tunic and collar TIMOR etc. MDXLIX. R. Oval shield, very heavily garnished in different style. EDWARD VI etc., *mm*. bow (2469)	175	650

Bust 3

Bust 4

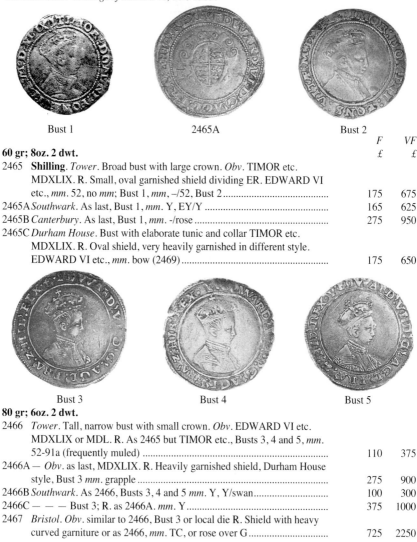

Bust 5

		F £	*VF* £
80 gr; 6oz. 2 dwt.			
2466	*Tower*. Tall, narrow bust with small crown. *Obv*. EDWARD VI etc. MDXLIX or MDL. R. As 2465 but TIMOR etc., Busts 3, 4 and 5, *mm*. 52-91a (frequently muled)	110	375
2466A	— *Obv*. as last, MDXLIX. R. Heavily garnished shield, Durham House style, Bust 3 *mm*. grapple	275	900
2466B	*Southwark*. As 2466, Busts 3, 4 and 5 *mm*. Y, Y/swan	100	300
2466C	— — — Bust 3; R. as 2466A. *mm*. Y	375	1000
2467	*Bristol*. *Obv*. similar to 2466, Bust 3 or local die R. Shield with heavy curved garniture or as 2466, *mm*. TC, or rose over G	725	2250

2466C

2468

		F £	VF £
2468	*Canterbury*. As 2466, Bust 3 and 4 *mm*. T, T/t, t/T, t	125	400

2470

2472

2470	*Durham House*. Bust as 2469. INIMICOS etc., no date. R. EDWARD etc.	165	600
2472	— Bust similar to 2466. EDWARD VI etc. R. INIMICOS etc.	135	425
2472A	— As last but legends transposed	300	950
2472B	*Tower*. Elegant bust with extremely thin neck. Bust 6, R. As 2466, *mm*. martlet	150	550
2472C	*Southwark*. As last, Bust 6, *mm*. Y	150	525

For coins of Edward VI countermarked, see p. 238

Third period, 1550-3

Very base issue (1551) 3oz. 2 dwt.

2473

Bust 6

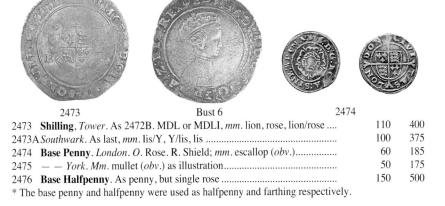

2474

2473	**Shilling**, *Tower*. As 2472B. MDL or MDLI, *mm*. lion, rose, lion/rose	110	400
2473A	*Southwark*. As last, *mm*. lis/Y, Y/lis, lis	100	375
2474	**Base Penny**. *London*. *O*. Rose. R. Shield; *mm*. escallop (*obv*.)	60	185
2475	— — *York*. *Mm*. mullet (*obv*.) as illustration	50	175
2476	**Base Halfpenny**. As penny, but single rose	150	500

* The base penny and halfpenny were used as halfpenny and farthing respectively.

Fine silver issue, (1551-3) 11oz. 3 dwt.

2478

		F £	VF £
2478	**Crown**. King on horseback with date below horse. R. Shield on cross; *mm*. y. 1551; tun, 1551-3 (1553, wire line inner circle may be missing) .	375	850

2479

2479	**Halfcrown**. Walking horse with plume; *mm*. y, 1551	325	750
2480	Galloping horse without plume; *mm*. tun, 1551-3	400	900
2481	Large walking horse without plume; *mm*. tun, 1553	750	2250

2482

2483

2482	**Shilling**. Facing bust, rose l., value XII r. *mm*. y, tun (several bust varieties)	80	240
2483	**Sixpence**. *London*. Similar, as illustration; *mm*. y/-, -/y, y, tun (bust varieties)	85	275
2484	*York*. As last, but CIVITAS ЄBORACI; *mm*. mullet	125	400

2485

2486

		F	*VF*
		£	£
2485	**Threepence**. *London*. As sixpence, but III; *mm*. tun	125	425
2486	*York*. As 2484, but III by bust	275	675

2487

2487A

2487	**Penny**. 'Sovereign' type; *mm*. tun	750	2250
2487A	**Farthing.** *O*. Portcullis, R Cross and Pellets (previously 2477)	725	2000

Mary brought English coins back to the sterling standard and struck all her gold coins at the traditional fineness of 23 c. 3 1/2 gr. The mintmarks usually appear at the end of the first or second word of the legends.

Pomegranate  Halved rose and castle 

GOLD

2488

		F £	VF £
2488	**'Fine' Sovereign** (30s.). Queen enthroned. R. Shield on rose, MDLIII, MDLIIII and undated, *mm*. pomegranate, half-rose (or mule)	2350	5500
2489	**Ryal** (15s.). As illus, MDLIII. R. As 1950 but A DNO etc. *mm*. pomegranate/-..	7500	20000

2489

2490

2490	**Angel** (10s.). Class I, annulet stops; *mm*. pomegranate...........................	700	1750
2490A	— Class II, pellet stops, *mm*. pomegranate (often muled with class I reverse)	650	1450
2490B	— Class III, pellet stops, large Roman letters, *mm*. half-rose and castle..	850	2000
2491	**Half-angel**. Similar; *mm*. pomegranate, pomegranate/-	1850	5000

SILVER

2492

		F £	*VF* £
2492	**Groat**. Crowned bust l. R. VЄRITAS, etc.; *mm*. pomegranate, pomegranate/-	70	250
2493	**Halfgroat**. Similar	600	1500
2494	**Penny**. Similar, but M. D. G. ROSA, etc.	425	1250

2495

2495	— As last. R. CIVITAS LONDON; no *mm*.	425	1250
2495A	— Base penny. Similar to 2474 but M.D.G. etc	*All late 19th cent. fabrications*	

The groats and smaller silver coins of this period have Mary's portrait only, but the shillings and sixpences show the bust of the queen's husband, Philip of Spain.

Mintmarks

Lis (105  Half-rose and castle 

GOLD

2496

		F £	VF £
2496	**Angel**. As illustration; wire line inner circles, calm sea, *mm*. lis	1800	4500
2496A	— — New-style, large wings, wire line i.c.	1850	4750
2496B	— — As above but beaded i.c	1850	4750
2497	**Half-angel**. Similar to 2496	4500	9500

SILVER

2498

2500

2498	**Shilling**. Busts face-to-face, full titles, undated, no *mm*.	200	675
2499	— — — also without mark of value	275	800
2500	— — 1554	250	750
2501	— English titles only 1554, 1555	250	800
2501A	— — undated	350	1000
2502	— — without mark of value, 1554, 1555 (rare)	275	850
2503	— — date below bust, 1554, 1555	1000	2500
2504	— — As last, but without ANG., 1555	1500	3250

2505

		F £	VF £
2505	**Sixpence**. Similar. Full titles, 1554 (and undated?)	200	700

2506

		F £	VF £
2506	— English titles only, 1555 (no *mm*., rare), 1557 (*mm*. lis, rounder garnishing)	225	750
2506A	— As last but heavy beaded i.c. on obv. 1555. (Irish 4d. obv. mule)	300	900
2507	— — date below bust, 1554, 1557 (very rare)	500	1250

2508

		F £	VF £
2508	**Groat**. Crowned bust of Mary 1. R. POSVIMVS etc.; *mm*. lis	75	275
2509	**Halfgroat**. Similar, but POSVIM, *mm*. lis	275	725

2510

		F £	VF £
2510	**Penny**. Similar to 2495, but P. Z. M. etc.; *mm*. lis	275	750
2510A	**Base penny**. Similar to 2495A, but P. Z. M . etc.; *mm*. halved rose and castle or castle/–, (used as a halfpenny)	65	200

Elizabeth's coinage is particularly interesting on account of the large number of different denominations issued. 'Crown' gold coins were again issued as well as the 'fine' gold denominations. In 1559 the base shillings of Edward VI's second and third coinages were called in and countermarked for recirculation at reduced values. Smaller debased coins were also devalued but not countermarked. The old debased groat became a three halfpence and other coins in proportion. The normal silver coinage was initially struck at .916 fineness as in the previous reign but between 1560 and 1577 and after 1582 the old sterling standard of .925 was restored. Between 1578 and 1582 the standard was slightly reduced and the weights were reduced by 1/32nd in 1601. Gold was similarly reduced slightly in quality 1578-82, and there was a slight weight reduction in 1601.

To help alleviate the shortage of small change, and to avoid the expense of minting an impossibly small silver farthing, a threefarthing piece was introduced to provide change if a penny was tendered for a farthing purchase. The sixpence, threepence, threehalfpence and threefarthings were marked with a rose behind the queen's head to distinguish them from the shilling, groat, half-groat and penny.

Coins of exceedingly fine workmanship were produced in a screw press introduced by Eloye Mestrelle, a French moneyer, in 1561. With parts of the machinery powered by a horse-drawn mill, the coins produced came to be known as 'mill money'. Despite the superior quality of the coins produced, the machinery was slow and inefficient compared to striking by hand. Mestrelle's dismissal was engineered in 1572 and six years later he was hanged for counterfeiting.

Mintmarks

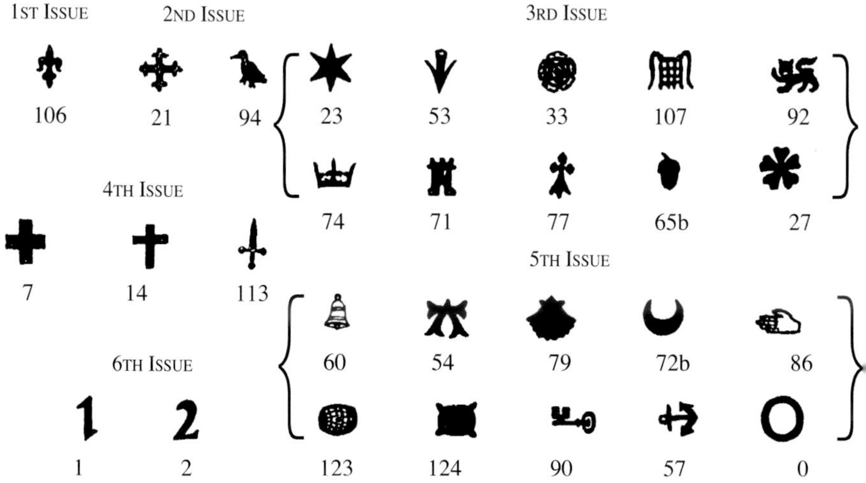

First Issue
1558-60 Lis (106)
Second Issue
1560-1 Cross crosslet (21)
Martlet (94)
Third Issue
1560-6 Star (23, milled)
1561-5 Pheon (53)
1565 Rose (33)
1566 Portcullis (107)
1566-7 Lion (92)
1567-70 Coronet (74)
Lis (105, milled)
1569-71 Castle (71)
1572-3 Ermine (77)
1573-4 Acorn (65b)
1573-7 Eglantine (27)
Fourth Issue
1578-9 Greek cross (7)
1580-1 Latin cross (14)
1582 Sword (113)
Fifth Issue
1582-3 Bell (60)
1582-4 A (54)
1584-6 Escallop (79)
1587-9 Crescent (72b)
1590-2 Hand (86)
1591-5 Tun (123)
1594-6 Woolpack (124)
1595-8 Key (90)
1597-1600 Anchor (57)
1600 **0**
Sixth Issue
1601-2 **1**
1602 **2**

N.B. *The dates for* mms *sometimes overlap. This is a result of using up old dies, onto which the new mark was punched.*

GOLD

Hammered Coinage

First to Third issues, 1559-78. ('Fine' gold of .994. 'Crown' gold of .916 fineness. Sovereigns of 240 gr.). Mintmarks; lis to eglantine.

		F £	*VF* £
2511	**'Fine' Sovereign** (30 s.) Queen enthroned, tressure broken by throne, reads Z not ET, no chains to portcullis. R. Arms on rose; *mm*. lis.	2500	6250

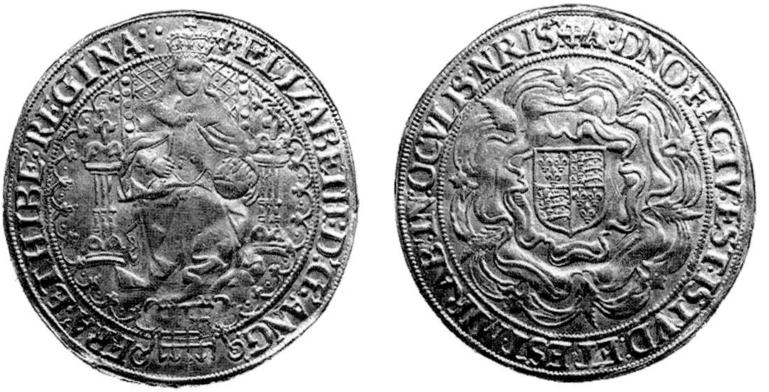

2512

2512	— — Similar but ET, chains on portcullis; *mm*. crosslet	2000	5250
2513	**Angel**. St. Michael. R. Ship. Wire line inner circles; *mm*. lis.................	625	1450
2513A	— Similar, but beaded i.c. on *obv*., *mm*. lis	600	1400
2514	— — Similar, but beaded inner circles; ship to r.; *mm*. 106, 21, 74, 27,..	350	800
2515	— — — Similar, but ship to l.; *mm*. 77-27..	350	825
2516	**Half Angel**. As 2513, wire line inner circles; *mm*. lis	950	2500
2516A	— As last, but beaded i.c.s, legend ends. Z.HIB	625	1500
2517	— As 2514, beaded inner circles; *mm*. 106, 21, 74, 77-27	325	750
2518	**Quarter Angel**. Similar; *mm*. 74, 77-27...	325	650

2513

2520A

2519	**Half Pound** (10 s.) Young crowned bust l. R. Arms. Wire line inner circles; *mm*. lis..	1250	3500
2520	— Similar, but beaded inner circles; *mm*. 21, 33-107.............................	525	1200
2520A	— — Smaller bust; *mm*. lion	900	2000
2520B	— — Broad bust, ear visible; *mm*. 92, 74, 71	625	1450
2521	**Crown**. As 2519; *mm*. lis...	1250	3500
2522	— Similar to 2520; *mm*. 21, 33-107..	525	1200
2522A	— Similar to 2520B; *mm*. 74, 71, 92	550	1250
2523	**Half Crown**. As 2519; *mm*. lis	1200	3250
2524	— Similar to 2520; *mm*. 21, 33-107 (2 busts)	500	1100
2524A	— Similar to 2520B; *mm*. 107-71...	525	1200

		F £	VF £

Fourth Issue, 1578-82 (`Fine' gold only of .992). *Mms* Greek cross, Latin cross and sword.

2525	**Angel**. As 2514; *mm*. 7, 14, 113	350	800
2526	**Half Angel**. As 2517; *mm*. 7, 14, 113	350	775
2527	— Similar, but without E and rose above ship; *mm*. latin cross	450	950
2528	**Quarter Angel**. As last; *mm*. 7, 14, 113	325	650

Fifth Issue, 1583-1600 (`Fine' gold of .979, `crown' gold of .916; pound of 174.5 grs. wt.). Mintmarks: bell to **O**.

2529

2529	**Sovereign** (30 s:). As 2512, but tressure not normally broken by back of throne; *mm*. 54-123	1850	4250

2530

2530	**Ryal** (15 s.). Queen in ship. R. Similar to 1950; *mm*. 54-86 (*rev*. only)	3500	9000

2531

2531	**Angel**. As 2514; *mm*. 60-123, 90-**O**	350	800
2532	**Half Angel**. As 2517; *mm*. 60-86, 90-57	350	750
2533	**Quarter Angel**. As 2518; *mm*. 60-123, 90-57/–	325	675

		F £	VF £
2534	**Pound** (20 s.). Old bust l., with elaborate dress and profusion of hair; *mm*., lion and tun/tun, 123-**O**	850	2000

2535

2535	**Half Pound**. Similar; *mm*. tun	675	1500
2535A	— Similar but smaller bust with less hair; *mm*. 123-**O**	625	1450

2536

2536	**Crown**. Similar to 2534; *mm*. 123-90. **O**	500	1200
2537	**Half Crown**. Similar; *mm*. -/123, 123-0, **O**	450	1000

Sixth Issue, 1601-3 ('Fine' gold of .994, 'crown' gold of .916; Pound of 172 gr.). Mintmarks: **1** and **2**

2538	**Angel**. As 2531; *mm*. **1, 2**	525	1250
2539	**Pound**. As 2534; *mm*. **1, 2**	850	2000
2540	**Half Pound**. As 2535A; *mm*. **1, 2**	800	1850
2541	**Crown**. As 2536; *mm*. **1, 2**	750	1650
2542	**Half Crown**. As 2537; *mm*. **1, 2**	725	1600

Milled Coinage, 1561-70

2543

2543	**Half Pound**. Crowned bust l.; *mm*. star, lis	950	3000
2544	**Crown**. Similar; *mm*. star, lis	925	2750
2545	**Half Crown**. Similar; *mm*. star, lis	1200	3500

For further details on both AV and AR milled coinage, *see* D. G. Borden *'An introduction to the milled coinage of Elizabeth I'*. BNJ 1983

SILVER

Hammered Coinage

Countermarked Edward VI base shillings (1559)

2546

2547

		Fair	F
		£	£
2546	**Fourpence-halfpenny**. Edward VI 2nd period 6oz and 8oz shillings .... cmkd on obv. with a portcullis; *mm*. 66, –/33, 52, t, 111, Y and 122	650	1500
2547	**Twopence-farthing**. Edward VI 3rd period 3 oz. shillings .... countermarked on obverse with a seated greyhound; *mm*. 92. 105, 35 and 87	750	1750

N.B. *Occasionally the wrong countermark was used*

First Issue, 1559-60 (.916 fine, shillings of 96 grs.)

2548

2551

		F	VF
		£	£
2548	**Shilling**. Without rose or date. ELIZABET(H), wire line inner circles, pearls on bodice, busts 1A, and 1B; *mm*. lis..	325	850
2549	— Similar, ELIZABETH, wire line and beaded inner circles, no pearls on bodice, busts 1D, 2A and 2B; *mm*. lis	110	375
2550	**Groat**. Without rose or date, wire line or no inner circles (two busts); *mm*. lis	125	450

1A

1B

1D

2A

2B

2551	— Similar, wire line and beaded inner circles, circles *mm*. lis	50	200
2551A	— — Small bust and shield (from halfgroat punches); *mm*. lis	85	275

		F £	VF £
2552	**Halfgroat**. Without rose or date, wire line inner circles; *mm*. lis	150	500
2553	**Penny**. Without rose or date, wire line inner circles; *mm*. lis	200	575
2554	— Similar but dated 1558 on *obv*.; *mm*. lis	425	1250

Second Issue, 1560-1 (.925 fineness, shilling of 96 gr.)

2555

2559

2560

		F	VF
2555	**Shilling**. Without rose or date, beaded inner circles. ET instead of Z busts 3A, 3B, 3C and 3J; *mm*. 21, 94	65	200
2555A	— large bust with pearls on bodice as 2548; *mm*. 21, bust 1A, 94, bust 1B	110	425
2556	**Groat**. Without rose or date, bust as 2551; *mm*. 21, 94	45	170
2557	**Halfgroat**. Without rose or date; *mm*. 21, 94	30	100
2558	**Penny**. Without rose or date (three bust varieties); *mm*. 21, 94	20	60

3A

3B

3C

3J

Third Issue, 1561-77 (Same fineness and weight as last)

		F	VF
2559	**Sixpence**. With rose and date, large flan (27 *mm*. or more), large bust with hair swept back, 1561; *mm*. pheon	135	525
2560	— Similar, small bust, 1561; *mm*. pheon	60	225

		F £	VF £
2561	— Smaller flan (26.5 *mm*.). Small regular bust, 1561-6; *mm*. 53-107	35	110

2561

2561B

2562

2563

2561B	— Similar, very large bust, with rose, 1563-5; *mm*. pheon	70	250
2562	— Intermediate bust, ear shows, 1566-74; *mm*. 92-65b (also 1567 *mm*. 71/74)	30	100
2562A	— Similar, without date; *mm*. lion, coronet, ermine	300	750
2563	— Larger bust, 1573-7; *mm*. 77-27	35	110
2564	**Threepence**. With rose and date 1561, large flan (20.5 *mm*.); *mm*. pheon	35	125
2565	— smaller flan (19 *mm*.). Regular bust, 1561-7; *mm*. 53-92	30	95
2566	— taller bust, ear shows, 1566-77; *mm*. 92-27, 27/-, 27/65b	30	90
2566A	— Similar, without rose, 1568; *mm*. coronet	225	525

2567

2571

2567	**Halfgroat**. Without rose or date; *mm*. 107-71	60	175
2568	**Threehalfpence**. With rose and date 1561, large flan (17 *mm*.) *mm*. pheon	35	135
2569	— — Smaller flan (16 *mm*.); 1561-2, 1564-70, 1572-7; *mm*. 53-27	25	85
2570	**Penny**. Without rose or date; *mm*. 33-71, 65b, 27, 33/107, 92/107, 74/107	20	65
2571	**Threefarthings**. With rose and date 1561-2, 1564, 1567, 1568, 1572-7; *mm*. 53, 74, 77-27	65	160

Fourth Issue, 1578-82 (.921 fineness, shilling of 95.6 gr.)

2572

2573

2572	**Sixpence**. As 2563, 1578-82; *mm*. 7-113, 14/113, 14/7	30	100
2573	**Threepence**. As 2566, 1578-82; *mm*. 7-113	25	85
2574	**Threehalfpence**. As 2569, 1578-9, 1581-2; *mm*. 7-113	30	95
2575	**Penny**. As 2570; *mm*. 7-113, 7/14, 14/7	20	65
2576	**Threefarthings**. As 2571, 1578-9, 1581-2; *mm*. 7-113	70	170

Fifth Issue, 1582-1600 (.925 fineness, shilling of 96 gr.)

2577

2578A

2581

		F £	*VF* £
2577	**Shilling**. Without rose or date, ELIZAB; ear concealed, busts 3B and 6A *mm*. 60-72b, ear shows. bust 6B *mm*. 79-**0** (mules occur)	60	185
2578	**Sixpence**. As 2572, ELIZABETH, 1582, 1583 *mm*. bell	40	120
2578A	— Similar, ELIZAB, 1582-1600; *mm*. 60-**0**, also 1583 *mm*. 79/54	30	95
2579	**Halfgroat**. Without rose or date, two pellets behind bust. R. CIVITAS LONDON; *mm*. 60-**0** (*mm*. bell sometimes without pellets)	15	50
2580	**Penny**. Without rose or date. R. CIVITAS LONDON; *mm*. 60-57, 90/-, 57/-, **0**/-	20	50
2581	**Halfpenny**. Portcullis. R. Cross and pellets; *mm*. none, 54-**0**	20	60

6A

6B

Sixth Issue, 1601-2 (.925 fineness, shilling of 92.9 gr.)

2582

2583

2582	**Crown**. As illustration, *mm*. **1, 2**	650	1400
2583	**Halfcrown**. As illustration, *mm*. **1, 2**	350	825
2584	**Shilling**. As 2577; bust 6B *mm*. **1, 2**	65	200
2585	**Sixpence**. As 2578A, 1601-2; *mm*. **1, 2**	35	100
2586	**Halfgroat**. As 2579, *mm*. **1, 2, 2/-**	20	50
2587	**Penny**. As 2580, *mm*. **1, 2, 2/-**	20	50
2588	**Halfpenny**. As 2581, *mm*. **1, 2**	25	65

Milled coinage

		F £	VF £
2589	**Shilling**. Without rose or date; *mm*. star. Plain dress, large size (over 31 *mm*.)	450	1350
2590	— decorated dress, large size	175	650
2591	— — intermediate size (30-31 *mm*.)	110	375
2592	— — small size (under 30 *mm*.)	90	325

2593 2594 2595

		F £	VF £
2593	**Sixpence**. Small bust, large rose. R. Cross fourchee, 1561 *mm*. star	45	165
2594	Tall narrow bust with plain dress, large rose, 1561-2; *mm*. star	40	140
2595	— similar, but decorated dress, 1562	40	150

2596 2598

		F £	VF £
2596	Large broad bust, elaborately decorated dress, small rose, 1562; *mm*. star	40	150
2597	— — cross pattée on *rev*., 1562, 64 *mm*. star	50	175
2598	— similar, pellet border, 1563-4	75	275
2598A	Bust with low ruff, raised rim, 1564, 1566 (both overdates)	90	325

2599 2600 2601

		F £	VF £
2599	Small bust, 1567-8, R. As 2593; *mm*. lis	50	170
2600	Large crude bust breaking legend; 1570, *mm*. lis; 1571/0, *mm*. castle (over lis)	170	575
2601	**Groat**. As illustration	110	400
2602	**Threepence**. With rose, small bust with plain dress, 1561	125	450
2603	Tall narrow decorated bust with medium rose, 1562	65	225
2604	Broad bust with very small rose, 1562	70	240
2605	Cross pattee on *rev*., 1563, 1564/3	150	475

2606

		F £	VF £
2606	**Halfgroat**. As groat	100	375

		F £	VF £
2607	**Threefarthings**. E . D . G . ROSA, etc., with rose. R. CIVITAS LONDON, shield with 1563 above	1250	3500

Portcullis money

Trade coins of 8, 4, 2, and 1 Testerns were coined at the Tower Mint in 1600/1 for the first voyage of the incorporated 'Company of Merchants of London Trading into the East Indies'. The coins bear the royal arms on the obverse and a portcullis on the reverse and have the *mm*. **O**. They were struck to the weights of the equivalent Spanish silver 8, 4, 2 and 1 reales.

2607A

2607A	Eight testerns	1000	2500

2607B

2607B	Four testerns	525	1250

2607C

2607D

2607C	Two testerns	500	1200
2607D	One testern	425	950

THE HOUSE OF STUART, THE COMMONWEALTH, AND THE HOUSE OF ORANGE, 1603-1714

JAMES I, 1603-25

With the accession of James VI of Scotland to the English throne, the royal titles and coat of arms are altered on the coinage; on the latter the Scottish rampant lion and the Irish harp now appear in the second and third quarters. In 1604 the weight of the gold pound was reduced and the new coin became known as the 'Unite'. Fine gold coins of 23 c. 3 $^{1}/_{2}$ carat and crown gold of 22 c. were both issued, and a gold four-shilling piece was struck 1604-19. In 1612 all the gold coins had their values raised by 10%; but in 1619 the Unite was replaced by a new, lighter 20s. piece, the 'Laurel', and a lighter rose-ryal, spur-ryal and angel were minted.

In 1613 the king granted Lord Harington a licence to coin farthings of copper as a result of repeated public demands for a low value coinage; this was later taken over by the Duke of Lennox. Towards the end of the reign coins made from silver sent to the mint from the Welsh mines had the Prince of Wales's plumes inserted over the royal arms.

Mintmarks

First coinage

1603-4 Thistle (125)
1604-5 Lis (105)

Second coinage

1604-5 Lis (105)
1605-6 Rose (33)
1606-7 Escallop (79)
1607 Grapes (84)
1607-9 Coronet (74)
1609-10 Key (90)
1610-11 Bell (60)
1611-12 Mullet (25)
1612-13 Tower (71)
1613 Trefoil (45)
1613-15 Cinquefoil (32)
1615-16 Tun (123)
1616-17 Book on lectern (132)
1617-18 Crescent (72b, gold)
1618-19 Plain cross (7a)
1619 Saltire cross (16, gold)

Third coinage

1619-20 Spur rowel (24)
1620-1 Rose (33)
1621-3 Thistle (125)
1623-4 Lis (105)
1624 Trefoil (46)

GOLD

First coinage, 1603-4 (Obverse legend reads D' . G' . ANG : SCO : etc.)

		F £	*VF* £
2608	**Sovereign** (20s.). King crowned r., half-length, first bust with plain armour. R. EXVRGAT, etc.; *mm.* thistle	750	1800
2609	— second bust with decorated armour; *mm.* thistle, lis	800	1850

2610

2612

2610	**Half-sovereign**. Crowned bust r. R. EXVRGAT, etc.; *mm.* thistle	1500	4000
2611	**Crown**. Similar. R. TVEATVR, etc.; *mm.* 125, 105/125	950	2750
2612	**Halfcrown**. Similar; *mm.* thistle, lis	500	1250

N.B. *The Quarter-Angel of this coinage is considered to be a pattern (possibly a later strike), although coin weights are known.*

Second coinage, 1604-19 (Obverse legend reads D' G' MAG : BRIT : etc.)

2613

2614

2613	**Rose-ryal** (30s., 33s. from 1612). King enthroned. R. Shield on rose; *mm.* 33-90, 25-132	1000	2650
2614	**Spur ryal** (15s., 16s. 6d. from 1612). King in ship; *mm.* 33, 79, 74, 25-32, 132	1850	5250
2615	**Angel** (10s., 11s. from 1612). Old type but larger shield; *mm.* 33-74, 60-16	650	1600
2616	—— pierced for use as touch-piece	325	700
2617	**Half-angel** (5s., 5s. 6d. from 1612). Similar; *mm.* 71-132, 7a, 16	1450	4000

		F £	*VF* £
2618	**Unite** (20s., 22s. from 1612). Half-length second bust r. R. FACIAM etc.; *mm.* lis or rose	325	700
2619	— fourth bust; *mm.* rose to cinquefoil	300	650

2620

2622

2624

2620	— fifth bust; *mm.* cinquefoil to saltire	300	650
2621	**Double-crown**. Third bust r. R. HENRICVS, etc.; *mm.* lis or rose	250	525
2622	Fourth bust; *mm.* rose to bell	250	500
2623	Fifth bust; *mm.* key, mullet to saltire	225	475
2624	**Britain crown**. First bust r.; *mm.* lis to coronet	165	350
2625	Third bust; *mm.* key to cinquefoil	165	350
2626	Fifth bust; *mm.* cinquefoil to saltire	150	325

2627

2627	**Thistle crown** (4s.). As illus.; *mm.* lis to plain cross	165	375
2628	— IR on only one side or absent both sides; *mm.* 79, 74, 71-123	180	400
2629	**Halfcrown**. I' D' G' ROSA SINE SPINA. First bust; *mm.* lis to key	145	285
2630	Third bust; *mm.* key to trefoil, trefoil/tower	145	285
2631	Fifth bust; *mm.* cinquefoil to plain cross	140	275

Third coinage, 1619-25

2632	**Rose-ryal** (30s.; 196 1/2 grs.). King enthroned. R. XXX above shield; lis, lion and rose emblems around; *mm.* 24, 125, 105	1250	3750
2633	Similar but plain back to throne; *mm.* trefoil	1350	4250

2634

2635

		F £	VF £
2634	**Spur-ryal** (15s.). As illus. R. Somewhat like 2614, but lis are also crowned. *mm.* 24-125, 46	1750	5000
2635	**Angel** (10s.) of new type; *mm.* 24-46	800	1850
2636	— pierced for use as touch-piece	350	850
2637	**Laurel** (20s.; 140 1/2 gr.). First (large) laur, bust l.; *mm.* 24, 24/-	325	725
2638	Second, medium, square headed bust, `SS' tie ends; *mm.* 24, 33	300	600
2638A	Third, small rounded head, ties wider apart; *mm.* 33, 125	250	525

2638B

		F £	VF £
2638B	Fourth head, very small ties; *mm.* 105, 46	250	500
2638C	Fourth head variety, tie ends form a bracket to value; *mm.* lis	275	550
2639	Fifth, small rather crude bust; *mm.* trefoil	750	2000

2640

2641A

		F £	VF £
2640	**Half-laurel**. First bust; *mm.* spur rowel	300	650
2641	— As 2638A; *mm.* rose	300	650
2641A	— As 2638B; *mm.* 33-46, 105/-	225	450
2642	**Quarter-laurel**. Bust with two loose tie ends; *mm.* 24-105	135	275
2642A	Bust as 2638C; *mm.* 105, 46, 105/46	135	275

2642B

		F £	VF £
2642B	As last but beaded, i.c. on *rev.* or both sides; *mm.* 105, 46	140	300

Rev. mm. on 1/2 and 1/4 laurels normally follows REGNA.

SILVER

2643

First coinage, 1603-4

		F	VF
2643	**Crown**. King on horseback. R. EXVRGAT, etc., shield; *mm.* thistle, lis	625	1400
2644	**Halfcrown**. Similar	500	1650

2645

2646

		F	VF
2645	**Shilling**. First bust, square-cut beard. R. EXVRGAT, etc.; *mm.* thistle	80	350
2646	— Second bust, beard merges with collar; *mm.* thistle, lis	50	180
2647	**Sixpence**. First bust; 1603; *mm.* thistle	40	160

2649

2650

2651

		F £	VF £
2648	Second bust; 1603-4; *mm.* thistle, lis	30	125
2649	**Halfgroat**. As illustration 2650 but II; *mm.* thistle, lis	20	60
2650	**Penny**. First bust I behind head; *mm.* thistle, lis ?	45	125
2650A	— Second bust; *mm.* thistle, lis	15	45
2651	**Halfpenny**. As illustration; *mm.* thistle, lis	15	40

Second coinage, 1604-19

		F	VF
2652	**Crown**. King on horseback. R. QVAE DEVS, etc. *rev.* stops; *mm.* 105-84	475	1100

2653

		F	VF
2653	**Halfcrown**. Similar; *mm.* 105-79	850	2500
2654	**Shilling**. Third bust, beard cut square and stands out (*cf.* illus. 2657); *mm.* lis, rose	45	165
2655	— Fourth bust, armour plainer (*cf.* 2658); *mm.* 33-74, 90 over 74, or 60 over 74	45	170

2656

		F	VF
2656	— Fifth bust, similar, but hair longer; *mm.* 74-7a (several bust varieties)	50	180

2657

2658

		F	VF
		£	£
2657	**Sixpence**. Third bust; 1604-6; *mm*. lis, rose, escallop	35	120
2658	— Fourth bust; 1605-16; *mm*. rose to book, 90/60, 25/60	35	125
2658A	— Fifth bust, 1618; *mm*. plain cross	700	1650
2659	**Halfgroat**. As illus. but larger crown on *obv*.; *mm*. lis to coronet	15	45

2660

2663

2660	—— Similar, but smaller crown on *obv*.; *mm*. coronet to plain cross	15	45
2660A	As before, but TVEATVR legend both sides; *mm*. plain cross over book?	50	125
2661	**Penny**. As halfgroat but no crowns; *mm*. 105-32,7a and none, -/84, 32/-	15	35
2662	— As before but TVEATVR legend both sides; *mm*. mullet	40	100
2663	**Halfpenny**. As illus.; *mm*. 105- 25, 32; 132; all *mms* on *rev*. only	15	35

Third coinage, 1619-25

2664	**Crown**. As 2652, with plain or grass ground line, colon stops on *obv*., no stops on *rev*.; *mm*. 33-46	275	675

2665

2665	— — plume over shield; *mm*. 125-46	350	850

2666

		F £	VF £
2666	**Halfcrown**. As 2664 but normally plain ground line only; all have bird-headed harp; *mm*. 33-46	120	325
2666A	— — Similar but no ground line; *mm*. rose	400	950

2667

2669

		F £	VF £
2667	— — Plume over shield; groundline *mm*. 125-46	275	700
2668	**Shilling**. Sixth (large) bust, hair longer and very curly; *mm*. 24-46	65	200
2669	— — plume over shield; *mm*. 125-46	125	425

2670

2672

		F £	VF £
2670	**Sixpence**. Sixth bust; 1621-4; *mm*. 33-46; 1621/0, *mm*. rose	35	125
2671	**Halfgroat**. As 2660 but no stops on *rev*.; *mm*. 24-46 and none, 105 and 46, 46/- *mm*. 24 with *rev*. stops known	15	35
2671A	Similar but no inner circles; *mm*. lis, trefoil over lis	20	45
2672	**Penny**. As illus.; *mm*. 24, 105, two pellets, none, trefoil,	15	30
2672A	— Similar but without inner circles on one or both sides; *mm*. lis, two pellets	15	35
2673	**Halfpenny**. As 2663, but no *mm*.	15	30

COPPER

For further details see C. Wilson Peck, *English Copper, Tin and Bronze Coins in the British Museum, 1558-1958.*

2674

2675

2676

		F £	*VF* £
2674	**Farthing**. 'Harington', small size. 1a, (originally tinned surface). Mintmark on or below cushion of crown. *mm:* A, B, C, D, F, S, Ermine, Millrind, Pellet, :<	30	60
2675	— — 1b, (occasionally tinned surface). Mintmark replaces central jewel on circlet of crown. *mm:* Trefoil, Crescent, Mullet or crown unmodified	35	70
2676	— 2, normal size, mintmark on reverse only; *mm.* Cinquefoil, Cross saltire, Lis, Martlet, Mullet, Trefoil	20	40
2677	'Lennox'. 3a; mintmark on reverse only; *mm.* Bell, Tower	20	40

2678

2679

2680

2678	— 3b; *mm.* mintmark both sides; *mm:* Flower, Fusil	8	20
2679	— — 3c; mintmark on obverse only; *mm.* Annulet, Bell, Coronet, Crescent, Cross flory fitchée, Cross patée fourchée, Dagger, Eagle's head, Fusil, Grapes, Key, Lion passant, Mascle, Quatrefoil, Rose (double), Star, Star (pierced), Thistlehead, Trefoil, Triangle, Triangle (pellet below), Tun, Woolpack	8	20
2680	— — 3d; las 3c but with larger crowns; *mm:* A, Dagger, Fusil, Lion rampant, Lis (three), Mascle, Stirrip, Trefoil, Triangle, Tun	8	20
2681	— 4; oval flan, legend starts at bottom left; *mm:* Cross patée. Originally issued for use in Ireland.	50	100

2681

Numismatically, this reign is one of the most interesting. Some outstanding machine-made coins were produced by Nicholas Briot, a French die-sinker, but they could not be struck at sufficient speed to supplant hand-hammering methods. In 1637 a branch mint was set up at Aberystwyth to coin silver extracted from the Welsh mines. After the king's final breach with Parliament the parliamentary government continued to issue coins at London with Charles's name and portrait until the king's trial and execution. The coinage of copper farthings continued to be manufactured privately under licences held first by the Duchess of Richmond, then by Lord Maltravers and later by various other persons. The licence was finally revoked by Parliament in 1644.

During the Civil War coins were struck at a number of towns to supply coinage for those areas of the country under Royalist control. Many of these coins have an abbreviated form of the 'Declaration' made at Wellington, Shropshire, Sept., 1642, in which Charles promised to uphold the Protestant Religion, the Laws of England and the Liberty of Parliament. Amongst the more spectacular pieces are the gold triple unites and the silver pounds and half-pounds struck at Shrewsbury and Oxford, and the emergency coins, some made from odd-shaped pieces of silver plate during the sieges of Newark, Scarborough, Carlisle and Pontefract.

Mintmarks

Tower Mint under Charles I

1625	Lis (105)	1633-4	Portcullis (107)
1625-6	Cross Calvary (10)	1634-5	Bell (60)
1626-7	Negro's head (96)	1635-6	Crown (75)
1627-8	Castle (71)	1636-8	Tun (123)
1628-9	Anchor (57)	1638-9	Anchor (57)
1629-30	Heart (88)	1639-40	Triangle (119a)
1630-1	Plume (101)	1640-1	Star (23)
1631-2	Rose (35)	1641-3	Triangle in circle (119b)
1632-3	Harp (87)		

Tower Mint under Parliament

1643-4	P in brackets (98)
1644-5	R in brackets (112)
1645	Eye (81)
1645-6	Sun (120)
1646-8	Sceptre (109)

Mint mark no. 57 maybe upright, inverted, or horizontal to left or right.

Briot's Mint

1631-2	Flower and B (59)	1638-9	Anchor (57)
1632	**B**		Anchor and B (58)
			Anchor and mullet (58v)

On mint mark no. 58 the 'B' below the anchor is usually shown as

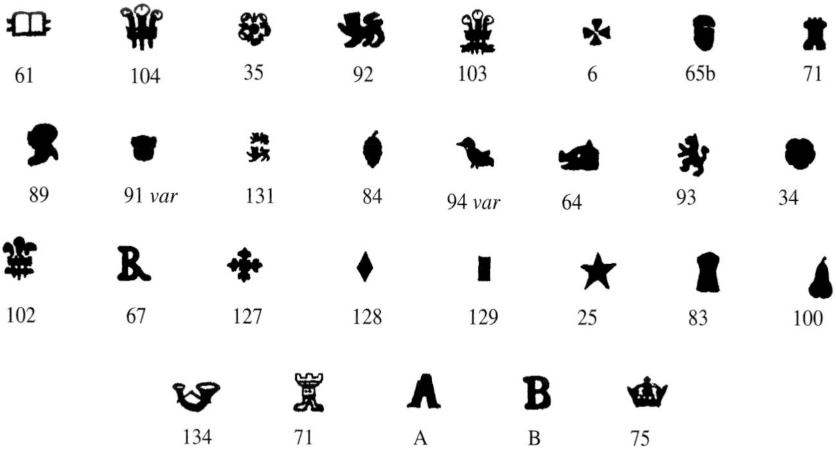

Provincial Mints

1638-42	Book (61, *Aberystwyth*)
1642	Plume (104, *Shrewsbury*)
	Pellets or pellet (*Shrewsbury*)
1642-3	Rose (35, *Truro*)
	Bugle (134, *Truro*)
1642-4	Lion (92, *York*)
1642-6	Plume (103, *Oxford*)
	Pellet or pellets (*Oxford*)
	Lis (105, *Oxford*)
1643	Cross pattee (6, *Bristol*)
	Acorn (65b, *Bristol*)
	Castle (71, *Worcester* or *Shrewsbury*)
	Helmet (89, *Worcester* and *Shrewsbury*)
1643-4	Leopard's head (91 *var. Worcester*)
	Two lions (131, *Worcester*)
	Lis (105, *Worcs.* or *Shrews.*)
	Bunch of grapes (84, *Worcs.* or *Shrews.*)
	Bird (94 var., *Worcs.* or *Shrews.*)
1643-4	Boar's head (64 *Worcs.* or *Shrews.*)
	Lion rampant (93, *Worcs.* or *Shrews.*)
	Rosette (34, *Worcs.* or *Shrews.*)
1643-5	Plume (102, *Bristol*)
	Br. (67, *Bristol*)
	Pellets (*Bristol*)
	Rose (35, *Exeter*)
	Rosette (34, *Oxford*)
1643-6	Floriated cross (127, *Oxford*)
1644	Cross pattee (6, *Oxford*)
	Lozenge (128, *Oxford*)
	Billet (129, *Oxford*)
	Mullet (25, *Oxford*)
1644-5	Gerb (83, *Chester*)
	Pear (100, *Worcester*)
	Lis (105, *Hereford?*)
	Castle (71, *Exeter*)
1645-6	Plume (102, *Ashby, Bridgnorth*)
1645	A (*Ashby*)
1646	B (*Bridgnorth*)
1648-9	Crown (75, *Aberystwyth Furnace*)

GOLD

Tower mint, under the King, 1625-42

Tower Gold		*F* £	*VF* £
2682	**Angel**. As for James I last issue, but *rev*. reads AMOR POPVLI etc; without mark of value; *mm*. lis and cross calvary	1100	3500
2683	— — pierced for use as touch-piece	475	1000
2684	— X in field to r.; *mm*. 96-88, 71 and 96/71, 57 and 71/57	1000	3250
2685	— — — pierced for use as touch-piece	475	1000
2686	— X in field to l.; *mm*. 96, 88, 35-23	1000	3250

2687

2687	— — — pierced for use as touch-piece	450	950
2688	**Unite** (20s.). First bust with ruff and collar of order, high double-crown. R. Square-topped shield; *mm*. lis.	300	725
2688A	— Similar, but extra garnishing to shield; *mm*. lis	325	750
2689	— Similar, but flat single-arched crown; *mm*. lis, cross calvary	300	750
2689A	R. As 2688A. *mm*. lis	350	800

2690

2690	Second bust with ruff and armour nearly concealed with scarf; R. Square-topped shield with slight garnishing *mm*. 10-88	300	700
2690A	Similar but more elongated bust, usually dividing legend. *mm*. 57-101, 88/101	275	650
2691	— As 2690A but *mm*. anchor below bust	700	1800
2691A	*Obv*. as 2690A. R. As next: *mm*. plume	650	1650
2692	Third bust, more armour visible. R. Oval shield with CR at sides; *mm*. 101, 35.	300	650
2693	Fourth bust, small lace collar with large high crown usually breaking i.c., long hair. Garter ribbon on breast. R. Oval shield with crowned CR at sides; *mm*. harp, portcullis	325	700
2693A	Similar, but unjewelled crown, within or touching i.c.; *mm*. 107-23	300	650
2694	Sixth (Briot's) bust, large lace collar. R. Similar; *mm*. 119a-119b	350	800
2695	Briot's hammered issue, (square-topped shield); *mm*. anchor	2250	6000

2696

2696A

2697

		F	*VF*
		£	£
2696	**Double-crown**. First bust. As 2688. R. Square-topped shield; *mm.* lis....	325	800
2696A	Similar to last but wider flatter double-arched crown; *mm.* 105, 10.........	275	650
*2697	Second bust. R. Similar to 2690; *mm.* 10-57	250	525
*2697A	Similar to 2690A: *mm.* 57-101	250	525
2697B	*Obv.* as last. R. As next: *mm.* plume	375	850
2698	Third bust. Flat or domed crown. R. Oval shield with CR at sides; *mm.* plume, rose	325	700
2699	Fourth bust, large head, high wide crown. R. Oval shield with crowned CR at sides; *mm.* portcullis..	275	600
2699A	— Similar to last, but flat crown, jewelled outer arch: *mm.* 87-123........	250	550
2699B	— Similar, but smaller head, unjewelled crown: *mm.* 60-57..................	250	550
2699C	— Sim. to 2699, but bust within i.c.; *mm.* bell	325	675
2700	Fifth bust (Early Aberystwyth style). R. Similar; *mm.* anchor	375	800
2700A	— (Late Aberystwyth style). R. *mm.* anchor, triangle	350	725
2701	Sixth bust. R. Normal; *mm.* 119a-119b..	300	650
2702	— R. Briot's square-topped shield; *mm.* anchor......................................	1250	3500

*For these coins inner circles are sometimes omitted on *obv.*, *rev.*, or both. *See also 2704, 2704A and 2707.*

2703

2707

2703	**Crown**. First bust with small round crown. R. Square-topped shield; *mm.* lis, cross calvary	145	325
2703A	As 2696A. *mm.* cross calvary..	150	350
2704	Second bust as 2690. R. Similar; *mm.* 10-71	140	300
2704A	As 2690A. *mm.* 57-101, 88/-, 57/-, 101/-..	140	300
2704B	As 2691. Wire line i.c.s on *rev.*..	300	650
2705	*Obv.* as 2690A. R. As next; 101, 35, 101/-	165	375
2706	Third bust. R. Oval shield with CR at sides; *mm.* plume.........................	275	625
2707	Fourth bust. R. Oval shield with crowned CR at sides; *mm.* -/87, 87-119b, 23/119a, 107/60..	150	325
2708	Fifth (Aberystwyth style) bust. R. Similar; *mm.* anchor	250	525
2709	Sixth (Briot's) bust. R. Similar; *mm.* anchor..	675	1500

Tower mint, under Parliament, 1642-9. All Charles I types

		F £	*VF* £
2710	**Unite**. Fourth bust, as 2693A; *mm*. (P), (P)/-	475	1000
2711	Sixth bust, as 2694 but crude style; *mm*. (P), (R), 119b	525	1250

2712

2712	Seventh bust, crude r style; *mm*. eye, sun, sceptre	625	1500
2713	**Double-crown**. Fourth bust, as 2699B; *mm*. eye	650	1450
2714	Fifth bust, as 2700A; *mm*. sun, sceptre	425	950
2715	Sixth bust, as 2701; *mm*. (P)	350	750
2716	Eighth, dumpy bust with single flat-arched crown; *mm*. sun	700	1600
2717	**Crown**. Fourth bust, as 2707 jewelled crown; *mm*. -/98 , 98/-, 98-120	200	450
2717A	Sim. but unjewelled crown. R. Small crude shield; *mm*. 81-109	225	475

Nicholas Briot's coinage, 1631-2

2718	**Angel**. Type somewhat as Tower but smaller and neater; *mm*. -/B	2500	6500

2719

2719	**Unite**. As illustration. R. FLORENT etc.; *mm*. flower and B/B	1250	3250
2720	**Double-crown**. Similar but X. R. CVLTORES, etc. *mm*. flower and B/B	975	2500
2720A	Similar but King's crown unjewelled: *mm*. flower and B/B, B	975	2500
2721	**Crown**. Similar; *mm*. B	1450	4500

Briots Hammered Gold: See No. 2695, 2702 and 2709

Provincial issues, 1638-49

Chester mint, 1644

2722	**Unite**. As Tower. Somewhat like a crude Tower sixth bust. R. Crowned, oval shield, crowned CR, *mm*. plume	9500	32500

Shrewsbury mint, 1642 (See also 2749)

2723	**Triple unite**, 1642. Half-length figure l holding sword and olive-branch; *mm*.: R. EXVRGAT, etc., around RELIG PROT, etc., in two wavy lines. III and three plumes above, date below	*Extremely rare*	

Oxford mint, 1642-6

		F	*VF*
		£	£
2724	**Triple unite**. As last, but *mm*. plume, tall narrow bust, 1642	2250	6250
2725	Similar, but 'Declaration' on continuous scroll, 1642-3	2750	7250
2725A	Large bust of fine style. King holds short olive branch; *mm*. small lis	7500	25000
2726	As last, but taller bust, with scarf behind shoulder, 1643, *mm*. plume	2500	6500

2727

2727	Similar, but without scarf, longer olive branch, 1643	2400	6000
2728	Similar, but OXON below 1643, rosette stops	3250	10000
2729	Smaller size, olive branch varies, bust size varies, 1644 OXON	2750	6500
2730	— Obv. as 2729, 1644 / OX	3000	7250
2731	**Unite**. Tall thin bust. R. 'Declaration' in two wavy lines, 1642; *no mm*.	800	1750
2732	— R. 'Declaration' in three lines on continuous scroll, 1642-3	825	1800
2733	Tall, well-proportioned bust. R. Similar, 1643, no *mm*.	950	2400
2734	Shorter bust, king's elbow not visible. R. Similar, 1643; *mm*. plume/-	700	1600
2735	Similar but longer olive branch curving to l. 1644 / OX; *mm*. plume	800	1750

2735A

2735A	Similar, but dumpy bust breaking lower i.c., small flan	825	1800
2736	Tall bust to edge of coin. R. Similar, 1643	1350	3500
2737	As 2734. R. 'Declaration' in three straight lines, 1644 / OX	1500	4250
2738	Similar to 2734, but smaller size; small bust, low olive branch. 1645	1250	3000
2739	— R. Single plume above 'Declaration', 1645-6 / OX; *mm*. plume, rosette, none	1250	2750
2740	**Half-unite**. 'Declaration' in three straight lines, 1642	1350	3500
2741	'Declaration' on scroll; *mm*. plume; 1642-3	1250	2750

2742

		F	VF
		£	£
2742	Bust to bottom of coin, 1643; Oxford plumes	825	1800
2743	— 1644 / OX. Three Shrewsbury plumes (neater work)	1500	3500
	Bristol mint, 1645		
*2744	**Unite**. Somewhat as 2734; Two busts known. *mm.* Br. or Br/ plumelet.; 1645	7000	18500
2745	**Half-unite**. Similar 1645	*Extremely rare*	
	Truro mint, 1642–3		
2745A	**Half-Unite**. Crowned bust l. (similar to Tower 4th bust). R. CVLT, etc., crowned shield	*Extremely rare*	
	Exeter mint, 1643–4		
2746	**Unite**. *obv.* sim. to early Oxford bust. R. FLORENT, etc., crowned oval shield between crowned CR, *mm.* rose	10000	32500
2747	— R. CVLTORES, etc., similar but no CR	9500	30000
	Worcester mint, 1643-4		
2748	**Unite**. Crude bust R. FLORENT, etc., double annulet stops, crowned oval shield, lion's paws on either side of garniture, no *mm.*	8500	27500
	Salopia (Shrewsbury) mint, 1644		
2749	**Unite.** *Obv.* bust in armour. R. Cr. shield, crowned CR. *mm.* lis/-	*Extremely rare*	
	Colchester besieged, 1648		
2750	**Ten Shillings** Gateway of castle between CR; below OBS CO L 16 S/X 48. Uniface – now considered a later concoction		
	Pontefract besieged, 1648-9. After the death of Charles I, in the name of Charles II		
2751	**Unite**. DVM : SPIRO : SPERO around CR crowned. CAROLVS : SECVИDVS : 16 48, castle, OBS on l., PC above	*Extremely rare*	
2752	**Unite.** CAROL : II, etc., around HANC : DEVS, etc. R. POST : MORTEM, etc., around castle. *Octagonal*	*Extremely rare*	

SILVER

	Tower mint, under the King, 1625-42		
2753	**Crown**. King on horseback with raised sword. 1a. Horse caparisoned with plume on head and crupper. R. Square-topped shield over long cross fourchee; *mm.* lis, cross calvary	325	750
2754	— 1b. Similar, but plume over shield, no cross; *mm.* 105, 10, 71	650	1650
2755	— 2a. Smaller horse, plume on hd. only, cross on housings, king holds sword on shoulder. R. Oval garnished shield over cross fourchee, CR above; *mm.* harp	300	675
2756	— $2b^1$. — — plume divides CR, no cross; *mm.* plume, rose	350	750
2757	— $2b^2$. — — — with cross; *mm.* harp	425	1000

2758

		F	*VF*
		£	£
2758	— 3a. Horse without caparisons. R. Oval shield without CR; *mm*. 60-23	300	700
2759	— 3b. — — plume over shield; *mm*. 107, 75, 123	325	800
2760	'Briot' horse with ground-line; *mm*. triangle in circle	2500	5500
2761	**Halfcrown**. As 2753. 1a^{1}. Rose on housings, ground-line; *mm*. lis	150	475

2761

2762	— 1a^{2}. Similar, but no rose or ground-line; *mm*. 105, 10 over 105	100	275
2762A	— —, with ground-line, *mm*. lis	325	800
2763	— 1a^{3}. As last but shield not over cross; *mm*. 10 sometimes over lis on one or both sides, 96	125	300
2763A	— Similar but only slight garnishing to shield; *mm*. 10, 71	135	350
2763B	— As 2763, light weight (204 grains as standard) *mm* 10, (usually over lis)	250	650
2765	— 1b. Heavy garnishing, plume over shield; *mm*. 105, 10, 96	450	1000
2765A	— Similar but only slight garnishing; *mm*. 96-57	450	1000
2766	— 2/1b. As 2755 but rose on housings. R. As last; *mm*. heart, plume	600	1500
2767	— 2a. As 2755. R. Flattened oval garnished shield without cross; *mm*. 101/35 plume, rose, (CR above, divided by rose (rare), lis over rose (rare), lis)	90	275
2768	— 2b. Similar, but large plume between the CR; *mm*. plume, rose	125	425
2769	— 2c. As 2a, but differently garnished oval shield with CR at sides; *mm*. harp, portcullis, 107/87	50	165
2770	— 2d. Similar, but with plume over shield; *mm*. harp	650	1750

2773

2775

		F £	VF £
2771	— 3a^{1}. No caparisons on horse, upright sword, scarf flies out from waist. R. Round garnished shield, no CR; *mm.* 60-119a, 60/75	45	140
2772	— 3b. — — plume over shield; *mm.* 107-123	110	325
2773	— 3a^{2}. — cloak flies from king's shoulder; R. Shields vary; *mm.* 123-23, 119b, 119b over 119a/119b	40	125
2774	— — — — rough ground beneath horse; R. Shields vary; *mm.* 119a, 23,	40	135
2775	— 4. Foreshortened horse, mane before chest, tail between legs; *mm.* 23, 119b	35	120

Most late Tower halfcrowns have irregular flans.

2776

2776A

		F £	VF £
2776	**Shilling**. 1. Bust in ruff, high crown, jewelled arches. R. Square-topped shield over cross fourchee; *mm.* lis, (normal weight 92.9 gr.)	60	240
2776A	— Similar but larger crown, plain inner arch; *mm.* 105, 10 over 105	50	200
2777	Similar but light weight (81.75 grs.); *mm.* 105, 10 over 105	70	250
2778	— 1b^{1}. As 2776A, but plume over shield, no cross; *mm.* 105, 10 over 105	350	950
2779	— 1a. Bust in ruff and armour concealed by scarf. R. As 2776; 10-71	60	200
2780	— — — — light weight; *mm.* cross Calvary (often extremely small XII)	65	230
2781	— 1b^{2}. As 2779, but plume over shield, no cross; *mm.* 10-101 (five bust varieties)	95	300
2781A	— — light weight 1b^{2} *mm.* 10	125	350
2782	— 1b^{3}, — — — cross; *mm.* negro's head	700	1750
2783	— 2a. More armour visible. R. Oval shield, CR above; *mm.* 35, 101, 101 over 88/101, (two bust varieties)	45	165
2784	— 2b. — — plume over shield; *mm.* 101, 35, 101 over 88/101, (three bust varieties)	120	350
2785	— 3^{1}. Bust with lace collar, (six bust varieties). R. Flattish oval shield, CR at sides; *mm.* harp, portcullis	35	135
2786	— 3^{2}. — — plume over shield; *mm.* harp (three bust varieties)	450	1250

2787

2793

		F £	VF £
2787	— 3a. — no inner circles, rounder shield without CR; *mm.* 60-123 (five bust varieties)	30	120
2788	— 3b. — — plume over shield; *mm.* 60-123 (Two bust varieties)	70	200
2789	— 4^{1}. Large Aberystwyth bust, medium or small XII. R. Square-topped shield over cross fleury; *mm.* tun, 57 over 123 (obv.) small neat cross ends	50	175
2790	— 4^{1}. var. Similar, but rounder shoulders, large XII; *mm.* 57, 119a, (cross ends vary)	35	125
2790A	— *O* as above. R As Briot hammered issue *mm* Δ over anchor	200	575
2791	— 4^{2}. Smaller Aberystwyth bust with small double-arched crown, small XII, *mm.* tun, small neat cross ends; large XII, *mm.* tun, anchor	45	170
2792	— 4^{3}. — single-arches, large XII; *mm.* 123, 57, 119a, 119b (cross ends vary)	35	125
2793	— 4^{4}. Older (Briot's style) bust, very pointed beard; *mm.* 119a-119b	30	120
2793A	— *Obv.* as last. R. As 2790A (Briot hammered). *mm.* Δ/Δ over anchor...	200	550
2794	**Sixpence**. 1. As 2776, but dated 1625-6; small bust *mm.* lis, large bust *mm.* lis. 10 (*rare*)	50	160
2794A	— Lightweight, 40.85 grains; large bust *mm* 10, 1625-6	100	325
2795	— $1a^{1}$. As 2779, but dated 1625-9; *mm.* 10-88 (busts vary)	65	200
2795A	Lightweight, 40.85 grains, 1626 *mm* 10	95	275
2796	— $1a^{2}$. — no cross, 1630; *mm.* heart, plume	165	525

2797

2799

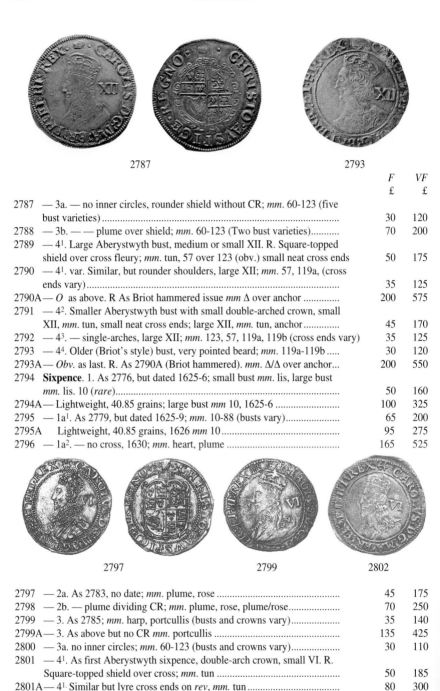

2802

		F £	VF £
2797	— 2a. As 2783, no date; *mm.* plume, rose	45	175
2798	— 2b. — plume dividing CR; *mm.* plume, rose, plume/rose	70	250
2799	— 3. As 2785; *mm.* harp, portcullis (busts and crowns vary)	35	140
2799A	— 3. As above but no CR *mm.* portcullis	135	425
2800	— 3a. no inner circles; *mm.* 60-123 (busts and crowns vary)	30	110
2801	— 4^{1}. As first Aberystwyth sixpence, double-arch crown, small VI. R. Square-topped shield over cross; *mm.* tun	50	185
2801A	— 4^{1} Similar but lyre cross ends on *rev*, *mm.* tun	80	300
2802	— 4^{1}. var. — similar, but large VI; *mm.* tun, anchor	35	140
2803	— 4^{2}. Second Aberystwyth bust, single-arched crown; *mm.* 123, 57, 119a	35	150

		F £	*VF* £
2804	— 4^{2}. larger bust, *mm.* triangle	40	165
2805	— 4^{3}. Older (Briot's style) bust; *mm.* 119a-119b (moline cross ends)	30	135

2806

2808

2818

		F £	*VF* £
2806	**Halfgroat**. 1. Crowned rose type. Beaded and/or wire line inner circles on one or both sides. *mm* 105, 105/–, 10	20	50
2807	— 1a. —— similar but without inner circles, *mm* 96–101	25	65
2808	— 2a. King's 2nd bust in ruff and mantle. R. Oval shield; *mm.* plume, rose	25	65
2809	— 2b. Similar, but with plume over shield; *mm.* plume, rose, plume/-	30	100
2809A	— — 2a Var. 3rd bust, with more armour. breaks i.c. at top. R. As last; *mm.* plume, rose	25	65
2809B	— — Sim. but plume over shield; *mm.* plume	30	100
2810	— 3^{1}. Bust with lace collar. R. Oval shield between CR; no inner circles; *mm.* rose, harp, portcullis, crown	15	45
2811	— 3^{2}. — — inner circles *mm.* harp, portcullis	15	40
2812	— 3^{3}. — — inner circle on R. *mm.* harp, portcullis	15	45
2813	— 3^{4}. — — inner circle on O. *mm.* harp, portcullis	15	45
2814	— 3^{5}. — — no CR, no inner circles; *mm.* portcullis	20	50
2815	— 3^{6}. — — — inner circles on *obv.*; *mm.* portcullis, harp	20	50
2816	— $3a^{1}$. — R. Rounder shield, different garniture, no i.cs.; *mm.* 60-119a.	15	40
2817	— $3a^{2}$. — — inner circle on *obv.*; *mm.* triangle, anchor	20	60
2818	— $3a^{3}$. — — inner circles both sides; *mm.* 119a-119b	15	45
2819	— $3a^{4}$. Aberystwyth bust, no inner circles; *mm.* anchor	30	80
2820	— $3a^{5}$. — inner circle on *rev.*; *mm.* anchor	30	85
2821	— $3a^{6}$. Very small bust, no inner circles; *mm.* anchor	40	100

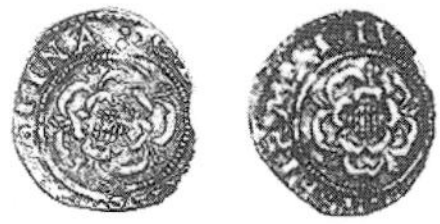

2822

2828

2831

		F £	*VF* £
2822	**Penny**. 1. Rose each side; i.cs.; *mm.* 96, :/lis, lis/:, one or two pellets, lis	12	30
2823	— 1a. — no i.cs.; *mm.* lis, one or two pellets, anchor	12	30
2824	— 1b. — i.c. on *rev.*; *mm.* negro's head/two pellets	25	80
2825	— 2. Bust in ruff and mantle. R. Oval shield; i.cs.; *mm.* plume, plume/rose, rose	20	65
2826	— 2^{1}. — — no i.cs.; *mm.* plume, rose	20	60
2827	— $2a^{1}$. More armour visible; no i.cs.; *mm.* plume, rose, plume/rose	15	50
2828	— $2a^{2}$. — i.c. on *obv.*; *mm.* plume, rose, plume over rose	15	50
2829	— $2a^{3}$. — i.cs. both sides; *mm.* plume, rose	15	50
2830	— $2a^{4}$. — i.c. on *rev.*; *mm.* rose over plume	20	60
2831	— 3^{1}. Bust in lace collar. R. CR at sides of shield; no i.cs.; *mm.* harp, one or two pellets. ··/harp (also *obv.* i.c. *mm.* harp)	12	30
2832	— 3^{2}. — similar but no CR; *mm.* 87, 107, 107/··, pellets, none	12	30
2833	— 3^{3}. — — i.c. on *obv.*; *mm.* harp,··,	12	35

		F £	*VF* £
2834	— 3^4. — — i.c. on *rev*.; *mm*. harp	15	45
2835	— $3a^1$. — similar, but shield almost round and with scroll garniture; no i.cs.; *mm*. bell, triangle, one to four pellets, none, bell/	12	30
2835A	— $3a^1$ variety — i.c. on *obv*., *rev*. or both sides; *mm*. triangle/two pellets, Δ,··,	15	45
2836	— $3a^3$. Aberystwyth bust; i.c. on *obv*. or none; *mm*. one or two pellets or triangle or none, or mule of these *mms*.	15	40

2837

2837	**Halfpenny**. Rose each side; no legend or *mm*.	15	35

Many small denominations have uneven irregular flans.

Tower mint, under Parliament, 1642-8. All Charles I type

2838	**Crown**. 4. Foreshortened horse; *mm*. (P) to sun	325	800
2839	— 5. Tall spirited horse; *mm*. sun	425	975
2840	**Halfcrown**. $3a^3$. As 2773, but coarse work; *mm*. (P) to sun, 81/120	35	125
2841	— 4. Foreshortened horse; *mm*. (P)	150	450
2842	— 5. Tall horse; *mm*. sun, sceptre	50	150
2843	**Shilling**. 4^4. Briot style bust, *mm*. (P), (R); coarse work; *mm*. eye, sun ...	30	110

2844

2845

2844	— 4^5. Long narrow coarse bust; *mm*. sun, sceptre	40	145
2845	— 4^6. Short bust with narrow crown; *mm*. sceptre	45	165

2845A

2845A	— — Short broad bust, as illus., broader crown; *mm*. sceptre	60	225
2846	**Sixpence**. 4^3. Briot style bust; *mm*. (P) (R)	70	250

2847

2848

		F	*VF*
		£	£
2847	— 4^4. Late Aberystwyth bust modified; *mm.* (P) to sceptre	50	165
2848	— 4^5. Squat bust of crude style; *mm.* eye, sun over eye	100	350
2849	**Halfgroat**. $3a^3$. Sim. to 2818; *mm.* (P) to eye, sceptre, 98/119b	20	50
2850	— $3a^7$. Older, shorter bust, pointed beard; *mm.* eye to sceptre	20	50
2851	**Penny**. $3a^2$. Older bust; *mm.* pellets, i.c. on *obv.* only	20	55

Nicholas Briot's coinage, 1631-9

First milled issue, 1631-2

2852	**Crown**. King on horseback. R. Crowned shield between CR crowned; *mm.* flower and B / B	375	1000

2853

2853	**Halfcrown**. Similar	225	650
2854	**Shilling**. Briot's early bust with falling lace collar. R. Square-topped shield over long cross fourchee; R. Legend starts at top or bottom (extr. rare) *mm.* flower and B/B, B	175	500

2855

2855	**Sixpence**. Similar, but VI behind bust; *mm.* flower and B/B, flower and B/-	75	250

Carlisle
Scarborough
York
Pontefract
Chester
Newark
Ashby-de-la-Zouch
Shrewsbury
Bridgenorth
Aberystwyth
(Dovey Furnace)
1648-9
Aberystwyth
(1638-42)
Hartlebury Castle
Worcester
Hereford
Oxford
Tower of
London
(Parliament)
Bristol
Exeter
Truro

2856

2856A

		F £	VF £
2856	**Halfgroat**. Briot's bust, B below, II behind. R. IVSTITIA, etc., square-topped shield over long cross fourchee	30	80
2856A	Pattern halfgroat. Uncrowned bust in ruff r. R. crowned, interlocked Cs. (North 2687). (Included because of its relatively regular appearance.)	30	75
2857	**Penny**. Similar, but I behind bust, B below bust; position of legend may vary	35	90

Second milled issue, 1638-9

2859

2858	**Halfcrown**. As 2853, but *mm*. anchor and B	165	450
2859	**Shilling**. Briot's late bust, the falling lace collar is plain with broad lace border, no scarf. R. As 2854 but cross only to inner circle; *mm*. anchor and B, anchor or muled	85	250
2860	**Sixpence**. Similar, but VI; *mm*. anchor, anchor and mullet/anchor	45	120

The two last often exhibit flan reduction marks.

Briot's hammered issue, 1638-9

2861	**Halfcrown**. King on Briot's style horse with ground line. R. Square-topped shield; *mm*. anchor, triangle over anchor. Also muled with Tower *rev*.	525	1400
2862	**Shilling**. Briot's first hammered issue, Sim. to 2859; R. Square-topped shield over short cross fleury, contraction stops on *obv.,* pellet stops *rev. mm.* anchor	500	1350
2862A	— Briot's second hammered issue. As 2862 but lozenge stops both sides. *mm.* anchor, triangle over anchor or triangle	275	700

Provincial and Civil War issues, 1638-49

York mint, 1643-4. *Mm*. lion

2863	**Halfcrown**. 1. Ground-line below horse. R. Square-topped shield between CR	325	900
2864	— 2. — R. Oval shield as Tower 3a, groundline grass or dotted	300	800
2865	— 3. No ground-line. R. Similar	300	800
2866	*— 4. As last, but EBOR below horse with head held low. Base metal, often very base	85	225
2867	— 5. Tall horse, mane in front of chest, EBOR below. R. Crowned square-topped shield between CR, floral spray in legend	225	600

**These pieces are contemporary forgeries (Besly, the York mint of Charles I, BNJ 54, 1984)*

2868

		F £	VF £
2868	— 6. As last, but shield is oval, garnished (*rev.* detail variations)	165	400
2869	— 7. Similar, but horse's tail shows between legs. R. Shield as last, but with lion's skin garniture, no CR or floral spray	150	375

2870

2870	**Shilling**. 1. Bust in scalloped lace collar similar to 3^1. R. EBOR above square-topped shield over cross fleury	110	325
2871	— 2. Similar, but bust in plain armour, mantle; coarse work	125	375
2872	— 3. *Obv.* as above illustration. — R. EBOR below oval shield	125	400
2873	— 4. — Similar, but crowned oval shield (*obv.* finer style)	110	325
2874	— 5. — As last, but lion's skin garniture	110	325
2875	**Sixpence**. *Obv.* Sim. to 2870. Crowned oval shield	175	525

2876

2877

2876	— — Crowned CR at sides	150	450
2877	**Threepence**. As type 1 shilling, but III behind bust. R. As 2870	35	105

Aberystwyth mint, 1638/9-42. *Mm.* book.

Plume 1=with coronet and band. Plume 2=with coronet only

2878	**Halfcrown**. Horseman similar to 2773, but plume 2 behind. R. Oval garnished shield with large plume above. *Obv.* plume 2, *rev.* plume 1. ...	450	1250
2879	— Similar to 2774, plume 1 behind King, ground below horse. *Obv.* squat plume 1, *rev.* plume 1	525	1500

		F £	*VF* £
2880	As 2773 but more spirited horse, no ground. FRAN ET HIB, plume 2/1	500	1350

2881

		F £	*VF* £
2881	**Shilling**. Bust with large square lace collar, plume 2 before, small XII. R. As before. No inner circles	200	625
2882	— inner circle on *rev*.	185	550
2883	As 2881, but large plume 1 or 2, large XII, inner circles, large or small shield	185	550

2884

		F £	*VF* £
2884	As last, but small narrow head, square lace collar, large or square plume	225	700
2885	Small Briot style face, small crown, plume 2	350	950
2885A	**Sixpence**. *Obv*. as Tower bust 3a, plume before. R. as 2889; *mm*. book (*obv*. only)	275	825

2886

		F £	*VF* £
2886	Somewhat as 2881, but double-arched crown, small VI; no inner circles	150	475
2887	Similar to 2886, but single arched crown, plume 2, inner circle *obv*. Large VI	165	550
2888	Similar, but with inner circles both sides	165	550
2889	— — *Rev*. with small squat-shaped plume above, sometimes no *rev*. *mm*.	150	500
2890	Bust as the first Oxford sixpence; with crown cutting inner circle	275	850

2891

2894

2895

No.	Description	F £	VF £
2891	**Groat**. Large bust, lace collar, no armour on shoulder. Crown breaks or touches inner circle. R. Shield, plume 1 or 2	30	90
2892	— Similar, armour on shoulder, shorter collar. R. Similar	35	100
2893	— Smaller, neater bust well within circle. R. Similar	30	85
2894	**Threepence**. Small bust, plume 2 before. R. Shield, plume 1 or 2 above, *obv.* legend variations	25	70
2895	— Similar, but crown cuts i.c. squat pl. on *obv.*, R. Pl. 2, *Obv.* legend variations	30	80
2900	**Halfgroat**. Bust as Tower type 3. R. Large plume. No inner circles, *mm.* pellet/book,book	35	100

2900A

2905

2907

No.	Description	F £	VF £
2900A	Bust as 2886. R. As last, no inner circle	45	125
2901	Bust with round lace collar; single arch crown, inner circles, colon stops	35	95
2902	After Briot's bust, square lace collar: inner circles	35	100
2903	**Penny**. As 2901; CARO; no inner circles	50	150
2904	As 2901; CARO; inner circles	45	125
2905	As last but reads CAROLVS; inner circles	55	180
2906	*Obv.* similar to 2890, tall narrow bust, crown touches inner circle	60	200
2907	**Halfpenny**. No legend. *O.* Rose. R. Plume	135	425

Aberystwyth-Furnace mint, 1648/9. *Mm.* crown

No.	Description	F £	VF £
2908	**Halfcrown**. King on horseback. R. Sim. to 2878	1350	3250
2909	**Shilling**. Aberystwyth type, but *mm.* crown	1500	4000
2910	**Sixpence**. Similar	950	2500

2911

2913

No.	Description	F £	VF £
2911	**Groat**. Similar	165	425
2912	**Threepence**. Similar	150	375
2913	**Halfgroat**. Similar. R. Large plume	225	600
2914	**Penny**. Similar	625	1500

Uncertain mint (? Hereford) 1644-5

2915

2930/1

No.	Description	F £	VF £
2915	**Halfcrown**. As illustration, dated 1645 or undated	1250	2750
2915A	— Scarf with long sash ends. CH below horse. R. Oval shield 1644	1500	4500
2915B	— R. Crowned oval shield, lion paws	1500	4500

Shrewsbury mint, 1642. Plume without band used as *mm.* or in field.

No.	Description	F £	VF £
2917	**Pound**. King on horseback, plume behind, similar to Tower grp. 3 crowns. R. Declaration between two straight lines, XX and three Shrewsbury plumes above, 1642 below; *mm.* pellets, pellets/-	1250	3000
2918	Similar, but Shrewsbury horse walking over pile of arms; no *mm.*, pellets	1100	2500
2919	As last, but cannon amongst arms and only single plume and XX above Declaration, no *mm.*	1450	3250
2920	**Half-pound**. As 2917, but X; *mm.* pellets	625	1450
2921	Similar, but only two plumes on *rev.*; *mm.*, pellets	950	2500
2922	Shrewsbury horseman with ground-line, three plumes on *rev.*; *mm.*, none, pellets/-	650	1500
2923	— with cannon and arms or arms below horse; *mm.* pellets/-	650	1500
2924	— no cannon in arms, no plume in *obv.* field; *mm.* plume/pellets, plume/-	450	975
2925	**Crown**. Aberystwyth horseman, no ground line	5250	15000

2926

No.	Description	F £	VF £
2926	Shrewsbury horseman with ground-line; *mm.* -/pellets, pellets/-, none	450	1000
2927	**Halfcrown**. *O.* From Aberystwyth die; (S2880); *mm.* book. R. Single plume above Declaration, 1642	650	1850
2928	Sim. to Aberystwyth die, fat plume behind. R. Three plumes above Declaration; *mm.* pellets, pellets/-	275	800

		F £	*VF* £
2929	Shrewsbury horseman, no ground line. R. As 2927, single plume, no *mm.*	375	1100
2929A	— — R. As 2933	300	750
2930	— R. 2: plume; 6, above Declaration	650	1750
2931	— with ground-line. R. Similar	650	1750
2932	— — R. As 2927, single plume	400	1100
2933	— — R. Three plumes above Declaration; *mm.* none or pellets	275	725
2933A	— — R. Aberystwyth die, plume over shield; *mm.* -/book	725	2250
2934	As 2933 but no plume behind king; *mm.* plume/pellets	275	650
2935	**Shilling**. *O.* From Aberystwyth die; S2885 *mm.* book. R. Declaration type	725	1750
2936	*O.* From Shrewsbury die. R. Similar	750	2000

Oxford mint, 1642-6. *Mm.* usually plume with band, except on the smaller denominations when it is lis or pellets. There were so many dies used at this mint that we can give only a selection of the more easily identifiable varieties.

For many years Oxford Halfcrowns and Shillings have been catalogued according to Morrieson obverse die varieties. In many cases, these are very small and difficult to identify. We have, therefore, simplified the obverse classification and used the available space to expand the listing of the more interesting reverse varieties.

Numbers in brackets following each entry refer to numbers employed in previous editions.

2937

		F £	*VF* £
2937	**Pound**. Large horseman over arms, no exergual line, fine workmanship. R. Three Shrewsbury plumes and XX above Declaration, 1642 below; *mm.* plume/pellets	1750	4500
2938	— Similar, but three Oxford plumes, 1643; *mm.* as last	1600	4000
2939	Shrewsbury horseman trampling on arms, exergual line. R. As last, 1642	1250	2750
2940	— — cannon amongst arms, 1642-3; *mm.* similar	1050	2250
2941	— as last but exergue is chequered, 1642; *mm.* similar	1400	3250
2942	Briot's horseman, 1643; *mm.* similar	2500	5500
2943	*O.* As 2937. R. Declaration in cartouche, single large plume above, 1644 OX below	2850	6750
2944	**Half-pound**. Shrewsbury horseman over arms, Oxford plume behind. R. Shrewsbury die, 1642; mm. plume/-	475	1100
2945	— R. Three Oxford plumes above, 1642; mm. plume/-	425	1000
2945A	— — 1643; *mm.* plume/- (2945)	450	1050

No.	Description	F £	VF £
2946	**Crown.** Shrewsbury die with groundline. R. Three Oxford plumes, 1642; no mm.	425	950
2946A	— — 1643; no *mm.* (2946)	425	950
2947	Oxford horseman, grass below. R. Three Oxford plumes, 1643; *mm.* plume/-	650	1650

2948

No.	Description	F £	VF £
2948	Rawlins' crown. King riding over a view of the city. R. Floral scrolls above and below Declaration, date in script, 1644 OXON; *mm.* floriated cross/- *(Electrotypes and copies of this coin are common)*	6000	17500
2949	**Halfcrown.** *O.* Shrewsbury die with groundline, plume behind. R. Oxford die, declaration in two lines, three Oxford plumes above, 1642 below; no *mm.*	350	900
2950	— no plume behind. R. as last, 1642; *mm.* plume/- (2949)	250	600
2951	Shrewsbury horseman with groundline, Oxford plume behind. R. Shrewsbury die, 1642; *mm.* plume/- (2950)	250	625
2952	— R. Three Oxford plumes, 1642; *mm.* plume/- (2951)	135	400
2953	— — without groundline, 1642; *mm.* plume/- (2952)	135	400

2954

No.	Description	F £	VF £
2954	Oxford horseman without groundline, 1643; *mm.* plume/-	125	350
2954A	— — R. Shrewsbury die, 1642; *mm.* plume/- or no *mm.*	250	625
2955	— with groundline. R. Three Oxford plumes, 1643; *mm.* plume/- (2953)	125	375
2956	Briot horseman, grassy, rocky or uneven ground. R. Three Oxford plumes, 1643; *mm.* plume/-, plume & rosette/- (2955, 57)	135	400
2957	— — 1643 OX; *mm.* plume/rosette, rosette (2955, 57)	150	450
2958	— — 1644 OX; *mm.* plume/- (2959, 63, 64)	150	450
2958A	— — lozenges by OX, 1644 OX; *mm.* plume/- (2959, 63, 64)	150	475

		F £	VF £
2959	— — 1645 OX; *mm.* plume/-, plume/rosette (2959, 63, 64, 66, 68)	140	425
2959A	— — pellets by date, 1645 OX; *mm.* plume/- (2967)	175	525
2960	— — 1646 OX; *mm.* plume/- (2966, 68)	150	450
2961	— — pellets or annulets by plumes and date, 1646 OX; *mm.* plume/- (2967)	165	500
2962	— R. Large central plume and two Oxford plumes, 1643; *mm.* plume/- (2956)	165	525
2963	— — 1643 OX; *mm.* plume/-, rosette/-, plume & rosette/rosette, plume & rosette/- (2956, 58)	150	450
2964	— — rosettes by OX, 1643 OX; *mm.* rosette/-, plume & rosette/- (2958)	175	550

2965 2965A

		F £	VF £
2965	— — plain, pellets or lozenges by plumes and/or OX, 1644 OX; *mm.* plume/- plume/rosette, rosette (2956, 58, 60, 65)	135	425
2965A	— — date in script, 1644 OX; *mm.* plume/- (2961)	160	500
2966	— — rosettes by plume and date, 1644 OX; *mm.* plume & rosette/rosette (2958)	185	550
2967	— — small plumes by date, 1644 OX; *mm.* plume & rosette/-, rosette (2962)	225	650
2968	— R. Large central plume and two small Shrewsbury plumes, lozenges in field, date in script, 1644 OX; *mm.* plume/rosette (2960A)	225	625
2969	— — small plumes by date, pellets by OX, 1644 OX; *mm.* plume/- (2962)	275	750
2970	**Shilling.** *O.* Shrewsbury die. R. Declaration in three lines, three Oxford plumes above, 1642; *mm.* plume/-	450	1250
2971	Oxford bust (small). R. Three Oxford plumes, 1642; *mm.* Oxford plume/-,	150	425
2972	Oxford bust (small or large). R. Three Oxford plumes, 1643; *mm.* Oxford plume/-, Oxford plume/rosette (2971, 72, 73, 75)	140	400
2972A	— — pellets by date, 1644; *mm.* plume/- (2975)	165	525
2972B	— — 1644 OX; mm. plume/rosette (2974)	150	475
2973	— R. Oxford and two Shrewsbury plumes, lozenges by date, 1644 OX; *mm.* plume/- (2976)	225	600

2974

		F £	VF £
2974	— R. Three Shrewsbury plumes, 1643; *mm.* plume/- (2972, 73)	175	500

2975

		F	*VF*
		£	£
2975	Fine Oxford bust. R. Three Oxford plumes, lozenges in field, 1644 OX; *mm.* Shrewsbury plume/- (2974)	160	475
2975A	— — large date in script, 1644 OX; *mm.* plume/- (2974A)	210	600
2976	— 1645 OX; *mm.* plume/- (2974)	700	1750
2976A	— R. Oxford and two Shrewsbury plumes, 1644 OX; *mm.* plume/- (2974)	200	575
2977	— R. Three Shrewsbury plumes, 1644 OX; *mm.* plume/- (2974)	175	500
2978	— — annulets or pellets at date, 1646; *mm.* plume/floriated cross, plume/- (2979)	165	475
2979	Rawlins' die. Fine bust with R. on truncation. R. Three Oxford plumes, rosettes or lozenges by plumes, lozenges by date, 1644 OX; *mm.* Shrewsbury plume/rosette, Shrewsbury plume/- (2978)	350	850
2979A	— — pellets by date, no OX, 1644; *mm.* plume/- (2977)	375	900
2979B	— R. Oxford and two Shrewsbury plumes, 1644 OX; *mm.* plume/- (2978)	525	1200

2980

2980	**Sixpence.** O. Aberystwyth die R. Three Oxford plumes, 1642; *mm.* book/-	185	525
2980A	— — 1643; *mm.* book/- (2980)	160	450
2981	— R. Three Shrewsbury plumes, 1643; *mm.* book/-	145	400
2982	— R. Shrewsbury plume and two lis, 1644 OX (groat rev. die); *mm.* book/-	450	1100
2983	**Groat.** *O.* Aberystwyth die. R. Shrewsbury plume and two lis, 1644 OX; *mm.* book/-	125	350
2984	— R. Three Shrewsbury plumes, 1644 OX; mm. book/-	135	375

2985

2985	Oxford bust within inner circle. R. As 2983, 1644 OX; mm. floriated cross/-	75	190

No.	Description	*F* £	*VF* £
2985A	— R. Three Shrewsbury plumes, 1644 OX; *mm.* floriated cross/-	125	350
2985B	— R. Single plume, 2 scrolls and OX monogram over Decl, 1645; *mm.* floriated cross/- (2989)	175	475
2986	Large bust to top of coin. R. As 2983, 1644 OX; *mm.* lis/-	150	425
2987	Large bust to bottom of coin. R. As 2983, 1644 OX; no *mm.*	175	475
2988	— R. Single plume, 2 scrolls and OX monogram over Decl, 1645; no *mm.* (2990)	100	365
2989	Rawlins' die, no inner circle, R on shoulder. R. As 2983, 1644 OX; no *mm.* (2988)	160	425
2990	— R. Single plume, Declaration in cartouche, 1645; no *mm.* (2991)	150	410

2990

No.	Description	*F* £	*VF* £
2991	— — 1646/5; no mm.	145	400
2992	**Threepence.** *O.* Aberystwyth die. R. Three lis over Declaration, 1644 OX; *mm.* book/-	95	275
2993	Rawlins; die, R below shoulder. R. Aberystwyth die, oval shield; *mm.* lis/book	95	275
2994	— R. Three lis over Declaration, 1644; *mm.* lis/-	60	140

2995

3000

No.	Description	*F* £	*VF* £
2995	Crown breaks inner circle, no R. R. Three lis, 1646/4; *mm.* lis/-	70	185
2996	**Halfgroat.** Small bust, beaded or wireline inner circle. R. Large plume in field; *mm.* mullet/lis, lis, -/lis	75	225
2997	— R. Three lis over Delcaration, 1644 OX; *mm.* lis	80	240
2998	**Penny.** *O.* Aberystwyth die, CARO. R. Small plume in field; *mm.* book/-	95	265
2999	Aberystwyth die, CAROLVS; R. Large plume; *mm.* book/-	100	275
3000	Rawlins' die, CARO. R. Small plume; *mm.* lis/mullet, lis/-	200	500
3001	Broad bust, CAROL. R. Small plume; *mm.* lis	185	475
3002	— R. Three lis over Declaration, 1644; *mm.* lis	600	1250

Bristol mint, 1643-5. *Mm.* usually plume or Br., except on small denominations

No.	Description	*F* £	*VF* £
3003	**Halfcrown**. *O.* Oxford die with or without ground-line. R. Declaration, three Bristol plumes above, 1643 below	275	750
3004	— Obv. as above. R as above, but *mm.* Br. 1643	300	800
3005	King wears unusual flat crown, *obv. mm.* acorn? between four pellets. R. As 3003, 1643	240	675
3006	— Obv. as above. R as 3004 but 1643-4	225	600
3007	Shrewsbury plume behind king. R. As last	170	450
3008	— Obv. as above. R as 3004 but Br below date instead of as *mm* . 1644.	175	475

3009

No.	Description	*F* £	*VF* £
3009	— Obv. as 3007 but Br below horse. R as above but 1644-5..................	170	450
3010	— Obv. as above. R as 3004 but Br. as *mm.* as well as 1644-5...............	185	500
3011	**Shilling**. *O*. Oxford die. R. Declaration, 1643, 3 crude plumes above, no *mm.*	225	575

3012

3014

No.	Description	*F* £	*VF* £
3012	— — R Similar, but *mm.* Br., 1643-4, less crude plumes........................	185	500
3013	—Obv. Coarse bust. R. As 3011, no *mm.*	250	650
3014	— — Coarse bust, R. as 3012, *mm.* Br, but 1644....................................	225	600

3015

3017

No.	Description	*F* £	*VF* £
3015	Obv. Bust of good style, plumelet before face. R. As 3012 *mm.* Br. but 1644-5	180	500
3016	— — R.as 3012, 1644, but Br below date instead of *mm.*........................	200	550
3016A	— — R as 3012, 1644 but plume and plumelet either side	175	475
3017	—Obv. Taller bust with high crown, no plumelets before, *mm.* Br. on its side. R As 3016 Br.below 1644-5	225	600
3018	—Obv. As 3017 but no *mm.* R as above but *mm..* no Br. below 1644-5..	250	675
3018A	— — R as above but plume and plumelets, 1645....................................	300	800
3019	**Sixpence**. Small bust, nothing before. R. Declaration surrounded by CHRISTO etc., 1643; *mm.* ./Br...	325	800

3020

		F £	VF £
3020	Fine style bust. Plumelet before face, 1644; *mm.* ./Br. (on its side)	150	425
3021	**Groat**. Bust l. R. Declaration, 1644	150	450
3022	— Plumelet before face, 1644	135	350
3023	— Br. below date, 1644	135	350
3023A	— Similar, but larger bust and more spread plume before. Mm. pellet/Br; nothing below 1644	140	400

3024

3026

3027

3024	**Threepence**. *O*. As 2992. Aberystwyth die; *mm.* book. R. Declaration, 1644	150	425
3025	Bristol die, plume before face, no *mm.*, 1644	225	575
3026	**Halfgroat**. Br. in place of date below Declaration	200	525
3027	**Penny**. Similar bust, I behind. R. Large plume with bands	300	750

This penny may belong to the late declaration issue. It has the same reverse plume punch as 3044.

Late 'Declaration' issues, 1645-6

(Previously given as Lundy Island and/or Appledore and Barnstaple/Bideford, it seems likely that coins marked A, 1645 may be Ashby de la Zouch and the coins marked B or plumes, 1646 may be Bridgnorth on Severn.)

3028	**Halfcrown**. A below horse and date and as *rev. mm.* 1645	1500	4000
3029	Similar but *rev.* from altered Bristol die (i.e. the A's are over Br.)	1500	4000
3030	As 3028 but without A below date 1645	1250	3750
3031	A below horse, A or B over A as (*rev. mm.*) and as *rev. mm.* Scroll above Declaration, B or nothing below 1646	1650	4500
3032	Plumelet below horse struck over A. R. *Mm.* Shrewsbury plumes; scroll above Declaration, 1646	600	1750

3033

		F £	VF £
3033	— Similar, but plumelet below date	650	1800
3034	**Shilling**. Crowned bust l., *mm.* plume. R. Declaration type; *mm.* A and A below 1645	650	1800

3035

		F £	VF £
3035	— Similar, but plumelet before face	750	2000
3036	— — Scroll above 'Declaration', 1646; *mm* plume/plumelet	275	725
3036A	— Bristol obv. die, no plumelet, similar to 3018 *mm.* Br. R. As last but *mm.* pellet. 1646.	350	900
3037	Obv as above, but Shrewsbury plume before face. plume over Br. *mm.* R. As above	300	800
3038	**Sixpence**. *O.* Plumelet before face; *mm.* A; R. 1645, 3 plumelets over 'Dec'	600	1400

3039

		F £	VF £
3039	*O.* Large Shrewsbury plume before face; *mm.* B. R. Scroll above Declaration, 1646, Shrewsbury plume and two plume plumelets	125	350
3040	**Groat**. As 3038	525	1350
3041	Somewhat similar, but *obv. mm.* plumelet; R *mm.* pellet or plume,1646 .	110	300
3042	**Threepence**. Somewhat as last but only single plumelet above Declaration, no line below, 1645; no *mm.*	325	850

		F £	VF £
3043	— Scroll in place of line above, 1646 below	110	275
3044	**Halfgroat**. Bust l., II behind. R. Large plume with bands dividing 1646; no *mm.*	400	950

Truro mint, 1642-3. *Mm.* rose except where stated

Entries for the Truro and Exeter mints have been re-ordered to follow E. Besly (BNJ 1992). They have been renumbered, as the original numbers from 3045 to 3092 (which are given in brackets) are no longer sequential.

		F £	VF £
3045	**Crown.** King on horseback, head in profile, sash flies out in two ends. R. CHRISTO, etc., round garnished shield (3048)	250	550
3046	**Halfcrown**. King on walking horse, groundline below, R. Oblong shield, CR above, *mm.* bugle/– (3048A)	850	2250
3047	Galloping horse, king holds baton. R. Oblong shield, CR at sides (3050)	1350	4000

3048

3052

		F £	VF £
3048	Walking horse, king holds sword. R. Similar (3054)	650	1600
3049	— R. Similar, but CR above (3055)	700	1650
3050	Galloping horse, king holds sword. R. Similar, but CR at sides (3051)	850	2500
3051	— R. Similar, but CR above (3052)	950	2650
3052	Trotting horse. R. Similar, but CR at sides (3053)	625	1500
3053	**Shilling**. Small bust of good style. R. Oblong shield (3056)	2000	6250

Exeter mint, 1643-6. Undated or dated 1644-6 *Mm.* rose except where stated

		F £	VF £
3054	**Half-pound**. King on horseback, face towards viewer, sash in large bow. R. CHRISTO, etc., round garnished shield. Struck from crown dies on a thick flan (3045)	*Extremely rare*	
3055	**Crown**. King on horseback, sash in large bow. R. Round garnished shield (3046)	225	500
3056	— Shield garnished with twelve even scrolls (3047)	250	600
3057	As 3055, R Date divided by *mm.* 16 rose 44 (3070)	275	675
3058	— R Date to l. of *mm.* 1644 (3071)	225	525
3059	— *mm*: rose/EX, 1645 (3072)	250	600
3060	King's sash flies out in two ends; *mm.* castle/rose, 1645 (3073)	375	900
3061	— *mm.* castle/EX, 1645 (3074)	250	575
3062	— *mm.* castle, 1645 (3075)	225	475
3063	**Halfcrown**. King on horseback, sash tied in bow. R. Oblong shield CR at sides (3062)	500	1250
3064	— R. Round shield with eight even scrolls (3063)	200	500

3065

		F £	VF £
3065	— R. Round shield with five short and two long scrolls (3064)	165	400
3066	— R. Oval shield with angular garnish of triple lines	525	1350

3067

3071

3067	Briot's horseman with lumpy ground. R. As 3064 (3067)	375	900
3068	— R. As 3065 (3069)	250	625
3069	— R. As 3066 (3068)	525	1350
3070	— R. As 3065, date to 1. of *mm.* 1644 (3079)	350	825
3071	King on spirited horse galloping over arms. R. Oval garnished shield, 1642 in cartouche below (3049)	1350	3500
3072	— R. As 3070, date to 1. of *mm.* 1644-5 (3076)	1750	5250
3073	— R. *mm.* castle, 1645 (3077)	1850	5500
3074	Short portly king, leaning backwards on ill-proportioned horse, 1644, 16 rose 44 (3078)	575	1400
3075	Horse with twisted tail, sash flies out in two ends R. As 3064 (3065)	350	825

3076

3076	— R. As 3070, date divided by *mm.* 16 rose 44, or date to 1. of *mm.* 1644-5 (3080)	275	675

		F £	*VF* £
3077	— R. *mm*. castle, 1645 (3081)	375	900
3078	— R. *mm*. EX, 1645 (3082)	350	850
3079	— R. Declaration type; *mm*. EX. 1644-5 (3083)	1250	3250
3080	— R. Similar, EX also below declaration, 1644 (3084)	1200	3000
3081	**Shilling.** Large Oxford style bust. R. Round shield with eight even scrolls (3057)	750	1850
3082	— R. Oval shield with CR at sides (3058)	700	1750
3083	Normal bust with lank hair. R. As 3081 (3060)	600	1250
3083A	— R. As 3082 (3059)	650	1500
3084	— R. Round shield with six scrolls (3061)	425	950

3085

3087A

3085	— R. Similar, date 1644, 45 to left of rose *mm.* 16 rose 44 (rare), 1644 to right of rose (very rare)	225	600
3086	— R. Declaration type, 1645	800	1850
3087	**Sixpence**. Similar to 3085, large bust and letters 1644 rose	200	550
3087A	— Smaller bust and letters from punches used on 3088, small or large VI, 16 rose 44	200	525
3088	**Groat**. Somewhat similar but 1644 at beginning of *obv.* legend	85	180

3089

3091

3092

3089	**Threepence**. Similar. R. Square shield, 1644 above	95	225
3090	**Halfgroat**. Similar, but II. R. Oval shield, 1644	150	400
3091	— R. Large rose, 1644	165	425
3092	**Penny**. As last but I behind head	275	675

Worcester mint 1643-4

3093	**Halfcrown**. King on horseback l., W below; *mm*. two lions. R. Declaration type 1644 altered from 1643 Bristol die; *mm*. pellets	850	2000
3094	— R. Square-topped shield; *mm*. helmet, castle	575	1500
3095	— R. Oval shield; *mm*. helmet	625	1600

3096

		F £	*VF* £
3096	Similar but grass indicated; *mm.* castle. R. Square-topped shield; *mm.* helmet or pellets.	550	1450
3097	— R. Oval draped shield, lis or lions in legend	625	1600
3098	— R. Oval shield CR at sides, roses in legend	625	1650
3099	— R. FLORENT etc., oval garnished shield with lion's paws each side.	675	1750
3100	Tall king, no W or *mm.* R. Oval shield, lis, roses, lions or stars in legend	525	1400
3101	— R. Square-topped shield; *mm.* helmet	575	1500
3102	— R. FLORENT, etc., oval shield; no *mm.*	625	1600
3103	Briot type horse, sword slopes forward, ground-line. R. Oval shield, roses in legend; *mm.* 91v, 105, none (combinations)	625	1650
3104	— Similar, but CR at sides, 91v/-	675	1700
3105	Dumpy, portly king, crude horse. R. As 3100; *mm.* 91v, 105, none	625	1600

3106

3106	Thin king and horse. R. Oval shield, stars in legend; *mm.* 91v, none	525	1400

Worcester or Salopia (Shrewsbury) 1643-4

3107	**Shilling**. Bust of king l., adequately rendered. R. Square-topped shield; *mm.* castle	900	2400
3108	— R. CR above shield; *mm.* helmet and lion	900	2400
3109	— R. Oval shield; *mm.* lion, pear	800	2000
3110	— Bust a somewhat crude copy of last (two varieties); *mm.* bird, lis. R. Square-topped shield with lion's paws above and at sides; *mm.* boar's head, helmet	950	2650

3111

		F	VF
		£	£
3111	— — CR above	950	2650
3112	— R. Oval shield, lis in legend; *mm.* lis	800	2200
3113	— R. Round shield; *mm.* lis, 3 lis	800	2000
3114	Bust r.; *mm.* pear/-, pear/lis. R. draped oval shield with or without CR. (Halfcrown reverse dies)	1650	4500
3115	**Sixpence**. As 3110; *mm.* castle, castle/boar's hd	750	2000

3116

3117

3116	**Groat**. As 3112; *mm.* lis/helmet, rose/helmet	425	950
3117	**Threepence**. Similar; *mm.* lis	225	500
3118	**Halfgroat**. Similar; *mm.* lis (*O.*) various (R.)	425	975

Salopia (Shrewsbury) mint, 1644

3119	**Halfcrown**. King on horseback l. SA below; *mm.* lis. R. (*mm.* lis, helmet, lion rampant, none). Cr. oval shield; CHRISTO etc. *mm.* helmet	2250	6250
3120	— R. FLORENT, etc., crowned oval shield, no *mm.*	2250	6250
3121	— SA erased or replaced by large pellet or cannon ball; *mm.* lis in legend, helmet. R. As 3119	1350	3250
3122	Tall horse and king, nothing below; *mm.* lis. R. Large round shield with crude garniture; *mm.* helmet	650	1600
3123	— R. Uncrowned square-topped shield with lion's paw above and at sides; *mm.* helmet	700	1750
3124	— R. Small crowned oval shield; *mm.* various	600	1450

3125

		F	VF
		£	£
3125	— R. As 3120	650	1600
3126	Finer work with little or no mane before horse. R. Cr. round or oval shield	725	1750
3127	Grass beneath horse. R. Similar; *mm.* lis or rose	850	2000
3128	Ground below horse. R. As 3120	900	2250

Hartlebury Castle (Worcs.) mint, 1646

3129

3129 **Halfcrown**. *O. Mm.* pear. R. HC (Hartlebury Castle) in garniture below shield; *mm.* three pears ... 900 2250

Chester mint, 1644

3130

3130 **Halfcrown**. As illus. R. Oval shield; *mm.* three gerbs and sword ... 550 1350

3131 — Similar, but without plume or CHST; R. Cr. oval shield with lion skin;

		F £	VF £
	mm. prostrate gerb; -/cinquefoil, -/∴.	600	1500
3132	— R. Crowned square-topped shield with CR at sides both crowned *rev.*; *mm.* cinquefoil	850	2250
3133	As 3130, but without plume or CHST. R. Declaration type, 1644 *rev.*; *mm.* plume	825	2000
3133A	**Shilling**. Bust l. R. Oval garnished shield; *mm.* ∴ (obv. only)	850	2250
3133B	— R. Square-topped shield; *mm.* as last	950	2500
3133C	— R . Shield over long cross	950	2500
3134	**Threepence**. R. Square-topped shield; *mm.*-/ prostrate gerb	850	2000

Welsh Marches mint? 1644

3135

3135	**Halfcrown**. Crude horseman, l. R. Declaration of Bristol style divided by a dotted line, 3 plumes above, 1644 below	675	1500

Carlisle besieged, 1644-5

3136	**Three shillings**. Large crown above C R between rosettes III. S below. *rev.* OBS . CARL / . 1645, rosette below	3250	7500

3137

3139

3137	Similar but :- OBS :/-: CARL :./.1645, rosette above and below	3000	7250
3138	**Shilling**. Large crown above C R between trefoil of pellets, XII below. *rev.* as 3136	2250	5500
3139	R. Legend and date in two lines	2500	6500

Note. *(3136-39) Round or Octagonal pieces exist.*

Newark besieged, several times 1645-6, surrendered May 1646

3140 3144

3140	**Halfcrown**. Large crown between CR ; below, XXX. *rev.* OBS / NEWARK / 1645 or 1646	375	850
3141	**Shilling**. Similar but crude flat shaped crown, NEWARKE, 1645	350	750
3142	Similar but normal arched crown, 1645	325	700
3143	— NEWARK, 1645 or 1646	325	700
3144	**Ninepence**. As halfcrown but IX, 1645 or 1646	300	600
3145	— NEWARKE, 1645	325	650

3146

3146	**Sixpence**. As halfcrown but VI, 1646	350	700

Pontefract besieged, June 1648-March 1648-9

3147 **Two shillings** (lozenge shaped). DVM : SPIRO : SPERO around CR crowned. R. Castle surrounded by OBS, PC, sword and 1648 .... *Extremely rare*

3148

3148 **Shilling** (lozenge shaped, octagonal or round). Similar 800 1800

3149

3150

3149 — Similar but XII on r. dividing PC 750 1650

After the death of Charles I (30 Jan. 1648/9), in the name of Charles II

3150 **Shilling** (octagonal). *O*. As last. R. CAROLVS : SECVИDVS : 1648, castle gateway with flag dividing PC, OBS on l., cannon protrudes on r........... 800 1800

3151 CAROL : II : etc., around HANC : DE / VS : DEDIT 1648. R. POST : MORTEM : PATRIS : PRO : FILIO around gateway etc. as last............ 900 2000

Scarborough besieged, July 1644-July 1645

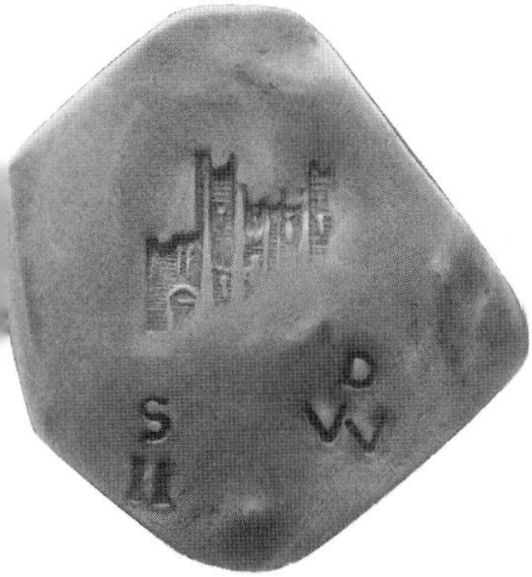

3156

3165

3169

Type I. Large Castle with gateway to left, SC and value Vs below

3152	**Crown.** (various weights)	15000

Type II. Small Castle with gateway, no SC, value punched on flan

3153	**Five shillings and eightpence.**	9500
3154	**Crown.** Similar	14000
3155	**Three shillings.** Similar	9000
3156	**Two shillings and tenpence.** Similar	8500
3157	**Two shillings and sevenpence.** Similar	8500
3158	**Halfcrown.** Similar	12000
3159	**Two shillings and fourpence.** Similar	8250
3161	**One shilling and ninepence.** *Struck from a different punch, possibly of later manufacture*	
3162	**One shilling and sixpence.** Similar to 3159	7000
3163	**One shilling and fourpence.** Similar	7000
3164	**One shilling and threepence.** Similar	7000
3165	**Shilling.** Similar	9500
3166	**Sixpence.** Similar	9000
3167	**Groat.** Similar	6250

Type III. Castle gateway with two turrets, value punched below

3168	**Two shillings and twopence**	6000
3169	**Two shillings.** Castle punched twice	6250
3170	**One shilling and sixpence.** Similar to 3168	5500
3171	**One shilling and fourpence.** Similar	5500
3172	**One shilling and threepence.** Similar	5500
3173	**One shilling and twopence.** Similar	5250
3174	**One shilling and one penny.** Similar	5250
3175	**Shilling.** Similar	7000
3176	**Elevenpence.** Similar	5000
3177	**Tenpence.** Similar	5000
3178	**Ninepence.** Similar	5000
3178A	**Eightpence.** Similar	4500
3179	**Sevenpence.** Similar	4500
3180	**Sixpence.** Similar	6500

COPPER

For further details see C. Wilson Peck, *English Copper, Tin and Bronze Coins in the British Museum, 1558-1958.*

3181

3183

		F £	*VF* £
3181	**Royal farthing**. 'Richmond' 1a, colon stops, CARO over IACO; *mm.* on *obv.* only; *mm:* Coronet, Crescent with mullet, Dagger, Mascle	8	20
3182	— — 1b, CARA; (Contemporary forgeries manufactured from official punches. Usually F for E in REX *mm.* on *obv.* only; *mm:* Annulet, Coronet, Cross patée fourchée, Dagger, Fusil, Key, Mascle, Trefoil, Tun	75	150
3183	— — 1c. CARO; *mm.* on *obv.* only; *mm:* A, A with pellet, Annulet, Annulet with pellet within, Bell, Book, Cinquefoil, Crescent (large and small), Cross (pellets in angles), Cross calvary, Cross patée, Cross patée fitchée, Cross patonce, Cross patonce in saltire, Cross saltire, Dagger, Ermine, Estoile, Estoile (pierced), Eye, Fish hook, Fleece, Fusil, Fusils (two), Gauntlet, Grapes, Halberd, Harp, Heart, Horseshoe, Leaf, Lion passant, Lis (large), Lis (demi), Lis (three), Martlet, Mascle with pellet within, Nautilus, Rose (single), Shield, Spearhead, Tower, Trefoil, Woolpack, Woolpack over annulet	6	18

3184

3185

3184	— — 1d, apostrophe stops, eagle-headed harp, *mm.* on *obv.* only; *mm:* Crescent (large), Lion rampant, Rose (double), Trefoil	10	20
3185	— 1e. Beaded harp, *mm* Rose (double) on *obv.* only	8	20

3186

3186	— 1f. Scroll-fronted harp, 5 jewels on circlet *mm* Rose (double) on *obv.* only	12	35
3187	— 1g. Scroll-fronted harp, 7 jewels on circlet *mm* Rose (double) on *obv.* only	6	18

3187A

		F £	VF £
3187A	— 1g on uncut square flan	150	300
	— Longer strips of two to nine farthings also exist	*Extremely Rare*	

3188

3192

		F £	VF £
3188	Transitional issue 2, double-arched crowns *mm* on *obv.* only; *mm:* Harp, Quatrefoil	18	45
3189	'Maltravers' 3a; inner circles *mm.* on *obv.* only; *mm:* Bell, Rose (double) Woolpack	18	45
3190	— 3b. *mm.* both sides; *mm:* Bell, Cross patée, Lis (large), Lis (small), Martlet, Rose (double), Woolpack	7	20
3191	— 3c. Different *mm.* on each side; *mm:* Bell/Cross patée fitchée, Cross patée fitchée/Bell, Harp/Bell, Harp/billet, Harp/Woolpack, Lis/Portcullis Martlet/Bell, Woolpack/Portcullis, Woolpack/Rose (double).	6	18
3192	'Richmond' oval. 4a. CARO over IACO; legend starts at bottom left, *mm:* Cross patéee on both sides.	45	90
3193	— 4a, *mm.* Cross patée on *obv.* only	45	90

3194

3200

		F £	VF £
3194	— 4b. CARO, colon stops; *mm.* Lis (demi) on *obv.* only	30	50
3195	— — — *mm.* on *rev.* only; *mm:* Martlet, Millrind	30	50
3196	— — — *mm.* on both sides; *mm:* Crescent/Crescent, Scroll/Scroll, 9/9, Lis (demi)/Scroll	30	50
3197	— 4c. apostrophe stops; *mm.* Rose (double) on *obv.* only	30	60
3198	— — — *mm.* Rose (double) both sides	45	80
3199	— — — *mm.* Rose (double) on *obv.*; Scroll on *rev.*	30	60
3200	'Maltravers' oval. 5, no inner circles, legend starts bottom left, *mm.* Lis (large) on both sides	45	80

3192 to 3200, the oval farthings, were originally issued for use in Ireland

		F	*VF*
		£	£
3201	**Rose farthing**. 1a. Double-arched crowns; sceptres within inner circle, BRIT; *mm.* on *obv.* or *rev.* or both; *mm:* Lis, Cross pattée	12	25
3202	— 1b. similar but sceptres just cross inner circle, BRIT; *mm.* Lis on *obv.* or both sides or not present.	10	20
3203	— 1c. similar but sceptres almost to outer circle, BRIT; *mm.*s as 3201 ...	12	25

3204

3207

3204	— 1d. similar but BRI; *mm.* on *obv.* or *rev.* or both sides or different each side; *mm:* Lis, Mullet, Cross pattée	10	20
3205	Transitional mules of 1d or (rarely) 1c and 2, double and single arched crowns; *mm.* as 3204; *mm:* Lis, Mullet, Crescent	6	18
3206	— 2. Single-arched crowns; *mm.* as 3204	4	12
3207	— 3. Sceptres below crown; *mm.* Mullet on both sides	30	50

The coins struck during the Commonwealth have inscriptions in English instead of Latin which was considered to savour of too much popery. St. George's cross and the Irish harp take the place of the royal arms. The silver halfpenny was issued for the last time. Coins with *mm.* anchor were struck during the protectorship of Richard Cromwell.

Mintmarks

1649-57 Sun  1658-60 Anchor 

GOLD

3208 3209

	F £	*VF* £		*F* £	*VF* £
3208 **Unite.** As illustration; *mm.* sun,					
1649	525	1200	1654	500	1100
1650	525	1200	1655	850	2000
1651	475	1000	1656	650	1450
1652	500	1100	1657	575	1350
1653	475	975			
3209 Similar, *mm.* anchor,					
1658	*Extremely Rare*		1660	1350	3250
3210 **Double-crown.** Similar; but X; *mm.* sun,					
1649	450	1000	1654	450	1000
1650	400	900	1655	*Extremely Rare*	
1651	375	800	1656	650	1500
1652	475	1100	1657	*Extremely Rare*	
1653	375	800			
3211 Similar, *mm.* anchor, 1660				1250	3000

3212

	F £	*VF* £		*F* £	*VF* £
3212 **Crown.** Similar, but V; *mm.* sun,					
1649	400	850	1654	375	800
1650	350	750	1655	*Extremely Rare*	
1651	375	800	1656	*Extremely Rare*	
1652	350	750	1657	650	1450
1653	350	750			

F £	VF £		F £	VF £
3213 Similar *mm.* anchor,					
1658	1250	3250	1660	Extremely rare	

SILVER

3215

3214 **Crown.** Same type; *mm.* sun,					
1649	1350	3500	1653	400	750
1651	725	1750	1654	450	950
1652	425	850	1656	400	800

3215 **Halfcrown.** Similar; *mm.* sun,					
1649	300	675	1654	165	400
1651	175	450	1655	550	1400
1652	175	450	1656	150	375
1653	150	360	1657	1200	2750

3216 Similar, *mm.* anchor					
1658	525	1100	1660	575	1200
1659	1500	3500			

3217 **Shilling.** Similar; *mm.* sun,					
1649	145	350	1654	110	240
1651	100	225	1655	200	450
1652	100	225	1656	125	275
1653	100	225	1657	375	900

3218

3218 Similar, *mm.* anchor					
1658	325	700	1660	325	675
1659	1250	2750

	F £	VF £		F £	VF £
3219 **Sixpence.** Similar; *mm.* sun,					
1649	110	275	1654	100	225
1651	90	200	1655	250	675
1652	100	225	1656	100	225
1653	90	200	1657	325	700
3220 Similar; *mm.* anchor,					
1658	325	700	1660	325	675
1659	750	1750			

3221

3222

	F £	VF £
3221 **Halfgroat**.	20	65
3222 **Penny**. Similar, but I above shields	15	45

3223

	F £	VF £
3223 **Halfpenny.**	20	50

Oliver Cromwell, 'the Great Emancipator' was born on 25th April 1599 in Huntingdon, he married Elizabeth Bourchier in August 1620 and had 3 children. The Protectorate was established on 16th December 1653, with work on the production of portrait coins authorised in 1655. Although often referred to as patterns, there is in fact nothing to suggest that the portrait coins of Oliver Cromwell were not intended for circulation. Authorised in 1656, the first full production came in 1657 and was followed by a second more plentiful one before Cromwell's death on 3rd September 1658. All coins were machine made, struck from dies by Thomas Simon in the presses of the Frenchman, Pierre Blondeau. Later, some of Simon's puncheons were sold in the Low Countries and an imitation Crown was made there. Other Dutch dies were prepared and some found their way back to the Mint, where in 1738 it was decided to strike a set of Cromwell's coins. Shillings and Sixpences were struck from the Dutch dies, and Crowns from new dies prepared by John Tanner. Thomas Simon who was born in 1618, later died in the Great Plague of 1665.

GOLD

		F £	*VF* £	*EF* £
3224	**Fifty shillings**. Laur. head l. R. Crowned Shield of the Protectorate, die axis ↑↓ 1656. Inscribed edge	3500	9500	20000

3225

3225	**Broad.** of Twenty Shillings. Similar, but grained edge die axis ↑↓ 1656.	2500	4000	6500

SILVER

3226

3226	**Crown.** Dr. bust l. R. Crowned shield, 1658/7. Inscribed edge ↑↓	1200	1850	2500
3226A	**Crown.** Dutch copy, similar with AИG legend 1658................	1650	2500	3500
3226B	**Crown.** Tanner's copy (struck 1738) dated 1658.......................	1650	2500	3500
3227	**Halfcrown.** Similar, 1656 different obverse legend ↑↓	1450	2750	4000

3227A

	F	VF	EF
	£	£	£
3227A Halfcrown. 1658 HIB type legend die axis ↑↓	500	950	1750

3228

3228 Shilling. Similar, but grained edge, 1658 ↑↓	350	600	950
3229 Sixpence. Similar 1658 ↑↓	*Extremely rare*		

COPPER

3230

3230 Farthing. Dr. bust l. R. CHARITIE AND CHANGE, shield ↑↓	2250	4250	—

There are also other reverse types for this coin.

For the first two years after the Restoration the same denominations, apart from the silver crown, were struck as were issued during the Commonwealth although the threepence and fourpence were soon added. Then, early in 1663, the ancient hand hammering process was finally superceded by the machinery of Blondeau.

For the emergency issues struck in the name of Charles II in 1648/9, see the siege pieces of Pontefract listed under Charles I, nos. 3150-1.

Hammered coinage, 1660-2

Mintmark: Crown. 

3301

3302

GOLD

		F	*VF*
	First issue. Without mark of value; *mm.* crown on *obv.* only	£	£
3301	**Unite** (20s.). Type as illustration	850	2250
3302	**Double-crown**. As illustration	650	1650
3303	**Crown**. Similar	675	1750

3303

3304

	Second issue. With mark of value; *mm.* crown on *obv.* only		
3304	**Unite.** Type as illustration	700	1650
3305	**Double-crown**. As illustration	550	1400
3306	**Crown**. Similar	575	1450

SILVER

3307

		F	VF
	First issue. Without inner circles or mark of value; *mm.* crown on *obv.* only	£	£
3307	**Halfcrown.** Crowned bust, as 3308	650	1750

3308

3309

3308	**Shilling**. Similar	200	575
3309	**Sixpence**. Similar	175	450
3310	**Twopence**. Similar	30	85
3311	**Penny**. Similar	25	65
3312	As last, but without mintmark	25	70

3313

3322

	Second issue. Without inner circles, but with mark of value; *mm.* crown on *obv.* only		
3313	**Halfcrown**. Crowned bust	800	2000
3314	**Shilling**. Similar	375	975
3315	**Sixpence**. Similar	1000	2500
3316	**Twopence**. Similar, but mm. on obv. only	85	240

3310

3317

3326

		F £	VF £
3317	Similar, but mm. both sides (machine made)	15	40
3318	Bust to edge of coin, legend starts at bottom l. (machine made, single arch crown)	15	40
3319	**Penny**. As 3317	15	45
3320	As 3318 (single arch crown)	15	35

3321

Third issue. With inner circles and mark of value; *mm.* crown on both sides

		F £	VF £
3321	**Halfcrown**. Crowned bust to i.c. (and rarely to edge of coin)	125	475
3322	**Shilling**. Similar, rarely *mm.* crown on *obv.* only	90	275
3323	**Sixpence**. Similar	80	250
3324	**Fourpence**. Similar	25	60
3325	**Threepence**. Similar	25	55
3326	**Twopence**. Similar	20	40
3327	**Penny**. Similar	20	50

Grading of Early and Later Milled Coinage

Milled coinage refers to coins that are struck by dies worked in a mechanical coining press. The early period is defined from the time of the successful installation of Peter Blondeau's hand powered machinery at the mint, initiated to strike the first portrait coins of Oliver Cromwell in 1656. The early period continuing until the advent of Matthew Boulton's steam powered presses from 1790. The coinage of this early period is therefore cruder in it's execution than the latter. When grading coins of the early peiod, we only attribute grades as high as extremely fine, and as high as uncirculated for the latter period. Most coins that occur of the early period in superior grades than those stated will command considerably higher prices, due to their rarity. We suggest the following definitions for grades of preservation:

Milled Coinage Conditions

Proof A very carefully struck coin from speciallly prepared dies, to give a superior definition to the design, with mirror-like fields. Occurs occasionally in the Early Milled Coinage, more frequently in the latter period. Some issues struck to a matt finish for Edward VII.

FDC *Fleur-de-coin.* Absolutely flawless, untouched, without wear, scratches, marks or hairlines. Generally applied to proofs.

UNC *Uncirculated.* A coin in as new condition as issued by the Mint, retaining full lustre or brilliance but, owing to modern mass-production methods of manufacture and storage, not necessarily perfect.

EF *Extremely Fine.* A coin that exhibits very little sign of circulation, with only minimal marks or faint wear, which are only evident upon very close scrutiny.

VF *Very Fine.* A coin that exhibits some wear on the raised surfaces of the design, but really has only had limited circulation.

F *Fine.* A coin that exhibits considerable wear to the raised surfaces of the design, either through circulation, or damage perhaps due to faulty striking

Fair *Fair.* A coin that exhibits wear, with the main features still distinguishable, and the legends, date and inscriptions still readable.

Poor *Poor.* A coin that exhibits considerable wear, certainly with milled coinage of no value to a collector unless it is an extremely rare date or variety.

Examples of Condition Grading

Early Milled

Gold AV

Silver AR

Copper Æ

Extremely Fine

Gold AV | Silver Æ | Copper Æ

Very Fine

Fine

James II
Two Guineas

William III
Crown

George III
Halfpenny

Later Milled

Gold AV | Silver Æ | Copper Æ

Uncirculated

Gold AV | Silver AR | Copper Æ

Extremely Fine

Very Fine

Fine

Victoria
Sovereign

Victoria
Halfcrown

George III
Twopence

CHARLES II (1660-85)

Charles II was born at St James Palace on 29th May 1630. He spent a long exile in France and returned after the fall of the Protectorate in 1660. The Restoration commenced and he married Catherine Braganza, but he bore no legitimate successor. Charles II died on 6th February 1685.

Early in 1663, the ancient hand hammering process was finally superceded by the machinery of Blondeau. John and Joseph Roettier, two brothers, engraved the dies with a safeguard against clipping, the larger coins were made with the edge inscribed DECVS ET TVTAMEN and the regnal year. The medium-sized coins were given a grained edge.

The new gold coins were current for 100s., 20s. and 10s., and they came to be called 'Guineas' as the gold from which some of them were made was imported from Guinea by the Africa Company (whose badge was the Elephant and Castle). It was not until some years later that the Guinea increased in value to 21s. and more. The Africa Co. badge is also found on some silver and so is the plume symbol indicating silver from the Welsh mines. The four smallest silver denominations, though known today as 'Maundy Money', were actually issued for general circulation: at this period the silver penny was probably the only coin distributed at the Royal Maundy ceremonies. Though never part of the original agreement, smaller coins were eventually also struck by machinery.

A good regal copper coinage was issued for the first time in 1672, but later in the reign, farthings were struck in tin (with a copper plug) in order to help the Cornish tin industry.

Engravers and designers: John Roettier (1631-1700), Thomas Simon (1618-1665)

GOLD

3328

Milled coinage

3328 Five Guineas. First laur. bust r., pointed trun., regnal year on edge in words, die axis ↑↓ (e.g. 1669=VICESIMO PRIMO), R. crowned cruciform shields, sceptres in angles

	F £	*VF* £	*EF* £		*F* £	*VF* £	*EF* £
1668 VICESIMO	1250	2250	5000	1675 V. SEPTIMO	1250	2250	5000
1669 – PRIMO	1250	2250	5000	1676 – OCTAVO	1400	2500	5500
1670 – SECVNDO	1250	2250	5000	1676 – SEPTIMO	1400	2250	5250
1671 – TERTIO	1400	2500	5500	1677 – NONO	1250	2250	5000
1672 – QVARTO	1250	2250	5000	1678/7 – TRICESIMO	1250	2250	5000
1673 – QVINTO	1250	2250	5000	1678 – TRICESIMO	1400	2250	5250
1674 – SEXTO	1400	2500	5500				

3329 Five Guineas.— with elephant below bust, die axis ↑↓

	F £	*VF* £	*EF* £		*F* £	*VF* £	*EF* £
1668 VICESIMO	1250	1950	4750	1675 V. SEPTIMO	1500	2750	6000
1669 – PRIMO	1500	2750	6000	1677/5 – NONO			*Extremely rare*

3330

3330 Five Guineas.— with elephant and castle below bust, die axis ↑↓

	F £	VF £	EF £		F £	VF £	EF £
1675 – SEPTIMO	*Extremely rare*			1678 TRICESIMO.....	1500	2750	6000
1676 – OCTAVO.....	1250	2250	5000	1678/7– TRICESIMO..	1500	2750	6000
1677 – NONO..........	1400	2500	5500				

3331 Five Guineas. Second laur. bust r., rounded trun. die axis ↑↓

	F £	VF £	EF £		F £	VF £	EF £
1678/7 TRICESIMO..	1500	2500	5500	1682 T. QVARTO	1250	2250	5000
1679 – PRIMO.........	1250	2250	5000	1683 – QVINTO	1250	2250	5000
1680 – SECVNDO ..	1250	2250	5000	1683/2—QVINTO	1500	2750	6000
1681 – TERTIO	1250	2250	5000	1684 – SEXTO...........	1250	1950	5000

3332 Five Guineas. Second laur. bust r., with elephant and castle below, die axis ↑↓

	F £	VF £	EF £		F £	VF £	EF £
1680 T. SECVNDO........	*Extremely rare*			1683 T. QVINTO.	1500	2500	5750
1681 – TERTIO......	1500	2500	5500	1684 – SEXTO.....	1250	2250	5000
1682 – QVARTO ...	1250	2250	5000				

3333

3334

3333 Two Guineas. First laur. bust r., pointed trun. die axis ↑↓

	F £	VF £	EF £		F £	VF £	EF £
1664	650	1500	3000	1669	*Extremely rare*		
1665	*Extremely rare*			1671	700	1750	3250

3334 Two Guineas.— with elephant below bust, die axis ↑↓

	F £	VF £	EF £
1664	600	1200	2750

3335 Two Guineas. Second laur. bust r., rounded trun, die axis ↑↓

	F £	VF £	EF £		F £	VF £	EF £
1675	800	1750	3250	1680	850	1850	3500
1676	600	1400	2750	1681	600	1400	2750
1677	600	1400	2750	1682	600	1400	2750
1678/7	600	1400	2750	1683	600	1400	2750
1679	600	1400	2750	1684	650	1500	3000

3335

3339

	F	*VF*	*EF*		*F*	*VF*	*EF*
	£	£	£		£	£	£

3336 Two Guineas.— with elephant and castle below bust, die axis ↑↓

1676	600	1400	3000	1682	600	1400	3000
1677		*Extremely rare*		1683	700	1750	3500
1678	600	1400	3000	1684	700	1750	3500

3337 Two Guineas.— with elephant only below, die axis ↑↓ 1678 .... *Extremely rare*

Overstruck dates are listed only if commoner than the normal date or if no normal date is known.

3338 Guinea. First laur. bust r., die axis ↑↓ 1663 ....475 1500 3000

3339 Guinea. — with elephant below bust, die axis ↑↓ 1663 ....425 1450 2750

3340 Guinea. Second laur. bust r., die axis ↑↓ 1664 ....375 1200 2500

3341

3341 Guinea. — with elephant below bust, die axis ↑↓ 1664 .... *Extremely rare*

3342 Guinea.Third laur. bust r. die axis ↑↓

1664	300	1100	2250	1669	300	1200	2500
1665	275	1100	2000	1670	275	1000	2000
1666	275	1100	2000	1671	275	1000	2000
1667	275	1100	2000	1672	325	1300	2500
1668	275	1100	2000	1673	350	1450	2750

3342

3344

3345

3343 Guinea. Third laur. bust r., with elephant below die axis ↑↓

1664	400	1350	2750	1668			*Extremely rare*
1665	350	1200	2500				

3344 Guinea. Fourth laur. bust r., rounded trun. die axis ↑↓

	F £	*VF* £	*EF* £
1672	250	850	1800
1673	250	850	1800
1674	300	1200	2500
1675	280	1000	2250
1675 CRAOLVS error	*Extremely rare*		
1676	225	750	1750
1677	225	750	1750
1678	225	750	1750
1679	225	750	1750
1680	225	750	1750
1681	280	1000	2250
1682	250	850	1800
1683	225	750	1750
1684	250	850	1800

3345 Fourth laur. bust r., with elephant and castle below, die axis ↑↓

	F £	*VF* £	*EF* £
1674	*Extremely rare*		
1675	350	1200	2500
1676	275	900	2000
1677	300	1000	2200
1677 GRATIR error	*Extremely rare*		
1678	350	1200	2500
1679	350	1200	2500
1680	450	1450	3250
1681	350	1100	2500
1682	300	1000	2250
1683	450	1450	3250
1684	300	1100	2250

3346 Guinea. — — with elephant below bust, die axis ↑↓

	F £	*VF* £	*EF* £
1677	*Extremely rare*		
1678	*Extremely rare*		

3347

3348

3347 Half-Guinea. First laur. bust r., pointed trun. die axis ↑↓

	F £	*VF* £	*EF* £
1669	300	750	2000
1670	250	650	1750
1671	325	850	2200
1672	325	850	2200

3348 Half-Guinea. Second laur. bust r., rounded trun. die axis ↑↓

	F £	*VF* £	*EF* £
1672	275	700	1900
1673	375	950	2500
1674	425	1000	2750
1675	*Extremely rare*		
1676	275	650	1750
1677	275	700	1900
1678	300	750	2000
1679	250	650	1750
1680	375	950	2500
1681	375	950	2500
1682	375	950	2500
1683	275	700	1900
1684	250	650	1750

3349 Half-Guinea with elephant and castle below bust, die axis ↑↓

	F £	*VF* £	*EF* £
1676	425	1250	—
1677	380	1000	2750
1678/7	325	850	2200
1680	*Extremely rare*		
1681	*Extremely rare*		
1682	380	1000	2750
1683	*Extremely rare*		
1684	280	750	2000

SILVER

3350

3350 Crown. First dr. bust r., rose below, edge undated, die axis ↑↓ 1662...85 450 2000

3350A Crown. — II of legend at 12 o'clock.. *Extremely rare*

3351 Crown.— — edge dated, die axis ↑↓ 1662...95 475 2000

3352 Crown.— no rose, edge dated, die axis ↑↓ 1662................................100 550 2250

3353 Crown.— — edge not dated, die axis ↑↓ 1662....................................95 500 2250

3354 Crown.— legend re-arranged shields altered, 1663, regnal year on edge in Roman figures ANNO REGNI XV die axis ↑↓..................................100 550 2250

3355 Crown. Second dr. bust r., regnal year on edge in Roman figures (e.g. 1664 = XVI), die axis ↑↓

1664 edge XVI..........	75	350	2000	1666 XVIII	75	400	2200
1665 XVI		*Extremely rare*		1666 XVIII RE·X...........		*Extremely rare*	
1665/4 XVII..............	500	1000	—	1667 XVIII	1500	—	—
1665 XVII.................	500	1000	—				

3356 – RE•X

3356

3356 Crown. — — elephant below bust, die axis ↑↓

1666 XVIII	175	650	—	1666 XVIII RE·X.....	250	800	—

3357

3357 Crown. Regnal year on edge in words (e.g. 1667= DECIMO NONO) die axis ↑↓

	F £	VF £	EF £
1667 D. NONO	75	350	1750
1667 — AN.· REG.·	75	350	1750
1668 VICESIMO	60	300	1650
1668/7 VICESIMO	75	350	1750
1668/5 VICESIMO	*Extremely rare*		
1669 V· PRIMO	200	600	—
1669/8 V· PRIMO	200	600	—
1670 V. SECVNDO	95	400	1850
1670/69 V. SECVND	100	450	1850
1671 V· TERTIO	75	375	1850
1671 — T/R in ET	500	—	—
1671 — ET over FR	750	1750	—

3358

3359

3358 Crown. Third dr. bust r. die axis ↑↓

	F £	VF £	EF £
1671 V. TERTIO	70	350	1750
1671 V. QVARTO	*Extremely rare*		
1672 V. QVARTO	70	350	1750
1673 V. QVARTO	*Extremely rare*		
1673 V. QVINTO	70	350	1750
1673/2 V. QVINTO	100	550	2200
1674 V. SEXTO	*Extremely rare*		
1675/3 V. SEPTIMO	500	1500	—
1675 —	750	2500	—
1675 — EGNI error	650	—	—
1676 V. OCTAVO	70	350	1750
1676 OCCTAVO	80	450	—
1677 V. NONO	90	450	2000
1677/6 V. NONO	100	550	—
1678/7 TRICESIMO	100	550	—
1679 T. PRIMO	75	350	1750
1680/79 T. SECVNDO	90	375	1850
1680 T. SECVNDO	100	500	2250

3359 Crown. Fourth dr. bust r. die axis ↑↓

	F £	VF £	EF £
1679 T. PRIMO	70	350	1650
1680 T. SECVNDO	75	350	1750
1680/79 T. SECVNDO	100	500	—
1681 T. TERTIO	75	350	1750
1682/1 T. QVARTO	70	350	1750
1682 T. QVARTO	500	1250	3500
1682 QVRRTO error	200	800	—
1683 T. QVINTO	300	900	—
1684 T. SEXTO	200	600	—

3360 Crown.— elephant and castle below bust, die axis ↑↓ 1681 T. TERTIO..1500 3500 —

3361

3362

		F £	VF £	EF £
3361	**Halfcrown.** First dr. bust r., regnal year on edge in Roman figures die axis ↑↓			
	1663 XV	75	325	1450
	1663 XV V/S in CAROLVS	125	500	—
	1663 XV no stops on obverse	100	425	—
3362	**Halfcrown.** Second dr. bust r., die axis ↑↓ 1664 XVI	100	500	2000
3363	**Halfcrown.** Third dr. bust r., die axis ↑↓ 1666 XVIII	650	2250	—
3364	**Halfcrown.** — elephant below bust, die axis ↑↓ 1666 XVIII	500	1000	—

3364

3365

3365 **Halfcrown.** Third dr bust r. regnal date on edge in words (eg. 1667=DECIMO NONO) ↑↓

	F	VF	EF		F	VF	EF
1667/4 D. NONO	*Extremely rare*			1669 — R/I in PRIMO	*Extremely rare*		
1668/4 VICESIMO	150	500	—	1670 V. SECVNDO	65	250	1500
1669/4 V. PRIMO	150	450	—	1670 – MRG for MAG	300	750	—
1669 V. PRIMO	350	800	—				

3366

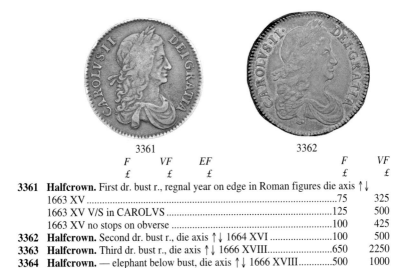

3367

3366 **Halfcrown.** Third bust variety r. die axis ↑↓

	F	VF	EF		F	VF	EF
1671 V. TERTIO	60	250	1250	1672 V. TERTIO	*Extremely rare*		
1671/0 V. TERTIO	85	325	1750	1672 V. QVARTO	60	250	1500

3367 Halfcrown. Fourth dr. bust r. die axis ↑↓

	F £	*VF* £	*EF* £
1672 V. QVARTO	90	350	1750
1673 V. QVINTO	60	225	1250
1673 —A/R in FRA	*Extremely rare*		
1673 — B/R in BR	*Extremely rare*		
1674 V. SEXTO	95	300	1750
1674/3 V. SEXTO	150	—	—
1675 V. SEPTIMO	70	275	1500
1675 — Retrograde 1	75	325	1750
1676 V. OCTAVO	55	200	1100
1676 — Retrograde 1	65	250	1250
1677 V. NONO	60	250	1350
1678 TRICESIMO	150	400	—
1679 T. PRIMO	60	225	1250
1679 — GRATTA error	*Extremely rare*		
1679 — REGИI error	*Extremely rare*		
1679 — DECNS error	150	450	—
1679 — DNCVS error	200	—	—
1679 — PRICESIMO	200	500	—
1679 — inverted A's for V's on edge	200	—	—
1680 T. SECVNDO	120	375	—
1680 T. SECVNꓷO error	*Extremely rare*		
1681 T. TERTIO	70	275	1500
1681/0 —	100	—	—
1682 T. QVARTO	80	325	1650
1682/79 T. QVARTO	*Extremely rare*		
1683 T. QVINTO	60	225	1250
1684/3 T. SEXTO	125	450	—

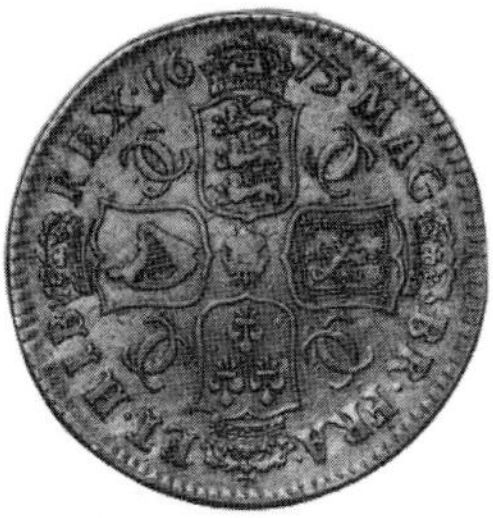

3369

3370

3368 Halfcrown. plume below bust, die axis ↑↓

	F £	*VF* £	*EF* £
1673 V. QVINTO	1000	—	—
1683 T. QVINTO	*Extremely rare*		

3369 Halfcrown.— plume below bust and in centre of *rev*., die axis ↑↓ 1673 V. QVINTO *Extremely rare*

3370 Halfcrown. elephant and castle below bust, die axis ↑↓ 1681 T. TERTIO 1350 — —

SHILLINGS

First bust

First bust variety

Second bust

Third bust

First bust

First bust var.

First bust and first bust variety

Second bust

3371

3371 – transposed shield

	F £	VF £	EF £
3371 Shilling. First dr. bust r., die axis ↑↓			
1663 die axis ↑↑ (en medaille)	75	375	850
1663 die axis ↑↓ as usual	60	225	500
1663 GARTIA error die axis ↑↓	550	—	—
1663 Transposed shields of Scotland and Ireland die axis ↑↓	125	650	1100
1663 A over G in FRA die axis ↑↓	500	—	—

3372

3374

3372 Shilling. First bust variety r. die axis ↑↓

	F £	VF £	EF £		F £	VF £	EF £
1663	60	225	500	1668	300	750	—
1666		*Extremely rare*		1669/6		*Extremely rare*	

	F £	VF £	EF £
3373 Shilling. First bust variety r. elephant below bust, die axis ↑↓ 1666	300	850	2250
3374 Shilling. Guinea head, elephant below bust, die axis ↑↓ 1666	950	2250	—

3375

3376

3375 Shilling. Second dr. bust r. die axis ↑↓

	F £	VF £	EF £		F £	VF £	EF £
1666	1000	3000	—	1676	65	300	600
1668	50	225	500	1676 higher bust		*Extremely rare*	
1668/7	65	300	650	1676/5	75	325	700
1669		*Extremely rare*		1677	65	300	600
1670	80	350	800	1678	80	350	800
1671	100	400	900	1678/7	80	350	800
1672	65	300	650	1679	65	300	600
1673	100	400	900	1679/7	80	350	800
1673/2	150	550	1100	1680		*Extremely rare*	
1674	125	450	950	1681	95	400	900
1674/3	100	400	850	1681/0	95	400	900
1675	150	550	1100	1682/1	350	800	—
1675/4	150	550	1100	1683		*Extremely rare*	

F £	VF £	EF £		F £	VF £	EF £

3376 Shilling.— plume below bust and in centre of *rev.* die axis ↑↓

1671	150	500	1400	1676	165	550	1500
1673	165	550	1500	1679	200	650	1750
1674	150	500	1400	1680	275	800	2000
1675	165	550	1500	1680/79	275	800	2000

3377 3378

3377 Shilling. plume *rev.* only, die axis ↑↓ 1674250 850 2000

3378 Shilling. — plume *obv. only* die axis ↑↓

| 1677 | 400 | 1250 | 2500 | 1679 | 350 | 1000 | 2250 |

3379 Shilling. — elephant and castle below bust, die axis ↑↓ 1681/0.......1250 — —

3380 3381

3380 Shilling. Third dr. (large) bust r. die axis ↑↓

| 1674 | 200 | 750 | 2000 | 1675/3 | 150 | 550 | 1500 |
| 1675 | 150 | 550 | 1500 | | | | |

3381 Shilling. Fourth dr. (large) bust r., older features, die axis ↑↓

| 1683 | 120 | 400 | 1000 | 1684 | 100 | 300 | 850 |

3382

3382 Sixpence. Dr. bust r. die axis ↑↓

1674	35	150	300	1679	50	175	350
1675	35	150	300	1680	75	250	500
1675/4	50	200	400	1681	35	125	250
1676	75	250	500	1682	75	250	500
1676/5	75	250	500	1682/1	50	175	350
1677	35	150	300	1683	35	150	300
1678/7	50	175	350	1684	60	175	350

3383

	F £	VF £	EF £
3383 Fourpence. Undated. Crowned dr. bust l. to edge of coin, value behind. R. Shield die axis ↑↓	15	40	90

3384

3386

3384 Fourpence. Dated. O. As illustration 3384. R. Four interlinked Cs die axis ↑↓

	F	VF	EF		F	VF	EF
1670	12	30	75	1678	10	20	60
1671	10	25	70	1678/6	10	25	70
1672/1	10	20	65	1678/7	10	25	70
1673	10	20	65	1679	10	20	60
1674	10	20	65	1680	10	20	60
1674/4 sideways	12	30	100	1681	10	20	60
1674 7 over 6	10	25	70	1681 B/R in HIB	12	30	100
1675	10	20	65	1681/0	10	25	70
1675/4	10	25	70	1682	10	20	60
1676	10	20	65	1682/1	10	25	70
1676 7 over 6	10	25	70	1683	10	20	60
1676/5	10	25	70	1684	10	25	70
1677	10	20	60	1684/3	10	20	60

	F	VF	EF
3385 Threepence. Undated. As 3383 die axis ↑↓	10	25	70

3386 Threepence. Dated. As illustration die axis ↑↓

	F	VF	EF		F	VF	EF
1670	6	18	60	1678	6	15	50
1671	6	15	50	1678 on 4d flan	6	15	50
1671 GR∀TIA	10	30	100	1679	6	15	50
1671 GRΛTIA	8	20	70	1679 O/A in CAROLVS	10	30	100
1672/1	6	15	50	1680	6	15	50
1673	6	15	50	1681	6	15	50
1674	6	15	50	1681/0	7	20	60
1675	6	18	60	1682	6	15	50
1676	6	15	50	1682/1	7	20	60
1676/5	7	20	60	1683	6	15	50
1676 ERA for FRA	10	30	100	1684	6	15	50
1677	6	18	60	1684/3	7	20	60

	F	VF	EF
3387 Twopence. Undated. As 3383 (double arch crown) die axis ↑↓	6	20	50

3388 3390

	F £	*VF* £	*EF* £		*F* £	*VF* £	*EF* £

3388 Twopence. Dated. As illustration die axis ↑↓

	F	VF	EF		F	VF	EF
1668 die axis ↑↑	8	20	60	1679	6	15	50
1670	6	15	50	1679 HIB over FRA	10	30	100
1671	6	15	50	1680	6	15	50
1672/1	6	15	50	1680/79	8	20	60
1673	8	20	60	1681	6	15	50
1674	6	15	50	1682/1	8	20	60
1675	6	15	50	1682/1 ERA for FRA	10	30	100
1676	6	15	50	1683	6	15	50
1677	8	20	60	1683/2	8	20	60
1678	6	15	50	1684	8	20	60
1678/6	8	20	60				

	F	VF	EF
3389 Penny. Undated. As 3383 (double arch crown) die axis ↑↓	6	25	80

3390 Penny. Dated. As illustration die axis ↑↓

	F	VF	EF		F	VF	EF
1670	8	20	70	1678 ᗡRATIA error	10	30	100
1671	8	20	70	1678	9	25	90
1672/1	8	20	70	1679	9	25	90
1673	8	20	70	1680	8	20	70
1674	8	20	70	1680 on 2d flan		*Extremely rare*	
1674 ᗡRATIA error	10	30	100	1681	10	30	100
1675	8	20	70	1682	9	25	80
1675 ᗡRATIA error	10	30	100	1682/1	10	30	100
1676	9	25	90	1682 ERA for FRA	10	30	100
1676 ᗡRATIA error	10	30	100	1683/1	8	20	70
1677	8	20	70	1684	9	25	90
1677 ᗡRATIA error	10	30	100	1684/3	10	30	100

	F	VF	EF
3391 Maundy Set. Undated. The four coins	85	200	350

3392 Maundy Set. Dated. The four coins. Uniform dates

	F	VF	EF		F	VF	EF
1670	70	120	275	1678	70	150	350
1671	60	100	275	1679	65	110	300
1672	70	120	325	1680	60	100	275
1673	60	100	275	1681	70	150	350
1674	60	100	275	1682	65	110	300
1675	65	110	300	1683	60	100	275
1676	65	110	300	1684	65	110	300
1677	65	110	300				

COPPER AND TIN

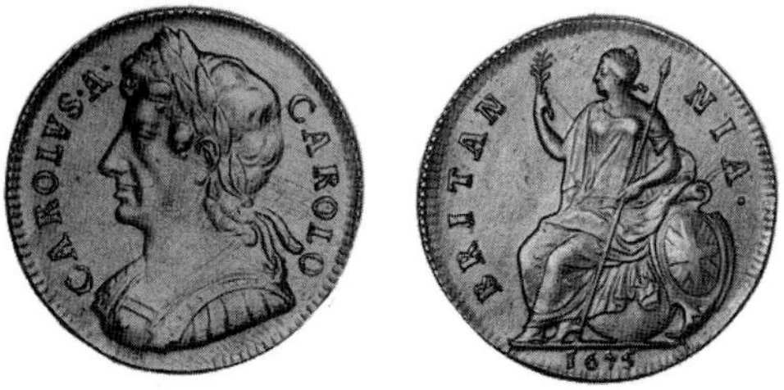

3393

	F £	VF £	EF £
3393 Copper **Halfpenny** Cuir. bust l. die axis ↑↓			
1672	50	150	500
1672 CRAOLVS error	*Extremely rare*		
1673	40	120	450
1673 CRAOLVS error	*Extremely rare*		
1673 no stops on obv.	*Extremely rare*		
1673 no rev. stop	70	250	—
1675	45	125	475
1675 no stops on obv.	60	200	—

3394

3395

	F £	VF £	EF £
3394 Copper **Farthing.** As illustration die axis ↑↓			
1672	40	110	275
1672 Rev. loose drapery	50	150	450
1672 no stops on obv.	60	175	500
1673	40	110	275
1673 CAROLA error	75	225	—
1673 BRITINNIA error	*Extremely rare*		
1673 no stops on obv.	*Extremely rare*		
1673 no rev. stop	*Extremely rare*		
1674	50	140	325
1675	40	110	275
1675 no stop after CAROLVS	*Extremely rare*		
1679	50	140	325
1679 no rev. stop	60	175	500

Prices for tin coinage based on corrosion free examples, and in the top grades with some lustre

	Fair £	F £	VF £	EF £
3395 Tin **Farthing.** Somewhat similar, but with copper plug, edge inscribed NUMMORVM FAMVLVS, and date on edge only die axis ↑↓				
1684 various varieties of edge	35	95	400	1000
1685	*Extremely rare*			

James II, brother of Charles II, was born on 14th October 1633, he married Anne Hyde with whom he produced 8 children. He lost control of his reign when the loyalist Tories moved against him over his many Catholic appointments. Parliament invited his protestant daughter Mary with husband William of Orange to jointly rule. James II abdicated and died in exile in France.

During this reign the dies continued to be engraved by John Roettier (1631-1700), the only major difference in the silver coinage being the ommission of the interlinked C's in the angles of the shields on the reverses. Tin halfpence and farthings provided the only base metal coinage during this short reign. All genuine tin coins of this period have a copper plug.

GOLD

	F	*VF*	*EF*		*F*	*VF*	*EF*
	£	£	£		£	£	£

3396 Five Guineas. First laur. bust l., sceptres misplaced date on edge in words (e.g. 1686 = SECVNDO) die axis ↑↓ 1686 SECVNDO 1300 3000 6000

3397

3397 Five Guineas. — sceptres normal. die axis ↑↓

1687 TERTIO..........1000	2750	5500		1688 QVARTO 1000	2750	5500	

3397A

3397A Five Guineas. Second laur. bust l. die axis ↑↓

1687 TERTIO..........1000	2750	5500		1688 QVARTO 1000	2750	5500	

3398

	F £	VF £	EF £		F £	VF £	EF £
3398 Five Guineas. First laur. bust l. Elephant and castle below bust die axis ↑↓							
1687 TERTIO	1250	2500	6000	1688 QVARTO	1250	3000	6000

3399

	F £	VF £	EF £		F £	VF £	EF £
3399 Two Guineas. Similar die axis ↑↓							
1687	750	2000	4000	1688/7	750	2000	4250
3400 Guinea. First laur. bust l. die axis ↑↓							
1685	275	1000	2500	1686	300	1100	2750
3401 Guinea. — elephant and castle below die axis ↑↓							
1685	350	1250	3000	1686		*Extremely rare*	

3402

	F £	VF £	EF £		F £	VF £	EF £
3402 Guinea. Second laur. bust l. die axis ↑↓							
1686	250	900	2000	1688	275	1000	2500
1687	250	900	2000				

3403	F £	VF £	EF £	3404	F £	VF £	EF £

3403 Guinea. — elephant and castle below die axis ↑↓

	F £	VF £	EF £		F £	VF £	EF £
1686	425	1500	3500	1688	300	1000	2500
1687	300	1000	2500				

3404 Half-Guinea laur. bust l. die axis ↑↓

	F £	VF £	EF £		F £	VF £	EF £
1686	225	600	1650	1688	275	650	1750
1687	325	750	2000				

3405 Half-Guinea elephant and castle below, die axis ↑↓ 1686 ....500 2000 —

SILVER

3406

3406 Crown. First dr. bust, l. regnal year on edge in words (e.g. 1686 = SECVNDO) die axis ↑↓

	F £	VF £	EF £
1686 SECVNDO	125	600	2250
1686 — No stops on obverse	275	750	—

3407

3407 Crown. Second dr. bust l. die axis ↑↓

	F £	VF £	EF £		F £	VF £	EF £
1687 TERTIO	100	400	1250	1688/7 —	125	550	1850
1688 QVARTO	100	450	1500				

3408 1st bust 2nd bust

3408 Halfcrown. First dr. bust, l. regnal year on edge in words (e.g. 1685 = PRIMO) die axis ↑↓

	F £	*VF* £	*EF* £		*F* £	*VF* £	*EF* £
1685 PRIMO	100	300	1000	1686 TERTIO	125	350	1250
1686 SECVNDO	100	300	1000	1687 TERTIO	100	300	1000
1686/5 —	200	500	—	1687/6 —	125	350	1250
1686 TERTIO V over S or B in JACOBVS	200	500	—	1687 — 6 over 8	*Extremely rare*		

3409 Halfcrown. Second dr. bust l. die axis ↑↓

	F £	*VF* £	*EF* £		*F* £	*VF* £	*EF* £
1687 TERTIO	125	350	1250	1688 QVARTO	100	300	1000

3410

3410 Shilling. Dr. bust l. die axis ↑↓

	F £	*VF* £	*EF* £		*F* £	*VF* £	*EF* £
1685	90	225	650	1687	120	350	850
1685 no stops on rev.	150	500	1250	1687/6	90	225	650
1686	100	300	750	1687 G/A in MAG	140	400	1000
1686/5	100	300	750	1688	100	300	750
1686 V/S in JACOBVS	100	300	750	1688/7	120	350	850

3411 Shilling. Plume in centre of *rev.*, die axis ↑↓ 1685..................Fair £3750

3412 3413

3412 Sixpence. R. Early type shields die axis ↑↓

	F £	*VF* £	*EF* £		*F* £	*VF* £	*EF* £
1686	75	200	400	1687/6	85	250	450
1687	85	250	450				

3413 Sixpence — R. Late type shields die axis ↑↓

	F £	*VF* £	*EF* £		*F* £	*VF* £	*EF* £
1687	75	200	400	1687 Later/early shields	85	250	450
1687/6	75	225	450	1688	75	225	450

3414

3415

	F £	VF £	EF £		F £	VF £	EF £
3414 Fourpence. O. As illus. R. IIII crowned die axis ↑↓							
1686	8	25	80	1688	8	25	80
1686 Date over crown	8	25	80	1688 1 over 8	20	50	125
1687/6	6	20	70	1688/7	8	25	80
1687 8 over 7	8	25	80				
3415 Threepence. – R. III crowned die axis ↑↓							
1685	5	22	70	1687	6	25	80
1685 Groat flan	30	75	150	1687/6	5	22	70
1686	5	22	70	1688	5	22	70
1686 4d obv. die	8	28	90	1688/7	6	25	80
3416 Twopence. – R. II crowned die axis ↑↓							
1686	7	20	70	1687 ERA for FRA	20	40	100
1686 IΛCOBVS	10	30	90	1688	8	25	80
1687	7	20	70	1688/7	8	25	80

3416

3417

	F £	VF £	EF £		F £	VF £	EF £
3417 Penny. – R. I crowned die axis ↑↓							
1685	8	25	80	1687/8	15	30	90
1686	8	25	80	1688	8	25	80
1687	8	25	80	1688/7	8	25	80
1687/6	8	25	80				
3418 Maundy Set. As last four. Uniform dates							
1686	75	180	350	1688	75	180	350
1687	75	180	350				

TIN

3419

Prices for tin coinage based on corrosion free examples, and in the top grades with some lustre

3419 Halfpenny. Dr. bust r.; date on edge die axis ↑↓

1685 various varieties of edge	45	100	300	1000
1686	55	120	350	1100
1687	45	100	300	1000

3420

3420 Farthing. Cuir. bust r.; date on edge die axis ↑↓

1684			*Extremely rare*	
1685 various varieties of edge	40	90	250	850
1686 two varieties of edge	45	100	275	900
1687			*Extremely rare*	

3421

3421 Farthing. Dr. bust r.; date on edge, 1687 various varieties of edge ↑↓	50	100	300	1000

Mary Stuart was born on 30 April 1662, and married William of Orange as part of Charles II's foreign policy. She eventually became William's loyal servant but bore him no children. The Bill and the Claim of Rights were both passed in 1689 and forbade the Royal and Perogative rights of Monarchs. Mary died from smallpox on 28 December 1694.

Due to the poor state of the silver coinage, much of it worn hammered coin, the Guinea, which was valued at 21s. 6d. at the beginning of the reign, circulated for as much as 30s. by 1694. The tin Halfpennies and Farthings were replaced by copper coins in 1694. The rampant Lion of Nassau is now placed as an inescutcheon on the centre of the royal arms.

Engravers and designers: George Bower (d.1689), Henry Harris (d.1704), John Roettier (1631-1700), James Roettier (1663-1698), Norbert Roettier (b.1665)

GOLD

3422

	F	*VF*	*EF*		*F*	*VF*	*EF*
	£	£	£		£	£	£

3422 Five Guineas. Conjoined busts r. regnal year on edge in words (e.g. 1691 = TERTIO) ↑↓

1691 TERTIO	1000	2000	5000	1694/2 SEXTO	1100	2200	5500
1692 QVARTO	1000	2000	5000	1694 SEXTO	1200	2500	6000
1693 QVINTO	1000	2000	5000				

3423

3424

3423 Five Guineas. — elephant and castle below, die axis ↑↓

1691 TERTIO	1100	2250	5500	1694/2 SEXTO	1100	2500	5750
1692 QVARTO	1100	2250	6000	1694 SEXTO	1200	2750	6000
1693 QVINTO	1250	2500	6000				

3424 Two Guineas. Conjoined busts r. die axis ↑↓

1693	600	1450	3250	1694/3	600	1450	3250

3425 Two Guineas. — elephant and castle below, die axis ↑↓

1691		*Extremely rare*		1694/3	700	1750	4000
1693	700	1750	4000				

3426

3427

	F £	VF £	EF £		F £	VF £	EF £
3426 Guinea. Conjoined busts r. die axis ↑↓							
1689	275	1100	2500	1692	300	1200	3000
1690	300	1100	2750	1693	300	1100	2750
1691	300	1100	2750	1694	275	1100	2750
3427 Guinea. Conjoined busts r. elephant and castle below die axis ↑↓							
1689	300	1100	2750	1692	300	1200	3000
1690	375	1250	3250	1693	*Extremely rare*		
1691	300	1200	3000	1694	300	1200	3000
3428 Guinea. — elephant only below, die axis ↑↓							
1692	375	1250	3250	1693	*Extremely rare*		

Overstruck dates are listed only if commoner than the normal date or if no normal date is known.

3429

3430

	F £	VF £	EF £		F £	VF £	EF £
3429 Half-Guinea. First busts r. 1689 die axis ↑↓					350	1100	2250
3430 Half-Guinea. Second busts r. R. Second shield die axis ↑↓							
1690	250	950	2000	1693	*Extremely rare*		
1691	275	1100	2250	1694	250	950	2000
1692	300	950	2000				
3431 Half-Guinea. — — elephant and castle below, die axis ↑↓							
1691	250	900	2000	1692	275	1000	2250
3432 Half-Guinea. — — elephant only below, die axis ↑↓ 1692					*Extremely rare*		

SILVER

3433

3433 Crown. Conjoined busts r. regnal year on edge in words (e.g. 1691 = TERTIO) die axis ↑↓

	F £	VF £	EF £		F £	VF £	EF £
1691 TERTIO	200	600	2000	1692 QVARTO	200	600	2000
1691 I/E in legend	400	1000	—	1692/7 QVARTO	300	850	—
1691 TERTTIO	*Extremely rare*			1692/7 QVINTO	200	600	2000

3434

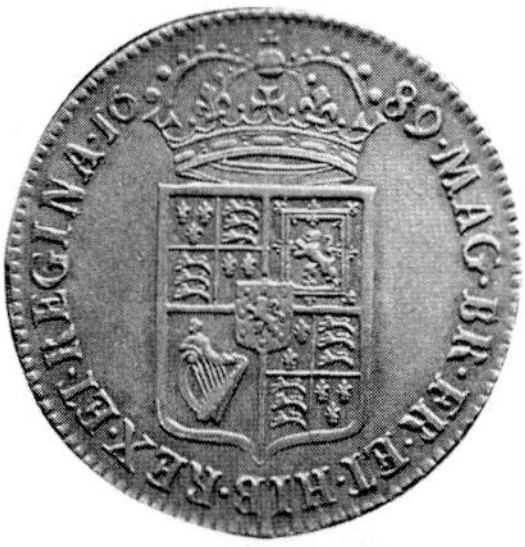

3435

	F £	VF £	EF £
3434 **Halfcrown.** First busts, r. R. First shield, 1689 PRIMO R. Crown with caul and interior frosted, with pearls die axis ↑↓	50	150	700
1689— 2nd L/M in GVLIELMVS	60	175	750
1689 — 1st V/A in GVLIELMVS, only caul frosted	60	175	750
1689 — — interior also frosted, no pearls	60	175	750
1689 Caul only frosted, pearls	50	150	700
1689 — no pearls	55	175	750
1689 No frosting, pearls	55	175	750
1689 No stops on obverse	60	175	750
1689 FRA for FR	95	250	850

3435 **Halfcrown.**— R. second shield die axis ↑↓

	F £	VF £	EF £
1689 PRIMO R. Caul and interior frosted with pearls	65	200	750
1689 — — no pearls	75	225	800
1689 — — — ĿT for ET error	*Extremely rare*		
1689 GVLI ĿMVS error	*Extremely rare*		
1689 Caul only frosted pearls	60	175	750
1689 interior frosted, no pearls	65	200	750
1689 Caul only frosted, no pearls	65	200	750
1689 no frosting, pearls	60	175	750
1689 no frosting, no pearls	60	175	750
1690 SECVNDO —	75	250	850
1690 — GRETIA error	150	500	1400
1690 TERTIO	100	350	1100

3436

	F £	VF £	EF £		F £	VF £	EF £

3436 Halfcrown. Second busts r. R. Crowned cruciform shields, WM monogram in angles ↑↓

1691 TERTIO	65	250	850	1693 QVINTO	65	225	800
1692 QVARTO	65	250	850	1693 3/inverted 3	75	250	850
1692 R/G in REGINA		*Extremely rare*		1693 inverted 3	150	450	1200
1692 QVINTO	125	400	—				

3437 3438

3437 Shilling. Conjoined busts r. R. Similar die axis ↑↓

1692	85	350	850	1693 9/0	120	400	950
1692 inverted 1	100	400	900	1693	80	300	650
1692 RE/ET on R.		*extremely rare*					

3438 Sixpence. Similar die axis ↑↓

1693	80	200	400	1694	95	225	550
1693 inverted 3	100	250	600				

3439 3440

3439 Fourpence. First busts, r. no tie to wreath. R. Crowned 4 die axis ↑↓

1689 GV below bust	8	20	70	1690	10	22	80
1689 G below bust	8	20	70	1690 6 over 5	10	20	80
1689 stop befor G	10	22	80	1691	12	30	100
1689 berries in wreath	10	22	80	1691/0	11	25	85
1689 GVLEELMVS	50	100	–	1694	12	30	100

3440 Fourpence. Second busts r. tie to wreath. R. Crowned 4 die axis ↑↓

	F £	VF £	EF £		F £	VF £	EF £
1692	11	25	85	1693/2	12	35	100
1692/1	12	35	100	1694	12	35	100
1692 MAR•IA	*Extremely rare*			1694 small lettering	12	35	100
1693	12	35	100				

3441 Threepence. First busts, r. no tie to wreath. R. Crowned 3 die ↑↓

	F £	VF £	EF £		F £	VF £	EF £
1689	7	20	60	1690 6 over 5	8	25	70
1689 No stops on rev.	10	30	80	1690 Large lettering	8	25	70
1689 LMV over MVS.	10	30	80	1690 9 over 6	8	25	70
1689 Hyphen stops on rev.	8	25	70	1691	30	80	175
1690	8	25	70				

3442 Threepence. Second busts, r. tie to wreath die axis ↑↓

	F £	VF £	EF £		F £	VF £	EF £
1691	10	30	90	1693 GV below bust	9	25	80
1692 G below bust	10	30	90	1694 G below bust	9	25	80
1692 GV below bust	10	30	90	1694 — MΛRIΛ error	10	30	90
1692 GVL below bust	10	30	90	1694 GV below bust	9	25	80
1693 G below bust	9	25	80	1694 GVL below bust	9	25	80
1693/2 G below bust	9	25	80				

3443 Twopence. Conjoined busts r. die axis ↑↓

	F £	VF £	EF £		F £	VF £	EF £
1689	8	20	70	1694/3	10	30	90
1691	8	20	70	1694/3 no stop after DG	10	30	90
1692	9	25	80	1694 MARLA error	12	35	100
1693	9	25	80	1694 HI for HIB	10	30	90
1693/2	10	30	90	1694 GVLI below bust.	10	30	90
1693 GV below bust	10	30	90	1694 GVL below bust	10	30	90
1694	10	30	90				

3444

3445

3444 Penny. Legend continuous over busts, die axis ↑↓

	F £	VF £	EF £		F £	VF £	EF £
1689	150	275	400	1689 MΛRIΛ	175	300	450
1689 GVIELMVS error	250	400	650				

3445 Penny. Legend broken by busts

	F £	VF £	EF £		F £	VF £	EF £
1690	14	40	130	1694 date spread	12	35	120
1691/0	12	35	120	1694 no stops on obv.	15	40	130
1692	14	40	130	1694 HI for HIB	15	40	130
1692/1	15	40	140	1694 — 9/6	15	40	130
1693	12	35	120				

3446

3446 Maundy Set. As last four. Uniform dates

	F £	VF £	EF £		F £	VF £	EF £
1689	250	500	750	1693	150	250	500
1691	95	175	400	1694	95	175	400
1692	150	250	500				

TIN AND COPPER

3447

Prices for tin coinage based on corrosion free examples, and in the top grades with some lustre

	Fair £	*F* £	*VF* £	*EF* £
3447 Tin **Halfpenny.** Small dr. busts r.; date on edge ↑↓ 1689	450	750	—	—
— — — obv. with star stops 1689			*Extremely rare*	

3448

	Fair £	*F* £	*VF* £	*EF* £
3448 Tin **Halfpenny.** — Large cuir. busts r.; date only on edge, die axis ↑↓				
1690 various edge varieties	60	120	350	1000
3449 Tin **Halfpenny.** date in ex. and on edge die axis ↑↓				
1691 various edge varieties	50	100	300	950
1691 in ex. 1692 on edge			*Extremely rare*	
1692	50	100	300	950
3450 Tin **Farthing.** Small dr. busts r. die axis ↑↓				
1689	175	400	950	—
1689, in ex. 1690 on edge			*Extremely rare*	

3451

	Fair £	*F* £	*VF* £	*EF* £
3451 Tin **Farthing.** Large cuir. busts r. die axis ↑↓				
1690, in ex. 1689 on edge			*Extremely rare*	
1690 various edge varieties	40	100	300	950
1691 various edge varieties	40	100	300	950
1692	50	125	350	1000

3452

	F £	VF £	EF £
3452 Copper **Halfpenny,** die axis ↑↓ 1694	50	120	450
1694 GVLIEMVS error	100	–	–
1694 MVRIA error	125	–	–
1694 MΛRIΛ error	100	–	–
1694 BRITΛNNI/Λ	100	–	–
1694 no rev. stop	100	–	–

3453

	F £	VF £	EF £
3453 Copper **Farthing**, die axis ↑↓ 1694	60	150	425
1694 MΛRIΛ error	100	–	–
1694 no stop after MΛRIΛ	100	–	–
1694 — BRITΛNNIΛ	125	–	–
1694 no stop on rev.	100	–	–
1694 no stop on obv.	100	–	–
1694 GVLIELMS, BRITΛNNIΛ errors	125	–	–
1694 BRITΛNNIΛ	100	–	–
1694 Broad heavier flan 25.5mm	175	–	–

William of Orange was born on 4th November 1650. He married Mary Stuart under Charles II's foreign policy and was invited to England by Parliament, where he proceeded to supress the Jacobite rebellion. The Bank of England was founded during this reign, and William ruled alone and without issue after Mary's death; until his own demise from a serious fall from his horse on 8th March 1702.

In 1696 a great re-coinage was undertaken to replace the hammered silver that made up most of the coinage in circulation, much of it being clipped and badly worn. Branch mints were set up at Bristol, Chester, Exeter, Norwich and York to help with the re-coinage. For a short time before they were finally demonetized, unclipped hammered coins were allowed to circulate freely provided they were officially pierced in the centre. Silver coins with roses between the coats of arms were made from silver obtained from the West of England mines.

Engravers and designers: Samuel Bull (d.c.1720), John Croker (1670-1740), Henry Harris (d.1704), John Roettier (1663-1698).

GOLD

3454

		F £	*VF* £	*EF* £		*F* £	*VF* £	*EF* £
3454	**Five Guineas.** First laur. bust r. regnal year on edge in words (e.g. 1699 = UNDECIMO) ↑↓							
	1699 UNDECIMO ..	1000	2250	4750	1700 DVODECIMO	1100	2500	5000
3455	**Five Guineas.**— elephant and castle below, 1699 UNDECIMO......					1350	3250	5500

3456

3457

		F	*VF*	*EF*
3456	**Five Guineas.** Second laur. bust r. ('fine work'), Plain or ornamental sceptres DECIMO TERTIO die axis ↑↓ 1701....................................	1000	3000	5750
3457	**Two Guineas.** ('fine work'), similar die axis ↑↓ 1701........................	1000	2000	3500

3458

	F	VF	EF		F	VF	EF
	£	£	£		£	£	£
3458 **Guinea**. First laur. bust r. die axis ↑↓							
1695	200	950	2000	1697	225	1000	2250
1696	225	1000	2250				
3459 **Guinea.** elephant and castle below die axis ↑↓							
1695	250	1000	2500	1696		*Extremely rare*	

3460

3463

ornamental sceptres

	F	VF	EF		F	VF	EF
3460 **Guinea.** Second laur. bust r. human-headed harp. die axis ↑↓							
1697	225	950	2250	1699	250	1000	2500
1698	200	850	1750	1700	200	850	1750
3461 **Guinea.** — elephant and castle below. die axis ↑↓							
1697	650	2000	—	1699		*Extremely rare*	
1698	300	1000	2500	1700	650	2000	—

	F	VF	EF
3462 **Guinea.** Second laur. bust. r. R. Human headed harp. Large lettering and large date, die axis ↑↓ 1698	200	850	1750
3463 **Guinea.** — R. Narrow crowns, plain or ornamented sceptres, die axis ↑↓ 1701	200	850	1750
3464 **Guinea.** — elephant and castle below, die axis ↑↓ 1701		*Extremely rare*	
3465 **Guinea.** Third laur. bust r. ('fine work'), die axis ↑↓ 1701	350	1100	3000

3466

3468

	F	VF	EF		F	VF	EF
3466 **Half-Guinea**. R. With early harp, die axis ↑↓ 1695					185	400	1500
3467 **Half-Guinea**. **—** elephant and castle. R. With early harp, die axis ↑↓							
1695	275	750	2000	1696	200	600	1750
3468 **Half-Guinea**. **—** R. With late harp, die axis ↑↓							
1697	240	650	1900	1700	150	300	1200
1698	150	300	1200	1701	150	300	1200
1699		*Extremely rare*					
3469 **Half-Guinea**. — elephant and castle, die axis ↑↓ 1698					225	600	2000

SILVER

3470

	F	VF	EF		F	VF	EF
	£	£	£		£	£	£

3470 Crown. First dr. bust, r. R.First harp, regnal year on edge in words (e.g. 1696 = OCTAVO) ↑↓

	F	VF	EF		F	VF	EF
1695 SEPTIMO	60	175	700	1696 G/D IN GRA	250	400	—
1695 OCTAVO	65	200	750	1696 — no stops	300	500	—
1695 OCTA∀O error	100	300	—	1696/5	300	500	—
1695 TVTA·EN error	*Extremely rare*			1696 GEI for DEI	275	600	—
1696 OCTAVO	50	150	600	1696 — no stops	300	—	—
1696 No stops on obverse	150	—	—				

3471

3471 Crown. Second dr. bust r. R. Second harp (hair across breast), 1696 (two varieties) die axis ↑↓ OCTAVO .... *Each unique*

3472

3472 Crown. Third dr. bust, r. R. First harp, die axis ↑↓ 1696 OCTAVO ....60 | 175 | 700

1696 TRICESIMO .... *Extremely rare*

		F £	VF £	EF £
3473	**Crown.** Second harp, die axis ↑↓ 1697 NONO	500	1250	8500

3474

3474	**Crown.** Third bust variety r. R. Third harp, ↑↓ 1700 DVODECIMO	65	200	700
	1700 D. TERTIO	80	250	900
	1700 ANN · error	250	—	—
	1700 ECIMO error		*Extremely rare*	
3475	**Halfcrown.** R. Small shields, 1696 die axis ↑↓ OCTAVO	45	125	400
	— — 1696 DECVS error	120	350	—
3476	**Halfcrown.** — B (*Bristol)* below bust, die axis ↑↓ 1696 OCTAVO	50	150	500

Chester Mint
3477

Exeter Mint
3478

3477	**Halfcrown.** — C (*Chester)* below bust, die axis ↑↓ 1696 OCTAVO	100	300	700
3478	**Halfcrown.** — E (*Exeter)* below bust, die axis ↑↓ 1696 OCTAVO	150	350	850
3479	**Halfcrown.** — N (*Norwich)* below bust, die axis ↑↓ 1696 OCTAVO	75	200	500
3480	**Halfcrown.** — y (*York)* below bust, die axis ↑↓ 1696 OCTAVO	100	300	700

3480

3481

3481	**Halfcrown** R. Large shield, early harp, die axis ↑↓ 1696 OCTAVO	50	125	400

		F £	VF £	EF £
3482	**Halfcrown.** — B (*Bristol)* below bust, die axis ↑↓ 1696 OCTAVO	50	150	400
3483	**Halfcrown.** — — C (*Chester)* below bust, die axis ↑↓ 1696 OCTAVO	60	200	500
3484	**Halfcrown.** — — E (*Exeter)* below bust, die axis ↑↓ 1696 OCTAVO	70	250	600
3485	**Halfcrown.** — — N (*Norwich)* below bust, die axis ↑↓ 1696 OCTAVO	95	300	750
3486	**Halfcrown.** — — y (*York)* below bust, die axis ↑↓ 1696 OCTAVO	65	200	500
	— — — die axis ↑↓ 1696 y *(York)*, Scots Arms at date		*Extremely rare*	
	— — die axis ↑↓ y over E 1696		*Extremely rare*	

3487

3488
Bristol Mint

3487 Halfcrown. R. Large shields, ordinary harp die axis ↑↓

	F £	VF £	EF £		F £	VF £	EF £
1696 OCTAVO	120	400	1000	1697 — GRR for GRA	*Fair* £750		
1697 NONO	40	100	350	1697/6 —	85	250	600

		F £	VF £	EF £
3488	**Halfcrown.** — — B (*Bristol)* below bust, die axis ↑↓ 1697 NONO	45	125	450
	1697 — no stops on reverse	60	200	500

3489

3489 Halfcrown. — — C *(Chester)* below bust die axis ↑↓

	F £	VF £	EF £		F £	VF £	EF £
1696 OCTAVO	95	300	750	1697 NONO	50	175	450

3490

Exeter Mint

	F £	VF £	EF £		F £	VF £	EF £

3490 Halfcrown. — — E *(Exeter)* below bust die axis ↑↓

1696 OCTAVO95	300	750	1697 NONO...............40	125	450
1696 NONO	*Extremely rare*		1697 — T▼TAMEN error	*Extremely rare*	
1697 OCTAVO...............	*Extremely rare*		1697 E over C or B under bust *Extremely rare*		

3491

3491 Halfcrown. — — N *(Norwich)* below bust die axis ↑↓

1696 OCTAVO100	350	850	1697 NONO...............50	175	450
1697 OCTAVO...............	*Extremely rare*		1697 — Scots Arms at date	*Fair* £550	

3492 Halfcrown. — — y *(York)* below bust, die axis ↑↓

1697 NONO...............40	125	450	1697 OCTAVO	*Extremely rare*

3493 Halfcrown. Second dr. bust r. (hair across breast), die axis ↑↓ 1696 OCTAVO *Unique*

3494

3494 Halfcrown. Dr. bust R. Modified large shields die axis ↑↓

1698 OCTAVO	*Extremely rare*		
1698 DECIMO	40	125	400
1698/7 —	*Extremely rare*		
1698 UNDECIMO	*Extremely rare*		
1699 UNDECIMO	70	200	550
1699 — Inverted A's for V's on edge	100	300	—
1699 — Scots Arms at date	*Extremely rare*		
1699 — Lion of Nassau inverted	250	—	—
1700 DVODECIMO	40	125	400
1700 D. TERTIO	50	175	500
1700 — DECVS error	85	225	600
1701 D. TERTIO	50	175	500
1701 — no stops on reverse	75	200	550

3495

3495 Halfcrown. – elephant and castle below bust, die axis ↑↓ 1701 D. TERTIO *Fair* 800

3496

3496 Halfcrown. – R. Plumes in angles, die axis ↑↓ 1701 D. TERTIO 125 350 900

First bust

Third bust

Third bust variety

3497
1st bust

3497
GVLELMVS error

3498
Bristol Mint

Exeter Mint
3500

	F	*VF*	*EF*		*F*	*VF*	*EF*
	£	£	£		£	£	£
3497 Shilling. First dr. bust die axis ↑↓							
1695	30	75	300	1697	20	50	175
1696	20	50	175	1697 E/A in DEI.............	*Extremely rare*		
1696 no stops on reverse	40	85	350	1697 GRI for GRA error	*Extremely rare*		
1696 MAB for MAG error	*Extremely rare*			1697 Arms of Scot/Ireland transposed..............	*Extremely rare*		
1696 GVLIEMVS error..	*Extremely rare*			1697 Irish Arms at date ..	*Extremely rare*		
1696 GVLIELMAS error	*Extremely rare*			1697 no stops on reverse	30	80	300
1696 GAVLIELMVS error	*Extremely rare*			1697 GVLELMVS error.	*Extremely rare*		
1696 GVLELMVS:	*Extremely rare*			1697 GVLIELMAS error	*Extremely rare*		
1696 2nd L over M.........	*Extremely rare*			1697 L/M in legend	*Extremely rare*		
1696-1669 error.........	500	—	—				
3498 Shilling. — B (*Bristol*) below bust die axis ↑↓							
1696	35	80	250	1697	35	85	275

3499

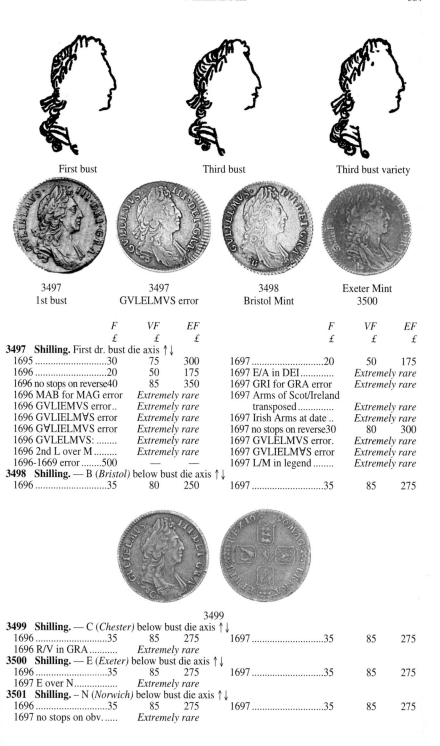

	F	*VF*	*EF*		*F*	*VF*	*EF*
3499 Shilling. — C (*Chester*) below bust die axis ↑↓							
1696	35	85	275	1697	35	85	275
1696 R/V in GRA...........	*Extremely rare*						
3500 Shilling. — E (*Exeter*) below bust die axis ↑↓							
1696	35	85	275	1697	35	85	275
1697 E over N................	*Extremely rare*						
3501 Shilling. – N (*Norwich*) below bust die axis ↑↓							
1696	35	85	275	1697	35	85	275
1697 no stops on obv......	*Extremely rare*						

F	VF	EF		F	VF	EF
	£	£	£		£	£	£

3502 Shilling. y *(York)* below bust die axis ↑↓

| 1696 |35 | 85 | 275 | 1697 Arms of Scot/Ireland | | | |
| 1697 |35 | 88 | 275 | transposed............. | *Extremely rare* | | |

1697 Arms of France/Ireland
transposed *Extremely rare*

3503 Shilling. —Y *(York)* below bust die axis ↑↓

| 1696 |45 | 90 | 300 | 1697 |45 | 90 | 275 |

1697 Y over *Extremely rare*

3504 3503
2nd bust York Mint – Y

3504 Shilling. Second dr. bust r. (hair across breast), die axis ↑↓ 1696............. *Unique*

3505 3507 3511
3rd bust Chester Mint 3rd bust var.

3505 Shilling. Third dr. bust r., die axis ↑↓ 169725 60 175

3506 Shilling. — B *(Bristol)* below bust, die axis ↑↓ 169745 100 300

3507 Shilling. — C *(Chester)* below bust die axis ↑↓

1696	100	250	700	1697 no stops on reverse60	125	450	
1697 FR.A error..........60	125	500	1697 Arms of Scotland				
1697	40	75	250	at date....................	*Extremely rare*		

3508 Shilling. — E *(Exeter)* below bust, die axis ↑↓

| 1696 | | *Extremely rare* | 1697 |45 | 90 | 300 |

3509 Shilling. — N *(Norwich)* below bust, die axis ↑↓ 169745 90 300

3510 Shilling. — y *(York)* below bust die axis ↑↓

| 1696 | | *Extremely rare* | 1697 |45 | 90 | 300 |

3511 Shilling. Third bust variety r. die axis ↑↓

| 1697 GⱯLIELMVS error | *Extremely rare* | 1697 GVLIELMⱯS error | *Extremely rare* |
| 1697 |20 | 50 | 175 | 1698 |30 | 75 | 250 |

3512 Shilling. — B *(Bristol)* below bust, die axis ↑↓ 169740 80 300

3513 Shilling. — C *(Chester)* below bust, die axis ↑↓ 1697......................80 200 550

3514 Shilling. — R. Plumes in angles, die axis ↑↓ 1698100 250 700

Third bust

Fourth bust

Fifth bust

3515
4th bust

3516
5th bust

	F £	*VF* £	*EF* £		*F* £	*VF* £	*EF* £
3515 Shilling Fourth dr. bust ('flaming hair') r. die axis ↑↓							
1698	70	200	700	1699	70	200	700
1698 No stops on reverse		*Extremely rare*					
3516 Shilling. Fifth dr. bust (hair high) r. die axis ↑↓							
1699	50	125	400	1700 Tall O's no stops			
1700	30	60	175	on reverse	45	75	225
1700 Circular small				1701	50	100	300
O's in date	35	65	200	1701 DEI/GRA		*Extremely rare*	
1700 no stop after DEI		*Extremely rare*					

3517

	F £	*VF* £	*EF* £		*F* £	*VF* £	*EF* £
3517 Shilling. — R. Plumes in angles die axis ↑↓							
1699	75	200	550	1701	75	200	500

3518

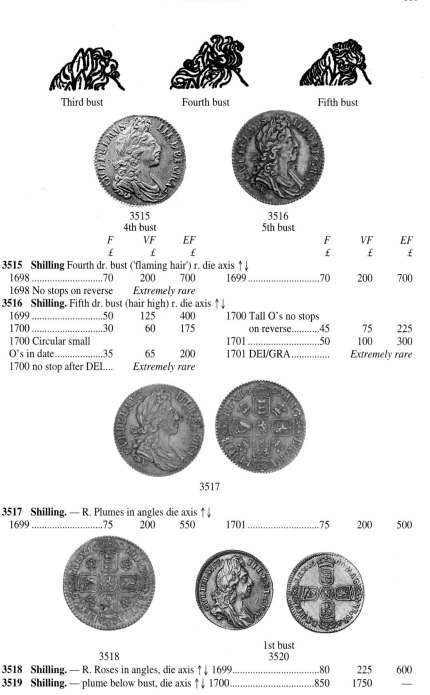

1st bust
3520

	F £	*VF* £	*EF* £
3518 Shilling. — R. Roses in angles, die axis ↑↓ 1699	80	225	600
3519 Shilling. — plume below bust, die axis ↑↓ 1700	850	1750	—

First bust

Third bust

Early harp. large crown.

Later harp, small crown.

		F	VF	EF		F	VF	EF
		£	£	£		£	£	£
3520	**Sixpence.** First dr. bust r. R. early harp die axis ↑↓							
	1695	35	75	275	1696/5	25	65	200
	1696	15	35	100	1696 no stops on obverse	25	65	200
	1696 French Arms at date	*Extremely rare*			1696 DFI for DEI	*Extremely rare*		
	1696 Scots Arms at date	*Extremely rare*						
3521	**Sixpence.** — — B *(Bristol)* below bust, die axis ↑↓ 1696					20	40	125
	— — 1696 B over E					*Extremely rare*		
3522	**Sixpence.** — — C *(Chester)* below bust, die axis ↑↓ 1696					30	65	200
3523	**Sixpence.** — — E *(Exeter)* below bust, die axis ↑↓ 1696					35	75	250
3524	**Sixpence.** — — N *(Norwich)* below bust, die axis ↑↓ 1696					50	100	275

3525

		F	VF	EF		F	VF	EF
3525	**Sixpence.** — — y *(York)* below bust, die axis ↑↓ 1696					20	50	150
3526	**Sixpence.** — — Y *(York)* below bust, die axis ↑↓ 1696					35	75	250
	— — — 1696 no stops on obverse					50	125	—
3527	**Sixpence.** — R. Later harp, large crowns, die axis ↑↓ 1696					45	100	275
	— — — 1696 no stops on obverse					50	125	300
3528	— — — B *(Bristol)* below bust die axis ↑↓							
	1696	40	100	275	1697	35	75	250
	1696 no stops on obv.	50	120	275				
3529	**Sixpence.** — — — C *(Chester)* below bust, die axis ↑↓ 1697					40	100	275
3530	**Sixpence.** — — — E *(Exeter)* below bust, die axis ↑↓ 1697					40	100	275
3531	**Sixpence.** — — small crowns die axis ↑↓							
	1696	40	90	250	1697 Arms of France/Ireland transposed	*Extremely rare*		
	1697 GVLIELMVS	50	125	250				
	1697	18	35	125				

Bristol Mint
3532

	F £	VF £	EF £		F £	VF £	EF £
3532 Sixpence. — — — B *(Bristol)* below bust die axis ↑↓							
1696	50	125	300	1697	30	65	175
1696 no stops on obverse	50	125	300	1697 B over E	40	100	225
3533 Sixpence. — — — C *(Chester)* below bust die axis ↑↓							
1696	50	125	375	1697 Irish shield at date..	*Extremely rare*		
1697	25	55	175				
3534 Sixpence. — — — E *(Exeter)* below bust, die axis ↑↓							
1697	30	65	200	1697 E over B	*Extremely rare*		
3535 Sixpence. — — — N *(Norwich)* below bust, die axis ↑↓							
1696	50	125	325	1697	20	40	125
1697 GVLIEMVS	*Extremely rare*						

3536

	F £	VF £	EF £		F £	VF £	EF £
3536 Sixpence. — — — y *(York)* below bust, die axis ↑↓							
1697	45	100	275	1697 Irish shield at date..	*Extremely rare*		

2nd bust
3537

Chester Mint
3540

	F £	VF £	EF £		F £	VF £	EF £
3537 Sixpence. Second dr. bust r. die axis ↑↓							
1696	200	375	—	1696 GVLELMVS	200	400	—
1697 GVLIELMVS	*Extremely rare*			1697	75	175	500
1697 G/I in GRA	*Extremely rare*			1697 GR/DE in GRA	*Extremely rare*		
1697 GVLIEMVS	*Extremely rare*						

3537A Sixpence. Third dr. bust, r. early harp, large crowns. E *(Exeter)* below bust, 1696 *Extremely rare*

3537B Sixpence. — — — Y *(York)* below bust, die axis ↑↓ 1696 *Extremely rare*

3538

	F £	VF £	EF £		F £	VF £	EF £
3538 Sixpence. Third dr. bust, r., R. Later harp, large crowns, die axis ↑↓							
1697 GVLIEIMVS ....Extremely rare							
1697	15	30	100	1699	45	120	300
1697 GVLIELMVS	*Extremely rare*			1700	20	35	95
1698	20	35	95	1701	25	45	150
3539 Sixpence.— — B *(Bristol)* below bust, die axis ↑↓							
1697	30	65	200	1697 IRA for FRA	*Extremely rare*		
3540 Sixpence.— — C *(Chester)* below bust, die axis ↑↓ 1697					40	85	250
3541 Sixpence.— — E *(Exeter)* below bust, die axis ↑↓ 1697					50	125	325
3542 Third dr. bust, r. R. Small crowns, die axis ↑↓							
1697	25	45	150	1697 G/D for GRA	*Extremely rare*		
3543 Sixpence.— — C *(Chester)* below bust, die axis ↑↓ 1697					35	75	225
3544 Sixpence.— — E *(Exeter)* below bust, die axis ↑↓ 1697					30	65	200

3545

3546

	F £	VF £	EF £		F £	VF £	EF £
3545 Sixpence.— — Y *(York)* below bust, die axis ↑↓ 1697					45	100	300
3546 Sixpence.— — R. Plumes in angles die axis ↑↓							
1698	25	60	175	1699	30	60	200
3547 Sixpence.— R. Roses in angles, die axis ↑↓							
1699	45	100	275	1699 GVLIELMVS	*Extremely rare*		

3548

3549

	F £	VF £	EF £		F £	VF £	EF £
3548 Sixpence.— plume below bust, die axis ↑↓ 1700					700	—	—
3549 Fourpence. R. 4 crowned die axis ↑↓							
1697			*Unique*	1700	11	25	90
1698	14	30	100	1701	14	30	100
1699	11	25	90	1702	10	25	80

3550

3551

3550 Threepence. R. 3 crowned die axis ↑↓

	F £	VF £	EF £		F £	VF £	EF £
1698	11	25	90	1701 GBA for GRA	15	35	100
1699	12	30	100	1701 small lettering	11	25	90
1700	11	25	90	1701 large lettering	12	30	90

3551 Twopence. R. Crown to edge of coin, large figure 2 die axis ↑↓

	F £	VF £	EF £
1698	15	40	100

3551A Twopence. – R Crown within inner circle of legend, smaller figure 2, die axis ↑↓

	F £	VF £	EF £		F £	VF £	EF £
1698	10	30	90	1700	9	25	80
1699	9	25	80	1701	9	25	80

3552 Penny. R. 1 crowned die axis ↑↓

	F £	VF £	EF £		F £	VF £	EF £
1698	10	25	80	1699	10	25	90
1698 IRA for FRA error	12	35	100	1700	10	25	90
1698 HI.BREX error	12	35	100	1701	10	25	90

3553

3553 Maundy Set. As last four. Uniform dates

	F £	VF £	EF £		F £	VF £	EF £
1698	75	150	350	1700	90	200	400
1699	90	200	400	1701	75	150	350

COPPER

3554

3554 Halfpenny. First issue. R. Britannia with r. hand raised die axis ↑↓

	F £	VF £	EF £		F £	VF £	EF £
1695	35	75	275	1697	25	65	225
1695 BRITΛNNIΛ error	100	—	—	1697 all stops omitted	125	—	—
1695 no stop on rev.	65	120	—	1697 I/E in TERTIVS	125	—	—
1695 no stops on obv.	65	120	—	1697 GVLILMVS, no rev. stop	*Extremely rare*		
1696	25	65	225	1697 no stop after TERTIVS	50	100	—
1696 GVLIEMVS, no rev. stop	*Extremely rare*			1698	35	85	300
1696 TERTVS error	100	—	—				

3555 Halfpenny. Second issue. R. Date in legend die axis ↑↓

	F £	VF £	EF £
1698 Stop after date	30	75	275
1699 no stop after date	25	65	225
1699 BRITΛNNIΛ error	100	—	—
1699 GVLIEMVS error	100	—	—
1699 BRITAN IA error	100	—	—

3556 Halfpenny. Third issue. R. Britannia with r. hand on knee die axis ↑↓

	F £	VF £	EF £
1699	25	65	225
1699 stop after date	100	—	—
1699 BRITΛNNIΛ error	75	150	—
1699 GVILELMVS error	125	—	—
1699 TERTVS error	125	—	—
1699 — no rev. stop	100	—	—
1699 no stops on obv.	75	150	—
1699 no stop after GVLIELMVS	75	150	—
1700	25	65	225
1700 no stops on obv.	75	150	—
1700 no stop after GVLIELMVS	75	150	—
1700 BRITΛNNIΛ error	35	75	300
1700 — no stop after	50	100	350
1700 BRIVANNIA error	*Extremely rare*		
1700 GVLIELMS	75	150	—
1700 GVLIEEMVS	50	100	350
1700 TER TIVS	40	85	325
1700 I/V in TERTIVS	125	—	—
1701	30	70	250
1701 BRITΛNNIΛ	50	100	350
1701 — no stops on obv.	125	—	—
1701 — inverted A's for V's	60	120	400

3557

3558

3557 Farthing. First issue die axis ↑↓

	F £	VF £	EF £
1695	35	95	350
1695 GVLIELMV error	100	—	—
1696	30	80	325
1697	25	70	300
1697 GVLIELMS error	125	—	—
1697 TERTIV error	100	—	—
1698	100	300	—
1698 B/G on rev.	100	—	—
1699	35	95	350
1699 GVLILEMVS•	50	120	—
1700	25	70	300
1700 RRITANNIA	125	—	—

3558 Farthing. Second issue. R. Date at end of legend die axis ↑↓

	F £	VF £	EF £
1698 Stop after date	40	125	450
1699 no stop after date	45	150	500
1699 no stop after GVLIELMVS	Extremely rare		
1699 — No stop before or after	*Extremely rare*		
1699 BRITΛNNIΛ	100	—	—
1699 BRITANNIA	100	—	—

Anne, the second daughter of James II, was born on 6th February 1665 and as a protestant succeeded to the throne on William III's death. Anne married Prince George of Denmark and produced 17 children, sadly none surviving to succeed to the throne. Anne died on 1st August 1714.

The Act of Union of 1707, which effected the unification of the ancient kingdoms of England and Scotland into a single realm, resulted in a change in the royal arms—on the Post-Union coinage the English lions and Scottish lion are emblazoned per pale on the top and bottom shields. After the Union the rose in the centre of the reverse of the gold coins is replaced by the Garter star.

Following a successful Anglo-Dutch expedition against Spain, bullion seized in Vigo Bay was sent to be minted into coin, and the coins made from this metal had the word VIGO placed below the Queen's bust.

Engravers and designers: Samuel Bull (d.c1720), Joseph Cave (d.c1760), James Clerk, John Croker (1670-1741), Godfrey Kneller (1646-1723)

GOLD

3560

Before Union with Scotland

	F	*VF*	*EF*		*F*	*VF*	*EF*
	£	£	£		£	£	£

3560 Five Guineas. Dr. bust l, regnal year on edge in words (e.g. 1705 = QVARTO) die axis ↑↓

1705 QVARTO	1500	2750	6500	1706 QVINTO	1250	2250	6000

3561 Five Guineas. VIGO below bust, die axis ↑↓ 1703 (Three varieties)

SECVNDO	—	2000	40000

3562

3563

3562 Guinea. Dr. bust l. die axis ↑↓

1702	250	850	2500	1706	350	1000	2750
1705	350	1000	2750	1707	400	1100	2750

3565

3564

		F £	VF £	EF £		F £	VF £	EF £
3563	**Guinea.** VIGO below bust, die axis ↑↓ 1703					3500	8000	15000
3564	**Half-Guinea.** Dr bust l. die axis ↑↓							
	1702	250	750	2000	1705	250	750	2000
3565	**Five Guineas.** VIGO below bust, 1703					2750	7000	12500

3566

After Union with Scotland. The shields on the reverse are changed to Post-Union type die axis ↑↓

		F £	VF £	EF £
3566	**Five Guineas.** Dr. bust l., regnal year on edge in words 1706 QVINTO	1350	2500	5500

3567

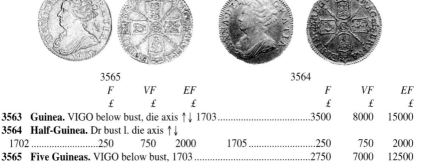

3568

		F £	VF £	EF £		F £	VF £	EF £
3567	**Five Guineas.** — R. Narrower shields, tall narrow crowns, larger rev. lettering, die axis ↑↓							
	1709 OCTAVO					1250	2200	5500
3568	**Five Guineas.** — R. Broader shields die axis ↑↓							
	1711 DECIMO	1250	2200	5500	1714/3 D. TERTIO	1250	2200	5500
	1713 DVODECIMO	1250	2200	5500	1714 D. TERTIO	1350	2500	6000

3569

	F £	VF £	EF £		F £	VF £	EF £
3569 Two Guineas. Dr. bust l. die axis ↑↓							
1709	500	1000	2500	1713	500	1000	2500
1711	500	1000	2500	1714/3	600	1250	2750
3570 Guinea. First dr. bust l. die axis ↑↓							
1707	250	750	1500	1708		*Extremely rare*	

3571 3574

	F	VF	EF		F	VF	EF
3571 Guinea. First dr. bust l. elephant and castle below, die axis ↑↓							
1707	450	1000	2750	1708		*Extremely rare*	
3572 Guinea. Second dr. bust l. die axis ↑↓							
1707		*Extremely rare*		1709	250	750	1750
1708	225	600	1500				
3573 Guinea. — elephant and castle below die axis ↑↓							
1708	450	1000	2500	1709	400	1000	2250
3574 Guinea. Third dr. bust l. die axis ↑↓							
1710	250	450	1250	1713	250	450	1250
1711	250	450	1250	1714	250	450	1250
1712	300	600	1500				

3575

	F	VF	EF		F	VF	EF
3575 Half-Guinea. Dr. bust l. die axis ↑↓							
1707	225	600	1500	1711	225	500	1250
1708	275	650	1650	1712	225	550	1500
1709	200	500	1250	1713	200	500	1250
1710	200	500	1250	1714	200	500	1250

SILVER

3576

	F £	VF £	EF £		F £	VF £	EF £

Before Union with Scotland

3576 Crown. VIGO below dr. bust, l., regnal year on edge in words (e.g. 1703 = TERTIO) die axis ↑↓
1703 TERTIO 175 600 2000

3577

3578

3577 Crown. Dr bust l. R. Plumes in angles, die axis ↑↓ 1705 QVINTO...350 1100 3000

3578 Crown. — R. Roses and plumes in angles die axis ↑↓
1706 QVINTO ....120 350 850 1707 SEXTO 135 400 950

3579

3579 Halfcrown . Dr. bust l. Regnal year on edge in words die axis ↑↓
1703 TERTIO..350 1000 —

3580 3581

	F	VF	EF		F	VF	EF
	£	£	£		£	£	£

3580 Halfcrown. VIGO below bust, die axis ↑↓ 1703 TERTIO 75 200 550

3581 Halfcrown. — R. Plumes in angles die axis ↑↓

1704 TERTIO............100 350 800 1705 QVINTO............85 250 700

3582 3583

3582 Halfcrown. — R. Roses and plumes in angles, die axis ↑↓

1706 QVINTO60 175 500 1707 SEXTO50 150 450

First bust Second bust

3583 Shilling. die axis ↑↓. First dr. bust l. 1702 ..50 200 400

3584

3584 Shilling. — R. Plumes in angles, die axis ↑↓ 1702...............................70 225 450

3585 Shilling. — VIGO below bust, die axis ↑↓

170260 175 450 1702 :ANNA *Extremely rare*

3586 3587

	F £	VF £	EF £		F £	VF £	EF £
3586 Shilling. Second dr. bust, l. VIGO below,die axis ↑↓ 1703					50	150	350
3587 Shilling. — plain, die axis ↑↓							
1704	400	850	—	1705	70	200	450
3588 Shilling. — R. Plumes in angles die axis ↑↓							
1704	75	225	500	1705	60	175	400
3589 Shilling. — R. Roses and plumes in angles die axis ↑↓							
1705	55	175	350	1707	55	175	375
3590 Sixpence. VIGO below dr. bust, l. die axis ↑↓ 1703					30	65	150
3591 Sixpence. Dr bust l., R. Angles plain, die axis ↑↓ 1705					45	100	250
3592 Sixpence. — R. Early shields, plumes in angles, die axis ↑↓ 1705					35	85	200

3593

Early Shield

Late Shield

	F	VF	EF		F	VF	EF
3593 Sixpence. – R. Late shields, plumes in angles, die axis ↑↓ 1705					45	95	225
3594 Sixpence. – R. Roses and plumes in angles die axis ↑↓							
1705	45	100	250	1707	35	75	175
3595 Fourpence. First dr. bust l. small face, curls at back of head point downwards. R Small crown above the figure 4 die axis ↑↓							
1703	8	25	70	1704	6	20	60

3595

3595C

	F	VF	EF		F	VF	EF
3595A Fourpence. Second dr. bust l. larger face, curls at back of head point upwards die axis ↑↓							
1705	8	25	70	1709	6	20	60
1706	6	20	60	1710	6	20	60
1708	6	20	60				
3595B –Fourpence. R Large crown with pearls on arch, larger serifs on the figure 4 die axis ↑↓							
1710	6	20	60	1713	6	20	60
3595C Fourpence. Second dr. bust l., but with re-engraved hair die axis ↑↓							
1710	6	20	60	1713	6	20	60
3596 Threepence. First dr. bust l., broader, tie riband pointing outwards. R. Crowned 3 die axis ↑↓							
1703 7 above crown	10	30	80	1703 7 not above crown	10	30	80

	F	*VF*	*EF*		*F*	*VF*	*EF*
	£	£	£		£	£	£

3596A Threepence. Second dr. bust l., taller and narrow, tie riband pointing inwards die axis ↑↓

1704	8	25	70	1706	6	20	60
1705	8	25	70				

3596B

3596B Threepence. Third dr. bust l., similar to first bust but larger and hair more finely engraved, die axis ↑↓

1707	6	20	60	1710	6	20	60
1708	6	20	60	1713	6	20	60
1708/7	6	20	60	1713 mule with 4d obv.			
1709	6	20	60	die	10	30	100

3597 Twopence. First dr. bust l., as fourpence, R. Crown to edge of coin, small figure 2 die axis ↑↓

1703	10	25	70	1705	6	20	50
1704	6	20	50	1706	7	20	60
1704 No stops on obv.	10	25	70	1707	7	20	60

3597A Twopence. Second dr. bust l., as fourpence, R Crown within inner circle of legend, large figure 2die axis ↑↓

1708	6	20	50	1710	6	20	50
1709	8	25	60	1713	6	20	50

3598 Penny. R. Crowned 1 die axis ↑↓

1703	10	25	80	1709	8	25	70
1705	8	25	70	1710	12	30	90
1706	8	25	70	1713/0	10	25	80
1708	12	30	90				

3599

	F	*VF*	*EF*		*F*	*VF*	*EF*
	£	£	£		£	£	£

3599 Maundy Set. As last four. Uniform dates

1703	75	125	350	1709	75	125	300
1705	75	125	350	1710	80	140	350
1706	65	100	250	1713	70	115	275
1708	80	140	350				

After Union with Scotland

The shields on the reverse are changed to the Post-Union types. The Edinburgh coins have been included here as they are now coins of Great Britain.

Edinburgh Mint
3600

	F £	VF £	EF £		F £	VF £	EF £
3600 Crown. Second dr. bust, l. E (Edinburgh) below, regnal year on edge in words, die axis ↑↓ (e.g. 1708 = SEPTIMO)							
1707 SEXTO	85	300	600	1708/7 SEPTIMO	100	375	700
1708 SEPTIMO	95	325	650				

3601

	F £	VF £	EF £		F £	VF £	EF £
3601 Crown. plain die axis ↑↓							
1707 SEPTIMO	80	250	600	1708 SEPTIMO	110	400	—
3602 Crown. — R. Plumes in angles, die axis ↑↓							
1708 SEPTIMO	125	400	850	1708 — BR for BRI	*Extremely rare*		

3603

	F £	VF £	EF £
3603 Crown. Third dr. bust. l. R. Roses and plumes, 1713 DVODECIMO	80	350	750

3604

	F £	VF £	EF £		F £	VF £	EF £
3604 Halfcrown. R. Plain, regnal year on edge in words (e.g. 1709 = OCTAVO), die axis ↑↓							
1707 SEPTIMO	45	125	400	1709 OCTAVO	40	100	400
1708 SEPTIMO	40	100	400	1713 DVODECIMO	50	125	400
3605 Halfcrown. — E below bust die axis ↑↓							
1707 SEXTO	40	100	400	1708 SEPTIMO	40	100	400
1707 SEPTIMO		*Extremely rare*		1709 OCTAVO	200	500	—

3606

Edinburgh Mint
3609

3606 Halfcrown. R. Plains in angles, die axis ↑↓ 1708 SEPTIMO.............60 200 450

3607

	F £	VF £	EF £		F £	VF £	EF £
3607 Halfcrown. – R. Roses and plumes in angles die axis ↑↓							
1710 NONO	60	200	475	1714 D. TERTIO	50	175	400
1712 UNDECIMO	50	125	450	1714/3 D. TERTIO	100	250	550
1713 DVODECIMO	60	200	450				

3608

3609A

	F £	VF £	EF £		F £	VF £	EF £

3608 Shilling. Second dr. bust, l. E *(Edinburgh)* below, die axis ↑↓

	F	VF	EF		F	VF	EF
1707	35	100	300	1708	70	175	400
1707 no stops on reverse	*Extremely rare*			1708 no rays to garter star	*Extremely rare*		

3609 Shilling. — E* *(Edinburgh)* below die axis ↑↓

	F	VF	EF		F	VF	EF
1707	70	200	450	1708/7	*Extremely rare*		
1708	45	120	325				

Third bust

Fourth bust

3610

3611

3610 Shilling Third dr. bust. l. R. Plain, die axis ↑↓

	F	VF	EF		F	VF	EF
1707	25	75	200	1709	25	75	200
1708	20	60	175	1711	100	300	600

3611 Shilling. — R. Plumes in angles die axis ↑↓

	F	VF	EF		F	VF	EF
1707	40	100	300	1708	35	75	250

3612 Shilling. — E below die axis ↑↓

	F	VF	EF		F	VF	EF
1707	35	75	250	1708/7	75	175	400
1708	55	150	350				

3613 Shilling. Second dr. bust l. R. Roses and plumes, die axis ↑↓ 1708 .....95 225 550

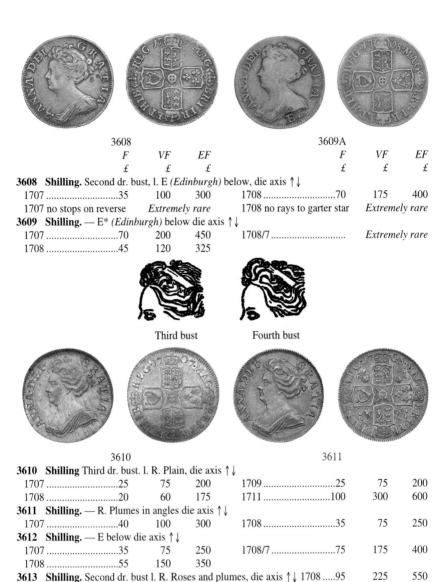

3614

3614 Shilling. Third dr. bust l. R. Roses and plumes die axis ↑↓

	F	VF	EF		F	VF	EF
1708	45	120	300	1710	25	65	200

3615
Edinburgh bust – E*

3620
Edinburgh Mint

3623

	F £	*VF* £	*EF* £		*F* £	*VF* £	*EF* £
3615 Shilling. 'Edinburgh' bust, E* below, die axis ↑↓							
1707	*Extremely rare*			1709	70	175	450
1708	65	150	400				
3615A Shilling. 'Edinburgh' bust E* below, struck from crude local dies, very large top two curls							
1708	800	—	—				
3616 Shilling. — E below, die axis ↑↓ 1709					200	500	—
3617 Shilling. Fourth dr. bust. l. R. Roses and plumes die axis ↑↓							
1710	50	150	350	1714	25	70	200
1712	25	70	200	1714/3		*Extremely rare*	
1713/2	30	85	250				
3618 Shilling. — plain, die axis ↑↓ 1711					20	60	125
3619 Sixpence. Normal dr. bust. l. R. Plain die axis ↑↓							
1707	20	45	120	1711	20	40	95
1707 BR. FRA error	*Extremely rare*			1711 Large Lis	20	40	95
1708	25	50	125				
3620 Sixpence. — E *(Edinburgh)* below bust die axis ↑↓							
1707	25	50	125	1708/7	40	90	200
1708	35	75	175				
3621 Sixpence. — E* *(Edinburgh)* below bust, die axis ↑↓							
1708	35	85	200	1708/7	40	95	225
3622 Sixpence. 'Edinburgh' bust, l. E* below, die axis ↑↓ 1708					40	95	225
3623 Sixpence. Normal dr. bust. l. R. Plumes in angles die axis ↑↓							
1707	20	60	175	1708	35	75	225
3624 Sixpence. — R. Roses and plumes in angles, die axis ↑↓ 1710					35	75	225

COPPER

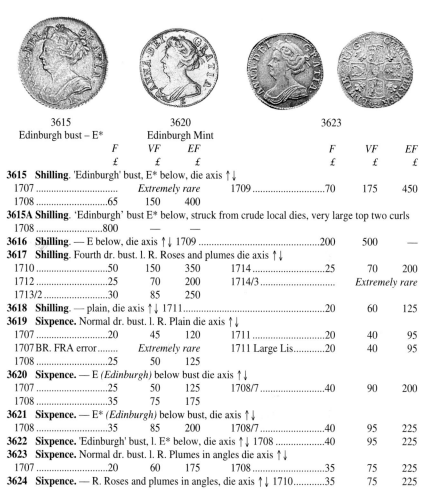

3625

	F £	*VF* £	*EF* £
3625 Farthing. Dr. bust l. 1714 pattern only, die axis ↑↓	175	250	450

GEORGE I, 1714-27

George I was born on 28th May 1660 son of Ernest, Elector of Hanover and Sophia grandaughter of James I, and inherited the English Throne on a technicality, Parliament considered him a better alternative than James Edward Stuart – Anne's half-brother. He was however, thoroughly German, did not want to learn English and spent over half his reign in Germany. He brought two mistresses with him to England while his wife ironically languished in a German prison on a charge of adultery. His reign created a government that could run independently of the King. The office of Prime Minister was created in 1721. He also kept England out of war for his entire reign, and he died on 11 June 1727.

The coins of the first of the Hanoverian kings have the arms of the Duchy of Brunswick and Luneberg on one of the four shields, the object in the centre of the shield being the Crown of Charlemagne. The King's German titles also appear, in abbreviated form, and name him 'Duke of Brunswick and Luneberg. Arch-treasurer of the Holy Roman Empire, and Elector', and on the Guinea of 1714, 'Prince Elector'. A Quarter-Guinea was struck for the first time in 1718, but it was of an inconvenient size, and the issue was discontinued.

Silver coined from bullion supplied to the mint by the South Sea Company in 1723 shows the Company's initials S.S.C.; similarly Welsh Copper Company bullion has the letters W.C.C. below the King's bust; and plumes and an interlinked CC in the reverse angles. Roses and plumes together on the reverse indicate silver supplied by the Company for Smelting Pit Coale and Sea Coale.

Engravers and Designers: Samuel Bull (d.c.1720), John Croker (1670-1741), John Rudulf Ochs Snr, (1673-c.1748), Norbert Roettier (b.1665)

Prime Minister: Sir Robert Walpole (1676 – 1745) –Whig, 1721-42

GOLD

3626

	F £	*VF* £	*EF* £		*F* £	*VF* £	*EF* £

3626 Five Guineas. Laur. head r. regnal year on edge in words (e.g. 1717 = TERTIO) die axis↑↓

1716 SECVNDO	1400	2750	6000	1720 SEXTO	1500	3000	6500
1717 TERTIO	1500	3000	6500	1726 D. TERTIO	1400	2750	6000

3627

	F	VF	EF		F	VF	EF
	£	£	£		£	£	£

3627 Two Guineas. Laur. head r. die axis ↑↓

| 1717 | 550 | 1100 | 2500 | 1726 | 450 | 900 | 2250 |
| 1720 | 500 | 1000 | 2500 | | | | |

3628 3630 3631

3628 Guinea. First laur. head r. R. Legend ends ET PR . EL (Prince Elector), die axis ↑↓

| 1714 | | | | 750 | 1500 | 2750 |

3629 Guinea. Second laur. head, r. tie with two ends, R.
normal legend ↑↓ 1715 275 750 2000

3630 Guinea. Third laur. head, r. no hair below truncation die axis ↑↓

| 1715 | 225 | 600 | 1750 | 1716 | 250 | 700 | 1750 |

3631 Guinea. — Fourth laur. head, r. tie with loop at one end die axis ↑↓

1716	200	650	1750	1720	200	650	1750
1717	225	700	1750	1721	225	700	2000
1718		*Extremely rare*		1722	200	650	1750
1719	200	650	1750	1723	225	700	1750
1719/6		*Extremely rare*					

3632 Guinea. — elephant and castle below die axis ↑↓

| 1721 | | *Extremely rare* | | 1722 | | *Extremely rare* | |

3633 3635

3633 Guinea. Fifth (older) laur. head, r. tie with two ends die axis ↑↓

1723	225	700	1750	1726	200	650	1650
1724	225	700	1750	1727	250	750	2250
1725	225	700	1750				

3634 Guinea. — elephant and castle below, die axis ↑↓ 1726 600 1750 —

	F	VF	EF		F	VF	EF
	£	£	£		£	£	£

3635 Half-Guinea. First laur. head r. die axis ↑↓

1715	200	400	850	1721		*Extremely rare*	
1717	175	350	750	1722	175	350	750
1718	150	300	700	1723		*Extremely rare*	
1719	150	300	700	1724	200	400	850
1720	225	450	900				

3636 Half-Guinea.— elephant and castle below, die axis ↑↓ 1721 .... *Extremely rare*

3637

3638

3637 Half-Guinea. Second (older) laur. head r. die axis ↑↓

1725	150	200	500	1727	175	300	850
1726	150	250	600				

3638 Quarter-Guinea. die axis ↑↓ 1718 ....60 100 250

SILVER

3639

3639 Crown. R. Roses and plumes in angles, regnal year on edge in words (e.g. 1716 = SECVNDO) die axis ↑↓

1716 SECVNDO	165	375	1100	1720 SEXTO	225	575	2250
1718/6 QUINTO	195	400	1500	1726 D. TERTIO	225	500	2000
1720/18 SEXTO	195	425	1500				

3640 Crown. – R. SSC (South Sea Company) in angles, die axis ↑↓
1723 DECIMO 195 400 1000

3641

3641 Halfcrown. R. Angles plain (pattern only), die axis ↑↓ 1715 *FDC* £4000

3642

3643

	F	*VF*	*EF*		*F*	*VF*	*EF*
	£	£	£		£	£	£

3642 Halfcrown. R. Roses and plumes in angles, regnal year on edge in words (e.g. 1717 = TIRTIO)

	F	*VF*	*EF*		*F*	*VF*	*EF*
1715 SECVNDO	95	275	750	1717 TIRTIO	120	325	850
1715 Edge wording out of order	200	400	1000	1720/17 SEXTO	95	275	750
1715 Plain edge	*Extremely rare*			1720 SEXTO	250	750	1600

3643 Halfcrown. – R. SSC in angles, die axis ↑↓ 1723 DECIMO 85 325 750

3644

3644 Halfcrown. – R. Small roses and plumes, die axis ↑↓ 1726 D. TERTIO..1250 3000 5000

3645

3646

3645 Shilling. First dr. bust. r. R. Roses and plumes in angles, die axis ↑↓

	F	*VF*	*EF*		*F*	*VF*	*EF*
1715	35	85	300	1720/18	85	250	600
1716	75	200	550	1721/0	40	110	350
1717	40	95	325	1721 — roses and plumes error	*Extremely rare*		
1718	35	85	300	1722	40	95	325
1719	70	175	525	1723	55	150	425
1720	40	95	325				

3646 Shilling. — plain (i.e. no marks either side) die axis ↑↓

	F	*VF*	*EF*		*F*	*VF*	*EF*
1720	35	85	300	1721/0	100	225	600
1720 large O	40	95	325	1721/19	120	275	700
1721	90	200	600				

3647

3649

	F £	VF £	EF £		F £	VF £	EF £

3647 Shilling. R. SSC in angles, die axis ↑↓

	F £	VF £	EF £		F £	VF £	EF £
1723	25	45	150	1723 C/SS in 3rd quarter	35	75	200
1723 French Arms at date	75	175	500				

3648 Shilling. Second dr. bust, r. bow to tie. R. Similar, die axis ↑↓ 1723 ...35 75 250

3649 Shilling. — R. Roses and plumes in angles die axis ↑↓

	F £	VF £	EF £		F £	VF £	EF £
1723	50	100	300	1726	400	900	—
1724	50	100	300	1727	375	850	—
1725	50	100	300	1727 no stops on rev.	400	900	—
1725 no stops on obv.	75	120	350				

3650

3651

3650 Shilling. — W.C.C. (Welsh Copper Company) below bust die axis ↑↓

	F £	VF £	EF £		F £	VF £	EF £
1723	225	450	1500	1725	225	450	1500
1724	225	450	1500	1726	225	450	1500

3651 Sixpence. R. Roses and plumes in angles, die axis ↑↓

	F £	VF £	EF £		F £	VF £	EF £
1717	45	100	300	1720/17	45	100	300
1717 Plain edge	*Extremely rare*						

3652

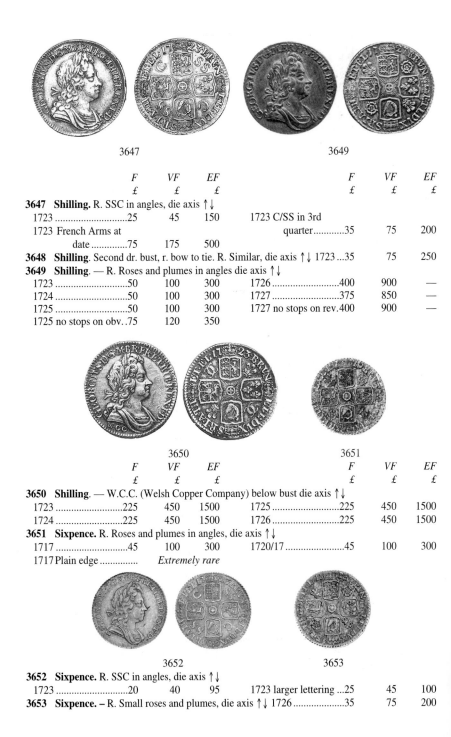

3653

3652 Sixpence. R. SSC in angles, die axis ↑↓

	F £	VF £	EF £		F £	VF £	EF £
1723	20	40	95	1723 larger lettering	25	45	100

3653 Sixpence. – R. Small roses and plumes, die axis ↑↓ 1726 ...35 75 200

F	VF	EF		F	VF	EF
	£	£	£		£	£	£

3654 Fourpence. Dr. bust r. R. crowned 4, die axis ↑↓

	F	VF	EF		F	VF	EF
1717	9	25	80	1723	9	25	80
1721	9	25	80	1727	12	30	90

3655 Threepence. R. crowned 3, die axis ↑↓

1717	8	25	70	1723	9	25	80
1721	9	25	80	1727 small lettering	9	25	80

3656 Twopence. R. crowned 2, die axis ↑↓

1717	6	18	45	1726	5	15	40
1721	5	15	40	1727 small lettering	8	20	50
1723	9	25	60				

3657 Penny. R. crowned 1, die axis ↑↓

1716	5	18	40	1723	6	20	45
1718	5	18	40	1725	5	18	40
1720	5	18	40	1726	8	25	50
1720 HIPEX error	10	50	80	1727 BRI·FR	10	40	70

3658

3658 Maundy Set. As last four. Uniform dates

1723	80	150	350	1727	75	130	325

COPPER

3659

3659 Halfpenny. 'Dump' issue obv. legend continuous over bust, plain edge, die axis ↑↓

1717	25	70	275	1718 no stops on obv.	50	150	—
1717 no stops on obv.	50	150	—	1719	350	—	—
1718	25	70	275	1719 grained edge	500	—	—

3660

3660 Halfpenny. Second issue, second obverse, plain left shoulder strap, less hair to the right of tie knot, plain edge, die axis ↑↓

	F £	*VF* £	*EF* £		*F* £	*VF* £	*EF* £
1719	35	85	300	1722	30	70	250
1719 grained edge	500	—	—	1722 ∀ for V on obv.	40	150	—
1720	25	65	225	1723	25	65	225
1721	30	70	250	1723 no stop on rev.	50	180	—
1721 stop after date	40	90	300	1724	25	65	225
1721/0	40	90	300				

3661

3662

3661 Farthing. 'Dump' issue, die axis ↑↓ 1717 ....120 300 500

3662 Farthing. Second issue die axis ↑↓

	F £	*VF* £	*EF* £		*F* £	*VF* £	*EF* £
1719	25	65	200	1721	25	65	200
1719 no stop on rev.	40	125	—	1721/0	35	85	275
1719 large lettering on obv.	50	150	—	1721 stop after date	35	80	250
				1722	30	75	250
1719 — no stops on obv.	40	150	—	1722 obv. large letters	40	100	300
				1723 R/ᴚ in REX	125	—	—
1719 — no stops on rev.	50	150	—	1723	30	75	250
1720	25	65	200	1724	30	75	250
1720 obv. large letters	50	150	—				

GEORGE II, 1727-60

George II was born on 30 October 1683 and was raised in Hanover, but upon his succession to the throne as George I's only child, he adapted himself to English society. His passions were the military, music and his wife – Caroline of Auspach, though he despised his eldest son Frederick as his own father despised him. George declared war on Spain in 1739 and he was the last King to have personally led troops into battle. Upon his death on 25 October 1760 the throne passed to his grandson George as Frederick had already died.

Silver was coined only spasmodically by the Mint during this reign; and no copper was struck after 1754. Gold coins made from bullion supplied by the East India Company bear the Company's initials. Some of the treasure seized by Admiral Anson during his circumnavigation of the globe, 1740-4, and by other privateers, was made into coin, which had the word LIMA below the king's bust to celebrate the expedition's successful harassment of the Spanish Colonies in the New World. Hammered gold was finally demonetized in 1733.

Engravers and designers: John Croker (1670-1741), John Rudolf Ochs Snr (1673-1748) and jnr (1704-88), Johann Sigismund Tanner (c.1706-75)

Prime Ministers: Sir Robert Walpole (1676-1745) Whig, 1721-43; Spencer Compton (1673-1743) Whig 1742-3; Henry Pelham (c.1695-1754) Whig 1743-54; William Cavendish (1720-1764) Whig 1756-7; Thomas Pelham-Holles (1693-1768) Whig 1754-6; 1757-62.

GOLD

3663A

	F £	VF £	EF £		F £	VF £	EF £
3663 Five Guineas. Young laur. head l. R. Crowned shield of arms, die axis ↑↓ regnal year on edge in words (e.g. 1729 = TERTIO) 1729 TERTIO					1000	2250	5250
3663A Five Guineas. — R. Revised shield garnish die axis ↑↓							
1731 QVARTO	1000	2000	5000	1741/35 D. QVARTO	1000	2000	5000
1735 OCTAVO	1000	2000	5000	1741 D. QVARTO	950	2000	4750
1738 DVODECIMO	1000	2000	5000				
3664 Five Guineas. — E.I.C. (East India Company) below; die axis ↑↓ 1729 TERTIO					1000	2250	5250

3665

	F £	VF £	EF £		F £	VF £	EF £
3665 Five Guineas. Old laur. head, l. LIMA below, ↑↓1746 D. NONO	1000	2250	5250				
3666 Five Guineas. — plain die axis ↑↓							
1748 V. SECVNDO	950	2000	4750	1753 V. SEXTO	950	2000	4750

3667

3667A

3667 Two Guineas. Young laur. head l. R Crown with rounded arches, die axis ↑↓

	F	VF	EF		F	VF	EF
1734/3	800	1750	—				

3667A* Two Guineas. – R. Crown with pointed arches, new type of shield garnishing die axis ↑↓

	F	VF	EF		F	VF	EF
1735	375	800	1750	1739	300	600	1500
1738	350	600	1250				

** Beware recent forgeries*

3668

3668* Two Guineas. Intermediate laur. head l. die axis ↑↓

	F	VF	EF		F	VF	EF
1739	350	600	1250	1740	375	600	1250

3669* Two Guineas. Old laur. head l. die axis ↑↓ 1740/39 500 850 1650

	F	VF	EF		F	VF	EF
1748	375	750	2000	1753	475	950	2500

**Beware recent forgeries.*
Overstruck dates are listed only if commoner than normal date or if no normal date is known.

F	VF	EF			F	VF	EF
	£	£	£			£	£	£

3670 Guinea. First young laur. head, l. small lettering, die axis ↑↓ 1727 ...500 1250 2750

	3671					3674		
	F	VF	EF			F	VF	EF
	£	£	£			£	£	£

3671 Guinea. larger lettering, smaller shield, die axis ↑↓

1727	300	750	2000	1728	350	850	2250

3672 Guinea. Second (narrower) young laur. head l. die axis ↑↓

1730	300	750	2000	1732	300	750	2000
1731	250	650	1750				

3673 Guinea. — E.I.C. below die axis ↑↓

1729	450	1100	2500	1732	350	850	2250
1731	400	800	2250				

3674 Guinea. — larger lettering on *obv.* die axis ↑↓

1732	275	700	1750	1736	250	650	1750
1733	200	550	1500	1737	275	700	2000
1734	200	550	1500	1738	275	700	2000
1735	225	600	1650				

3675 Guinea. — — E.I.C. below, die axis ↑↓ 1732350 850 2250

3676 Guinea. Intermediate laur. head l. die axis ↑↓

1739	200	450	1500	1741/39		*Extremely rare*	
1740	225	500	1750	1743		*Extremely rare*	

3677 Guinea. — E.I.C. below, die axis ↑↓ 1739350 750 2500

3678 Guinea. — larger lettering on *obv.*, GEORGIVS die axis ↑↓

1745					275	600	2000

	3678A		3679		3680	

3678A Guinea. — as last but reads GEORGIVS die axis ↑↓

1746			250	450	1500

3679 Guinea. LIMA below, die axis ↑↓ 1745 ...650 1500 3000

3680 Guinea. Old laur. head l. die axis ↑↓

1747	200	350	1000	1753	175	275	900
1748	175	275	900	1755	200	375	1000
1749	175	275	900	1756	175	250	850
1750	200	300	900	1758	150	225	800
1751	175	250	850	1759	150	225	800
1752	175	250	850	1760	175	250	850

	F £	VF £	EF £		F £	VF £	EF £

3681 Half-Guinea. Young laur. head. l. R First shield, die axis ↑↓

1728	200	450	1250	1729	250	500	1500

3681A

3681A Half-Guinea. R. Modified garnished shield die axis ↑↓

1730	450	1000	—	1735			*?exists*
1731	300	700	2000	1736	200	450	1250
1732	250	500	1500	1737		*Extremely rare*	
1733			*?exists*	1738	175	400	1000
1734	175	400	1000	1739	175	400	1000

3682 Half-Guinea. — E.I.C. below die axis ↑↓

1729	300	700	2000	1732		*Extremely rare*	
1730	500	1000	—	1739		*Extremely rare*	
1731		*Extremely rare*					

3676

3683A

3683 Half-Guinea. Intermediate laur. head l. die axis ↑↓

1740	300	700	2000	1745	300	700	2000
1743		*Extremely rare*					

3683A Half-Guinea. — as last but reads GEORGIVS, die axis ↑↓ 1746......175 400 1000

3684

3685

3684 Half-Guinea. — LIMA below, die axis ↑↓ 1745 ....500 1500 3000

3685 Half-Guinea. Old laur. head l. die axis ↑↓

1747	250	550	1500	1753	150	300	600
1748	150	325	700	1755	125	275	550
1749		*Extremely rare*		1756	125	275	550
1750	175	350	850	1758	125	275	550
1751	175	350	800	1759	120	250	500
1752	175	350	800	1760	120	250	500

SILVER

3686

	F £	VF £	EF £		F £	VF £	EF £

3686 Crown. Young dr. bust. l. R. Roses and plumes in angles, regnal year
on edge in words (e.g. 1736 = NONO), die axis ↑↓

1732 SEXTO	120	350	850	1734 No A in ANNO	200	600	1400
1732 Proof, plain edge *FDC* £3000				1735 OCTAVO	120	350	850
1734 SEPTIMO	150	400	1000	1736 NONO	100	325	800

3687 Crown. — R. Roses in angles die axis ↑↓

1739 DVODECIMO	125	300	850	1741 D. QVARTO	100	300	750

3688

3688 Crown. Old dr. bust l. R. Roses in angles, die axis ↑↓ 1743 D.
SEPTIMO ..100 300 750

3689 Crown. — LIMA below, die axis ↑↓ 1746 D. NONO.......................100 300 750

3690 3691

3690 Crown. — Plain (i.e. no marks either side) die axis ↑↓
1746 Proof only, VICESIMO *FDC* £2500

1750 V. QVARTO	150	350	850	1751 V. QVARTO	175	400	900

3691 Halfcrown. Young dr. bust l. R. plain (pattern only), 1731 *FDC* £2500

3692

3693

	F £	VF £	EF £		F £	VF £	EF £
3692 Halfcrown. Young dr. bust l. R. Roses and plumes, regnal year on edge in words (e.g. 1732 = SEXTO), die axis ↑↓							
1731 QVINTO	65	200	650	1735 OCTAVO	75	225	700
1732 SEXTO	65	200	650	1736 NONO	95	250	800
1734 SEPTIMO	75	225	700				
3693 Halfcrown. — R. Roses in angles die axis ↑↓							
1739 DVODECIMO	50	125	500	1741 D. QVARTO	60	150	550
1741 Large *obv.* letters	75	200	600	1741/39 D. QVARTO	120	300	750
3694 Halfcrown. Old dr. bust. l. GEORGIUS R. Roses in angles die axis ↑↓							
1743 D. SEPTIMO	45	100	450	1745/3 D. NONO	65	125	500
1745 D. NONO	45	100	450				
3695 Halfcrown. — LIMA below die axis ↑↓				1745 D. NONO	35	85	275
3695A Halfcrown. — as last but reads GEORGIVS die axis ↑↓							
1746 D. NONO	35	85	275	1746/5 D. NONO	50	120	450

3696

3696 Halfcrown. — R. Plain angles die axis ↑↓

1746 proof only VICESIMO *FDC* £850

	F £	VF £	EF £		F £	VF £	EF £
1750 V. QVARTO	75	200	650	1751 V. QVARTO	90	250	800

3697

3697 Shilling. Young dr. bust. l. R. Plumes in angles, die axis ↑↓

	F £	VF £	EF £		F £	VF £	EF £
1727	50	225	600	1731	65	250	700

3698

3699

3698 Shilling. R. Roses and plumes in angles, die axis ↑↓

Date	F £	VF £	EF £	Date	F £	VF £	EF £
1727	35	85	300	1731	35	85	300
1728	45	95	350	1732	45	95	350
1729	45	95	350				

3699 Shilling. — larger lettering. R. Roses and plumes in angles die axis ↑↓

Date	F £	VF £	EF £	Date	F £	VF £	EF £
1734	30	70	250	1736/5	50	120	350
1735	30	70	250	1737	30	70	250
1736	30	70	250				

3700

3701

3700 Shilling. — R. Plain, die axis ↑↓ 1728 ... 125 | 300 | 600

3701 Shilling. — R. Roses in angles die axis ↑↓

Date	F £	VF £	EF £	Date	F £	VF £	EF £
1739	25	60	200	1741	30	65	225
1739/7	*Extremely rare*			1741/39	300	600	—
1739 smaller garter star	85	200	550				

3702

3703A

3702 Shilling. Old dr. bust, l. GEORGIUS R. Roses in angles die axis ↑↓

Date	F £	VF £	EF £	Date	F £	VF £	EF £
1743	20	45	200	1745/3	50	150	350
1745	30	75	225	1747	25	65	200

3703 Shilling. — LIMA below die axis ↑↓ 1745 ... 15 | 45 | 175

3703A Shilling. – as last but reads GEORGIVS die axis ↑↓

Date	F £	VF £	EF £	Date	F £	VF £	EF £
1746	85	175	550	1746/5	100	200	600

3704

3704 Shilling. — R. plain angles die axis ↑↓

	F £	VF £	EF £
1746 Proof only *FDC* £600			
1750	30	75	300
1750/6	50	100	350
1750 Wide O	50	100	350
1751	50	150	400
1758	15	25	65

3705

3706

3707

	F £	VF £	EF £
3705 Sixpence. Young dr. bust. l. R. Angles plain, die axis ↑↓ 1728	60	150	300
3706 Sixpence. — R. Plumes in angles die axis ↑↓ 1728	40	90	200

3707 Sixpence. — R. Roses and plumes in angles die axis ↑↓

	F £	VF £	EF £
1728	20	50	120
1731	20	50	120
1732	20	50	120
1734	30	60	175
1735	30	60	175
1735/4	35	75	225
1736	25	55	150

3708

3711

3708 Sixpence. Young dr. bust l., R. Roses in angles, die axis ↑↓

	F £	VF £	EF £
1739	20	50	125
1739 O/R in legend	50	150	300
1741	20	50	125

3709

3709 Sixpence. Old dr. bust. l. R. Roses in angles die axis ↑↓

	F £	VF £	EF £
1743	20	50	125
1745	20	50	125
1745/3	30	60	150

3710 Sixpence. — LIMA below bust die axis ↑↓

	F £	*VF* £	*EF* £		*F* £	*VF* £	*EF* £
1745					15	40	85

3710A Sixpence. – as last but reads GEORGIVS die axis ↑↓

1746	10	35	80	1746/5	20	70	140

3711 Sixpence. — plain die axis ↑↓

1746 *proof only FDC* £350

1750	30	65	175	1758	10	15	30
1751	35	90	225	1758 DEI error	25	50	100
1757	10	15	30	1758/7	15	30	50

3712 Fourpence. Young dr. bust l. R. Small dome-shaped crown without pearls on arch, figure 4

1729	8	20	50	1731	8	20	50

3712A Fourpence. – R.Double arched crown with pearls, large figure 4, die axis ↑↓

1732	8	20	50	1740	8	20	50
1735	8	20	50	1743	8	20	50
1737	8	20	50	1743/0	15	60	120
1739	8	20	50	1746	6	15	45
				1760	8	20	50

3713 Threepence. Young dr. bust l. R. Crowned 3, pearls on arch, die axis ↑↓

1729					8	20	50

3713A Threepence. – R. Ornate arch die axis ↑↓

1731 Smaller lettering	8	20	50	1731	8	20	50

3713B Threepence. R. Double arched crown with pearls, die axis ↑↓

1732	8	20	50	1743 Large lettering	6	15	45
1732 with stop over head	10	25	60	1743 Small lettering	6	15	45
1735	8	20	50	1743 — stop over head	7	20	50
1737	6	15	45	1746	6	15	45
1739	6	15	45	1746/3	7	20	50
1740	6	15	45	1760	6	15	45

3714 Twopence. Young dr. bust l. R. Small crown and figure 2, die axis ↑↓

1729	4	15	35	1731	4	15	35

3714A Twopence. Young dr. bust l. R. Large crown and figure 2 die axis ↑↓

1732	4	15	35	1743/0	5	15	40
1735	4	15	35	1746	4	15	35
1737	4	15	35	1756	4	15	35
1739	5	15	40	1759	4	15	35
1740	8	20	50	1760	4	15	35
1743	4	15	35				

3715 Penny. Young dr. bust l. head. R. Date over small crown and figure 1, die axis ↑↓

1729	6	20	40	1731	5	15	35

3715A Penny. R. Large crown dividing date die axis ↑↓

1732	5	15	35	1753/2	6	20	45
1735	6	20	45	1753	4	15	35
1737	6	20	40	1754	4	15	35
1739	5	15	35	1755	4	15	35
1740	5	15	35	1756	4	15	35
1743	5	15	35	1757	4	15	35
1746	5	15	35	1757 Colon after			
1746/3	6	20	45	GRATIA	6	25	45
1750	4	15	35	1758	4	15	35
1752	4	15	35	1759	4	15	35
1752/0	6	20	45	1760	6	20	45

3716

	F	*VF*	*EF*		*F*	*VF*	*EF*
	£	£	£		£	£	£
3716 Maundy Set. As last four. Uniform dates							
1729	60	125	275	1739	50	100	250
1731	60	125	275	1740	50	100	250
1732	50	100	250	1743	60	125	275
1735	50	100	250	1746	45	100	250
1737	50	100	250	1760	75	175	275

COPPER

3717

3717 Halfpenny. Young cuir. bust l. die axis ↑↓							
1729	15	45	150	1732 rev. no stop	20	75	200
1729 rev. no stop	20	50	175	1733	12	40	120
1730	12	45	125	1734	12	40	120
1730 GEOGIVS error	20	75	200	1734/3	30	95	—
1730 stop after date	20	50	175	1734 no stops on obv.	30	95	—
1730 no stop after				1735	12	40	120
REX on rev.	25	85	250	1736	15	50	150
1731	12	40	120	1737	15	50	150
1731 rev. no stop	20	75	200	1738	10	35	120
1732	12	45	125	1739	12	40	120
3718 Halfpenny. Old cuir. bust l., GEORGIUS die axis ↑↓							
1740	10	35	100	1743	10	35	100
1742	10	35	100	1744	10	35	100
1742/0	20	70	200	1745	10	35	100

3719

	F £	VF £	EF £		F £	VF £	EF £

3719 Halfpenny. Old cuir. bust l. GEORGIVS, die axis ↑↓

1746	10	30	100	1751	10	30	100
1747	10	35	120	1752	10	30	100
1748	10	35	120	1753	10	30	100
1749	10	30	100	1754	10	35	120
1750	10	35	120				

3720 3722

3720 Farthing. Young cuir. bust l. die axis ↑↓

1730	12	35	125	1735 3 over 5	20	75	200
1731	12	35	125	1736	12	35	125
1732	15	40	150	1736 triple tie ribands	30	75	200
1733	12	35	125	1737 small date	10	30	100
1734	15	40	150	1737 large date	10	30	100
1734 no stop on obv.	30	75	200	1739	10	30	100
1735	10	30	100	1739/5		*Extremely rare*	

3721 Farthing. Old cuir. bust. GEORGIUS die axis ↑↓

1741	15	40	125	1744	10	25	95

3722 Farthing. — GEORGIVS die axis ↑↓

1746	8	25	85	1750	15	40	120
1746 V over U		*Extremely rare*		1754	5	14	40
1749	15	40	120	1754/0	25	75	175

George III, grandson of George II was born on 4 June 1738. He married Charlotte of Mecklenburg and they had nine sons and six daughters. The French Revolution and the American War of Independence both happened in his long reign, the longest yet of any King. The naval battle of Trafalgar and the Battle of Waterloo also took place during his reign. Later in his reign, he was affected by what seems to be the mental disease porphyria, and the future George IV was appointed as regent. George III died at Windsor Castle on 29 January 1820.

During the second half of the 18th century very little silver or copper was minted. In 1797 Matthew Boulton's 'cartwheels', the first copper Pennies and Twopences, demonstrated the improvement gleaned from the application of steam power to the coining press.

During the Napoleonic Wars bank notes came into general use when the issue of Guineas was stopped between 1799 and 1813, but gold 7s. pieces, Third-Guineas; were minted to relieve the shortage of smaller money. As an emergency measure Spanish 'Dollars' were put into circulation for a short period after being countermarked, and in 1804 Spanish Eight Reales were overstruck and issued as Bank of England Dollars.

The transition to a 'token' silver coinage began in 1811 when the Bank of England had 3s and 1s. 6d. tokens made for general circulation. Private issues of token money in the years 1788-95 and 1811-15 helped to alleviate the shortage of regal coinage. A change over to a gold standard and a regular 'token' silver coinage came in 1816 when the Mint, which was moved from its old quarters in the Tower of London to a new site on Tower Hill, began a complete re-coinage. The Guinea was replaced by a 20s. Sovereign, and silver coins were made which had an intrinsic value lower than their face value. The St. George design used on the Sovereign and Crown was the work of Benedetto Pistrucci.

Engravers and Designers:– Conrad Heinrich Kuchler (c.1740-1810), Nathaniel Marchant (1739-1816), John Rudulf Ochs Jnr. (1704-88), Lewis Pingo (1743-1830), Thomas Pingo (d.1776) Benedetto Pistrucci (1784-1855), Johann Sigismond Tanner (c.1706-75), Thomas Wyon (1792-1817), William Wyon (1795-1851), Richard Yeo (d.1779).

Prime Ministers:– Thomas Pelham-Holles, (1693-1768) Whig, 1757-62; John Stuart, (1713-1792) Tory 1762-3; George Grenville, (1712-1770), Whig 1763-5; William Pitt 'The Elder', (1708-1778), Whig 1766-8; Augustus Henry Fitzroy, (1735-1811), Whig 1767-70; Lord North, (1732-1790), Tory 1770-82; Charles Wentworth, (1730-1782), Whig 1765-6, 1782; William Petty, (1737-1805), Whig 1782-3; Henry Addington, (1757-1844) Tory, 1801-4; William Pitt 'The Younger' (1759-1806), Tory 1783-1801, 1804-6; William Wyndham Grenville, (1759-1854), Whig, 1806-7; William Bentinck, (1738-1809) Tory 1783, 1807-9; Spencer Perceval, (1762-1812) Tory 1809-12; Robert Banks Jenkinson, (1770-1828) Tory 1812-27 .

GOLD

Early Coinages

3723

3723 Five Guineas. Pattern only, laur. bust r. die axis ↑↑ (en medaille)

1770 *FDC* £40,000
1773 *FDC* £40,000
1777 *FDC* £40,000

3724

3724

3724 Two Guineas. Pattern only, laur. bust r. die axis ↑↑ (en medaille)

1768	*FDC* £17,500	1777	*FDC* £15,000
1773	*FDC* £17,500		

There are six different bust varieties for 3723 and 3724, for further details see select bibliography

3725

	F £	*VF* £	*EF* £
3725 Guinea. First laur. head r., 1761 (varieties with two or three leaves at top of wreath). R. crowned shield of arms die axis ↑↓	650	1750	3000

3726

3726 Guinea. Second laur. head r. die axis ↑↓

	F	*VF*	*EF*		*F*	*VF*	*EF*
1763	350	850	2000	1764	300	700	1750

3727

3728

3729

	F	VF	EF		F	VF	EF
	£	£	£		£	£	£
3727 Guinea. Third laur. head r. die axis ↑↓							
1765	150	300	500	1770	175	350	600
1766	125	250	400	1771	150	300	500
1767	175	350	600	1772	125	250	400
1768	125	300	500	1773	125	250	400
1769	125	300	500	1773 7 over 1	200	400	—
3728 Guinea. Fourth laur. head r. die axis ↑↓							
1774	100	200	350	1781	110	225	375
1775	100	200	350	1782	110	225	375
1776	125	250	400	1783	110	225	375
1777	100	200	350	1784	110	225	375
1778	125	250	400	1785	100	200	350
1779	110	225	375	1786	100	200	350
3729 Guinea. Fifth laur. head r. R. 'Spade'-shaped shield, die axis ↑↑							
1787	95	175	300	1794	95	175	300
1788	95	175	300	1795	120	225	400
1789	95	175	300	1796	120	225	400
1790	95	175	300	1797	95	175	300
1791	95	175	300	1798*	95	175	300
1792	100	200	350	1799	125	250	450
1793	95	175	300	** Beware counterfeits*			

3730

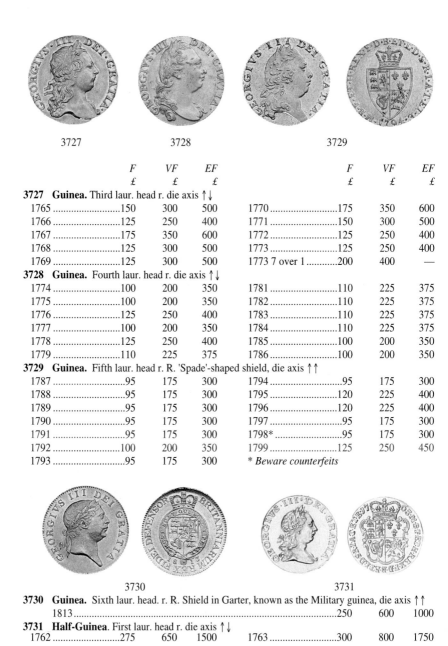

3731

3730 Guinea. Sixth laur. head. r. R. Shield in Garter, known as the Military guinea, die axis ↑↑

	F	VF	EF
1813	250	600	1000

3731 Half-Guinea. First laur. head r. die axis ↑↓

	F	VF	EF		F	VF	EF
1762	275	650	1500	1763	300	800	1750

3732

3733

3732 Half-Guinea. Second laur. head r. die axis ↑↓

	F £	VF £	EF £		F £	VF £	EF £
1764	100	250	600	1772	*Extremely rare*		
1765	300	600	—	1773	100	250	600
1766	100	250	600	1774	200	400	1000
1768	100	250	600	1775	250	500	1200
1769	125	300	750				

3734

3735

3733 Half-Guinea Third laur. head (less fine style) r. die axis ↑↓

1774	*Extremely rare*			1775	500	950	2000

3734 Half-Guinea Fourth laur. head r. die axis ↑↓

1775	75	150	300	1781	80	175	400
1776	75	150	300	1783	300	800	—
1777	70	125	275	1784	75	150	300
1778	80	175	350	1785	70	125	275
1779	100	200	500	1786	70	125	275

3735 Half-Guinea Fifth laur. head. r. R. 'Spade' shaped shield, date below, die axis ↑↑

1787	70	120	250	1794	75	150	300
1788	70	120	250	1795	100	200	450
1789	85	175	350	1796	75	150	300
1790	70	120	250	1797	70	125	250
1791	75	150	300	1798	70	125	250
1792	400	1000	—	1800	125	350	—
1793	70	120	250				

3736

3736 Half-Guinea Sixth laur. head. r. R. Shield in Garter, date below die axis ↑↑

1801	50	75	150	1803	55	85	175
1802	55	85	175				

3737 3738 3739

	F	VF	EF		F	VF	EF
	£	£	£		£	£	£

3737 Half-Guinea Seventh laur. head. r. with short hair. R. As last die axis ↑↑

1804	50	75	150	1809	55	85	175
1805		*Extremely rare*		1810	55	85	175
1806	55	85	175	1811	100	200	450
1808	55	85	175	1813	75	150	350

3738 Third-Guinea. First laur. head r. R. Crown, date in legend, die axis ↑↑

1797	40	65	150	1799	45	85	200
1798	40	65	150	1800	40	65	150

3739 Third-Guinea. – R. Similar but date below crown, die axis ↑↑

1801	40	65	150	1803	40	65	150
1802	40	65	150				

3740 3741

3740 Third-Guinea. Second laur. head r. with short hair, R. Similar, die axis ↑↑

1804	40	65	150	1810	40	65	150
1806	40	65	150	1811	175	350	750
1808	40	65	150	1813	100	200	400
1809	40	65	150				

3741 Quarter-Guinea. die axis ↑↓ 1762 ...50 125 250

For gold of the 'new coinage', 1817-20, see page 354.

SILVER

3742 3746

3742 Shilling. Young dr. bust, r. known as the 'Northumberland' shilling, die axis ↑↓

1763	150	300	500

3743 Shilling. Older dr. bust, R. No semée of hearts in Hanoverian

shield, ↑↑ 1787	15	25	50
3744 Shilling. — No stop over head, die axis ↑↑ 1787	20	40	75
3745 Shilling. — No stops at date, die axis ↑↓ 1787	25	50	95
3745A Shilling. — No stops on *obv.*, die axis ↑↓ 1787	150	350	750
3746 Shilling. — R. With semée of hearts, die axis ↑↓ 1787	15	25	50
1787 1/1 retrograde	30	75	150

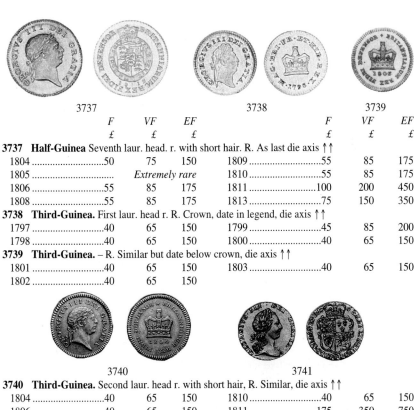

no semée of hearts

with semée of hearts

3747

	F	*VF*	*EF*		*F*	*VF*	*EF*
	£	£	£		£	£	£

3747 **Shilling** No stop over head, 1798: known as the 'Dorrien and Magens' shilling *UNC* £4500

3748 **Sixpence.** R. Without semée of hearts, die axis ↑↑ 1787 ...... 10 | 20 | 40

3749 **Sixpence.** — R. With semée of hearts, die axis ↑↓ 1787 ...... 10 | 20 | 40

3749

3750

3750 **Fourpence**. Young dr. bust r. R. Crowned 4, die axis ↑↓

	F	VF	EF		F	VF	EF
1763	4	12	25	1772/0	5	18	30
1765	200	400	750	1776	4	15	25
1766	5	18	30	1780	4	15	25
1770	5	18	30	1784	5	18	30
1772	5	18	30	1786	6	20	35

3751

3753

3755

3751 **Fourpence**. Older dr. bust. R. Thin 4 ('Wire Money'), die axis ↑↑ 1792 10 | 30 | 60

3752 **Fourpence**. — R. Normal 4, die axis ↑↑

	F	VF	EF		F	VF	EF
1795	5	15	30	1800	5	15	30

3753 **Threepence.** Young dr. bust r. R. Crowned 3, die axis ↑↓

	F	VF	EF		F	VF	EF
1762	3	10	20	1772 small III	4	15	25
1763	3	10	20	1772 very large III	4	15	25
1765	150	300	650	1780	4	15	25
1766	5	18	30	1784	5	18	30
1770	5	18	30	1786	4	15	25

3754 **Threepence.** Older dr. bust. r. R. Thin 3 ('Wire Money'), die axis ↑↑ 1792...10 | 30 | 60

3755 **Threepence.** — R. Normal 3, die axis ↑↑

	F	VF	EF		F	VF	EF
1795	5	15	30	1800	5	15	30

3756 Twopence. Young dr. bust r. R. Crowned 2, die axis ↑↓

	F £	VF £	EF £		F £	VF £	EF £
1763	6	20	30	1776	4	15	25
1765	100	250	550	1780	4	15	25
1766	4	15	25	1784	4	15	25
1772	4	15	25	1786	3	12	25
1772 second 7/6	5	18	30	1786 large obv. lettering	3	12	25

3756

3757 Twopence Older dr. bust. r. R. Thin 2 ('Wire Money'), die axis ↑↑ 1792..10 25 60

3758 Twopence — R. Normal 2, die axis ↑↑

1795	3	12	25	1800	3	12	25

3759 Penny. Young dr. bust r. R. Crowned 1, die axis ↑↓

1763	5	18	30	1779	4	15	25
1766	4	15	25	1780	5	18	30
1770	3	10	20	1781	3	10	20
1772	4	15	25	1784	3	10	20
1776	4	15	25	1786	3	10	20

3760 Penny. Older dr. bust. r. R. Thin 1 ('Wire Money'), die axis ↑↑ 1792....8 25 50

3761 Penny. — R. Normal 1, die axis ↑↑

1795	3	10	25	1800	3	10	25

3762 Maundy Set. Young dr. bust. r. Uniform dates

1763	50	100	225	1780	50	100	225
1766	50	100	225	1784	50	100	225
1772	50	100	225	1786	50	100	225

3763 Maundy Set. — Older dr. bust. r. R. Thin numerals ('Wire Money'), 1792.....90 175 350

3764 Maundy Set. — R. Normal numerals. Uniform dates

1795	40	95	150	1800	35	85	125

Emergency Issue, die axis ↑↑

3765A

3765 Dollar. Pillar type (current for 4s 9d). Spanish American 8 Reales, oval countermark with head of George III.

	F £	VF £	EF £
Mexico City Mint — m̊	350	650	1250
Bolivia, Potosi Mint – PTS monogram	650	1250	—
Peru, Lima Mint – LIMÆ monogram	600	1100	—

No.	Description	F £	VF £	EF £
3765A	**Dollar.** Portrait type, oval countermark.			
	Mexico City Mint — m̊	95	200	350
	Bolivia, Potosi Mint — PTS monogram	110	300	—
	Chile, Santiago Mint — s̊	500	1000	—
	Guatemala Mint — NG	400	850	—
	Spain, Madrid Mint	250	550	1250
	Spain, Seville Mint	200	450	1000
	Peru, Lima Mint — LIMÆ monogram	125	275	500
3765B	**Dollar.** — Oval countermark on French Ecu		*Extremely rare*	
3765C	**Dollar.** — Oval countermark on USA Dollar		*Of highest rarity*	

3766

3767

No.	Description	F £	VF £	EF £
3766	**Dollar** octagonal countermarks with head of George III			
	Mexico City Mint — m̊	200	450	700
	Bolivia, Potosi Mint — PTS monogram	400	—	—
	Guatamala Mint — NG	650	1250	—
	Peru, Lima Mint — LIME monogram	250	500	1000
	Spain, Madrid Mint	350	750	—
	Spain, Seville Mint	400	850	—
3766A	**Dollar.** — Octagonal countermark on French Ecu		*Of highest rarity*	
3766B	**Dollar.** — Octagonal countermark on USA Dollar		*Extremely rare*	
3767	**Half-Dollar.** With similar oval countermark. Mints of Potosi, Santiago, Madrid & Seville *from*	100	225	425

Bank of England Issue

3768

3768 Dollar. (current for 5s.). laur. and dr. bust of king. r. R. Britannia seated l., several varieties occur, die axis ↑↑

	F	VF	EF
1804	100	200	375

These dollars were re-struck from Spanish-American 8-Reales until at least 1811. Dollars that show dates and Mint marks of original coin are worth rather more.

3769

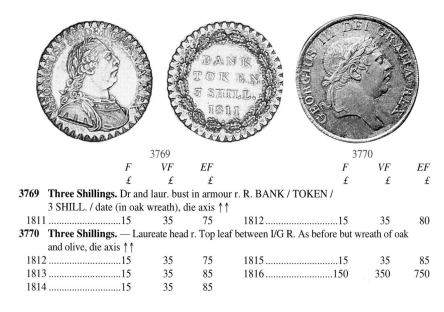

3770

3769 Three Shillings. Dr and laur. bust in armour r. R. BANK / TOKEN / 3 SHILL. / date (in oak wreath), die axis ↑↑

	F £	VF £	EF £		F £	VF £	EF £
1811	15	35	75	1812	15	35	80

3770 Three Shillings. — Laureate head r. Top leaf between I/G R. As before but wreath of oak and olive, die axis ↑↑

	F £	VF £	EF £		F £	VF £	EF £
1812	15	35	75	1815	15	35	85
1813	15	35	85	1816	150	350	750
1814	15	35	85				

3771

3772

3771 Eighteenpence. Dr. and laur. bust r. in armour R BANK/TOKEN/Is. 6D./date (in oak wreath) ↑↑

	F £	*VF* £	*EF* £		*F* £	*VF* £	*EF* £
1811	10	25	60	1812	10	25	65

3772 Eighteenpence. Laureate head r. die axis ↑↑

	F £	*VF* £	*EF* £		*F* £	*VF* £	*EF* £
1812	10	25	60	1815	10	30	75
1813	10	30	75	1816	10	30	75
1814	10	30	75				

3773

3773 Ninepence. Similar, Laur. head 1812, R. 9D type (pattern only) die axis ↑↑ *FDC* £800

3773A

3773A Ninepence. —— 1812, R. 9 pence type (pattern only) die axis ↑↑ FDC. *Extremely rare*

COPPER

First Issue — Tower Mint, London

3774

3775

	F £	VF £	EF £		F £	VF £	EF £
3774 Halfpenny. Cuir. bust r. R. Britannia, die axis ↑↓							
1770	12	35	100	1772 no incuse hair coil	10	30	100
1770 no stop on rev.	20	50	125	1772 — no stop on rev.	20	50	125
1771	10	30	100	1773	10	30	100
1771 no stop on rev.	20	50	125	1773 no stop after REX	18	45	110
1771 ball below spear blade	10	30	100	1773 no stop on rev.	20	50	125
1772 incuse hair coil on rev.	10	30	100	1774 different obv. profile	18	45	125
1772 GEORIVS error	35	75	175	1775 —	10	30	100
1772 ball below spear blade	10	30	100				
3775 Farthing. Similar, die axis ↑↓							
1771	20	50	120	1774	12	30	75
1773	10	25	65	1775	12	30	75
1773 no stop on rev.	15	35	85	1775 struck en medaille ↑↑	25	60	125
1773 no stop after REX	25	60	125				

Second Issue—Soho Mint. Birmingham 'Cartwheel' coinage, die axis ↑↓

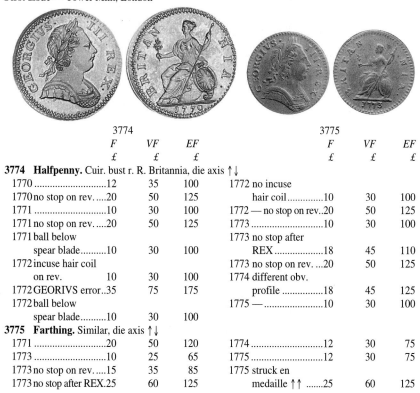

3776

3776 Twopence. Legends incuse on raised rim, 1797 .... 20 85 200

3777

	F £	VF £	EF £	UNC £
3777 Penny. 1797. Similar, 10 leaves in wreath on obv.	10	35	120	450
1797 11 leaves in wreath on obv.	10	35	120	450

Halfpence and Farthings of this issue are patterns.

Third Issue—Soho Mint, Birmingham, die axis ↑↓

3778

3779

	VF £	EF £	UNC £
3778 Halfpenny. Dr. bust r.,			
1799 Ship on rev. with 5 gunports	10	35	75
1799 Ship with 6 relief gunports	10	35	75
1799 Ship with 9 relief gunports	15	50	100
1799 Ship with plain hull	15	50	100
1799 — raised line on hull	15	50	100
3779 Farthing.			
1799 Obv. with 3 berries in wreath	8	25	60
1799 Obv. with 4 berries in wreath	8	25	60

Fourth Issue—Soho Mint, Birmingham, die axis ↑↓

3780

	VF £	*EF* £	*UNC* £		*VF* £	*EF* £	*UNC* £
3780 Penny. Shorter haired, dr. bust r. date below							
1806 incuse hair curl by tie knot	10	30	95	1807	10	35	110
1806 no incuse hair curl	15	40	120				

3781

3782

	VF £	*EF* £	*UNC* £		*VF* £	*EF* £	*UNC* £
3781 Halfpenny							
1806 rev. no berries	6	25	75	1807	8	30	85
1806 rev. 3 berries	10	50	100				
3782 Farthing							
1806 K. on tr.	6	22	65	1807	8	28	75
1806 incuse dot on tr	35	75	175				

Last or new coinage, 1816-20

The year 1816 is a landmark in the history of our coinage. For some years at the beginning of the 19th century Mint production was virtually confined to small gold denominations, regular full production being resumed only after the Mint had been moved from the Tower of London to a new site on Tower Hill. Steam powered minting machinery made by Boulton and Watt replaced the old hand-operated presses and these produced coins which were technically much superior to the older milled coins.

In 1816 for the first time British silver coins were produced with an intrinsic value substantially below their face value, the first official token coinage. The old Guinea was replaced by a Sovereign of twenty shillings in 1817, the standard of 22 carat (.916) fineness still being retained.

Mint Master or Engraver's and/or designer's initials: WWP (William Wellesley Pole)
B.P. (Benedetto Pistrucci)

GOLD

3783

3783 Five Pounds. 1820 (Pattern only) die axis ↑↓ *FDC*. £35,000

3784

3784 Two Pounds. 1820 (Pattern only) die axis ↑↓ *FDC*. £12,500

3785

3785A

	F £	*VF* £	*EF* £	*UNC* £		*F* £	*VF* £	*EF* £	*UNC* £

3785 Sovereign. laur. head r. coarse hair, legend type A (Descending colon after BRITANNIAR, no space between REX and F:D:). R. St. George and dragon, die axis ↑↓

	F	VF	EF	UNC		F	VF	EF	UNC
1817	100	175	450	650	1819	*Extremely rare*			
1818	110	200	500	800					

3785A Sovereign. — legend type B (Ascending colon after BRITANNIAR, space between REX and F:D:) ↑↓

	F	VF	EF	UNC
1818	110	200	500	800

3785B Sovereign. laur head r. Hair with tighter curls, legend type A. (as above) die axis ↑↓

	F £	VF £	EF £	UNC £		F £	VF £	EF £	UNC £
1818	*Extremely rare*								

3785C

3785C – small date

3785C Sovereign. — legend type B. (as above) die axis ↑↓

	F £	VF £	EF £	UNC £		F £	VF £	EF £	UNC £
1818	*Extremely rare*				1820	100	175	450	600
1820 Roman I	200	400	800	—	1820 short date	150	250	500	750
1820 Small O	150	250	500	750					

3786

3786 Half-Sovereign. laur head r. R. Crowned shield, die axis ↑↓

	F £	VF £	EF £	UNC £		F £	VF £	EF £	UNC £
1817	60	100	175	300	1820	65	110	200	350
1818	65	110	200	350					

SILVER

3787

3787 Crown. Laur. head r. R. Pistrucci's St. George and dragon within Garter, die axis ↑↓

		F £	VF £	EF £	UNC £
1818, edge	LVIII	25	55	165	350
1818	LVIII error edge inscription	*Extremely rare*			
1818	LIX	25	55	165	350
1819	LIX	20	50	150	325
1819	LIX no stops on edge	45	100	200	500
1819/8	LIX	50	125	275	—
1819	LX	30	60	185	375
1820	LX	25	55	165	350
1820/19	LX	75	200	350	—

3788

3788 Halfcrown. Large laur. bust or 'bull' head r. die axis ↑↓

	F £	VF £	EF £	UNC £		F £	VF £	EF £	UNC £
1816	20	45	100	250	1817	20	45	100	250
1817 D/T in DEI	30	75	—	—					

3789

3789 Halfcrown. Small laur. head r. die axis ↑↑

	F £	VF £	EF £	UNC £		F £	VF £	EF £	UNC £
1817	20	45	100	250	1819	20	45	100	250
1817 Reversed s's in garter	*Extremely rare*				1819/8	*Extremely rare*			
1818 Reversed s's in garter	*Extremely rare*				1820	30	65	150	350
1818	25	50	120	275					

3790

3790 Shilling. laur head r. R. Shield in Garter, die axis ↑↑

	F £	VF £	EF £	UNC £		F £	VF £	EF £	UNC £
1816	10	15	30	65	1819/8	20	40	80	175
1817	10	18	35	70	1819	10	18	35	90
1817 GEOE error	100	200	350	—	1820	10	18	35	90
1818	20	40	95	200	1820 I/S in HONI	40	80	175	350
1818 High 8	30	75	120	250					

3791

	F £	VF £	EF £	UNC £		F £	VF £	EF £	UNC £
3791 Sixpence. laur head r. R. Shield in Garter, die axis ↑↑									
1816	6	12	25	50	1819 small 8	10	20	35	60
1817	8	15	30	55	1820	10	20	35	60
1818	10	20	35	60	1820 inverted 1	75	200	—	—
1819/8	12	25	40	70	1820 I/S in HONI	75	200	—	—
1819	10	20	35	60	1820 obv. no colons	100	300	—	—

3792

	VF £	EF £	UNC £		VF £	EF £	UNC £
3792 Maundy Set. (4d., 3d., 2d. and 1d.) die axis ↑↑							
1817	60	95	200	1820	60	95	200
1818	60	95	200				

		EF £	UNC £
3793 — **Fourpence.** 1817, 1818, 1820	*from*	14	30
3794 — **Threepence.** 1817, 1818, 1820	*from*	14	30
3795 — **Twopence.** 1817, 1818, 1820	*from*	8	20
3796 — **Penny.** 1817, 1818, 1820	*from*	8	15

George IV, oldest son of George III, was born on 12 August 1762 and was almost a complete opposite to his father. He was very extravagent and lived in the height of luxury. He especially influenced fashion of the time which has become known as the 'Regency' style. He had numerous mistresses, and had an arranged marriage with Caroline of Brunswick. She later moved to Italy with their only daughter, but returned to claim her place as Queen upon George's accession. George banned her from ever being coronated, and he died without ever conceiving a son on 26 June 1830, when his younger brother William acsended the throne.

The Mint resumed the coinage of copper farthings in 1821, and pennies and halfpennies in 1825. A gold Two Pound piece was first issued for general circulation in 1823. A full cased proof set of the new bare head coinage was issued in limited quantities in 1826.

Engraver's and/or designer's initials on the coins:

B. P. (Benedetto Pistrucci) W.W. P. (William Wellesley Pole) – Master of the Mint
J. B. M. (Jean Baptiste Merlen)

Engravers and Designers:– Francis Legett Chantrey (1781-1842) Jean Baptiste Merlen (1769-c.1850) Benedetto Pistrucci (1784-1855) William Wyon (1795-1851)
Prime Ministers:– Robert Banks Jenkinson, (1770-1828) Tory, 1812-27; George Canning, (1770-1827) Tory, 1827; Frederick Robinson, (1782-1859), Tory 1827-8; Arthur Wellesley, (1769-1852), Tory, 1828-30.

GOLD

3797

3797 **Five Pounds.** 1826 Bare head l. R. Crowned shield and mantle, inscribed edge, die axis ↑↓ Proof *FDC* £8000

3798

	VF £	*EF* £	*UNC* £
3798 **Two Pounds.** 1823 Proof *FDC* £3500			
1823. Large bare head. l. R. St. George, inscribed edge ↑↓	375	700	1250
3799 **Two Pounds.** — 1826. Type as 3797 inscribed edge die axis ↑↓ Proof *FDC* £3000			

F	*VF*	*EF*	*UNC*		*F*	*VF*	*EF*	*UNC*
	£	£	£	£		£	£	£	£

3800 Sovereign. Laur. head. l. R. St. George and dragon, die axis ↑↓

1821	100	175	425	575	1824	100	175	450	600
1822*	100	175	450	600	1825	200	475	1250	—
1823	200	475	1250	—					

**Beware counterfeits.*

3801 Sovereign. Bare head. l. R. Crowned shield, die axis ↑↓

1825	100	175	350	600	1828	700	2000	4500	—
1826	100	175	350	600	1829	120	200	400	650
— Proof *FDC* £2250					1830	120	200	400	650
1827*	120	200	400	650					

**Beware counterfeits*

	3802		3803

3802 Half-Sovereign. Laur. head. l. R. Ornately garnished shield. die axis ↑↓

1821	300	750	1350	2250

3803 Half-Sovereign. — R. Plain shield die axis ↑↓

1823	80	150	375	500	1825	70	125	325	450
1824	75	135	350	475					

	3804		3804A

3804 Half-Sovereign. — Bare head. l. R. Garnished shield die axis ↑↓

1826	70	120	300	450	1827	70	120	300	450
— Proof *FDC* £1000 ..					1828	65	110	275	425

3804A Half-Sovereign. — with extra tuft of hair to l. ear, much heavier border, die axis ↑↓

1826	70	120	300	450	1827	70	120	300	450
— Proof *FDC* £1000 ..					1828	65	110	275	425

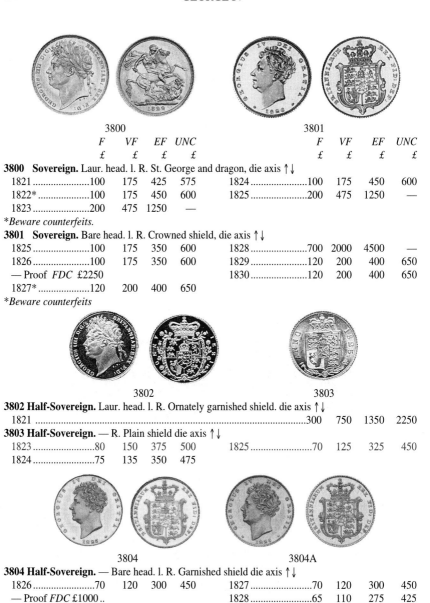

SILVER

3805

		F £	VF £	EF £	UNC £
3805 Crown. Laur. head. l. R. St. George, die axis ↑↓					
1821, edge	SECUNDO	25	85	400	1000
1821	SECUNDO Proof £1750				
1821	TERTIO Proof £2750				
1822 —	SECUNDO	30	100	450	1200
— —	TERTIO	27	90	400	1000

3806

3806 Crown. Bare head. l. R. Shield with crest inscribed edge, die axis ↑↓ 1826 Proof *FDC* £2500

3807

3807
Heavier garnishing

3807 Halfcrown. Laur. head. l. R. Garnished shield, die axis ↑↓

	F	VF	EF	UNC		F	VF	EF	UNC
1820	20	45	150	275	1823 —	450	1250	4000	—
1821	20	45	150	275					

	F	VF	EF	UNC
1821 Heavier shield garnishing	20	45	175	300

F	VF	EF	UNC		F	VF	EF	UNC
	£	£	£	£		£	£	£	£

3808 Halfcrown. R. Shield in garter and collar die axis ↑↓

| 1823 | 20 | 45 | 150 | 300 | 1824 | 25 | 60 | 200 | 375 |

3809 Halfcrown. Bare head. l. R. Shield with crest die axis ↑↓

1824		*Extremely rare*			1826 Proof *FDC* £550				
1825	25	50	100	250	1828	30	85	200	450
1826	20	40	95	250	1829	25	75	175	400

3810 3811 3812

3810 Shilling. Laur. head. l. R. Garnished shield, die axis ↑↓

| 1821 | 10 | 35 | 100 | 200 |

3811 Shilling. — R. Shield in Garter die axis ↑↓

| 1823 | 25 | 60 | 200 | 450 | 1825 | 18 | 45 | 120 | 250 |
| 1824 | 10 | 35 | 100 | 200 | 1825/3 | | *Extremely rare* | | |

3812 Shilling. Bare head l. R. Lion on crown die axis ↑↓

1825	10	35	90	150	1826/2		*Extremely rare*		
1825 Roman I		*Extremely rare*			1827	20	60	200	375
1826	8	25	75	125	1829	15	45	125	300
— Proof *FDC* £250									

3813 3814 3815

3813 Sixpence. Laur. head. l. R. Garnished shield, die axis ↑↓

| 1821 | 10 | 20 | 60 | 120 | 1821 BBITANNIAR | 50 | 175 | 550 | — |

3814 Sixpence. — R. Shield in Garter die axis ↑↓

| 1824 | 10 | 20 | 60 | 120 | 1826 | 20 | 60 | 175 | 350 |
| 1825 | 10 | 20 | 60 | 120 |

3815 Sixpence. Bare head. l. R. Lion on crown die axis ↑↓

1826	10	20	60	120	1828	10	25	85	175
— Proof *FDC* £175 ...					1829	10	20	60	120
1827	18	50	175	350

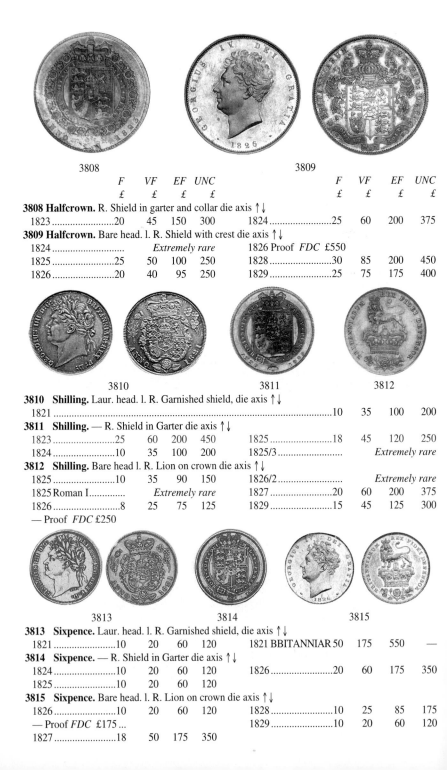

3816

	EF £	FDC £		EF £	FDC £
3816 Maundy Set. (4d., 3d., 2d. and 1d.) die axis ↑↓					
1822	90	150	1827	85	125
1823	85	125	1828	85	125
1824	95	150	1829	85	125
1825	85	125	1830	85	125
1826	85	125			
3817 Maundy Fourpence. 1822-30			*from*	12	20
3818 — Threepence. small head, 1822				25	40
3819 — — normal head, 1823-30			*from*	10	18
3820 — Twopence. 1822-30			*from*	9	15
3821 — Penny. 1822-30			*from*	7	12

COPPER

First Issue, 1821-6

3822

3824

	F £	VF £	EF £	UNC £		F £	VF £	EF £	UNC £
3822 Farthing. Laur. and dr. bust l. die axis ↑↓									
1821	2	10	30	60	1825 —	2	10	30	55
1822 leaf ribs raised	2	10	25	55	1825 leaf ribs raised	4	15	35	70
1823 —	3	12	35	65	1826 —	5	15	40	85
1823 — I for 1 in date	25	75	175	—					

3823

Second issue, 1825-30

3823 Penny. Laur. head. l. R. Britannia, with shield bearing saltire of arms die axis ↑↑

	F £	VF £	EF £	UNC £
1825	12	30	95	275
1826 plain saltire on rev.	10	30	80	275
1826 Proof *FDC*..*£250*				
1826 thin line on saltire	10	30	95	275
1826 thick line on saltire	15	50	125	325
1827 plain saltire	150	400	1000	—

3824 Halfpenny. Similar, die axis ↑↑

	F £	VF £	EF £	UNC £
1825	12	45	120	225
1826 rev. two incuse lines on saltire	8	20	60	100
1826 Proof *FDC*..*£175*				
1826 rev. raised line on saltire	10	25	85	150
1827 rev. two incuse lines on saltire	10	25	70	125

3825

3825 Farthing. Similar, die axis ↑↑

	F £	VF £	EF £	UNC £
1826	2	10	30	50
1826 Proof *FDC £140*				
1827	3	10	40	75
1828	2	10	35	70
1829	3	15	50	100
1830	2	10	35	70

3826

3827

3826 Half-Farthing. (for use in Ceylon). Similar, die axis ↑↑

	F £	VF £	EF £	UNC £
1828 rev. helmet intrudes legend	10	25	75	150
1828 rev. helmet to base of legend	10	25	75	150
1830 —	25	50	125	—
1830 rev. helmet intrudes legend	10	25	75	150

3827 Third-Farthing. (for use in Malta). Similar, die axis ↑↑

	VF £	EF £	UNC £
1827	15	40	85

Copper coins graded in this catalogue as UNC have full mint lustre.

PSI Proof Set, new issue, 1826. Five pounds to Farthing (11 coins) *FDC* £19500
PSIA — — Similar, including Maundy Set (15 coins) *FDC* £20000

William IV was born on 21 August 1765, and ascended the throne on his elder brother's death. Back in 1823 he was cohabiting with the actress Dorothea Jordan who bore him ten illegitimate children. After the death of George IV's daughter, William was forced into a legitimate marriage with Adelaide of Saxe-Coburg and Meinengein. She bore him two daughters who both died in childhood. His reign was most notable for the introduction of the Reform bill and abolition of slavery. William was the last King of Hanover, and died on 20 June 1837 when the throne passed to his niece Victoria.

In order to prevent confusion between the Sixpence and Half-Sovereign the size of the latter was reduced in 1834, although the weight remained the same. The smaller gold piece was not acceptable to the public and in the following year it was made to the normal size. In 1836 the silver Groat was again issued for general circulation: it is the only British silver coin which has a seated Britannia as the type. Crowns were not struck during this reign for general circulation; but proofs or patterns of this denomination were made and are greatly sought after. Silver Threepences and Three-Halfpence were minted for use in the Colonies.

Engraver's and/or designer's initials on the coins:

W. W. (William Wyon)

Engravers and Designers:– Francis Legett Chantry (1781-1842) Jean Baptiste Merlen (1769-c.1850) William Wyon (1795-1851).

Prime Ministers:– Earl Grey, (1764-1845), Whig, 1830-34; William Lamb, (1779-1848) Whig, 1834, 1835-47; Sir Robert Peel, (1788-1850), Tory, 1834-5.

GOLD

3828

3828 Two Pounds. bare head r. R. crowned shield and mantle, die axis ↑↓
1831 (proof only). .... *FDC* £4500

3829A

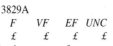

3829B

	F £	*VF* £	*EF* £	*UNC* £		*F* £	*VF* £	*EF* £	*UNC* £

3829 Sovereign. First bust. r. top of ear narrow and rounded, nose to 2nd N of BRITANNIAR, fine obv. beading. R. Crowned shield. Die axis ↑↓

1831	150	250	550	800	1832	125	200	525	800

— Proof plain edge *FDC £2500*

3829A Sovereign. — — WW without stops die axis ↑↓

1831 .... *Extremely rare*

3829B Sovereign. Second bust. r. top of ear broad and flat, nose to 2nd I in BRITANNIAR, coarser obv. beading. ↑↓

1832*	125	195	450	700	1836	125	195	450	700
1833	125	195	450	700	1836 N of ANNO struck in shield	*Extremely rare*			
1835	125	195	475	750	1837	140	225	500	775

3830

3831

	F £	VF £	EF £	UNC £		F £	VF £	EF £	UNC £
3830 Half-Sovereign. Small size, die axis ↑↓									
1831 Proof plain edge *FDC* £1250					1834	100	200	475	750
* *Beware of counterfeits*									
3831 Half-Sovereign. Large size, die axis ↑↓									
1835	100	200	450	650	1837	100	220	500	675
1836	120	250	550	700					
3832 *Obv.* struck from Sixpence. die in error, 1836						850	1500	2750	—

SILVER

3832

3833

3833 Crown. R. Shield on mantle, 1831 Proof only W.W. on trun. struck ↑↓ ....*FDC* £6000
1831 — W. WYON on trun. struck ↑↑ en medaille (medal die axis)................*FDC* £8000
1831 — — similar die axis ↑↓ *FDC* £8500
1834 — W.W. on trun. struck die axis ↑↓ ....*FDC* £12000

3834

WW script

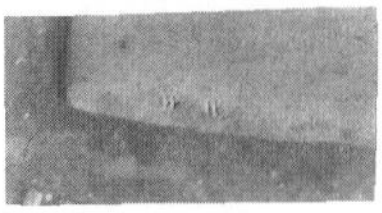

WW block

	F £	VF £	EF £	UNC £		F £	VF £	EF £	UNC £
3834 Halfcrown. WW in script on trun. R. Shield on mantle, die axis ↑↓									
1831 Proof *FDC* £600					1836/5	40	90	275	—
1834	20	50	150	300	1836	20	50	150	300
1835	30	90	250	500	1837	35	100	275	600
3834A Halfcrown. — block WW on trun.die axis ↑↓									
1831 Proof *FDC* £500									
1834						40	120	350	—

3835

3836

	F £	VF £	EF £	UNC £
3835 Shilling. R. Value in wreath, die axis ↑↓				
1831 Proof *FDC £275*				
1834	15	35	100	200
1835	20	40	120	225
1836	20	40	120	225
1837	28	60	175	375
3836 Sixpence. R. Value in wreath, die axis ↑↓				
1831	10	20	60	120
— Proof *FDC* £175				
1834	10	20	60	120
1835	10	20	60	120
1836	18	40	120	200
1837	15	35	120	200

3837

3839

	F £	VF £	EF £	UNC £
3837 Groat. R. Britannia seated, die axis ↑↑				
1836	5	15	35	60
1837	10	20	40	75
3838 Threepence (for use in the West Indies). As Maundy threepence but with a dull surface, ↑↓				
1834	4	12	60	120
1835	4	10	50	100
1836	4	12	60	120
1837	10	20	75	150
3839 Three-Halfpence (for Colonial use). R. Value, Crowned in wreath, die axis ↑↓				
1834	5	10	30	60
1835/4	6	15	35	75
1835	10	25	60	150
1836	6	15	35	75
1837	15	35	100	250

3840

	EF £	FDC £
3840 Maundy Set (4d., 3d., 2d. and 1d.). Die axis ↑↓		
1831	120	200
— Proof *FDC* £300		
1832	100	180
1833	95	160
1834	95	160
1835	95	160
1836	120	200
1837	120	200
3841 — Fourpence, 1831-7 *from*	12	20
3842 — Threepence, 1831-7 *from*	20	30
3843 — Twopence, 1831-7 *from*	8	15
3844 — Penny, 1831-7 *from*	9	16

COPPER

3845

3845 Penny. No initials on trun. die axis ↑↑

	F £	VF £	EF £	UNC £
1831	18	50	150	400
1831 Proof *FDC* ↑↓ *£275*				
1831 Proof *FDC* ↑↑ *£325*				
1834	20	60	175	425
1837	45	110	275	600

3846 Penny. incuse initials on trun. die axis ↑↑

	F £	VF £	EF £	UNC £
1831 W.W on trun	*Extremely rare*			
1831 .W.W on trun	30	85	250	500

3847 Halfpenny. As penny, die axis ↑↑

	F £	VF £	EF £	UNC £
1831	12	25	60	125
1831 Proof *FDC* ↑↓ *£200*				
1831 Proof *FDC* ↑↑ *£300*				
1834	12	25	60	125
1837	10	20	55	100

3847

3848

3848 Farthing. Similar, die axis ↑↑

	F £	VF £	EF £	UNC £
1831 rev. incuse line on saltire	2	10	35	60
1831 Proof *FDC* ↑↓ *£150*				
1831 Proof *FDC* ↑↑ £200				
1834 rev. raised line on saltire	2	10	35	60
1835 —	2	10	35	60
1835 rev. incuse line on saltire	2	10	35	60
1836 rev. raised line on saltire	2	10	35	60
1837 —	2	10	35	60

3849 Half-Farthing (for use in Ceylon). Similar, die axis ↑↑

	F £	VF £	EF £	UNC £
1837	45	100	200	—

3849

3850

3850 Third-Farthing (for use in Malta). Similar, die axis ↑↑

	F £	VF £	EF £	UNC £
1835	5	15	40	100

Copper coins graded in this catalogue as UNC have full mint lustre

PS2 Proof set. Coronation, 1831. Two pounds to farthing (14 coins). *FDC* £18500

Victoria was born on 24 May 1819, and enjoyed the longest reign of any Monarch so far. She marrried the German, Prince Albert with whom she enjoyed 17 years of Marriage. Upon Albert's death she became the 'Widow of Windsor' descending into a 25 year period of mourning. She skillfully avoided conflict with other European powers, and produced connections with many Royal houses all over Europe. The Great Exhibition of 1851 was a sign of the power of the largest Empire in the world. Victoria died on 22 January 1901 at the age of 81.

In 1849, as a first step towards decimalization, a silver Florin ($^{1}/_{10}$th pound) was introduced, but the coins of 1849 omitted the usual *Dei Gratia* and these so-called 'Godless' Florins were replaced in 1851 by the 'Gothic' issue. The Halfcrown was temporarily discontinued but was minted again from 1874 onwards. Between 1863 and 1880 reverse dies of the gold and silver coins were numbered in the course of Mint experiments into the wear of dies. The exception was the Florin where the die number is on the obverse below the bust.

The gold and silver coins were redesigned for the Queen's Golden Jubilee in 1887. The Double-Florin which was then issued, was abandoned after only four years; the Jubilee Sixpence of 1887, known as the 'withdrawn' type, was changed to avoid confusion with the Half-Sovereign. Gold and silver were again redesigned in 1893 with an older portrait of the Queen, but the 'old head' was not used on the bronze coinage until 1895. The heavy copper Penny had been replaced by the lighter bronze 'bun' Penny in 1860. In 1874-6 and 1881-2 some of the bronze was made by Heaton in Birmingham, and these have a letter H below the date. From 1897 Farthings were issued with a dark surface.

Early Sovereigns had a shield-type reverse, but Pistrucci's St. George design was used again from 1871. In order to increase the output of gold coinage, branches of the Royal Mint were set up in Australia at Sydney and Melbourne and, later, at Perth for coining gold of imperial type.

Engraver's and/or designer's initials on the coins:

W. W. (William Wyon 1795-1851)
L. C. W. (Leonard Charles Wyon 1826-91)
J. E. B. (Joseph Edgar Boehm 1834-90)
T. B. (Thomas Brock 1847-1922)
B. P. (Benedetto Pistrucci, 1784-1855)

Engravers and Designers: George William De Saulle, (1862-1903) William Dyce (1806-64), Jean Baptiste Merlen (1769-c.1850) Edward Poynter (1836-1919)

Prime Minister: William Lamb, (1779-1848), Whig, 1835-41; Sir Robert Peel, (1788-1850), Tory, 1841-6; Earl of Aberdeen, (1754-1860), Tory 1851-5, Viscount Palmerston, (1784-1865), Liberal, 1855-8 1859-65; Earl Russell, (1742-1878), Whig, 1846-51 1865-6; Earl of Derby, (1799-1861), Conservative, 1852, 1858-9 1866-8; Benjamin Disraeli, (1804-1881), Conservative, 1868, 1874-80; William Ewart Gladstone (1809-1898), 1868-74, 1880-85, 1886, 1892-94 ; Robert Arthur Talbot Gascoyne-Cecil, (1830-1903), Conservative, 1885-6. 1886-92, 1895-1902; Earl of Roseberry, (1847-1929), Liberal, 1894-5.

GOLD

Young Head Coinage, 1838-87

3851

3851 **Five Pounds.** 1839. Young filleted bust l. R. 'Una and the lion' (proof only) varieties occur, inscribed edge, die axis ↑↑ *FDC* £21,500

3852

3852 Sovereign. First (small) young head. l. R. First shield. London mint, die axis ↑↓

	F £	VF £	EF £	UNC £
1838	85	250	500	950
1839	125	300	900	1500
— die axis ↑↓ Proof *FDC* £2,000				
— die axis ↑↑ Proof *FDC* £2,000				
1841	600	950	2750	—
1842	65	75	125	225
1843	65	75	125	225
1843/2	95	150	300	1000
1844	65	75	125	225
1845	65	75	125	225
1846	65	75	125	225
1847	65	75	125	225
1848	200	—	—	—

3852A
Leaves differently arranged

3852B
Narrow shield

3852C
Second large head

3852A Sovereign. — R similar but leaves of the wreath arranged differently with tops of leaves closer to crown.

	F	VF	EF	UNC
1838	1250	3000	—	—

3852B Sovereign. — narrower shield. Considerably modified floral emblems, different leaf arrangement ↑↓

1843 .... *Extremely rare*

3852C Sovereign. Second (large) head. l. W W still in relief. R. Shield with repositioned legend die axis ↑↓

	F	VF	EF	UNC
1848	BV	65	110	195
1849	BV	65	110	195
1850	BV	65	115	225
1851	BV	65	110	195
1852	BV	65	100	195
1853	BV	70	110	195
1854	100	225	500	—
1855	80	125	200	—
1872	BV	60	100	195

3852D
WW Incuse

3852E
Extra line in ribbon

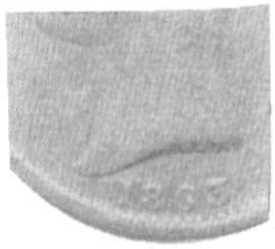

3852F/3853A
827 on truncation

3852D Sovereign. — — WW incuse on trun. die axis ↑↓

	F	VF	EF	UNC
1853	70	110	200	—
— Proof *FDC £6000*				
1854	BV	65	100	195
1855	BV	65	95	195
1856	BV	65	100	195
1857	BV	65	95	195
1858	BV	70	140	250
1859	BV	65	100	195
1860	BV	65	95	195
1861	BV	65	95	195
1861 Roman I	100	200	500	—
1862	BV	65	95	195
1863	BV	65	95	195

3852E Sovereign. — — As 3852D 'Ansell' ribbon. Additional raised line on the lower part of the ribbon ↑↓

	F	VF	EF	UNC
1859	125	300	1250	—

3852F Sovereign. — — As 3852D with die number 827 on trun. die axis ↑↓

	F	VF	EF	UNC
1863	1750	3500	—	—

3853
Die number location

3853B

	F	VF	EF	UNC			F	VF	EF	UNC
	£	£	£	£			£	£	£	£

3853 Sovereign.— As 3852D R. die number in space below wreath, above floral emblem, die axis ↑↓

1863	BV	65	90	175		1868	BV	65	90	175
1864	BV	65	85	150		1869	BV	65	85	150
1865	BV	65	90	200		1870	BV	65	100	225
1866	BV	65	85	150						

3853A Sovereign. — — As 3853 with die number 827 on trun. R. die number is always no. 22 die axis ↑↓

1863							1500	2500	—	—

3853B Sovereign. — — WW in relief on trun. R. die number below wreath, above floral emblem die axis ↑↓

1870	BV	65	90	175		1873	BV	65	90	175
1871	BV	65	85	150		1874	600	1250	3500	—
1872	BV	65	85	150						

Melbourne Mint mark
3854

Sydney Mint mark
3855

3854 Sovereign Second (large) head. l. WW in relief R. M below wreath for Melbourne Mint, Australia ↑↓

1872 M	BV	65	100	300		1882 M	BV	65	120	200
1872/1 M	65	100	600	1250		1883 M	70	200	425	650
1873 M		*Extremely rare*				1884 M	BV	65	110	775
1874 M	BV	55	100	600		1885 M	BV	65	100	425
1879 M		*Extremely rare*				1886 M	275	1000	2500	5000
1880 M	150	500	1800	3000		1887 M	200	750	2000	—
1881 M	BV	65	120	200						

3855 Sovereign. — — As 3854 R. with S below wreath for Sydney Mint, Australia die axis ↑↓

1871 S	BV	65	110	425		1881 S	BV	65	80	475
1872 S	BV	65	110	325		1882 S	BV	65	80	350
1873 S	BV	65	110	250		1883 S	BV	65	80	375
1875 S	BV	65	100	650		1884 S	BV	65	80	400
1877 S	BV	65	100	500		1885 S	BV	65	90	275
1878 S	BV	65	95	775		1886 S	BV	65	80	400
1879 S	BV	65	95	475		1887 S	BV	65	100	300
1880 S	BV	65	80	675						

3855A Sovereign. Second (large) head WW incuse on trun. R. with S below wreath for Sydney
Mint die axis ↑↓

1871 S							65	80	125	500

3856A
Horse with long tail
Small BP in exergue

3856C
Horse with short tail
No BP in exergue

	F	VF	EF	UNC		F	VF	EF	UNC
	£	£	£	£		£	£	£	£

3856 Sovereign. First young head. l. WW buried in narrow trun. R. St. George.
London mint. Horse with short tail. Large BP in ex. die axis ↑↓

1871..BV			65	85	150				

3856A Sovereign. — — As 3856 R. Horse with long tail. Small BP in ex.die axis ↑↓

1871	BV	65	75	125	1876	BV	65	75	150
1872	BV	65	75	140	1878	BV	65	75	125
1873	BV	65	75	125	1879	75	125	500	—
1874	BV	65	85	150	1880	BV	65	75	125

3856B Sovereign. — — As 3856 R. Horse with short tail, small BP in ex.die axis ↑↓

1880	BV	65	75	140	1885	BV	65	85	140
1884	BV	65	75	125					

3856C Sovereign. — — As 3856 R. Horse with short tail, no BP in ex.die axis ↑↓

1880..BV			65	75	125				

3856D Sovereign. Second head. l. WW complete, on broad trun. R.
 Horse with long tail, small BP in ex.die axis ↑↓

1880..BV			65	75	125				

3856E Sovereign. — — As 3856D R. Horse with short tail. No BP in ex. die axis ↑↓

1880..BV			65	75	125				

3856F Sovereign. — — As 3856E R. Horse with short tail, small BP in ex. die axis ↑↓

1880	65	85	110	150	1885	BV	65	85	140
1884	BV	65	85	145					

3857
Melbourne Mint
WW buried in truncation

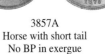

3857A
Horse with short tail
No BP in exergue

3857 Sovereign. — — First head. l. WW buried in trun. M below head for Melbourne Mint,
 Australia. R. Horse with long tail, small BP die axis ↑↓

1872 M	BV	65	500	1500	1877 M	BV	65	80	1000
1873 M	BV	65	110	500	1878 M	BV	65	80	550
1874 M	BV	65	100	850	1879 M	BV	65	80	500
1875 M	BV	65	150	600	1880 M	BV	65	80	550
1876 M	BV	65	160	750	1881 M	BV	65	80	1000

3857A Sovereign. — — As 3857 R. horse with short tail, no BP in ex die axis ↑↓

1881 M	BV	65	100	1000	1882 M	BV	65	75	300

	F	VF	EF	UNC		F	VF	EF	UNC
	£	£	£	£		£	£	£	£

3857B Sovereign. First head l. WW buried in trun. M below head for Melbourne Mint, Australia R. Horse with short tail, small BP in ex. die axis ↑↓

	F	VF	EF	UNC		F	VF	EF	UNC
1882 M	BV	65	75	300	1884 M	BV	65	75	450
1883 M	BV	65	75	300	1885 M	BV	65	75	550

3857C Sovereign. — — Second head. l. WW complete on broad truncation. R. Horse with short tail, small BP in ex.

	F	VF	EF	UNC		F	VF	EF	UNC
1882 M	BV	65	75	300	1885 M	BV	65	75	550
1883 M	BV	65	75	300	1886 M	BV	65	75	300
1884 M	BV	65	75	450	1887 M	BV	65	75	250

3858 Sovereign First head. l. WW buried in narrow trun. S below head for Sydney Mint, Australia, R. Horse with short tail, large BP in ex. die axis ↑↓

	F	VF	EF	UNC
1871 S	65	100	500	850

3858A Sovereign. — — As 3858 R. Horse with long tail, small BP in ex. die axis ↑↓

	F	VF	EF	UNC		F	VF	EF	UNC
1871 S	BV	65	300	600	1876 S	BV	65	110	750
1872 S	BV	65	140	350	1877 S	BV		*Extremely rare*	
1873 S	BV	65	140	450	1879 S	60	120	750	1500
1874 S	BV	65	120	1000	1880 S	BV	65	125	1250
1875 S	BV	65	100	850					

3858B Sovereign. — — As 3858 R. Horse with long tail, no BP in ex. die axis ↑↓

	F	VF	EF	UNC		F	VF	EF	UNC
1880 S	BV	65	120	1250	1881 S	BV	65	120	650

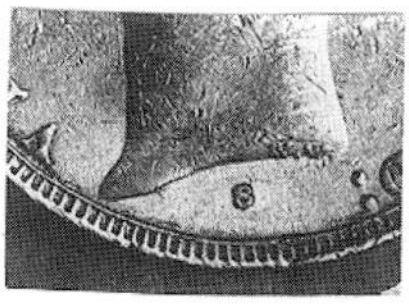

3858C
Sydney Mint
WW on broad truncation

3859
Type A1

3859A
Type A2

3858C Sovereign. Second head. l. WW complete on broad trun. R. Horse with long tail, small BP in ex. die axis ↑↓

	F	VF	EF	UNC
1880 S	BV	70	125	1250

3858D Sovereign. — — As 3858C R. Horse with short tail, no BP in ex. die axis ↑↓

	F	VF	EF	UNC		F	VF	EF	UNC
1881 S		65	120	650	1882 S	BV	65	75	300

3858E Sovereign. — — As 3858D R. Horse with short tail small BP in ex. die axis ↑↓

	F	VF	EF	UNC		F	VF	EF	UNC
1882 S	BV	65	75	300	1885 S	BV	65	75	400
1883 S	BV	65	75	300	1886 S	BV	65	75	300
1884 S	BV	65	75	300	1887 S	BV	65	75	300

3859 Half-Sovereign. Type A1. First (smallest) young head. l. R. First shield, die axis ↑↓

	F	VF	EF	UNC		F	VF	EF	UNC
1838	65	95	225	400	1850	105	225	750	—
1839 die axis ↑↓ or ↑↑ Proof only *FDC* £1250					1851	40	75	175	300
1841	65	100	275	450	1852	65	90	200	350
1842	40	75	150	275	1853	40	70	150	275
1843	65	100	275	450	— Proof *FDC* £3000				
1844	60	75	225	400	1854			*Extremely rare*	
1845	120	300	950	—	1855	40	75	160	275
1846	60	85	225	400	1856	40	75	160	275
1847	60	85	225	400	1857	65	90	200	350
1848	60	85	225	400	1858	65	90	200	350
1849	40	75	175	300					

3859A Half-Sovereign. Type A2, Second (larger) young head. l. R. First shield die axis ↑↓

	F	VF	EF	UNC		F	VF	EF	UNC
1858	40	70	160	275	1861	40	70	160	275
1859	40	70	160	275	1862	250	750	—	—
1860	40	70	160	275	1863	40	70	160	275

3860
Die number location

3860C

3860D
Type A3

3860E
Type A4

3860F

	F £	*VF* £	*EF* £	*UNC* £		*F* £	*VF* £	*EF* £	*UNC* £

3860 Half-Sovereign. Type A2, as last R. die number below shield, die axis ↑↓

1863	65	90	225	400	1867	40	70	150	275
1864	40	70	150	275	1869	40	70	150	275
1865	40	70	150	275	1870	60	80	160	275
1866	40	70	150	275	1871	40	70	150	275

3860A Half-Sovereign. — R. Re-engraved shield legend and rosettes closer to border, coarse boarder teeth both sides, with die number below shield die axis ↑↓

1870	85	200	550	—	1871	85	200	550	—

3860B Half-Sovereign. — R. As last but with normal border teeth and no die number below shield die axis ↑↓

1871 .... *Extremely rare*

3860C Half-Sovereign. — obv. with repositioned legend, nose now points to T in VICTORIA. R Similar to last but with die number below shield die axis ↑↓

1871	105	225	650	—	1872	90	200	550	—

3860DHalf-Sovereign. Type A3, Third (larger still) young head l. R. As 3860A, with die number below shield die axis ↑↓

1872	40	70	150	275	1875	40	65	150	250
1873	40	70	150	275	1876	40	65	150	250
1874	40	75	150	275	1877	40	65	150	250

3860E Half-Sovereign. Type A4. Fourth young head l. hair ribbon now narrow. R. As last with die number below shield die axis ↑↓

1876	40	65	140	250	1878	40	65	140	250
1877	40	65	140	250	1879	60	85	275	450

3860F Half-Sovereign. Type A5. Fifth young head l. in very low relief. R. As last with die number below shield die axis ↑↓

1880	40	75	275	450

3861
Type A5

3862
Sydney Mint

3861 Half-Sovereign. Obv. as last. R. Cross on crown buried in border. Legend and rosettes very close to heavy border, no die number below shield die axis ↑↓

1880	40	75	165	300	1884	40	65	125	200
1883	40	65	135	200	1885	40	65	125	200

3862 Half-Sovereign. Type A2, Second (larger) young head l. R. First shield with S below shield for Sydney Mint, Australia, die axis ↑↓

1871 S	40	85	500	—

3862A Half-Sovereign. — obv. with repositioned legend, nose now points to T in VICTORIA. R Re-engraved shield, S below shield die axis ↑↓

1872 S	40	90	600	—

3862B Half-Sovereign. Type A3. Third (larger still) young head l. R. As last die axis ↑↓

	F £	VF £	EF £	UNC £
1875 S	40	85	500	—

3862C Half-Sovereign. Type A4. Fourth young head l. hair ribbon now narrow. R. As last, die axis ↑↓

	F £	VF £	EF £	UNC £
1879 S	40	75	700	—

3862D Half-Sovereign. Type A5. Fifth young head,l. in low relief. R as last. die axis ↑↓

	F £	VF £	EF £	UNC £		F £	VF £	EF £	UNC £
1882 S	125	550	2250	—	1883 S	50	100	450	—

3862E Half-Sovereign. — R. Cross on crown buried in border. Legend and rosettes very close to heavy border, S below shield die axis ↑↓

	F £	VF £	EF £	UNC £		F £	VF £	EF £	UNC £
1880 S	40	60	600	—	1883 S	40	80	500	—
1881 S	40	100	650	—	1886 S	40	75	400	—
1882 S	100	550	2250	—	1887 S	40	70	300	1750

Melbourne Mint
3863

3863 Half-Sovereign. Type A. Third (larger still) young head l. R. Re-engraved shield with M below shield for Melbourne Mint, Australia die axis ↑↓

	F £	VF £	EF £	UNC £		F £	VF £	EF £	UNC £
1873 M	40	100	500	—	1877 M	40	100	400	—

3863A Half-Sovereign. Type A4, fourth young head l. hair ribbon now narrow. R. As last die axis ↑↓

	F £	VF £	EF £	UNC £		F £	VF £	EF £	UNC £
1877 M	40	100	400	—	1882 M	40	100	400	—

3863B Half-Sovereign. Type A5. Fifth young head l. in low relief. R. As last die axis ↑↓

	F £	VF £	EF £	UNC £		F £	VF £	EF £	UNC £
1881 M	60	150	500	—	1885 M	65	200	1250	—
1882 M	40	85	400	—	1886 M	40	100	1250	—
1884 M	50	200	1250	—	1887 M	75	200	1600	—

Jubilee Coinage, 1887-93, die axis ↑↑

3864

	F £	VF £	EF £	UNC £
3864* Five Pounds. R. St. George 1887	400	500	600	800

— Proof *FDC* £2,250

— Proof no B.P. in exergue £2,750

3864A* Five Pounds. R. St George, S on ground for Sydney Mint, Australia 1887S
Extremely rare

* *Beware recent forgeries*

3865

3866

	EF £	UNC £		F £	VF £	EF £	UNC £
3865* Two Pounds. Similar die axis ↑↑ 1887				150	200	275	350
— Proof *FDC* £750							

3865A* Two Pounds. R. St George, S on ground for Sydney Mint, Australia ↑↑ 1887S.... *Extremely rare*

3866* Sovereign. Normal JEB designer's initials on trun. R. St. George. London Mint die axis ↑↑

1887	60	95	1888	BV	60	95

3866A Sovereign. — with tiny JEB designer's initials on truncation die axis ↑↑

1887 .... *Extremely rare*

3866B Sovereign. Repositioned legend. G: of D:G: now closer to crown. Normal JEB designer's initials on trun. ↑↑

1887 Proof *FDC* £500.			1889	BV	60	95
1888	60	95	1890	BV	60	95

3866C Sovereign. Obv. as last. R. Horse with longer tail die axis ↑↑

1891	60	95	1892	BV	60	95

3867
Melbourne Mint

3869

3867 Sovereign. With small spread JEB designer's initials on trun. R. M on ground for Melbourne Mint, Australia, die axis ↑↑

1887M	BV	60	100

3867A Sovereign. With normal JEB designer's initials on trun. die axis ↑↑

1887M	BV	60	100

3867B Sovereign. Repositioned legend. G: of D: G: now closer to crown. Normal JEB initials on trun. die axis ↑↑

1887M	60	100	1889M	BV	60	100
1888M	60	120	1890M	BV	60	100

3867C Sovereign. Obv. as last. R. Horse with longer tail die axis ↑↑

1891M	60	100	1893M	BV	60	100
1892M	60	100				

3868 Sovereign. With small spread JEB initials on trun. R. S on ground for Sydney Mint, Australia die axis ↑↑

1887S	70	200	850

3868A Sovereign. With normal JEB designer's initials on trun. die axis ↑↑

1888S	BV	60	150

3868B Sovereign. Repositioned legend. G: of D:G: now closer to crown. Normal JEB initials on trun. die axis ↑↑

1888S	60	150	1890S	BV	70	400
1889S	60	200				

* *Beware recent forgeries*

	VF £	EF £	UNC £		F £	VF £	EF £	UNC £

3868C Sovereign. Obv. as last. R. Horse with longer tail die axis ↑↑

	VF	EF	UNC		F	VF	EF	UNC
1891S		60	100	1893S		BV	60	100
1892S		60	100					

3869 Half-Sovereign. Obv. normal JEB designer's initials. on trun. R. High shield die axis ↑↑

	VF	EF	UNC		F	VF	EF	UNC
1887		50	75	1890		100	200	—

— Proof *FDC* £250

3869A

3869B

3869C

3869A Half-Sovereign. Small close JEB designer's intitials. on trun. R. High shield die axis ↑↑

	VF	EF	UNC
1887	100	200	—

3869B Half-Sovereign. Normal JEB initials. on trun. R. Lower shield, date therefore spread apart, complete cross at top, die axis ↑↑

	VF	EF	UNC		F	VF	EF	UNC
1890	100	200	—	1892		100	200	—

3869C Half-Sovereign. No JEB initials on trun. R. High Shield die axis ↑↑

	VF	EF	UNC		F	VF	EF	UNC
1887	100	200	—	1891		100	200	—
1890	BV	50	85	1892		100	200	—

3869D Half-Sovereign. As last. R. Lower shield, date therefore spread apart die axis ↑↑

	VF	EF	UNC		F	VF	EF	UNC
1890	BV	50	85	1892		BV	50	85
1891	BV	70	100	1893		BV	80	110

3870

3870A

3870 Half-Sovereign. Small very spread JEB initials on trun. R. High shield, M below for Melbourne Mint, Australia, die axis ↑↑

	F	VF	EF	UNC
1887M	60	150	300	600

3870A Half-Sovereign. Small close JEB initials on trun. R. As last die axis ↑↑

	F	VF	EF	UNC
1887M	60	150	300	600

3870B Half-Sovereign. Normal JEB initials on trun. R. Lower shield, date therefore spread part die axis ↑↑

	F	VF	EF	UNC
1893M	60	175	400	—

3871 Half-Sovereign. Small very spread JEB initials on trun. R. High shield S below for Sydney Mint, Australia ↑↑

	F	VF	EF	UNC
1887S	50	100	250	—

3871A Half-Sovereign. Small close JEB initials on trun. R As last. die axis ↑↑

	F	VF	EF	UNC
1887S	50	100	250	—

VF	EF	UNC		F	VF	EF	UNC
	£	£	£		£	£	£	£

3871B Half-Sovereign. Normal JEB initials on trun. R. Lower shield, date therefore spread apart, S below for Sydney Mint, Australia die axis ↑↑

1889S ..50 100 400 —

3871C Half-Sovereign. Normal JEB initials on trun. R. High shield, S below for Sydney Mint, Australia die axis ↑↑

1891S ..60 125 450 950

3871D Half-Sovereign. No JEB initials on trun. R. As last die axis ↑↑

1891S ..60 125 500 2000

Old Head coinage, 1893-1901, die axis ↑↑

3872

3872* Five Pounds. R. St. George and dragon

1893 ..400 675 975 1250

— Proof *FDC* £2500

3873 3874

	EF	UNC		F	VF	EF	UNC
	£	£		£	£	£	£

3873* Two Pounds. Similar die axis ↑↑

1893 ..150 250 400 550

— Proof *FDC* £850

3874 Sovereign. R. St. George, London Mint die axis ↑↑

1893	95	1898		85
— Proof *FDC* £600		1899		85
1894	85	1900		85
1895	85	1901		85
1896	85			

3875 Sovereign. — R. St. George. M on ground for Melbourne Mint, Australia die axis ↑↑

1893 M	85	1898 M	85
1894 M	85	1899 M	85
1895 M	85	1900 M	85
1896 M	85	1901 M	85
1897 M	85		

** beware recent forgeries*

3876
Perth Mint mark

3877
Sydney Mint mark

	F	VF	EF	UNC		F	VF	EF	UNC
	£	£	£	£		£	£	£	£
3876 Sovereign. — — P on ground for Perth Mint, Australia die axis ↑↑									
1899 P		85	250	900	1901 P			75	150
1900 P			75	150					
3877 Sovereign. — — S on ground for Sydney Mint, Australia die axis ↑↑									
1893 S				100	1898 S				150
1894 S				85	1899 S				85
1895 S				85	1900 S				85
1896 S				100	1901 S				85
1897 S				85					

3878

	F	VF	EF	UNC		F	VF	EF	UNC
3878 Half-Sovereign. R. St. George. London Mint die axis ↑↑									
1893			50	95	1897			50	95
— Proof *FDC* £450					1898			50	95
1894			50	95	1899			50	95
1895			50	95	1900			50	95
1896			50	95	1901			50	95
3879 Half-Sovereign. — — M on ground for Melbourne Mint, Australia die axis ↑↑									
1893 M	500	—	—	—	1899 M	50	100	300	—
1896 M	50	100	250	—	1900 M	50	100	300	—
3880 Half-Sovereign. — — P on ground for Perth Mint, Australia die axis ↑↑									
1899 P	Proof only *unique*				1900 P	75	150	500	—
3881 Half-Sovereign.— — S on ground for Sydney Mint, Australia die axis ↑↑									
1893 S	60	100	250	—	1900 S	40	75	200	—
1897 S	40	75	200	—					

SILVER

Young head coinage, die axis ↑↓

3882

	F £	VF £	EF £	UNC £
3882 Crown. Young head. l. R. Crowned shield, regnal year on edge in Roman figures (eg 1847 = XI)				
1839 Proof only *FDC* £3250				
1844 Star stops VIII	30	95	650	1500
1844 Cinquefoil stops VIII	30	95	650	1500
1845 Star stops VIII	30	95	650	1500
1845 Cinquefoil stops VIII	30	95	650	1500
1847 XI	35	120	800	1750

3883

3885 Type 'A1'

3883*Crown. 'Gothic' type, as illustration; inscribed edge,

mdcccxlvii=1847 Undecimo on edge die axis ↑↓ 300 500 850 1750

— Proof, Plain edge die axis *FDC* £2000 ↑↑

**Beware of recent forgeries.*

3884 Crown. — — mdcccliii=1853. Septimo on edge die axis ↑↑ Proof *FDC* £4500

3885 Halfcrown. Type A^1. Young head l. with one ornate and one plain fillet binding hair. WW in relief on trun. Die axis ↑↓

1839 .... 250 750 2000 1839 Proof plain edge. *FDC* £650

3886 —Halfcrown. Type A^2 Similar, but two ornate fillets binding hair.die axis ↑↓

— 1839 Proof *FDC* £1500

3886A Halfcrown. — Type $A^{2/3}$ Similar, Two plain fillets, WW relief, die axis ↑↓ plain edge Proof *FDC* £2500

3887 Halfcrown. — Type A^3. Two plain fillets. WW incuse on trun. die axis ↑↓

1839 ....300 1000 2500 — 1840 ....30 75 300 500

3888 Halfcrown. — Type A[4]. Similar but no initials on trun. die axis ↑↓

	F £	*VF* £	*EF* £	*UNC* £
1841	85	300	850	1500
1842	25	75	300	500
1843	30	100	400	700
1844	20	50	250	450
1845	20	50	250	450
1846	20	50	250	450
1848/6	60	150	550	1100
1848	25	250	750	1250
1849 large date	30	80	350	600
1849 small date	40	100	425	700
1850	25	70	350	650
1853 Proof *FDC* £1000				

3889

3890

3889 Halfcrown. — Type A[5]. As last but design of inferior workmanship die axis ↑↓

	F £	*VF* £	*EF* £	*UNC* £
1874	15	35	90	200
1875	15	35	90	200
1876	15	40	100	225
1876/5	30	50	200	450
1877	15	35	90	200
1878	15	35	90	200
1879	15	40	120	250
1880	15	35	90	200
1881	15	35	90	200
1882	15	40	100	225
1883	15	35	90	200
1884	15	35	90	200
1885	15	35	90	200
1886	15	35	90	200
1887	20	45	110	250

3890 Florin. 'Godless' type A (i.e. without D.G.), WW behind bust within linear circle, die axis ↑↓

	F £	*VF* £	*EF* £	*UNC* £
1848 Plain edge (Pattern) *FDC* £600				
1848 Milled edge Proof *FDC* £1750				
1849 WW obliterated	35	70	175	300
1849	18	35	100	175

3891 Florin. 'Gothic' type B[1]. Reads brit:, WW below bust, date at end of obverse legend in gothic numerals (1851 to 1863) die axis ↑↓

	F £	*VF* £	*EF* £	*UNC* £
mdccclі		*Extremely rare*		
mdcccliі	18	40	100	200
mdcclii, ii/i	20	50	125	275
mdcccliii	18	40	100	200
— Proof *FDC £1000*				
mdcccliv	250	650	2000	—
mdccclv	25	75	150	300
mdccclvi	25	75	150	300
mdccclvii	20	45	110	225
mdcclviii	20	45	110	225
mdccclix	20	45	110	225
mdccclx	25	50	135	250
mdccclxii	50	150	500	1000
mdccclxiii	100	300	750	1500

3891

3892

3892 Florin. — Type B[2]. As last but die number below bust (1864 to 1867) die axis ↑↓

	F £	*VF* £	*EF* £	*UNC* £
mdccclxiv	20	45	110	225
— heavy flan		*Extremely rare*		
mdccclxv	40	100	200	350
mdccclxvi	35	75	175	300
mdccclxvii	30	70	175	300

	F	VF	EF	UNC		F	VF	EF	UNC
	£	£	£	£		£	£	£	£

3893 Florin. — Type B^3. Reads britt:, die number below bust (1868 to 1879) die axis ↑↓

mdccclxviii	30	85	200	400	mdccclxxiv	25	55	150	275
mdccclxix	25	75	200	350	mdccclxxiv iv/iii	35	75	200	350
mdccclxx	20	45	110	225	mdccclxxv	25	50	125	250
mdccclxxi	20	50	125	250	mdccclxxvi	20	45	110	225
mdccclxxii	18	40	85	175	mdccclxxvii	25	50	125	250
mdccclxxiii	20	50	120	200	mdccclxxix			*Extremely rare*	

3894 Florin. — Type B^4. As last but with border of 48 arcs and no WW below bust die axis ↑↓

1877 mdccclxxvii			*Extremely rare*	

3895 Florin. — Type B^5. Similar but 42 arcs (1867, 1877 and 1878) die axis ↑↓

mdccclxvii		*Extremely rare*			mdccclxxviii	20	45	110	225
mdccclxxvii	25	55	150	300					

3896 Florin. — Type $B^{5/6}$. As last but no die number below bust (1877, 1879) die axis ↑↓

mdccclxxvii	100	200	400	750	mdccclxxix	100	200	400	750

3897 Florin. — Type B^6. Reads britt:, WW; 48 arcs (1879) die axis ↑↓

mdccclxxix	20	45	110	225

3898 Florin. — Type B^7. As last but no WW, 38 arcs (1879) die axis ↑↓

mdccclxxix	20	45	110	225

3899 Florin.— Type $B^{3/8}$. As next but younger portrait (1880) die axis ↑↓

mdccclxxx			*Extremely rare*	

3900 Florin. — Type B^8. Similar but 34 arcs (1880 to 1887) die axis ↑↓

mdccclxxx	15	40	100	200	mdccclxxxiv	18	40	95	200
mdccclxxxi	18	40	95	200	mdccclxxxv	20	45	100	225
mdccclxxxi/xxri	30	75	150	300	mdccclxxxvi	15	35	85	175
mdccclxxxiii	18	40	95	200					

3901 Florin. — Type B^9. Similar but 46 arcs die axis ↑↓

1887 mdccclxxxvii	30	55	175	300

3902 Shilling. Type A^1. First head l., WW on trun. die axis ↑↑

1838	10	25	100	150	1839	10	25	100	150

3903 Shilling Type A^2. Second head, l. WW on trun. (proof only), 1839 die axis ↑↑ *FDC £250*

3904

3904 Shilling — Type A^3. Second head, l. no initials on trun. Die axis ↑↓

1839	10	25	85	175	— Proof *FDC £400*				
1840	15	50	135	225	1854	50	150	500	900
1841	15	50	135	225	1854/1	150	500	1400	—
1842	10	20	70	150	1855	10	20	60	125
1843	15	30	110	200	1856	10	20	60	125
1844	10	20	70	150	1857	10	20	60	125
1845	10	20	80	175	1857 REG F:Ɔ:error	125	275	600	—
1846	10	20	70	150	1858	10	20	60	125
1848 over 6	45	100	450	650	1859	10	20	60	125
1849	15	25	80	175	1860	15	25	90	175
1850	120	800	1200	—	1861	15	25	90	175
1851/49	150	600	1400	—	1862	20	40	125	225
1851	30	85	300	500	1863	25	60	250	450
1852	10	20	65	125	1863/1	75	175	400	—
1853	10	20	60	125					

3905 Shilling — Type A^4. As last, R. Die number above date die axis ↑↑

	F £	VF £	EF £	UNC £		F £	VF £	EF £	UNC £
1864	10	20	60	125	1866 BBITANNIAR	50	125	300	—
1865	10	20	60	125	1867	10	20	65	125
1866	10	20	60	125					

3906 Shilling — Type A^5. Third head, l. R. No die number above date die axis ↑↓

1867 Proof *Extremely rare* — 1867 Proof plain edge *Extremely rare*

3906A

Die number location

3906A Shilling — Type A^6. Third head, l. R. Die number above date die axis ↑↓

	F £	VF £	EF £	UNC £		F £	VF £	EF £	UNC £
1867	45	100	500	—	1874	10	20	60	125
1868	10	25	60	125	1875	10	20	60	125
1869	20	35	80	150	1876	15	30	65	125
1870	20	35	80	150	1877	10	20	60	125
1871	10	20	60	125	1878	10	20	60	125
1872	10	20	60	125	1879	25	60	200	350
1873	10	20	60	125					

3907 Shilling — Type A^7. Fourth head, l. R. No die number above date die axis ↑↓

	F £	VF £	EF £	UNC £		F £	VF £	EF £	UNC £
1879	10	20	50	110	1884	10	20	40	90
1880	10	20	40	90	1885	10	15	30	85
1881	10	20	40	90	1886	10	15	30	85
1882	15	40	80	160	1887	15	30	60	140
1883	10	20	40	90					

3907A Shilling. Type A7. Fourth head, L. R. Die number above date die axis ↑↓

1878 *Extremely rare* — 1879 *Extremely rare*

3908

3908 Sixpence. Type A^1. First head l. die axis ↑↓

	F £	VF £	EF £	UNC £		F £	VF £	EF £	UNC £
1838	8	15	40	75	1852	4	12	40	80
1839	8	15	40	75	1853	6	14	35	70
— Proof *FDC* £200					— Proof *FDC* £300				
1840	8	15	45	85	1854	50	120	400	750
1841	8	18	50	110	1855	6	14	35	85
1842	8	15	40	95	1855/3	12	25	50	110
1843	8	15	40	95	1856	7	15	40	95
1844 Small 44	6	14	35	85	1857	7	15	40	95
1844 Large 44	10	25	50	110	1858	7	15	40	95
1845	7	15	40	95	1859	6	14	35	85
1846	6	14	35	85	1859/8	10	20	40	100
1848	30	75	300	500	1860	7	15	40	90
1848/6 or 7	40	90	350	550	1862	30	80	300	500
1850	7	15	40	95	1863	18	50	200	400
1850/3	15	30	80	175	1866	*Extremely rare*			
1851	7	15	40	95					

3909
Die number location

3912
Type 'A5'

	F £	VF £	EF £	UNC £		F £	VF £	EF £	UNC £

3909 Sixpence. — Type A2. First head, R. die number above date die axis ↑↓

	F £	VF £	EF £	UNC £		F £	VF £	EF £	UNC £
1864 ∞	7	15	40	95	1866	7	15	40	95
1865	8	18	50	110					

3910 Sixpence. — Type A3. Second head, l. R. die number above date die axis ↑↓

	F £	VF £	EF £	UNC £		F £	VF £	EF £	UNC £
1867	10	18	55	125	1875	5	12	35	85
1868	10	18	55	125	1876	10	18	60	140
1869	10	20	80	175	1877	5	12	35	85
1870	10	20	80	175	1878	5	12	35	85
1871	7	15	40	95	1878 DRITANNIAR	30	80	275	—
1872	7	15	40	95	1878/7	35	100	300	—
1873	5	12	35	85	1879	10	18	60	140
1874	5	12	35	85					

3911 Sixpence. — Type A4. Second head, l. No die number die axis ↑↓

	F £	VF £	EF £	UNC £		F £	VF £	EF £	UNC £
1871	8	16	50	100	1879	7	15	40	85
1877	7	15	40	85	1880	8	16	50	100

3912 Sixpence. — Type A5. Third head l. die axis ↑↓

	F £	VF £	EF £	UNC £		F £	VF £	EF £	UNC £
1880	5	10	30	60	1884	5	10	25	55
1881	5	10	25	55	1885	5	10	25	55
1882	10	25	60	120	1886	5	10	25	55
1883	5	10	25	55	1887	4	8	20	50

3913

3913 Groat (4d.). R. Britannia seated r. die axis ↑↑

	F £	VF £	EF £	UNC £		F £	VF £	EF £	UNC £
1838	2	8	25	50	1846	4	10	32	65
1838/	3	16	35	85	1847/6 (or 8)	25	75	225	—
1839	3	9	28	55	1848/6	25	100	225	70
1839 die axis ↑↑ Proof *FDC* £150					1848	3	9	25	50
1839 die axis ↑↓ Proof *FDC* £200					1848/7	10	25	75	140
1840	3	9	25	55	1849	3	9	25	55
1840 small round o	5	15	30	75	1849/8	5	10	30	70
1841	4	10	35	65	1851	20	65	175	350
1842	4	10	32	65	1852	35	90	250	450
1842/1	5	15	35	85	1853	40	100	300	500
1843	4	10	32	65	— Proof *FDC* £300 milled edge				
1843 4 over 5	8	20	40	95	1854	3	9	25	55
1844	4	10	32	65	1855	3	9	25	55
1845	4	10	32	65					

Threepence. R. Crowned 3; as Maundy threepence but with a less prooflike surface

3914

3914 Threepence. Type A[1]. First bust, young head, high relief, ear fully visible. Dei axis ↑↓
R Tie ribbon closer to tooth border, cross on crown further from tooth border, figure 3

	F £	*VF* £	*EF* £	*UNC* £		*F* £	*VF* £	*EF* £	*UNC* £
1838*	5	10	50	85	1851	5	10	50	90
1838 BRITANNIAB....	*Extremely rare*				1851 5 over 8	10	20	80	—
1839*	5	18	65	120	1852*	60	175	400	—
— Proof (see Maundy)					1853	10	25	75	150
1840*	5	14	60	100	1854	5	10	50	90
1841*	5	18	66	120	1855	5	18	65	120
1842*	5	18	65	120	1856	5	10	45	85
1843*	5	12	50	85	1857	5	18	65	120
1844*	5	18	65	120	1858	5	10	45	85
1845	3	8	35	70	1858 BRITANNIAB ..	*Extremely rare*			
1846	10	20	75	150	1858/6	10	20	80	—
1847*	50	150	350	600	1858/5	8	18	65	—
1848*	40	125	325	—	1859	5	10	45	85
1849	5	18	65	120	1860	5	18	65	120
1850	3	8	40	65	1861	5	10	45	85

**Issued for Colonial use only.*

3914A
Type A2

3914C
Type A4

3914D
Type A5

3914A Threepence. Type A[2]. First bust variety, slightly older portrait with aquiline nose ↑↓

	F £	*VF* £	*EF* £	*UNC* £		*F* £	*VF* £	*EF* £	*UNC* £
1859	5	10	45	85	1865	5	18	65	120
1860	5	10	45	85	1866	5	10	45	85
1861	5	10	45	85	1867	5	10	45	85
1862	5	10	45	85	1868	5	10	45	85
1863	5	18	65	120	1868 RRITANNIAR ..	*Extremely rare*			
1864	5	10	45	85					

3914B Threepence. — Type A[3]. Second Bust, slightly larger, lower relief, mouth fuller, nose more pronounced, rounded truncation die axis ↑↓

	F £	*VF* £	*EF* £	*UNC* £
1867	5	18	65	120

	F	VF	EF	UNC		F	VF	EF	UNC
	£	£	£	£		£	£	£	£

3914C Threepence. Type A4. Obv. as last. R. Tie ribbon further from tooth border, cross on crown nearer to tooth border die axis ↑↓

1867	5	18	65	120	1874	3	8	30	55
1868	5	18	65	120	1875	3	8	30	55
1869	10	20	75	140	1876	3	8	30	55
1870	4	12	50	85	1877	4	10	40	65
1871	5	14	55	100	1878	4	10	40	65
1872	5	14	55	100	1879	4	10	40	65
1873	3	8	30	55	1884	3	6	25	50

3914DThreepence. — Type A5. Third bust, older features, mouth closed, hair strands leading from 'bun' vary

1880	4	10	40	65	1885	3	6	25	50
1881	3	6	25	50	1886	3	6	25	50
1882	5	10	50	95	1887	4	10	40	65
1883	3	6	25	50					

3914E Twopence. Young head. R Date divided by a crowned 2 within a wreath, die axis ↑↓

1838	3	7	18	40	1848	5	10	22	50

3915

3915 Three-Halfpence. (for Colonial use). R. Value, etc. die axis ↑↓

1838	5	12	25	55	1843	3	6	15	45
1839	4	10	20	50	1843/34	8	20	70	150
1840	8	22	65	120	1860	6	18	50	95
1841	5	14	30	70	1862	6	18	50	95
1842	5	14	30	70					

3916

3916 Maundy Set. (4d., 3d., 2d. and 1.) die axis ↑↓

	EF £	FDC £		EF £	FDC £
1838	65	120	1862	55	90
1839	75	130	1863	55	90
— Proof die axis ↑↑ *FDC* £300			1864	55	90
1840	75	130	1865	55	90
1841	85	150	1866	55	90
1842	75	130	1867	55	90
1843	75	130	1868	55	90
1844	75	130	1869	60	100
1845	65	110	1870	50	85
1846	85	150	1871	50	85
1847	75	130	1872	50	85
1848	75	130	1873	50	85
1849	85	150	1874	50	85
1850	55	95	1875	50	85
1851	55	95	1876	50	85
1852	65	110	1877	50	85
1853	65	110	1878	50	85
— Proof *FDC* £350			1879	50	85
1854	65	110	1880	50	85
1855	65	110	1881	50	85
1856	60	100	1882	50	85
1857	60	100	1883	50	85
1858	60	100	1884	50	85
1859	60	100	1885	50	85
1860	55	90	1886	50	85
1861	55	90	1887	55	95

	EF £	FDC £
3917 — **Fourpence,** 1838-87 ... *from*	8	14
3918 — **Threepence**, 1838-87 ... *from*	12	25
3919 — **Twopence**, 1838-87 ... *from*	6	10
3920 — **Penny**, 1838-87 ... *from*	5	8

Maundy Sets in the original dated cases are worth approximately £10, and £5 for undated cases more than the prices quoted.

Jubilee Coinage 1887-93, die axis ↑↑

3921

3921 Crown. R. St. George and dragon, die axis ↑↑

	F £	*VF* £	*EF* £	*UNC* £
1887	15	25	40	85
— Proof *FDC* £375				
1888 narrow date	15	30	60	110
1888 wide date	40	100	200	—
1889	15	25	40	85
1890	15	30	60	110
1891	15	30	65	130
1892	20	40	80	160

3922

3922 Double-Florin (4s.). R. Cruciform shields. Roman I in date, die axis ↑↑

	F £	*VF* £	*EF* £	*UNC* £
1887	12	20	30	60
— Proof *FDC* £250				

3923 Double-Florin — R. Similar but Arabic 1 in date, die axis ↑↑

	F £	*VF* £	*EF* £	*UNC* £
1887	12	20	30	60
— Proof *FDC* £175				
1888	12	20	35	75
1888 inverted 1 for I in VICTORIA	25	50	120	250
1889	12	20	30	65
1889 inverted 1 for I in VICTORIA	25	50	120	250
1890	12	20	35	70

3924 3925

3924 Halfcrown. R. Shield in garter and collar, die axis ↑↑

	F £	VF £	EF £	UNC £
1887	7	12	20	45
— Proof *FDC* £100				
1888	10	15	35	70
1889	10	18	45	80
1890	10	18	45	80
1891	10	18	45	80
1892	10	18	45	80

3925 Florin. R. Cruciform shields, sceptres in angles, die axis ↑↑

	F £	VF £	EF £	UNC £
1887	5	8	15	30
— Proof *FDC* £75				
1888	6	12	22	45
1889	6	12	24	50
1890	10	25	60	130
1891	20	50	125	275
1892	20	45	110	250

3926 3927

3926 Shilling. Small head. R. Shield in Garter, die axis ↑↑

	F £	VF £	EF £	UNC £
1887	3	5	10	20
— Proof *FDC £60*				
1888/7	5	9	18	35
1889	35	90	300	450

3927 Shilling. Large head. R. As before, die axis ↑↑

	F £	VF £	EF £	UNC £
1889	5	9	25	45
1890	5	10	30	50
1891	5	10	35	55
1892	5	10	35	55

3928 3929 3930

3928 Sixpence. JEB designer's initials below trun. R. Shield in Garter (withdrawn type), die axis ↑↑

	F £	VF £	EF £	UNC £
1887	2	5	10	18
1887 R/V in VICTORIA	10	35	75	125
1887 JEB on trun.	15	40	85	150
—Proof *FDC* £45				

3929 Sixpence. — R. Value in wreath

	F £	VF £	EF £	UNC £
1887	2	5	10	18
1888	4	8	15	30
1889	4	8	15	30
1890	4	8	16	35
1891	5	10	18	40
1892	5	10	18	40
1893	175	500	1500	—

3930 Groat (for use in British Guiana). R. Britannia seated, die axis ↑↑

	F £	VF £	EF £	UNC £		F £	VF £	EF £	UNC £
1888						8	20	35	65

3931 Threepence. As Maundy but less prooflike surface, die axis ↑↑

	F £	VF £	EF £	UNC £		F £	VF £	EF £	UNC £
1887	—	1	4	10	1890	1	3	7	15
— Proof *FDC* £30					1891	1	3	7	15
1888	2	5	12	25	1892	2	5	12	25
1889	1	3	7	15	1893	15	40	100	200

2932

3932 Maundy Set. (4d., 3d., 2d. and 1d.) die axis ↑↑

	EF £	FDC £		EF £	FDC £
1888	55	80	1891	55	80
1889	55	80	1892	55	80
1890	55	80			

		EF £	FDC £
3933 — Fourpence, 1888-92	*from*	9	15
3934 — Threepence, 1888-92	*from*	10	20
3935 — Twopence, 1888-92	*from*	5	10
3936 — Penny, 1888-92	*from*	5	10

Maundy Sets in the original dated cases are worth approximately £10 and £5 for undated cases more than the prices quoted.

Old Head Coinage 1893-1901, die axis ↑↑

3937

3937 Crown. R. St. George. Regnal date on edge, die axis ↑↑

	F £	*VF* £	*EF* £	*UNC* £
1893 edge LVI	15	30	100	200
1893 Proof *FDC* £400				
1893 LVII	25	60	175	350
1894 LVII	15	40	125	275
1894 LVIII	15	40	125	275
1895 LVIII	15	35	110	250
1895 LIX	15	35	110	250
1896 LIX	18	50	150	300
1896 LX	15	35	110	250
1897 LX	15	35	110	250
1897 LXI	15	35	110	250
1898 LXI	25	60	175	350
1898 LXII	15	40	125	275
1899 LXII	15	40	125	275
1899 LXIII	15	40	125	275
1900 LXIII	20	50	150	300
1900 LXIV	20	50	175	350

3938

3938 Halfcrown. R. Shield in collar, die axis ↑↑

	F £	*VF* £	*EF* £	*UNC* £		*F* £	*VF* £	*EF* £	*UNC* £
1893	8	15	30	60	1897	8	15	30	60
— Proof *FDC* £120					1898	10	16	35	70
1894	10	18	50	90	1899	10	16	35	70
1895	9	16	35	70	1900	10	16	35	70
1896	9	16	35	70	1901	10	16	35	70

3939

	F £	VF £	EF £	UNC £		F £	VF £	EF £	UNC £

3939 Florin. R. Three shields within garter, die axis ↑↑

1893	5	10	30	50	1897	6	12	30	55
— Proof *FDC* £100					1898	6	15	35	65
1894	8	16	50	85	1899	6	12	30	55
1895	7	18	40	65	1900	6	12	30	55
1896	6	12	30	55	1901	6	12	30	55

3940 Shilling. R. Three shields within Garter, small rose, die axis ↑↑

1893	4	8	15	30	1894	5	10	20	45
1893 small lettering	6	15	30	50	1895	10	20	40	75
1893 Proof *FDC* £65									

3940 3941

3940A Shilling. Second reverse, larger rose, die axis ↑↑

1895	4	9	18	40	1899	4	10	20	40
1896	4	9	18	35	1900	4	10	20	40
1897	4	9	18	35	1901	4	10	20	40
1898	4	9	18	35					

3941 Sixpence. R. Value in wreath, die axis ↑↑

1893	3	6	12	25	1897	4	8	12	25
— Proof *FDC* £50					1898	4	8	12	25
1894	5	10	16	30	1899	4	8	14	25
1895	4	8	12	25	1900	4	8	14	25
1896	4	8	12	25	1901	4	8	14	25

3942 Threepence. R. Crowned 3. As Maundy but less prooflike surface, die axis ↑↑

1893	1	2	5	12	1897	1	2	6	15
— Proof *FDC* £35					1898	1	2	6	15
1894	1	3	7	18	1899	1	2	5	12
1895	1	3	7	18	1900	1	2	5	12
1896	1	2	6	15	1901	1	2	6	15

3943

3943 Maundy Set. (4d., 3d., 2d. and 1d.), die axis ↑↑

	EF £	FDC £		EF £	FDC £
1893	45	60	1898	45	60
1894	50	65	1899	55	65
1895	45	60	1900	55	65
1896	45	60	1901	45	60
1897	45	60			

		EF £	FDC £
3944 — Fourpence. 1893-1901	*from*	5	10
3945 — Threepence. 1893-1901	*from*	10	20
3946 — Twopence. 1893-1901	*from*	5	10
3947 — Penny. 1893-1901	*from*	5	10

Maundy Sets in the original dated cases are worth approximately £5 more than the prices quoted.

3948

Rev. with ornamental trident prongs (OT)

Young Head Copper Coinage, 1838-60, die axis ↑↑

3948 Penny. R. Britannia

	F £	VF £	EF £	UNC £
1839 Bronzed proof *FDC*£300				
1841 Rev. OT	5	10	30	70
1841 OT. no colon after REG	5	10	30	70
1843 OT. —		*Extremely rare*		
1843 OT REG:	35	100	500	—
1844 OT	10	15	40	90
1845 OT	15	25	75	175
1846 OT	10	20	60	150
1846 OT colon close to DEF	15	25	70	175
1847 — —	8	15	40	95
1847 OT DEF—:	8	15	40	95
1848/7 OT	5	15	35	85
1848 OT	5	15	35	85
1848/6 OT	20	50	175	—
1849 OT	50	100	500	—
1851 OT	10	20	60	150
1851 OT DEF:	10	20	60	150
1853 OT DEF—:	5	12	30	70
1853 Proof *FDC £275*				
1853 Plain trident, (PT) DEF:	10	20	50	125
1854 PT	5	12	30	70
1854/3 PT	12	25	60	150
1854 OT DEF—:	8	15	35	80
1855 OT —	5	12	30	70
1855 PT DEF:	5	12	30	70
1856 PT DEF:		*Extremely rare*		
1856 OT DEF—:	25	50	125	400
1857 OT DEF—:	8	15	35	80
1857 PT DEF:	5	10	30	70
1858 OT DEF—:	5	10	30	70
1858/7 — —	5	10	30	70
1858/3	25	60	200	—
1858 no ww on trun.	5	10	30	70
1859	5	10	30	70
1860/59	175	450	1200	—

**The 1860 large copper pieces are not to be confused with the smaller and commoner bronze issue with date on reverse (nos. 3954, 3956 and 3958).*

3949

	F £	VF £	EF £	UNC £
3949 Halfpenny. R. Britannia, die axis ↑↑				
1838	5	12	25	60
1839 Bronzed proof FDC *£200*				
1841	4	10	20	55
1843	25	45	90	225
1844	6	15	30	70
1845	50	125	350	—
1846	8	18	35	85
1847	8	18	35	85
1848	10	20	40	95
1848/7	8	18	35	85
1851	5	15	30	75
1851 Rev. incuse dots on shield	5	15	30	75
1852 —	8	18	35	85
1852 Rev. normal shield	8	18	35	85
1853 Rev. incuse dots on shield	3	8	15	40
1853 — Proof FDC *£150*				
1853/2 —	15	35	75	175
1854 —	3	8	15	40
1855 —	3	8	15	40
1856 —	5	15	30	75
1857 —	4	10	20	50
1857 Rev. normal shield	4	10	20	50
1858 —	5	10	25	65
1858/7 —	5	10	25	65
1858/6 —	5	10	25	65
1859 —	5	10	25	65
1859/8 —	10	20	50	110
1860 —	600	1750	3000	—

Overstruck dates are listed only if commoner than normal date, or if no normal date is known.

3950

	F £	VF £	EF £	UNC £
3950 Farthing. R. Britannia die axis ↑↑				
1838 WW raised on trun.	5	10	25	55
1839	4	8	20	50
1839 Bronzed Proof *FDC £150*				
1840	4	8	20	50
1841	4	8	20	50
1842	15	35	85	175
1843	4	8	20	50
1843 I for 1 in date	50	175	—	—
1844	45	100	300	—
1845	8	10	25	60
1846	8	15	40	90
1847	5	10	25	60
1848	5	10	25	60
1849	30	60	200	—
1850	5	10	25	60
1851	10	20	45	110
1851 D/◡in DEI	25	50	125	—
1852	10	20	45	110
1853	5	10	25	60
1853 WW incuse on trun.	10	30	75	175
1853 Proof *FDC £275*				
1854	5	10	25	40
1855	5	10	30	65
1855 WW raised	8	15	35	75
1856 WW incuse	8	20	40	100
1856 R/E in VICTORIA	15	40	90	—
1857	5	10	25	60
1858	5	10	25	60
1859	10	20	45	110
1860	750	1750	3000	—

3951

	F £	VF £	EF £	UNC £		F £	VF £	EF £	UNC £
3951 Half-Farthing. R. Value, die axis ↑↑									
1839	5	10	30	60	1851	5	10	35	60
1839 Bronzed proof *FDC* £275					1852	4	10	35	60
1842	5	10	30	60	1853	5	15	40	85
1843		5	20	35	1853 Proof *FDC £250*				
1844		3	15	30	1854	8	25	65	110
1844 E/N in REGINA	10	20	65	125	1856	8	25	65	110
1847	4	8	22	50	1856 Large date	50	100	250	500

**Thes1860 large copper pieces are not to be confused with the smaller and commoner bronze issue with date on reverse (nos. 3954, 3956 and 3958).*

3951

3952

3953

	F £	VF £	EF £	UNC £		F £	VF £	EF £	UNC £
3952 Third-Farthing (for use in Malta). R. Britannia die axis ↑↑									
1844	20	35	75	150	1844 RE for REG	30	60	250	500
3953 Quarter-Farthing (for use in Ceylon). R. Value, die axis ↑↑									
1839	10	18	35	65	1853	10	20	40	75
1851	10	20	40	75	1853 Proof *FDC £700*				
1852	10	18	35	65					

Copper coins graded in this catalogue as UNC have full mint lustre.

Bronze Coinage, 'Bun Head' Issue, 1860-95, die axis ↑↑

When studying an example of the bronze coinage if the minutiae of the variety is not evident due to wear from cirulation, then the coin will not be of any individual significance.

3954

H Mint mark location

3955

3954 Penny. R. Britannia, die axis ↑↑

	F £	VF £	EF £	UNC £
1860 Beaded border	10	40	100	250
1860 — R. shield of treble incuse lines	10	25	50	150
1860 —lowered eye	50	100	250	550
1860 — R. sea extends beyond linear circle..	30	60	150	400
1860 — —eye lower.	8	40	100	250
1860 Beaded/R. toothed border	100	350	725	1500
1860 Toothed/beaded border	100	350	725	1500
1860 Toothed border...	5	15	30	80
1860 — heavy flan	*Extremely rare*			
1860 — rose complete. on bust	5	15	35	80
1860 — — R. LCW below foot......	75	150	300	550
1860 — L C WYON below bust	2	10	35	90
1860 — no LC WYON	6	25	75	175
1860 — — 16 leaves in wreath...........	15	50	150	300
1861 Toothed border	20	50	125	275
1861 — R. no LCW	25	80	200	450
1861 — — sea crosses linear circle....	20	50	125	300
1861 — LC WYON lower on bust	50	100	200	425
1861 — LC WYON below bust	3	15	40	100
1861 — — heavy flan .	*Extremely rare*			
1861 — — R. no LCW	100	250	525	1200
1861 — — — sea crosses linear circle	8	40	100	250
1861 — no LC WYON	2	10	35	90
1861 — — R. no LCW.	*Extremely rare*			
1861 — — — sea crosses linear circle	100	200	400	900
1861 — — 16 leaves in wreath...........	2	10	35	90
1861 — — — 6 over 8	*Extremely rare*			
1861 — — — R. .	100	250	500	—
no LCW	8	40	100	225
1861 — — — — sea crosses linear circle.......	2	10	35	90
1861 — — — — — 8 over 6	*Extremely rare*			
1862 L C WYON on bust	Extremely rare			
1862 no LC WYON .	2	10	35	90
1862 — 8 over 6.........	*Extremely rare*			
1862 — Halfpenny numerals	*Extremely rare*			
1863	2	10	35	90
1863 Die number below	*Extremely rare*			
1863 slender 3	*Extremely rare*			
1864 Upper serif.....	20	75	250	650
1864 Crosslet 4.......	25	85	300	900
1865	8	20	65	175
1865/3	40	100	200	550
1866	5	15	45	110
1867	8	25	65	200
1868	15	35	100	300
1869	50	175	400	1000
1870	8	25	75	200
1871	25	75	250	450
1872	5	15	40	110
1873	5	15	40	110
1874	5	15	55	175
1874 narrow date	25	50	100	225
1874 older features .	10	30	60	150
1875	2	10	35	100
1875 narrow date	3	10	25	65
1877	2	10	35	100
1877 narrow date	*Extremely rare*			
1878	3	15	50	175
1879	10	20	65	200
1879 Double incuse leaf veins..........	2	7	25	75
1879 narrow date	25	50	100	225
1880	3	15	65	150
1880 3 rings on trident shaft	3	15	65	150
1881	4	15	50	175
1882*	*Extremely rare*			
1883	3	10	35	90
1884	2	8	25	60
1885	2	8	25	60
1886	2	10	25	70
1887	2	8	25	60
1888	2	10	25	70
1889	2	8	20	60
1890	2	8	20	60
1891	2	7	18	55
1892	2	8	20	60
1893	2	8	20	60
1894	3	15	40	95

* not to be confused with Heaton Mint

3955 Penny. R. Britannia, H Mint mark below date – (struck by Ralph Heaton & Sons, Birmingham)

	F £	VF £	EF £	UNC £
1874 H	5	20	50	120
1874 H narrow date .	10	30	80	200
1875 H	35	95	350	—
1876 H	2	15	35	90
1876 H wide date	10	30	80	200
1881 H	3	15	35	100
1882 H	2	10	25	75
1882/1 H	10	25	60	200

3956

3956 Halfpenny. R. Britannia, die axis ↑↑

	F £	VF £	EF £	UNC £
1860 Beaded border ..	1	5	20	50
1860 no tie to wreath ..	5	15	50	120
1860 Toothed border .	2	10	30	85
1860 round top light house		15	50	120
1860 5 berries in wreath	4	12	40	100
1860 — 15 leaves, 4 berries	3	10	35	85
1860 — rounded lighthouse	4	12	40	100
1860 — Double incuse leaf veins	5	15	50	120
1860 — 16 leaves wreath	10	30	85	200
1860 TB/BBmule	*Extremely rare*			
1861 5 berries in wreath	10	30	75	175
1861 15 leaves in wreath	6	20	50	120
1861 — R. no hemline to drapery	10	30	75	175
1861 — R. Door on lighthouse	5	15	50	120
1861 4 leaves double incuse veins	2	10	30	85
1861 16 leaves wreath.	5	15	50	120
1861 — R. LCW incuse on rock	10	30	75	175
1861 — R. no hemline to drapery	3	12	40	100
1861 — R. door on lighthouse	1	5	20	50
1861 HALP error	*Extremely rare*			
1861 6 over 8	*Extremely rare*			
1862	1	4	15	45
1862 Die letter A B or C to left of lighthouse	*Extremely rare*			
1863 small 3	2	6	35	90
1863 large 3	2	6	35	90
1864	2	10	40	100
1865	3	15	50	175
1865/3	40	100	200	450
1866	2	10	40	100
1867	3	15	50	175
1868	2	10	45	120
1869	10	40	150	300
1870	2	8	35	90
1871	15	50	175	325
1872	2	7	30	85
1873	2	10	40	100
1873 R. hemline to drapery	2	10	40	100
1874	5	25	85	250
1874 narrow date	15	50	150	—
1874 older features	5	25	85	250
1875	1	6	30	80
1877	1	6	30	80
1878	3	15	50	175
1878 wide date	50	100	225	375
1879	1	5	20	60
1880	2	7	30	85
1881	2	7	30	85
1883	1	7	30	85
1883 rose for brooch obv.	*Extremely rare*			
1884	1	4	20	50
1885	1	4	20	50
1886	1	4	20	50
1887	1	4	15	40
1888	1	4	20	50
1889	1	4	20	50
1889/8	10	20	50	120
1890	1	4	15	40
1891	1	4	15	40
1892	1	6	30	80
1893	1	4	20	50
1894	1	7	30	80

3957 Halfpenny. — R. Britannia, H Mint mark below date — (struck by Ralph Heaton & Sons, Birmingham)

	F £	VF £	EF £	UNC £
1874 H	1	5	30	70
1875 H	2	6	35	90
1876 H	1	5	30	70
1881 H	1	5	30	70
1882 H	1	5	30	70

3958

3960

3958 Farthing. R. Britannia die axis ↑↑

	F £	VF £	EF £	UNC £
1860 Beaded border		5	20	45
1860 Toothed border		3	15	35
1860 — small eye		3	18	40
1860 TB/BB mule		*Extremely rare*		
1861small eye		3	18	40
1861 larger eye		4	20	45
1862		3	18	40
1862 large 8		*Extremely rare*		
1863	20	45	125	300
1864 4 no serif		5	25	55
1864 4 with serif		8	30	65
1865		3	18	40
1865/2		10	25	75
1866		3	15	35
1867		4	20	50
1868		4	20	50
1869		10	30	75
1872		3	18	40
1873		2	12	40
1875 large date	5	10	30	80
1875 small date	10	25	80	225
1875 —older features	8	20	70	175
1877 Proof only £2,500				
1878		2	10	25
1879 large 9		5	15	40
1879 normal 9		2	10	25
1880		3	20	45
1881		2	10	30
1883	2	10	30	65
1884		1	8	15
1885		1	8	15
1886		1	8	15
1887		2	12	30
1888		2	10	25
1890		2	10	25
1891		1	8	20
1892	2	10	30	65
1893		1	8	20
1894		2	10	25
1895	10	20	50	110

Bronze coins graded in this catalogue as UNC have full mint lustre

3959 Farthing. — R. Britannia. H Mint mark below date
— (struck by Ralph Heaton & Sons, Birmingham)

	F	VF	EF	UNC
1874 H older features	5	10	25	55
1874 H,∩ over N's obv.		*Extremely rare*		
1875 H younger features	20	50	100	350
1875 H older features		2	8	25
1876 H large 6	10	28	60	110
1876 H normal 6	5	10	30	65
1881 H	2	5	12	35
1882 H	2	5	12	35

3960 Third-Farthing (for use in Malta). R. Value die axis ↑↑

	F	VF	EF	UNC
1866	1	3	10	25
1868	1	3	10	25
1876	2	4	12	30
1878	1	3	10	25
1881	2	4	12	30
1884	1	3	10	25
1885	1	3	10	25

Old Head Issue, 1885-1901, die axis ↑↑

3961

3961 Penny. R. Britannia, die axis ↑↑

	VF £	EF £	UNC £
1895	2	6	30
1896	2	5	25
1897	2	5	25
1897 O'NE flawed	*Extremely rare*		
1898	3	10	35
1899	2	5	25
1900		8	20
1901		3	10

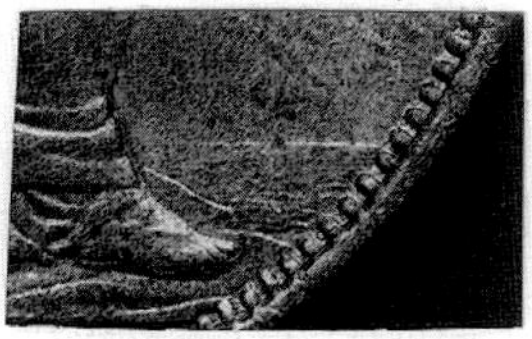

3961 'High Tide'
Horizon is level with folds in robe

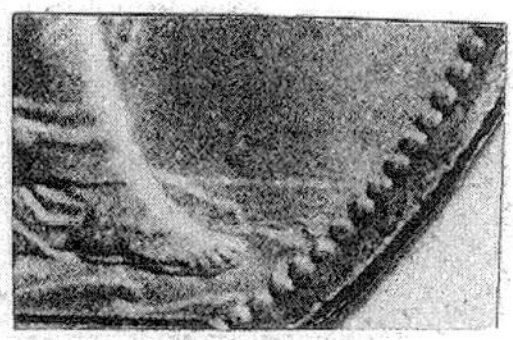

3961A 'Low Tide'
Horizon is level with hem line of robe

3961A Penny. As last but 'Low tide', 1895 .... 35 125 300

3962 Halfpenny. Type as Penny. R. Britannia, die axis ↑↑

	VF £	EF £	UNC £
1895	2	6	15
1896	2	5	12
1897	2	5	12
1897 Higher tide level.	5	10	20
1898	2	5	12
1899		5	12
1900		8	15
1901		2	8

3963 Farthing. R. Britannia. Bright finish, die axis ↑↑

	VF £	EF £	UNC £
1895	2	5	10
1896	2	5	10
1897	2	5	12

3962

3964

3964 Farthing. — Dark finish, die axis ↑↑

	VF £	EF £	UNC £
1897	2	5	10
1897 Higher tide level.	5	10	20
1898	2	5	10
1899	2	5	10
1900	3	8	15
1901		2	5

Proof Sets

PS3 Young head, **1839.** 'Una and the Lion' Five Pounds, and Sovereign to Farthing (15 coins) .... *FDC* £30,000

PS4 — **1853.** Sovereign to Half-Farthing, including Gothic type Crown (16 coins) .... *FDC* £25,000

PS5 Jubilee head. Golden Jubilee, **1887.** Five pounds to Threepence (11 coins) .*FDC* £5,000

PS6 — — **1887.** Crown to Threepence (7 coins) .... *FDC* £1000

PS7 Old head, **1893**. Five Pounds to Threepence (10 coins) .... *FDC* £6,000

PS8 — — **1893.** Crown to Threepence (6 coins) .... *FDC* £1100

THE HOUSE OF SAXE-COBURG-GOTHA, 1901-1910

EDWARD VII, 1901-10

'Edward the Peacemaker' was born on 9 November 1841, and married Princess Alexandra of Denmark. He indulged himself in every decadent luxury, while his wife tried to ignore his extra-marital activities. Edward travelled extensively and was crucial in negotiating alliances with Russia and France. Edward VII died on 6 May 1910.

Five Pound pieces, Two Pound pieces and Crowns were only issued in 1902. A branch of the Royal Mint was opened in Canada at Ottawa and coined Sovereigns of imperial type from 1908.

Unlike the coins in most other proof sets, the proofs issued for the Coronation in 1902 have a matt surface in place of the more usual brilliant finish.

Designer's initials: De S. (G. W. De Saulles)
B. P. (Benedetto Pistrucci, d. 1855)

Engravers and Designers: WHJ Blakemore, George WIlliam De Saulles (1862-1903), Benedetto Pistrucci (1784-1855)

Prime Ministers:– Robert Arthur Talbor Gascoyine-Cecil (1830-1903), Conservative 1895-1902, Arthur James Balfour (1848-1930), Conservative 1902-5, Sir Henry Campbell-Bannerman (1836-1908), Liberal 1905-8, Herbert Henry Asquith (1852-1928), Liberal 1908-16

GOLD

Die axis: ↑↑

3966

			EF	*UNC*	*F*	*VF*	*EF*	*UNC*
			£	£	£	£	£	£
3965	**Five Pounds.** 1902. R. St. George				400	575	700	850
3966	**Five Pounds.** — Proof. 1902. *Matt surface FDC* £750							
3966A	**Five Pounds.** — Proof 1902S. S on ground for Sydney Mint, Australia							*Extremely rare*

3967

3969

3967	**Two Pounds.** 1902. Similar	175	225	300	400
3968	**Two Pounds.** — Proof. 1902. *Matt surface FDC* £300				
3968A	**Two Pounds.** — Proof 1902S. S on ground for Sydney Mint, Australia				*Extremely rare*

3969 Sovereign. R . St. George. London mint, die axis ↑↑

1902 Matt proof *FDC* £125		1906	85
1902	85	1907	85
1903	85	1908	85
1904	85	1909	85
1905	85	1910	85

3970 Sovereign. — C on ground for Ottawa Mint, Canada

1908 C (Satin proof only) *FDC* £2000			1910 C	BV	80	150
1909 C	80	150				

UNC £		UNC £

3971 Sovereign. R. St. George M on ground for Melbourne Mint, Australia, die axis ↑↑

1902 M	95	1907 M	85
1903 M	85	1908 M	85
1904 M	85	1909 M	85
1905 M	85	1910 M	85
1906 M	85		

3972 Sovereign. — P on ground for Perth Mint, Australia die axis ↑↑

1902 P	95	1907 P	85
1903 P	85	1908 P	85
1904 P	85	1909 P	85
1905 P	85	1910 P	85
1906 P	85		

3973 Sovereign. — S on ground for Sydney Mint, Australia die axis ↑↑

1902 S	95	1906 S	85
— Proof	*Extremely rare*	1907 S	85
1903 S	85	1908 S	85
1904 S	85	1909 S	85
1905 S	85	1910 S	85

3974

	VF £	EF £	UNC £		VF £	EF £	UNC £

3974 Half-Sovereign. R. St. George. London Mint, die axis ↑↑

1902 Matt proof *FDC £85*				1906	BV	40	55
1902	BV	50	65	1907	BV	40	55
1903	BV	40	55	1908	BV	40	55
1904	BV	40	55	1909	BV	40	55
1905	BV	40	55	1910	BV	40	55

3975 Half-Sovereign. — M on ground for Melbourne Mint, Australia, die axis ↑↑

1906 M	40	60	140	1908 M	BV	60	150
1907 M	40	60	140	1909 M	BV	60	140

3976 Half-Sovereign. — P on ground for Perth Mint, Australia, die axis ↑↑

1904 P		150	500	—	1909 P	125	300	—
1908 P		150	500	—				

3977 Half-Sovereign. — S on ground for Sydney Mint, Australia, die axis ↑↑

1902 S	40	100	250	1906 S	40	100	300
— Proof	*Extremely rare*			1908 S	40	100	300
1903 S	40	65	125	1910 S	40	100	225

SILVER

3978

	F £	VF £	EF £	UNC £
3978 Crown. R. St. George and dragon die axis ↑↑				
1902	35	65	100	150
3979 Crown. — Matt proof *FDC £150*				

3980

3980 Halfcrown. R. Crowned Shield in Garter, die axis ↑↑

	F £	VF £	EF £	UNC £
1902	15	35	60	100
— Matt proof *FDC* £100				
1903	65	250	600	1100
1904	50	200	450	900
1905*	175	450	950	2000
1906	20	45	175	400
1907	20	45	175	400
1908	25	50	300	600
1909	20	45	250	450
1910	15	35	150	300

3981 Florin. R. Britannia standing on ship's bow die axis ↑↑

	F £	VF £	EF £	UNC £
1902	8	20	50	85
— Matt proof *FDC* £60				
1903	10	25	90	250
1904	12	30	100	275
1905	50	125	400	750
1906	10	25	90	250
1907	10	30	100	275
1908	15	40	175	400
1909	15	40	150	350
1910	10	20	75	200

**Beware of recent forgeries.*

3981

3982

3983

3982 Shilling. R. Lion rampant on crown die axis ↑↑

	F £	VF £	EF £	UNC £		F £	VF £	EF £	UNC £
1902	5	15	45	75	1906	5	10	45	110
— Matt proof *FDC* £70					1907	5	10	50	125
1903	8	20	85	225	1908	10	20	85	250
1904	8	15	75	175	1909	10	20	85	250
1905	50	150	450	950	1910	3	10	40	90

3983 Sixpence. R. Value in wreath die axis ↑↑

	F £	VF £	EF £	UNC £		F £	VF £	EF £	UNC £
1902	5	10	30	50	1906	4	10	30	70
— Matt proof *FDC* £50					1907	5	10	35	75
1903	4	10	30	70	1908	5	12	40	80
1904	6	15	45	95	1909	4	10	35	75
1905	5	12	35	80	1910	3	5	25	45

3984 Threepence. As Maundy but dull finish die axis ↑↑

	F £	VF £	EF £	UNC £		F £	VF £	EF £	UNC £
1902		4	8	15	1906	2	7	25	45
— Matt proof *FDC* £15					1907	1	7	25	45
1903	1	7	25	45	1908	1	2	10	25
1904	3	7	35	60	1909	1	7	25	45
1905	2	7	25	45	1910		1	10	30

3985

3985 Maundy Set (4d., 3d., 2d. and 1d.) die axis ↑↑

	EF £	FDC £		EF £	FDC £
1902	45	60	1906	45	55
— Matt proof *FDC* £55			1907	45	55
1903	45	55	1908	45	55
1904	45	55	1909	55	80
1905	45	55	1910	55	80

		EF £	FDC £
3986 — **Fourpence.** 1902-10	*from*	5	10
3987 — **Threepence**. 1902-10	*from*	5	12
3988 — **Twopence.** 1902-10	*from*	5	8
3989 — **Penny.** 1902-10	*from*	6	10

Maundy sets in the original dated cases are worth approximately £5 more than the prices quoted.

BRONZE

3990A

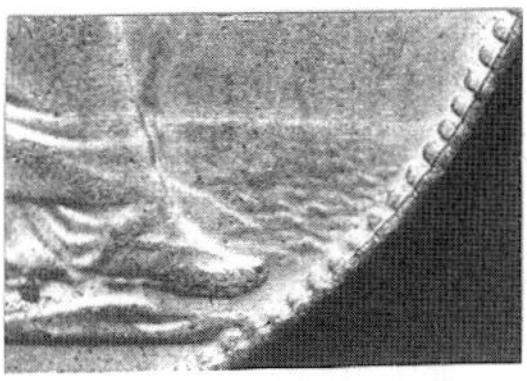

3990 'High Tide'

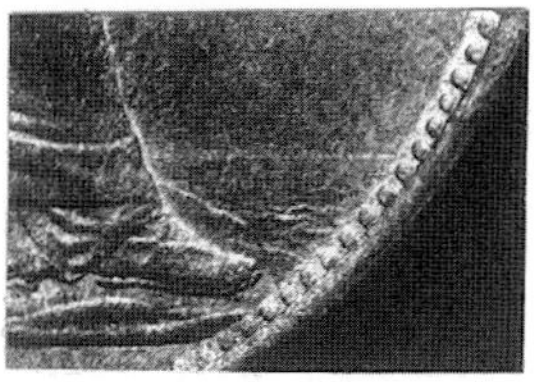

3990A 'Low Tide'

	F £	VF £	EF £	UNC £
3990 Penny. R. Britannia die axis ↑↑				
1902		1	4	20
1903 Normal 3		2	8	30
1903 Open 3		20	50	—
1904		3	12	40
1905		2	10	35
1906		2	8	30
1907		2	8	30
1908		2	8	30
1909		2	8	30
1910		1	7	25
3990A Penny.— R. As last but 'Low tide', 1902	5	10	30	65

3991

3991 Halfpenny. R. Britannia die axis ↑↑

	F £	VF £	EF £	UNC £
1902		1	4	12
1903		2	8	20
1904		2	8	25
1905		2	8	25
1906		2	8	20
1907		1	5	15
1908		1	5	15
1909		2	8	25
1910		2	7	20

3991A Halfpenny. — R. As last but 'Low tide', 1902 ....10 25 40 75

3992

3993

3992 Farthing. Britannia. Dark finish die axis ↑↑

	VF £	EF £	UNC £
1902		5	12
1903	1	5	12
1904	2	7	15
1905	1	5	12
1906	1	5	12
1907	1	5	12
1908	1	5	12
1909	1	5	12
1910	2	7	15

3993 Third-Farthing (for use in Malta) die axis ↑↑.

	EF £	UNC £
1902	8	20

No proofs of the bronze coins were issued in 1902

Proof Sets

PS9 Coronation, **1902.** Five Pounds to Maundy Penny, matt surface, (13 coins) *FDC* £1,600

PS10 — **1902.** Sovereign to Maundy Penny, matt surface, (11 coins) ....*FDC* £600

THE HOUSE OF WINDSOR, 1910-

GEORGE V, 1910-36

George V was born on 3 June 1865 and married Mary of Teek who bore him four sons and a daughter. He was King through World War I and visited the front on several occassions. He suffered a fall breaking his pelvis on one of these visits, an injury that would pain him for the rest of his life. He watched the Empire divide; Ireland, Canada, Australia, New Zealand and India all went through changes. He died on 2nd January 1936 only months after the Silver Jubilee.

Paper money issued by the Treasury during the First World War replaced gold for internal use after 1915 but the branch mints in Australia and South Africa (the main Commonwealth gold producing countries) continued striking Sovereigns until 1930-2. Owing to the steep rise in the price of silver in 1919/20 the issue of standard (.925) silver was discontinued and coins of .500 silver were minted.

In 1912, 1918 and 1919 some Pennies were made under contract by private mints in Birmingham. In 1918, as Half-Sovereigns were no longer being minted, Farthings were again issued with the ordinary bright bronze finish. Crown pieces had not been issued for general circulation but they were struck in small numbers about Christmas time for people to give as presents in the years 1927-36, and in 1935 a special commemorative Crown was issued in celebration of the Silver Jubilee.

As George V died in January, it is likely that all coins dated 1936 were struck during the reign of Edward VIII.

Engravers and Designers:– George Kuger Gray (1880-1943), Bertram MacKennal (1863-1931), Benedetto Pistrucci (1784-1855) Percy Metcalfe (1895-1970)
Prime Ministers:– Herbert Henry Asquith (1852-1928), Liberal 1908-16, David Lloyd George, (1863-1945) Liberal 1916-22, Andrew Bonor Law (1858-1923), Conservative, 1922-3, Stanley Baldwin, (1867-1947) Conservative, 1923, 1924-1, 1935-7, James Ramsey MacDonald, (1866-1931) Labour 1924-7, 1929-35
Designer's initials:
B. M. (Bertram Mackennal) P. M. (Percy Metcalfe)
K. G. (G. Kruger Gray) B. P. (Benedetto Pistrucci; d. 1855)

Die axis: ↑↑

GOLD

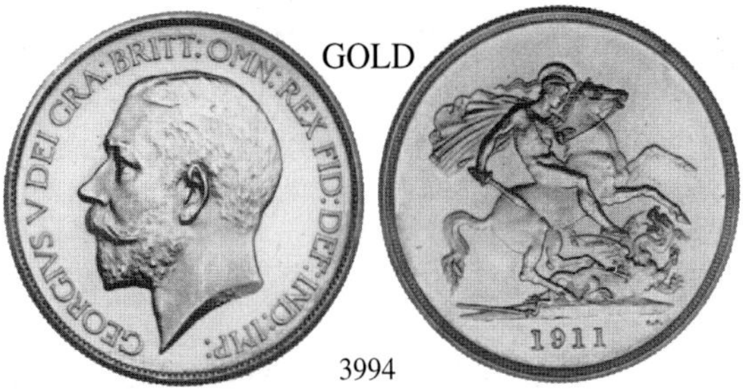

3994

	FDC £
3994 Five Pounds.* R. St. George, 1911 (Proof only)	1200
3995 Two Pounds.* R. St. George, 1911 (Proof only)	450

3996

3996 Sovereign. R. St. George. London Mint die axis: ↑↑

Date	£	Date	VF £	EF £	UNC £
1911	85	1915			85
— Proof *FDC* £250		1916			95
1912	85	1917*	1500	3500	—
1913	85	1925			75
1914	85				

**Forgeries exist of these and of most other dates and mints.*

3997 Sovereign. R. St George, C on ground for the Ottawa Mint, Canada die axis: ↑↑

Date	VF £	EF £	UNC £
1911 C	BV	85	110
1913 C	90	400	—
1914 C	125	250	—
1916 C*	3000	6000	—
1917 C	BV	85	110
1918 C	BV	85	110
1919 C	BV	85	110

** Beware of recent forgeries*

3997
Canada Mint mark

3998
India Mint mark

4004
South Africa Mint mark

3998 Sovereign. — I on ground for Bombay Mint, India 1918 75

3999 Sovereign. — M on ground for Melbourne Mint, Australia die axis: ↑↑

Date	VF £	EF £	UNC £
1911 M			75
1912 M			75
1913 M			75
1914 M			75
1915 M			75
1916 M			75
1917 M			75
1918 M			75
1919 M			90
1920 M	750	1750	—
1921 M	1250	3500	6000
1922 M	1200	3000	—
1923 M			75
1924 M			75
1925 M			75
1926 M			75
1928 M	575	1400	2000

4000 Sovereign. — small head die axis: ↑↑

Date	VF £	EF £	UNC £
1929 M	500	1250	—
1930 M	95	175	—
1931 M	150	250	—

4000

4001

4001 Sovereign. — P on ground for Perth Mint, Australia die axis: ↑↑

Date	VF £	EF £	UNC £
1911 P			75
1912 P			75
1913 P			75
1914 P			75
1915 P			75
1916 P			75
1917 P			75
1918 P			75
1919 P			75
1920 P			75
1921 P			75
1922 P			75
1923 P			75
1924 P	60	85	100
1925 P	90	110	250
1926 P	125	500	1750
1927 P	90	125	500
1928 P	75	90	110

VF	EF	UNC		VF	EF	UNC
	£	£	£		£	£	£

4002 Sovereign. — — small head die axis: ↑↑

1929 P			75	1931 P			75
1930 P			75				

4003 Sovereign. — S on ground for Sydney Mint, Australia die axis: ↑↑

1911 S			75	1919 S			75
1912 S			75	1920 S		*Extremely rare*	
1913 S			75	1921 S	400	900	1500
1914 S			75	1922 S	3000	9500	—
1915 S			75	1923 S	2000	4500	—
1916 S			75	1924 S	425	850	1250
1917 S			75	1925 S			75
1918 S			75	1926 S	4500	850	15000

4004 Sovereign. — SA on ground for Pretoria Mint, South Africa die axis: ↑↑

1923 SA	800	1400	2500	1926 SA			75
1923 SA Proof *FDC* £300				1927 SA			75
1924 SA	1250	2250	—	1928 SA			75
1925 SA			75				

4005 Sovereign. — — small head die axis: ↑↑

1929 SA			75	1931 SA			75
1930 SA			75	1932 SA			90

4002 4003 4006

4006 Half-Sovereign. R. St. George. London Mint die axis: ↑↑

1911	BV	35	50	1913		35	50
— Proof *FDC* £175				1914		35	50
1912	BV	35	50	1915		35	50

4007 Half-Sovereign. — M on ground for Melbourne Mint, Australia die axis: ↑↑

1915 M					45	70	125

4008 Half-Sovereign. — P on ground for Perth Mint, Australia die axis: ↑↑

1911 P	45	70	100	1918 P	125	275	450
1915 P	45	70	100				

4009 Half-Sovereign. — S on ground for Sydney Mint, Australia die axis: ↑↑

1911 S	45	70	90	1915 S	35	50	60
1912 S	45	70	90	1916 S	35	50	60
1914 S	40	60	75				

4010 Half-Sovereign. — SA on ground for Pretoria Mint, South Africa die axis: ↑↑

1923 SA Proof *FDC* £250				1926 SA	BV	35	50
1925 SA	BV	35	50

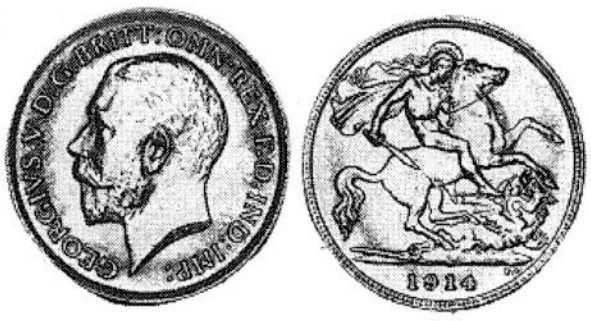

SILVER

First Coinage. Sterling silver (.925 fine)

4011

4011 Halfcrown. R. Crowned shield in Garter die axis: ↑↑

	F £	VF £	EF £	UNC £		F £	VF £	EF £	UNC £
1911	5	18	40	95	1915	4	10	25	65
— Proof *FDC* £80					1916	4	10	25	65
1912	6	25	55	110	1917	5	15	40	75
1913	8	30	65	125	1918	4	10	25	65
1914	4	10	25	65	1919	5	15	40	75

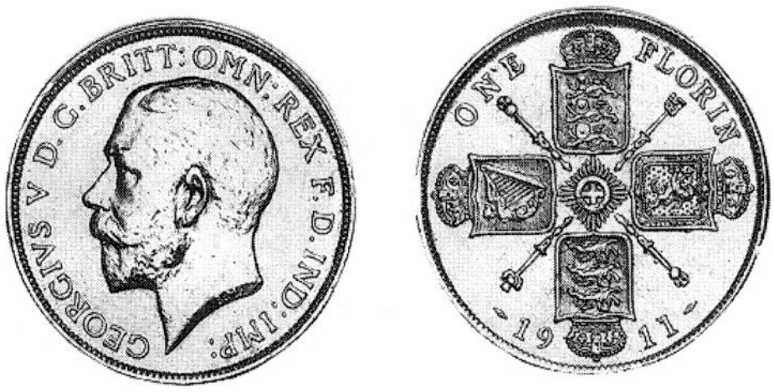

4012

4012 Florin. R. Cruciform shields die axis: ↑↑

	F £	VF £	EF £	UNC £		F £	VF £	EF £	UNC £
1911	5	10	35	80	1915	6	20	40	85
— Proof *FDC £75*					1916	4	10	25	60
1912	5	15	45	85	1917	6	12	30	70
1913	8	25	65	125	1918	4	10	25	60
1914	4	10	25	60	1919	6	12	30	70

4013 Shilling. R. Lion rampant on crown, within circle die axis: ↑↑

	F £	VF £	EF £	UNC £		F £	VF £	EF £	UNC £
1911	2	8	20	40	1915		4	20	40
— Proof *FDC £40*					1916		4	20	40
1912	4	12	30	60	1917		5	25	45
1913	8	15	45	80	1918		4	20	40
1914	3	10	25	45	1919	4	10	30	55

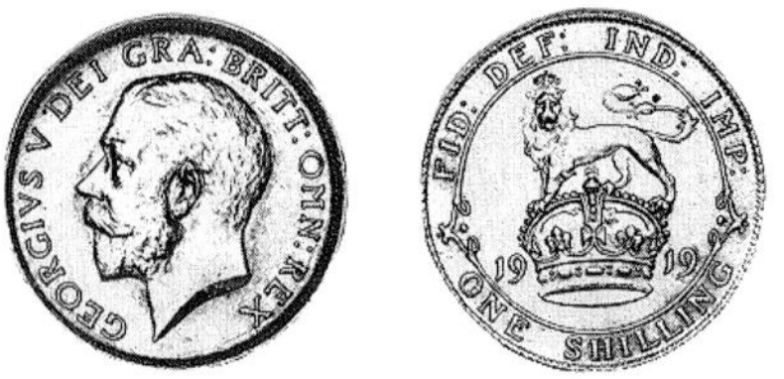

4013

4014

	F £	VF £	EF £	UNC £		F £	VF £	EF £	UNC £
4014 Sixpence. R. Similar die axis: ↑↑									
1911	2	8	15	30	1916	2	8	15	30
— Proof *FDC* £30					1917	5	15	30	60
1912	4	10	25	45	1918	2	8	15	30
1913	5	12	30	50	1919	4	10	20	40
1914	2	8	15	30	1920	4	10	25	45
1915	2	8	15	30					
4015 Threepence. As Maundy but dull finish die axis: ↑↑									
1911		1	5	15	1916		1	3	10
1912		1	5	15	1917		1	3	10
1913		1	5	15	1918		1	3	10
1914		1	5	15	1919		1	3	10
1915		1	5	15	1920		1	5	15

4016

	EF £	FDC £		EF £	FDC £
4016 Maundy Set (4d., 3d., 2d. and 1d.) die axis: ↑↑					
1911	50	70	1916	50	70
— Proof *FDC* £75			1917	50	70
1912	50	70	1918	50	70
1913	50	70	1919	50	70
1914	50	70	1920	50	70
1915	50	70			
4017 — Fourpence. 1911-20 *from*	7	12			
4018 — Threepence. 1911-20 *from*	8	15			
4019 — Twopence. 1911-20 *from*	6	10			
4020 — Penny. 1911-20 *from*	7	12			

Second Coinage. Debased silver (.500 fine). Types as before.

4021 Halfcrown. die axis: ↑↑

	F £	*VF* £	*EF* £	*UNC* £
1920	4	8	25	65
1921	5	10	30	75
1922	4	8	25	65
1923	3	5	15	40
1924	5	10	35	75
1925	20	50	175	300
1926	5	10	35	80
1926 No colon after OMN	10	25	85	150

4022 Florin. die axis: ↑↑

	F £	*VF* £	*EF* £	*UNC* £
1920	3	8	30	80
1921	3	8	30	60
1922	3	6	25	50
1923	2	5	20	45
1924	4	10	40	75
1925	25	45	125	200
1926	3	10	40	75

4023 Shilling. die axis: ↑↑

	F £	*VF* £	*EF* £	*UNC* £
1920	3	6	25	45
1921	4	10	30	65
1922	3	6	25	45
1923	2	5	20	40
1924	3	8	30	50
1925	5	10	45	80
1926	3	6	20	45

4024 Sixpence. die axis: ↑↑

	F £	*VF* £	*EF* £	*UNC* £
1920	2	4	12	25
1921	2	4	12	25
1922	2	5	15	30
1923	3	6	20	40
1924	2	4	12	25
1925	2	4	15	30

4025

4026

4025 Sixpence. — new beading and broader rim die axis: ↑↑

	F £	*VF* £	*EF* £	*UNC* £
1925	2	4	12	25
1926	2	4	15	25

4026 Threepence. die axis: ↑↑

	F £	*VF* £	*EF* £	*UNC* £
1920		1	3	15
1921		1	3	15
1922		1	10	20
1925	—	2	14	25
1926	1	3	15	30

4027 Maundy Set. (4d., 3d., 2d. and 1d.) die axis: ↑↑

	EF £	*FDC* £
1921	45	70
1922	45	70
1923	45	70
1924	45	70
1925	45	70
1926	45	70
1927	45	70
4028 — Fourpence. 1921-7 *from*	8	12
4029 — Threepence. 1921-7 *from*	8	15
4030 — Twopence. 1921-7 *from*	6	10
4031 — Penny. 1921-7 *from*	7	12

2nd coinage
BM more central on tr.

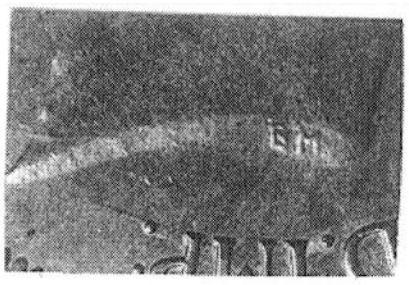

3rd coinage
Modified Effigy
BM to right of tr.

Third Coinage. As before but modified effigy, with details of head more clearly defined. The BM on truncation is nearer to the back of the neck and without stops; beading is more pronounced.

	F £	*VF* £	*EF* £	*UNC* £
4032 Halfcrown. die axis: ↑↑				
1926	5	10	35	60
1927	4	7	25	40
4033 Shilling. die axis: ↑↑				
1926	2	4	18	30
1927	2	6	25	40
4034 Sixpence. die axis: ↑↑				
1926		3	10	20
1927	2	4	15	25
4035 Threepence. die axis: ↑↑				
1926		1	8	25

Fourth Coinage. New types, 1927-36

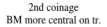

4036

4036 Crown. R. Crown in wreath die axis: ↑↑

1927 –15,030 struck Proof only *FDC £140*

	F £	*VF* £	*EF* £	*UNC* £
1928 –9034 struck	35	75	125	200
1929 –4994 struck	35	75	125	200
1930 -4847 struck.	35	75	125	200
1931 –4056 struck	35	85	150	225
1932 –2395 struck	85	120	225	350
1933 –7132 struck	35	75	125	200
1934 –932 struck	250	500	850	1500
1936 –2473 struck	65	100	200	300

4037

4038

4037 Halfcrown. R. Shield die axis: ↑↑

	F £	VF £	EF £	UNC £
1927 Proof only *FDC* £45				
1928	2	5	10	20
1929	2	5	10	20
1930	10	25	100	200
1931	2	5	10	25
1932	4	8	15	35
1933	2	5	10	20
1934	4	10	25	50
1935		5	10	20
1936		3	8	15

4038 Florin. R. Cruciform shields, sceptre in each angle die axis: ↑↑

	F £	VF £	EF £	UNC £
1927 Proof only *FDC* £45				
1928		3	10	20
1929		3	10	20
1930	2	5	10	25
1931	2	5	10	25
1932	20	50	125	250
1933		3	10	25
1935		3	10	20
1936		2	10	20

4039

4040

4039 Shilling. R. Lion rampant on crown, no inner circles die axis: ↑↑

	F £	VF £	EF £	UNC £
1927	2	4	15	30
— Proof *FDC* £30				
1928		3	10	20
1929		3	10	20
1930	3	6	20	40
1931	2	4	10	20
1932	2	4	10	20
1933		3	10	20
1934	2	5	16	30
1935		3	10	20
1936		3	8	20

4040 Sixpence. R. Three oak sprigs with six acorns die axis: ↑↑

	F £	VF £	EF £	UNC £
1927 Proof only *FDC* £25				
1928		2	4	12
1929		2	4	12
1930		2	4	12

4041 Sixpence. — closer milling die axis: ↑↑

	F £	VF £	EF £	UNC £
1931	2	3	8	20
1932	2	4	14	25
1933	2	3	8	18
1934	2	3	10	22
1935		2	6	15
1936		2	4	12

4042

4043

4042 Threepence. R. Three oak sprigs with three acorns die axis: ↑↑

	F £	*VF* £	*EF* £	*UNC* £		*F* £	*VF* £	*EF* £	*UNC* £
1927 Proof only *FDC £40*					1933			1	8
1928	1	3	14	35	1934			1	8
1930	1	3	14	35	1935			1	8
1931			1	8	1936			1	8
1932			1	8					

4043 Maundy Set. As earlier sets die axis: ↑↑

	EF £	*FDC* £		*EF* £	*FDC* £
1928	45	70	1933	45	70
1929	45	70	1934	45	70
1930	45	70	1935	45	70
1931	45	70	1936	45	70
1932	45	70			

The 1936 Maundy was distributed by King Edward VIII

		EF £	*FDC* £
4044 — Fourpence. 1928-36	*from*	8	12
4045 — Threepence. 1928-36	*from*	9	12
4046 — Twopence. 1928-36	*from*	7	12
4047 — Penny. 1928-36	*from*	8	15

Silver Jubilee Commemorative issue, die axis: ↑↑

4048

	VF £	*EF* £	*UNC* £
4048 Crown. 1935. R. St. George, incuse lettering on edge –714,769 struck	10	15	25
1935 — error edge		*Extremely rare*	
4049 Crown. — Specimen striking issued in box			40

4050 Crown. — raised lettering on edge 2,500 struck.Proof (.925 Æ) *FDC £250*

— error edge inscription Proof *FDC* £1000

— Proof in gold –28 struck £11,000

BRONZE

H Mint mark location – 4052

4052

KN Mint mark location – 4053

	F	VF	EF	UNC		F	VF	EF	UNC
	£	£	£	£		£	£	£	£

4051 Penny. R. Britannia die axis: ↑↑

1911			1	6	20	1918		1		8	25
1912			1	8	25	1919		1		8	25
1913			2	12	30	1920		1		8	25
1914			1	8	25	1921		1		8	25
1915			1	8	25	1922		4		18	35
1916			1	8	25	1926		5		22	45
1917			1	8	25						

4052 Penny. — R. Britannia, H (Heaton Mint, Birmingham, Ltd.) to l. of date die axis: ↑↑

1912 H		8	45	100	1919 H		10	100	225
1918 H		15	120	225					

4053 Penny. — R. Britannia KN (King's Norton Metal Co.) to l. of date die axis: ↑↑

1918 KN	3	25	150	300	1919 KN	3	30	175	350

4054 Penny. — modified effigy die axis: ↑↑

1926	15	75	500	950	1927			5	15

4055 Penny. — small head die axis: ↑↑

1928			5	15	1933		*Extremely rare*	
1929			5	15	1934		12	30
1930			8	18	1935		3	15
1931			8	20	1936		2	10
1932			15	35				

4056 Halfpenny. R. Britannia die axis: ↑↑

1911			5	20	1919			5	25
1912			5	25	1920			5	25
1913			5	25	1921			5	25
1914			5	25	1922			7	30
1915			5	25	1923			5	25
1916			5	25	1924			5	25
1917			5	25	1925			5	25
1918			5	25					

4057 Halfpenny. — modified effigy die axis: ↑↑

1925			8	30	1927			5	25
1926			6	25

4056

4058

4058 Halfpenny. Small head die axis: ↑↑

	EF £	UNC £		EF £	UNC £
1928	2	15	1933	2	15
1929	2	15	1934	4	20
1930	2	15	1935	2	15
1931	2	15	1936	1	10
1932	2	15			

4059

4062

4059 Farthing. R. Britannia. Dark finish die axis: ↑↑

1911	3	8	1915	4	10
1912	2	5	1916	2	5
1913	2	5	1917	1	5
1914	2	5	1918	9	20

4060 Farthing. — Bright finish, die axis: ↑↑ 1918-25 .... 1 5

4061 Farthing. — Modified effigy die axis: ↑↑

1926	1	3	1932	1	3
1927	1	3	1933	1	3
1928	1	3	1934	2	5
1929	1	3	1935	2	5
1930	1	3	1936	1	3
1931	1	3			

4062 Third-Farthing (for use in Malta). R. Value die axis: ↑↑

1913 .... 8 20

Proof Sets

PS11 Coronation, **1911.** Five pounds to Maundy Penny (12 coins) .... *FDC* £2,500

PS12 — **1911.** Sovereign to Maundy Penny (10 coins) .... *FDC* £750

PS13 — **1911.** Half crown to Maundy Penny (8 coins) .... *FDC* £400

PS14 New type, **1927.** Wreath type Crown to Threepence (6 coins) .... *FDC* £275

Abdicated 10 December. Created Duke of Windsor (1936-72)

Edward VIII was born 23 June 1894, and was very popular as Prince of Wales. He ruled only for a short time before announcing his intended marriage to the American divorcee Wallis Simpson; a potential religious and political scandal. Edward was not a traditionalist, as evidenced on the proposed coinage, where he insisted against all advice on having his effigy face the same way as his father's, instead of opposite. He abdicated in favour of his brother, and became Edward, Duke of Windsor marrying Mrs Simpson in France, where they lived in exile. He goverened the Bahamas from 1940-45 and died on 28 May 1972.

Abdicated 10 December. Created Duke of Windsor (1936-72)

No coins of Edward VIII were issued for currency within the United Kingdom bearing his name and portrait. The Mint had commenced work on a new coinage prior to the Abdication, and various patterns were made. No Proof Sets were issued for sale and only a small number of sets were struck.

Coins bearing Edward's name, but not his portrait, were issued for the colonial territories of British East Africa, British West Africa, Fiji and New Guinea. The projected U.K. coins were to include a Shilling of essentially `Scottish' type and a nickel brass Threepence with twelve sides which might supplement and possibly supersede the inconveniently small silver Threepence.

Engravers and Designers:– George Kruger Gray (1880-1943), Thomas Humphrey Paget (1893-1974), Benedicto Pistucci (1784-1855) Frances Madge Kitchener, Percy Metcalfe (1895-1970), H Wilson Parker (1896-1980)

Designer's initials:

H. P. (T. Humphrey Paget)
K. G. (G. Kruger Gray)
W. P. (H. Wilson Parker)
B.P. (Benedetto Pistrucci, d. 1855)
M. K. (Madge Kitchener)

Prime Minister:– Stanley Baldwin (1867-1947), Conservative 1935-7

Die axis ↑↑

4063 Proof Set

Gold, £5, £2 and £1, 1937 .... *not issued*

Silver Crown, Halfcrown, Florin,

	£
Sovereign,	*Extremely rare*
Crown,	*Extremely rare*
Halfcrown,	*Extremely rare*
Florin,	*Extremely rare*
Shilling,	*Extremely rare*
Sixpence,	*Extremely rare*
Threepence,	*Extremely rare*

Nickel brass. **Threepence**, 1937	*not issued*
Bronze. **Penny. Halfpenny and Farthing,** 1937	*not issued*

Pattern

4064 Nickel brass dodecagonal **Threepence**, 1937. R. Thrift plant of more naturalistic style than the modified proof coin. A small number of these coins were produced for experimental purposes and a few did get into circulation *Extremely rare*

GEORGE VI, 1936-52

George VI was born on 14 December 1895 and never expected to be King. He suffered ill-health through much of his life and had a stammer. He married Elizabeth Bowes Lyon and together they became very popular especially through the ravages of Word War II, when Buckingham Palace was bombed. The war took it's toll on George, and ever a heavy smoker he succumbed to lung cancer on 6th February 1952. His wife survives him and will have celebrated her 100th birthday in 2000.

Though they were at first issued concurrently, the twelve-sided nickel-brass Threepence superseded the small silver Threepence in 1942. Those dated 1943-4 were not issued for circulation in the U.K. In addition to the usual English 'lion' Shilling, a Shilling, of Scottish type was issued concurrently. This depicts the Scottish lion and crown flanked by the shield of St. Andrew and a thistle. In 1947, as silver was needed to repay the bullion lent by the U.S.A. during the war, silver coins were replaced by coins of the same type and weight made of cupro-nickel. In 1949, after India had attained independence, the title IND:IMP (*Indiae Imperator)* was dropped from the coinage. Commemorative Crown pieces were issued for the Coronation and the 1951 Festival of Britain.

Engravers and Designers:– Frances Madge Kitchener, George Kruger Gray (1880-1943), Percy Metcalfe (1895-1970) Thomas Humphrey Paget (1893-1974), H Wilson Parker (1896-1980), Benedetto Pistrucci (1784-1855)

Designer's initials:

K. G. (G. Kruger Gray)
H. P. (T. Humphrey Paget)
B. P. (Benedetto Pistrucci, d. 1855)
W. P. (Wilson Parker)

Prime Ministers:– Stanley Baldwin, (1867-1947) Conservative, 1935-37, Arthur Neville Chamberlain, (1869-1940) Conservative 1937-40, Sir Winston Leonard Spencer Churchill,(1874-1965) Conservative 1940-45. 1951-55, Clement Richard Attlee, (1883-1967) Labour 1945-51

Die axis ↑↑

GOLD

4074

4076

		FDC £
4074	**Five Pounds.** Bare head l. R. St. George, 1937. Proof plain edge only (5001 struck)..	550
4075	**Two Pounds.** Similar, 1937. Proof plain edge only (5001 struck)...............................	325
4076	**Sovereign.** Similar, 1937. Proof plain edge only (5001 struck)..................................	400
4077	**Half-Sovereign.** Similar, 1937. Proof plain edge only (5001 struck)..........................	150

SILVER

First coinage. Silver, .500 fine, with title IND:IMP

4078

	VF £	EF £	UNC £
4078 Crown. Coronation commemorative, 1937. R. Arms and supporters	10	18	25

4079 Crown. — — Proof *FDC* £35
— — Frosted 'VIP' Proof £300

4080

4081

4080 Halfcrown. R. Shield die axis: ↑↑

	EF £	*UNC* £		*UNC* £
1937		10	1942	8
— Proof *FDC* £15			1943	12
1938	5	25	1944	8
1939		12	1945	8
1940		12	1946	8
1941		12		

4081 Florin. R. Crowned rose, etc. die axis: ↑↑

	EF £	*UNC* £		*UNC* £
1937		8	1942	8
— Proof *FDC* £12			1943	8
1938	5	20	1944	8
1939		10	1945	8
1940		10	1946	8
1941		10		

4082

4083

4082 Shilling. 'English'. R. Lion rampant on large crown die axis: ↑↑

	EF £	*UNC* £		*UNC* £
1937		6	1942	8
— Proof *FDC* £10			1943	8
1938	4	20	1944	8
1939		10	1945	6
1940		10	1946	6
1941		10		

4083 Shilling. 'Scottish'. R. Lion seated facing on crown die axis: ↑↑

	EF £	*UNC* £
1937		6
— Proof *FDC* £10		
1938	4	20
1939		10
1940		10
1941		10

	VF £	*EF* £	*UNC* £
1942			9
1943			9
1944			8
1945			6
1946			6

4084

4085

4084 Sixpence. R. GRI crowned die axis: ↑↑

	EF £	*UNC* £
1937		5
— Proof *FDC* £6		
1938	3	10
1939		8
1940		8
1941		8

	VF £	*EF* £	*UNC* £
1942			5
1943			5
1944			5
1945			5
1946			5

4085 Threepence. R. Shield on rose die axis: ↑↑

	EF £	*UNC* £
1937		5
— Proof *FDC* £8		
1938		6
1939	4	12
1940		10

	VF £	*EF* £	*UNC* £
1941		2	10
1942*	4	10	25
1943*	4	10	30
1944*	10	20	45
1945*		*Extremely rare*	

**For colonial use only.*

4086

4086 Maundy Set. Silver, .500 fine. Uniform dates die axis: ↑↑

	FDC £
1937	55
— Proof *FDC* £60	
1938	70
1939	70
1940	70
1941	70

	FDC £
1942	70
1943	70
1944	70
1945	70
1946	70

		FDC £		FDC
4087 — Fourpence. 1937-46	*from*			10
4088 — Threepence. 1937-46	*from*			10
4089 — Twopence. 1937-46	*from*			10
4090 — Penny. 1937-46	*from*			15

Second coinage. Silver, .925 fine, with title IND:IMP (Maundy only)

4091 Maundy Set (4d., 3d., 2d. and 1d.). Uniform dates die axis: ↑↑

1947	70	1948	70

4092 — Fourpence, 1947-8	10
4093 — Threepence, 1947-8	10
4094 — Twopence, 1947-8	10
4095 — Penny, 1947-8	15

Third coinage. Silver, .925 fine, but omitting IND:IMP. (Maundy only)

4096 Maundy Set (4d., 3d., 2d. and 1d.). Uniform dates die axis: ↑↑

1949	70	1951	70
1950	70	1952	70

The 1952 Maundy was distributed by Queen Elizabeth II.

4097 — Fourpence, 1949-52	*from*	10
4098 — Threepence, 1949-52	*from*	10
4099 — Twopence, 1949-52	*from*	10
4100 — Penny, 1949-52	*from*	15

CUPRO-NICKEL

Second coinage. Types as first (silver) coinage, IND:IMP.

	UNC £		UNC £
4101 Halfcrown. R. Shield die axis: ↑↑			
1947	6	1948	6
4102 Florin. R. Crowned rose die axis: ↑↑			
1947	6	1948	6
4103 Shilling. 'English' type die axis: ↑↑			
1947	6	1948	5
4104 Shilling. — 'Scottish' type die axis: ↑↑			
1947	6	1948	5
4105 Sixpence. R. GRI crowned die axis: ↑↑			
1947	5	1948	4

Third coinage. Types as before but title IND:IMP. omitted

4106

	UNC £		VF £	EF £	UNC £
4106 Halfcrown. die axis: ↑↑					
1949	8	1951			15
1950	12	— Proof *FDC* £20			
— Proof *FDC* £15		1952			*Extremely rare*
4107 Florin. die axis: ↑↑					
1949	10	1951			15
1950	12	— Proof *FDC* £20			
— Proof *FDC* £15					
4108 Shilling. 'English' type die axis: ↑↑					
1949	10	1951			15
1950	12	— Proof *FDC* £15			
— Proof *FDC* £12					
4109 Shilling. — 'Scottish' type die axis: ↑↑					
1949	12	1951			15
1950	12	— Proof *FDC* £15			
— Proof *FDC* £12					

4110

	UNC £		VF £	EF £	UNC £
4110 Sixpence. As illustration die axis: ↑↑					
1949	6	1951			12
1950	6	— Proof *FDC* £10			
— Proof *FDC* £8		1952	3	15	40

Festival of Britain issue die axis: ↑↑

4111

	EF £	UNC £
4111 Crown. R. St. George, 1951. *Proof-like*	10	20
— — Frosted 'VIP' Proof £200		

NICKEL BRASS

First issue, with title IND:IMP.

4112

4113

4112 Threepence (dodecagonal). R. Thrift plant die axis: ↑↑

	VF £	EF £	UNC £
1937			5
—Proof *FDC* £6			
1938		4	12
1939		5	30
1940			10
1941			6
1942			5
1943			5
1944			6
1945			10
1946	10	40	150
1948		4	30

Second issue, omitting IND:IMP.

4113 Threepence. Similar die axis: ↑↑

	VF £	EF £	UNC £
1949	10	45	175
1950		10	35
— Proof *FDC* £30			
1951		15	55
— Proof *FDC* £35			
1952			8

BRONZE

First issue, with title IND:IMP.

4114

	UNC £		UNC £
4114 Penny. R. Britannia r. die axis: ↑↑			
1937	3	1944 —	12
— Proof *FDC* £10		1945 —	10
1938	5	1946 —	10
1939	8	1947 —	4
1940	30	1948 —	4
1940 Double exergue line	8		

4115

4116

4115 Halfpenny. R. Ship l. die axis: ↑↑			
1937	4	1943	4
— Proof *FDC* £5		1944	4
1938	5	1945	5
1939	6	1946	6
1940	8	1947	5
1941	4	1948	4
1942	4		

4116 Farthing. R. Wren l. die axis: ↑↑			
1937	2	1943	2
— Proof *FDC* £5		1944	2
1938	4	1945	2
1939	2	1946	2
1940	2	1947	2
1941	2	1948	2
1942	2		

Second issue, without IND.IMP. Types as before

4117 Penny. die axis: ↑↑

	VF £	*EF* £	*UNC* £
1949			4
1950	5	12	30
— Proof *FDC* £20			
1951	10	25	45
— Proof *FDC* £35			
1952 Proof only			*Unique*

4118

4119

4118 Halfpenny. die axis: ↑↑

1949	8
1950	6
— Proof *FDC* £5	
1951	12
— Proof *FDC* £10	
1952	5

4119 Farthing. die axis: ↑↑

1949	3
1950	3
— Proof *FDC* £5	
1951	4
— Proof *FDC* £10	
1952	3

The coins dated 1952 were issued during the reign of Elizabeth II.

Proof Sets

PS15 Coronation, **1937.** Five pounds to Half-sovereign (4 coins)	*FDC*	£1500
PS16 — **1937.** Crown to Farthing, including Maundy Set (15 coins)	*FDC*	£175
PS17 Mid-Century, **1950.** Halfcrown to Farthing (9 coins)	*FDC*	£75
PS18 Festival of Britain, **1951.** Crown to Farthing (10 coins)	*FDC*	£80

ELIZABETH II, acc. 1952

Elizabeth II born on 21 April 1926, our current Monarch has lived a long and glorious reign. She married Philip a distant cousin in 1947 and has four children, Charles, Anne, Andrew and Edward. Significantly she is the first Monarch to pay taxes and her coinage has been an interesting one with the change to decimal coinage and the numerous bust changes since 1953.

The earliest coins of this reign have the title BRITT:OMN, but in 1954 this was omitted from the Queen's titles owing to the changing status of so many Commonwealth territories. The minting of 'English' and 'Scottish' shillings was continued. A Coronation commemorative crown was issued in 1953, another crown was struck on the occasion of the 1960 British Exhibition in New York and a third was issued in honour of Sir Winston Churchill in 1965. A very small number of proof gold coins were struck in 1953 for the national museum collections, but between 1957 and 1968 gold sovereigns were minted again in quantity for sale in the international bullion market and to counteract the activities of counterfeiters.

Owing to inflation the farthing had now become practically valueless; production of these coins ceased after 1956 and the coins were demonetized at the end of 1960. In 1965 it was decided to change to a decimal system of coinage in the year 1971. As part of the transition to decimal coinage the halfpenny was demonetized in August 1969 and the halfcrown in January 1970. (See also introduction to Decimal Coinage.

Designer's initials:

A. V. (Avril Vaughan)
B. P. (Benedetto Pistrucci, 1784-1855)
B. R. (Bruce Rushin)
C. T. (Cecil Thomas)
D. C. (David Cornell)
E. F. (Edgar Fuller)
G. L. (Gilbert Ledward)
I. R. B. (Ian Rank-Broadley)
J. M. M. (John Mills)
M. G. (Mary Gillick)
M. M. D. (Mary Milner Dickens)
M. N. (Michael Noakes)
M. R. (Michael Rizzello)
N. S. (Norman Sillman)
P. N. (Philip Nathan)
R. D. M. (Raphael David Maklouf)
R. E. (Robert Elderton)
W. G. (William Gardner)
W. P. (Wilson Parker 1896-1980)
R. D. (Ron Dutton)
J. M. (Jeffrey Matthews)

Other designers whose initials do not appear on the coins:
Christopher Ironside
Arnold Machin (1911-99)
David Wynne
Professor Richard Guyatt
Eric Sewell
Oscar Nemon
Leslie Durbin
Derek Gorringe
Bernard Sindall

PRE-DECIMAL ISSUES
Die axis ↑↑
GOLD

First coinage, with title BRITT.OMN, 1953. *Proof only*.................. *of the highest rarity*
4120 Five Pounds. R. St. George .... *None issued for collectors*
4121 Two Pounds. Similar .... *None issued for collectors*
4122 Sovereign. Similar .... *None issued for collectors*
4123 Half-Sovereign. Similar .... *None issued for collectors*

Second issue, BRITT.OMN omitted

4125

4124 Sovereign. laur head r. R. St. George, fine graining on edge
1957 .... BV

4125 Sovereign. Similar, but coarser graining on edge

1958	BV	1965	BV
1959	BV	1966	BV
1962	BV	1967	BV
1963	BV	1968	BV
1964	BV		

SILVER

The Queen's Maundy are now the only coins struck regularly in silver.
The location of the Maundy ceremony is given for each year.

First issue, with title BRITT:OMN:

	FDC £
4126 Maundy Set (4d., 3d., 2d. and 1d.), 1953. St Paul's	300
4127 — Fourpence. 1953	50
4128 — Threepence. 1953	50
4129 — Twopence. 1953	50
4130 — Penny. 1953	100

Second issue, with BRITT:OMN: omitted

4131

FDC £

4131 Maundy Set (4d., 3d., 2d. and 1d.). Uniform dates

1954 *Westminster*	70	1963 *Chelmsford*	70
1955 *Southwark*	70	1964 *Westminster*	70
1956 *Westminster*	70	1965 *Canterbury*	70
1957 *St. Albans*	70	1966 *Westminster*	70
1958 *Westminster*	70	1967 *Durham*	70
1959 *Windsor*	70	1968 *Westminster*	70
1960 *Westminster*	70	1969 *Selby*	70
1961 *Rochester*	70	1970 *Westminster*	70
1962 *Westminster*	70		

4132 — Fourpence. 1954-70	*from*	10
4133 — Threepence. 1954-70	*from*	10
4134 — Twopence. 1954-70	*from*	10
4135 — Penny. 1954-70	*from*	15

CUPRO-NICKEL

First issue, 1953, with title BRITT.OMN.

4136

	EF	UNC	PROOF FDC
	£	£	£
4136 Crown. Queen on horseback. R. Crown in centre of emblematical cross, shield of Arms in each angle, 1953	6	10	25
—— Frosted 'VIP' proof £250			

4137 4138

	EF	UNC	PROOF FDC
4137 Halfcrown. with title BRITT:OMN: R. Arms, 1953		3	10
4138 Florin. R. Double rose, 1953		3	8

4139 4140 4141

	EF	UNC	PROOF FDC
4139 Shilling. 'English'. R. Three lions, 1953		1	6
4140 Shilling. '— 'Scottish'. R. Lion rampant in shield, 1953		1	6
4141 Sixpence. R. Interlaced rose, thistle, shamrock and leek, 1953		1	5
4142 Sixpence. Set of 9 uncirculated cu-ni, ni-br and Æ coins (2/6 to 1/4d.) in Royal Mint plastic envelope		25	

Second issue, similar types but omitting BRITT.OMN.

4143

4144

	EF	*UNC*
	£	£
4143 Crown, 1960. Bust r. R. As 4136	3	5
— — Similar, from polished dies (New York Exhibition issue)	6	25
— — 'VIP' *Proof,* frosted design *FDC* £300		
4144 Crown, — Churchill commemorative, 1965. As illustration. R. Bust of Sir Winston Churchill r.		1
— — Similar, "Satin-Finish". VIP *Specimen*		400

4145 Halfcrown. R. As 4137

	EF	*UNC*		*EF*	*UNC*		*EF*	*UNC*
	£	£		£	£		£	£
1954	3	18	1960		5	1965		3
1955		6	1961		3	1966		1
1956		8	1961 Polished die		8	1967		1
1957		4	1962		3	1970 Proof *FDC* £3		
1958	3	15	1963		3			
1959	5	25	1964		5			

4146

4146 Florin. R. As 4138

1954	5	40	1962	3
1955		5	1963	3
1956		5	1964	3
1957	5	40	1965	3
1958	4	18	1966	2
1959	5	35	1967	2
1960		4	1970 Proof *FDC* £3	
1961		4		

4147 Shilling. 'English' type. R. As 4139

	EF £	*UNC* £
1954		4
1955		4
1956		8
1957		3
1958	2	15
1959		3
1960		3
1961		1.50
1962		1
1963		0.75
1964		0.75
1965		0.75
1966		0.75

1970 Proof *FDC* £2

4148 Shilling. — 'Scottish' type. R. As 4140

	EF £	*UNC* £
1954		4
1955		5
1956		8
1957	2	15
1958		2
1959	2	15
1960		3
1961		5
1962		3
1963		0.75
1964		1
1965		1
1966		0.75

1970 Proof *FDC* £2

4149 Sixpence. R. As 4141

	UNC £
1954	5
1955	3
1956	3
1957	2
1958	2
1959	1
1960	2
1961	1
1962	0.75
1963	0.75
1964	0.75
1965	0.50
1966	0.50
1967	0.50

1970 Proof *FDC* £2

NICKEL BRASS

First issue, with title BRITT.OMN.

4152

4153

4152 Threepence (dodecagonal). R. Crowned portcullis, 1953 3

— Proof *FDC* £6

Second issue (omitting BRIT.OMN)

4153 Threepence Similar type

	UNC £
1954	5
1955	6
1956	6
1957	4
1958	7
1959	4
1960	4
1961	1
1962	0.75
1963	0.50
1964	0.50
1965	0.50
1966	0.35
1967	0.35

1970 Proof *FDC* £2

BRONZE

First issue, with title BRITT.OMN.

4154

4155

	VF £	*EF* £	*UNC* £	*Proof FDC* £
4154 Penny. R. Britannia (only issued with Royal Mint set in plastic envelope), 1953 Beaded border	1	4	8	10
1953 Toothed border			*Extremely rare*	
4155 Halfpenny. R. Ship, 1953			3	6
4156 Farthing. R. Wren, 1953			2	5

Second issue, omitting BRITT.OMN.

4157 Penny. R. Britannia (1954-60 *not issued)*

	UNC £		*UNC* £
1954	*Unique*	1965	0.35
1961	1	1966	0.35
1962	0.50	1967	0.25
1963	0.50	1970 Proof *FDC £3*	
1964	0.35		

4158 Halfpenny. R. Ship (1961 *not issued)*

1954	3	1960	0.50
1954 larger border teeth	4	1962	0.50
1955	2	1963	0.50
1956	2	1964	0.50
1957	2	1965	0.50
1957 calm sea	4	1966	0.25
1958	1	1967	0.25
1959	0.75	1970 Proof *FDC £2*	

4156

4159

4159 Farthing. R. Wren

	EF £		*EF* £	*UNC* £
1954	3	1956 Rev. with thin rim	2	5
1955 Rev. with thin rim	3			

Proof Sets

PS19 Coronation, **1953.** Crown to Farthing (10 coins)	*FDC*	60
PS20 'Last Sterling', **1970.** Halfcrown to Halfpenny plus medallion	*FDC*	15

All prices quoted assume coins are in their original case. Issued by the Royal Mint in official case from 1887 onwards, but earlier sets were issued privately by the engraver. All pieces have a superior finish to that of the current coins.

		No. of coins	*FDC £*
PS1	**George IV, 1826**. New issue, Five Pounds to Farthing	(11)	19,500
PS1A	— — Similar to above, including Maundy Set	(15)	20,000
PS2	**William IV, 1831.** Coronation, Two Pounds to Farthing	(14)	18,500
PS3	**Victoria, 1839.** Young head. "Una and the Lion" Five Pounds and Sovereign to Farthing	(15)	30,000
PS4	— **1853.** Sovereign to Half-Farthing, including Gothic type Crown	(16)	25,000
PS5	— **1887.** Jubilee bust for Golden Jubilee, Five Pounds to Threepence	(11)	5,000
PS6	— **1887.** Silver Crown to Threepence	(7)	1,000
PS7	— **1893.** Old bust, Five Pounds to Threepence	(10)	6,000
PS8	— **1893.** Silver Crown to Threepence	(6)	1,100
PS9	**Edward VII, 1902.** Coronation, Five Pounds to Maundy Penny. Matt finish to surfaces	(13)	1,600
PS10	— **1902.** Sovereign to Maundy Penny. Matt finish	(11)	600
PS11	**George V, 1911.** Coronation, Five Pounds to Maundy Penny	(12)	2,500
PS12	— **1911.** Sovereign to Maundy Penny	(10)	800
PS13	— **1911.** Silver Halfcrown to Maundy Penny	(8)	400
PS14	— **1927.** New Coinage. Wreath type Crown to Threepence	(6)	275
PS15	**George VI, 1937.** Coronation. Five Pounds to Half-Sovereign	(4)	1,500
PS16	— **1937.** Coronation. Crown to Farthing, including Maundy Set	(15)	175
PS17	— **1950.** Mid-Century, Halfcrown to Farthing	(9)	75
PS18	— **1951.** Festival of Britain, Crown to Farthing	(10)	80
PS19	**Elizabeth II, 1953.** Coronation. Crown to Farthing	(10)	60
PS20	— **1970.** "Last Sterling" set. Halfcrown to Halfpenny plus medallion	(8)	15

DECIMAL COINAGE

A decision to adopt decimal currency was announced in March 1966 following the recommendation of the Halsbury Committee of Enquiry which had been appointed in 1961. The date for the introduction of the new system was 15 February 1971 and it was evident that the Royal Mint facilities which had been located on Tower Hill for more than 150 years would be unable to strike the significant quantities of coins required on that site. The Government therefore decided to build a new mint at Llantrisant in South Wales.

The new system provided for three smaller bronze coins and very large numbers were struck and stock piled for D-Day but the five and ten new pence denominations with the same specifications as the former shilling and florin were introduced in 1968. A further change was the introduction of a 50 new pence coin to replace the ten shilling banknote.

In 1982 and 1983 two more new coins were introduced; the 20 pence which helped to reduce demand for five and ten pence pieces, and the first circulating non-precious metal £1 coin which replaced the bank note of the same value.

Increasing raw material costs, and inflation also play a part in the development of a modern coinage system and a smaller 50 pence was introduced in the autumn of 1997. The bimetallic circulating £2 was also introduced.

For the collector, many of these changes have been accompanied by special issues often in limited editions struck in precious metal. New designs, particularly on the £1 coins, have added interest to the coins that circulate, and may hopefully stimulate new collectors.

In the period since decimalisation there has been a marked increase in the issue of commemorative coins. The crown size pieces, which by virtue of their size allow much scope for interesting designs seem to be reserved for the commemoration of Royal events or anniversaries, and other denominations such as the £2 and the 50 pence have honoured other interesting themes.

The major change in the coinage in 1998 was the new, and fourth, portrait of H. M. The Queen. Designed by Ian Rank-Broadley, a whole new series has started which will stimulate interest among collectors everywhere.

GOLD

4201

4204

4201 **Five pounds.** As illustration
1980 Proof *FDC** £425
1981 Proof *FDC* (Issued: 5,400)** £450
1982 Proof *FDC** £450
1984 Proof *FDC* (Issued: 905) £450

4202 As 4201 but, 'U' in a circle to left of date
1984 (Issued: 15,104) *Unc* £400

4203 **Two pounds**
1980 Proof *FDC** £225
1982 Proof *FDC** £225
1983 Proof *FDC* (Issued: 12,500)** £200

** Coins marked thus were originally issued in Royal Mint Sets.*

*** Numbers include coins sold in sets.*

4204 Sovereign. As illustration

1974 .... Unc BV
1976 .... Unc BV
1978 .... Unc BV
1979 .... Unc BV
— Proof *FDC* (Issued: 50,000) £100
1980 .... Unc BV
— Proof *FDC* (Issued: 81,200) £85
1981 .... Unc BV
— Proof *FDC* (Issued: 32,960) £95
1982 .... Unc BV
— Proof *FDC* (Issued: 20,000) £95
1983 Proof *FDC* (Issued: 21,250)** £95
1984 Proof *FDC* (Issued: 12,880) £95

4205 Half-sovereign

1980 Proof *FDC* (Issued: 76.700) £60
1982 .... Unc £60
— Proof FDC (Issued: 19,090) £60
1983 Proof FDC (Issued: 19,710)** £60
1984 Proof FDC (Issued: 12,410) £60

*

SILVER

	FDC £
4211 Maundy Set (4p, 3p, 2p and 1p). Uniform dates. Types as 4131	
1971 *Tewkesbury Abbey*	85
1972 *York Minster*	85
1973 *Westminster Abbey*	85
1974 *Salisbury Cathedral*	85
1975 *Peterborough Cathedral*	85
1976 *Hereford Cathedral*	85
1977 *Westminster Abbey*	85
1978 *Carlisle Cathedral*	85
1979 *Winchester Cathedral*	85
1980 *Worcester Cathedral*	85
1981 *Westminster Abbey*	85
1982 *St. David's Cathedral*	85
1983 *Exeter Cathedral*	85
1984 *Southwell Minster*	85
1985 *Ripon Cathedral*	85
1986 *Chichester Cathedral*	85
1987 *Ely Cathedral*	75
1988 *Lichfield Cathedral*	75
1989 *Birmingham Cathedral*	75
1990 *Newcastle Cathedral*	75
1991 *Westminster Abbey*	75
1992 *Chester Cathedral*	75
1993 *Wells Cathedral*	75
1994 *Truro Cathedral*	75
1995 *Coventry Cathedral*	75
1996 *Norwich Cathedral*	80
1997 *Bradford Cathedral*	85
1998 *Portsmouth Cathedral*	90
1999 *Bristol Cathedral*	95
2000 *Lincoln Cathedral*	100
2001 *Westminster Abbey*	100
4212 — fourpence, 1971-96 .... *from*	13
4213 — threepence, 1971-96 .... *from*	13
4214 — twopence, 1971-96 .... *from*	13
4215 — penny, 1971-96 .... *from*	15

The place of distribution is shown after each date.

**Coins marked thus were originally issued in Royal Mint sets*
*** numbers include coins sold in sets*

NICKEL-BRASS

4221

4222

		UNC £
4221	**One pound** (Royal Arms design). Edge DECUS ET TUTAMEN	
	1983	5
	— Specimen in presentation folder (issued: 484,900)	5
	— Proof *FDC** £5 — Proof piedfort in silver *FDC* (Issued: 10,000) £100	
	— Proof in silver *FDC* (Issued: 50,000) £25	
4222	**One pound** (Scottish design). Edge NEMO ME IMPUNE LACESSIT	
	1984	5
	— Specimen in presentation folder (Issued: 27,960)	5
	— Proof *FDC** £5 — Proof piedfort in silver *FDC* (Issued: 15,000) £45	
	— Proof in silver *FDC* (Issued: 44,855) £21	

CUPRO-NICKEL

4223

4224

4223 **Fifty new pence** (seven-sided). R. Britannia r.

	UNC £		*UNC* £		*UNC* £
1969	2	1976	2	1979	2
1970	4	— Proof *FDC** £2		— Proof *FDC** £3	
1971 Proof *FDC** £4		1977	2	1980	2
1972 Proof *FDC** £5		— Proof *FDC** £2		— Proof *FDC** £2	
1974 Proof *FDC** £3		1978	2	1981	2
1975 Proof *FDC** £3		— Proof *FDC** £3		— Proof *FDC** £2	

4224 Accession to European Economic Community. R. Clasped hands, 1973 ...... 1.50
— Proof *FDC*** £3

** Coins marked thus were originally issued in Royal Mint sets as shown on page 483.*

*** Issued as an individual proof coin and in the year set shown on page 483.*

4225

4225 Fifty (50) pence. 'New' omitted. As illustration

1982	2	1983	2	1984*	3
— Proof *FDC** £2		— Proof *FDC** £2		— Proof *FDC** £2	

4226

4226 Twenty-five pence. Silver Wedding Commemorative, 1972 .... 1.25
— Proof *FDC** (in 1972 Set, See PS22) £4
— Silver proof in case *FDC* (Issued: 100,000) £24

4227

UNC
£

4227 Twenty-five pence Silver Jubilee Commemorative, 1977 .... 0.75
— Specimen in presentation folder 2
— Proof *FDC** (in 1977 Set, See PS27) £4
— Silver proof in case *FDC* (Issued: 377,000) £22

** Coins marked thus were originally issued in Royal Mint sets*

4228

4228 **Twenty-Five pence** Queen Mother 80th Birthday Commemorative, 1980 .... 1.25
— Specimen in presentation folder 2
— Silver proof in case *FDC* (issued: 83,672) £32.50

4229

4229 **Twenty-five pence.** Royal Wedding Commemorative, 1981 .... 1.25
— Specimen in presentation folder 2
— Silver proof in case *FDC* (Issued: 218,142) £30

4230

	UNC £		*UNC* £		*UNC* £
4230 **Twenty (20) pence.** R crowned rose					
1982	0.40	1983	0.40	1984	0.40
— Proof *FDC** £2		— Proof *FDC** £1		— Proof *FDC** £1	
— Proof piedfort in silver *FDC* (Issued: 10,000) £40					

** Coins marked thus were originally issued in Royal Mint sets*

4231

4232

4231 Ten new pence. R. Lion passant guardant.

1968	0.30	1974	0.40	1978 Proof *FDC** £4	
1969	0.30	— Proof *FDC** £1		1979	0.50
1970	0.30	1975	0.50	— Proof *FDC** £2	
1971	0.40	— Proof *FDC** £1		1980	0.75
— Proof *FDC** £2		1976	0.50	— Proof *FDC** £1	
1972 Proof *FDC** £3		— Proof *FDC** £1		1981	0.75
1973	0.40	1977	0.50	— Proof *FDC** £1	
— Proof *FDC** £2		— Proof *FDC** £2			

4232 Ten (10) pence. As illustration

1982*	3	1983*	3	1984*	2
— Proof *FDC** £1		— Proof *FDC** £2		— Proof *FDC** £1	

4233

4234

4233 Five new pence. R. Crowned thistle

1968	0.20	1974 Proof *FDC** £2		— Proof *FDC** £1	
1969	0.30	1975	0.20	1979	0.20
1970	0.30	— Proof *FDC** £1		— Proof *FDC** £1	
1971	0.20	1976 Proof *FDC** £2		1980	0.20
— Proof *FDC** £2		1977	0.20	— Proof *FDC** £1	
1972 Proof *FDC** £2		— Proof *FDC** £1		1981 Proof *FDC** £1	
1973 Proof *FDC** £2		1978	0.20		

4234 Five (5) pence. As illustration

1982*	2	1983*	2	1984*	2
— Proof *FDC** £2		— Proof *FDC** £2		— Proof *FDC** £1	

* *Coins marked thus were originally issued in Royal Mint sets.*

BRONZE

4235

4236

	UNC £		UNC £		UNC £

4235 Two new pence. R. Plumes

	UNC £		UNC £		UNC £
1971	0.10	1976...........................	0.20	— Proof *FDC** £1	
— Proof *FDC** £1		— Proof *FDC** £1		1980...........................	0.15
1972 Proof *FDC** £2		1977...........................	0.10	— Proof *FDC** £1	
1973 Proof *FDC** £2		— Proof *FDC** £1		1981...........................	0.15
1974 Proof *FDC** £2		1978...........................	0.30	— Proof *FDC** £1	
1975	0.20	— Proof *FDC** £1			
— Proof *FDC** £1		1979...........................	0.15		

4236 Two (2) pence. As illustration

	UNC £		UNC £		UNC £
1982*	1	— Error. R. as 4235	£250	1984*.........................	1
— Proof *FDC** £1		— Proof *FDC** £1..		— Proof *FDC** £1	
1983*	1				

4237

4238

4239

4240

4237 One new penny. R. Crowned portcullis

	UNC £		UNC £		UNC £
1971	0.10	1975...........................	0.20	— Proof *FDC** £1	
— Proof *FDC** £1		— Proof *FDC** £1		1979...........................	0.10
1972 Proof *FDC**£2		1976...........................	0.20	— Proof *FDC** £1	
1973	0.20	— Proof *FDC** £1		1980...........................	0.10
— Proof *FDC** £1		1977...........................	0.10	— Proof *FDC** £1	
1974	0.20	— Proof *FDC** £1		1981...........................	0.20
— Proof *FDC** £1		1978...........................	0.20	— Proof *FDC** £1	

4238 One (1) penny. As illustration

	UNC £		UNC £		UNC £
1982	0.10	1983...........................	0.20	1984*.........................	1
— Proof *FDC** £1		— *FDC** £1...........		— Proof *FDC** £1	

4239 Half new penny. R. Crown

	UNC £		UNC £		UNC £
1971	0.10	1975...........................	0.25	— Proof *FDC** £1	
— Proof *FDC** £1		— Proof *FDC** £1..		1979...........................	0.10
1972 Proof *FDC** £2		1976...........................	0.20	— Proof *FDC** £1	
1973	0.20	— Proof *FDC** £1..		1980...........................	0.10
— Proof *FDC** £1		1977...........................	0.10	— Proof *FDC** £1	
1974	0.20	— Proof *FDC** £1..		1981...........................	0.20
— Proof *FDC** £1		1978...........................	0.10	— Proof *FDC** £1	

4240 Half (1/2) penny. As illustration

	UNC £		UNC £		UNC £
1982	0.10	1983...........................	0.25	1984*.........................	2.00
— Proof *FDC** £1		— Proof *FDC** £1..		— Proof *FDC** £2	

** Coins marked thus were originally issued in Royal Mint sets.*

The new effigy was designed by Raphael David Maklouf, FRSA. It is the third portrait of the Queen to be used on UK coinage, the previous change of portrait being in 1968 with the introduction of decimal coins. The designer's initials R.D.M. appear on the truncation. There is no portrait change on the Maundy coins (see 4211-4215).

GOLD

4251

4253

4251 **Five pounds.** R. St. George

1985 Proof *FDC* (Issued: 281) £500

1990 Proof *FDC** £500	1993 Proof *FDC** £500	1996 Proof *FDC** £500
1991 Proof *FDC** £500	1994 Proof *FDC** £500	1997 Proof *FDC** £600
1992 Proof *FDC** £500	1995 Proof *FDC** £500	

4252 **Five pounds** R. St George, 'U' in a circle to left of date.

	UNC		*UNC*
1985 (Issued: 13,626).............	£400	1993 (Issued: 906)	£450
1986 (Issued: 7,723)...............	£400	1994 (Issued: 1,000)	£500
1990 (Issued: 1,226)...............	£425	1995 (Issued: 1,000)	£500
1991 (Issued: 976)..................	£450	1996 (Issued: 901)	£500
1992 (Issued: 797)..................	£450	1997 (Issued: 802)	£500

4253 **Five pounds** Uncouped portrait of Queen Elizabeth II. As illustration. R. St. George, 'U' in a circle to left of date.

1987 (Issued: 5,694)...............	£425	1988 (Issued: 3,315)	£425

4254 **Five pounds** 500th Anniversary of Sovereign. As illustration 4277

1989 (Issued: 2,937)............... £450 — — Proof *FDC** £500

4261 **Two pounds.** R. St. George

1985 Proof *FDC** £200	1991 Proof *FDC* (Issued: 620) £225
1987 Proof *FDC* (Issued: 1,801) £175	1992 Proof *FDC* (Issued: 476) £225
1988 Proof *FDC* (Issued: 1,551) £175	1993 Proof *FDC* (Issued: 414) £225
1990 Proof *FDC* (Issued: 716) £200	1996 Proof *FDC* £250

4263 **Two pounds** 500th Anniversary of Sovereign. As illustration 4277

1989 Proof *FDC* (Issued: 2,000) £250

The 1986 £2, 1994 £2 and two types of 1995 £2 commemorative coins in gold previously listed as 4262, 4264, 4265 & 4266 respectively are now shown in the section commencing 4311 with their respective types in other metals.

4271 **Sovereign.** R. St. George

1985 Proof FDC (Issued: 11,393) £125	1992 Proof FDC (Issued: 4,772) £160
1986 Proof FDC (Issued: 5,079) £125	1993 Proof FDC (Issued: 4,349) £160
1987 Proof FDC (Issued: 9,979) £125	1994 Proof FDC (Issued: 4,998) £160
1988 Proof FDC (Issued: 7,670) £125	1995 Proof FDC (Issued: 7,500) £160
1990 Proof FDC (Issued: 4,767) £150	1996 Proof FDC (Issued: 7,500) £160
1991 Proof FDC (Issued: 4,713) £150	1997 Proof FDC (Issued: 7,500) £160

** Coins marked thus were originally issued in Royal Mint sets. Where numbers of coins issued or the Edition limit is quoted, these refer to individual coins. Additional coins were included in sets which are listed in the appropriate section.*

4272 **Sovereign.** 500th Anniversary of Sovereign. As illustration 4277
1989 Proof *FDC* (Issued: 10,535) £175

4277

4276 **Half-sovereign.** R. St. George

1985 Proof *FDC* (Issued: 9,951) £65	1992 Proof *FDC* (Issued: 3,783) £80
1986 Proof *FDC* (Issued: 4,575) £65	1993 Proof *FDC* (Issued: 2,910) £85
1987 Proof *FDC* (Issued: 8,187) £65	1994 Proof *FDC* (Issued: 5,000) £85
1988 Proof *FDC* (Issued: 7,074) £65	1995 Proof *FDC* (Issued: 4,900) £85
1990 Proof *FDC* (Issued: 4,231) £80	1996 Proof *FDC* (Issued: 5,730) £85
1991 Proof *FDC* (Issued: 3,588) £80	1997 Proof *FDC* (Issued: 7,500) £85

4277 **Half-sovereign** 500th Anniversary of Sovereign. As illustration 4277
1989 Proof *FDC* (Issued: 8,888) £80

4281

	UNC £		*UNC* £
4281 **Britannia.** One hundred pounds. (1oz of fine gold) R. Britannia standing.			
1987..	BV	— Proof *FDC* (Issued: 626) £350	
— Proof *FDC* (Issued: 2,486) £350		1989	BV
1988..	BV	— Proof *FDC* (Issued: 338) £350	
4282 **Britannia.** One hundred pounds. (1oz of fine gold alloyed with silver) R. Britannia standing.			
1990..	BV	— Proof *FDC** £450	
— Proof *FDC* (Issued: 262) £350		1994	BV
1991..	BV	— Proof *FDC** £450	
— Proof *FDC* (Issued: 143) £400		1995	BV
1992..	BV	— Proof *FDC** £500	
— Proof *FDC** £450..............		1996	BV
1993..	BV	— Proof *FDC** £500	

Where numbers of coins are quoted, these refer to individual coins. Additional coins were included in sets which are listed in the appropriate section.

** Coins marked thus were originally issued in Royal Mint sets.*

4283

4283 **Britannia. One Hundred pounds.** (1 oz of fine gold, alloyed with silver) R. Standing figure of Britannia in horse drawn chariot. 10th Anniversary of Britannia issue
1997 Proof *FDC* (Issued: 164) £545

4286

4286 **Britannia. Fifty pounds.** (1/2oz of fine gold). R. Britannia standing.

1987.. BV
— Proof *FDC* (Issued: 2,485) £160
1988.. BV
— Proof *FDC** £160
1989 .... BV
— Proof *FDC** £175

4287 **Britannia. Fifty pounds.** (1/2oz of fine gold, alloyed with Silver)
R. Britannia standing.

1990.. BV
— Proof *FDC** £200
1991.. BV
— Proof *FDC** £200
1992.. **
— Proof *FDC** £250
1993.. BV
— Proof *FDC** £250
1994 .... BV
— Proof *FDC** £250
1995 .... BV
— Proof *FDC** £250
1996 .... BV
— Proof *FDC** £250

4288

4288 **Britannia. Fifty pounds.** (1/2 oz fine gold, alloyed with silver) R. Standing figure of Britannia in horse drawn chariot 10th Anniversay of Britannia issue
1997 Proof *FDC** £300

* *Coins marked thus were originally issued in Royal Mint sets*

** *Issues of bullion quality coins of these years were modest and should command a premium*

4291

4296

4291 **Britannia. Twenty five pounds.** (1/4oz of fine gold). R. Britannia standing.

1987.. BV
— Proof *FDC* (Issued: 3,500) £85
1988.. BV
— Proof *FDC** £85
1989.. BV
— Proof *FDC** £100

4292 **Britannia. Twenty five pounds.** (1/4oz of fine gold alloyed with silver). R. Britannia standing.

1990.. BV
— Proof *FDC** £120
1991.. BV
— Proof *FDC** £135
1992.. BV
— Proof *FDC** £135
1993.. ***
— Proof *FDC** £135
1994.. BV
— Proof *FDC** £135
1995.. BV
— Proof *FDC** £135
1996.. BV
— Proof *FDC** £135

4293

4293 **Britannia. Twenty five pounds.** (1/4 oz fine gold, alloyed with silver) R. Standing figure of Britannia in horse drawn chariot. 10th Anniversary of Britannia issue
1997 Proof *FDC* (Issued: 923) £135

4296 **Britannia. Ten pounds.** (1/10oz of fine gold). R. Britannia standing.

1987.. BV
— Proof *FDC* (Issued: 3,500) £50
1988.. BV
— Proof *FDC* (Issued: 2,694) £50
1989.. BV
— Proof *FDC* (Issued: 1,609) £55

4297 **Britannia. Ten pounds.** (1/10oz of fine gold alloyed with silver). R. Britannia standing.

1990.. BV
— Proof *FDC* (Issued: 1,571) £65
1991.. BV
— Proof *FDC* (Issued: 954) £65
1992.. *
— Proof *FDC* (Issued: 1,000) £65
1993.. BV
— Proof *FDC* (Issued: 997) £65
1994.. **
— Proof *FDC* (Issued: 994) £65
1995.. BV
— Proof *FDC* (Issued: 1,500) £65
1996.. BV
— Proof *FDC* (Issued: 2,379) £65

** Coins marked thus were originally issued in Royal Mint sets.*
*** Issues of bullion quality coins of these years were modest and coins should command a premium*
**** Extremely small numbers issued.*

4298

4298 Britannia. Ten pounds. (1/10 oz fine gold, alloyed with silver) R. Standing figure of Britannia in horse drawn chariot. 10th Anniversary of Britannia issue
1997 Proof *FDC* (Issued: 1,821) £65

SILVER

4300

4300 Britannia. Two pounds. (1 oz fine silver) R. Standing figure of Britannia in horse drawn chariot. 10th Anniversary of Britannia issue
1997 Proof *FDC* (Issued: 4,173) £35

4300A

4300A Britannia. One pound. (1/2 oz of fine silver) R. Standing figure of Britannia in horse drawn chariot. 10th Anniversary of Britannia issue
1997 Proof *FDC** £25

** Coins marked thus were originally issued in Royal Mint Sets.*

4300B

4300B Britannia. Fifty pence. (1/4 oz of fine silver) R. Standing figure of Britannia in horse drawn chariot. 10th Anniversary of Britannnia issue
1997 Proof *FDC** £20

4300C

4300C Britannia. Twenty pence. (1/4 oz of fine silver) R. Standing figure of Britannia in horse drawn chariot. 10th Anniversary of Britannia issue
1997 Proof *FDC* (Issued: 8,686) £15

CUPRO-NICKEL

4301

		UNC £
4301	**Five pounds (crown).** Queen Mother 90th birthday commemorative. 1990................	8
	— Specimen in presentation folder (Issued: 45,250)...	10
	— Proof in silver *FDC* (Issued: 56,102) £45	
	— Proof in gold FDC (Issued: 2,500) £600	

* *Coins marked thus were originally issued in Royal Mint Sets.*

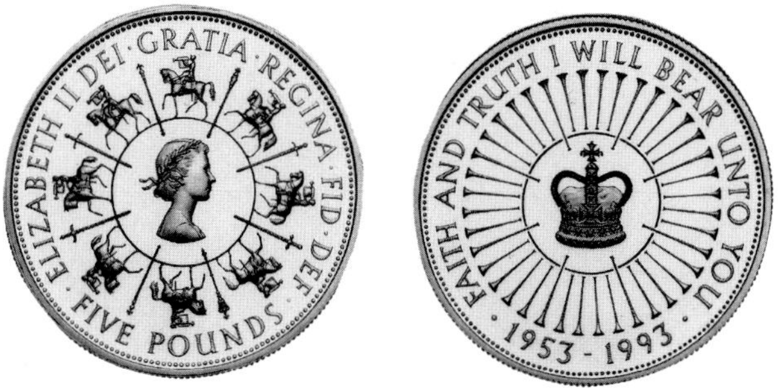

4302

4302 **Five pounds (crown).** 40th Anniversary of the Coronation. 1993 7
— Specimen in presentation folder 9
— Proof *FDC* (in 1993 set, see PS51)* £9
— Proof in silver *FDC* (Issued: 58,877) £32
— Proof in gold *FDC* (Issued: 2,500) £600

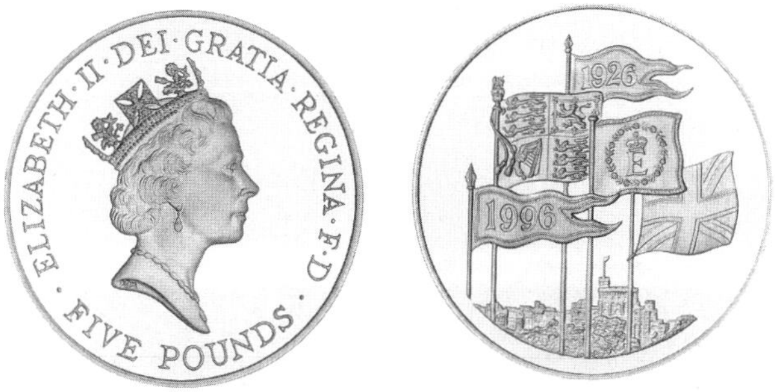

4303

4303 **Five pounds (crown).** 70th Birthday of Queen Elizabeth II. R. The Queen's personal flag, the Royal Standard, the Union Flag, two pennants bearing the dates '1926' and '1996' all against a backdrop of Windsor Castle. Edge: VIVAT REGINA ELIZABETHA.
1996 7
— Specimen in presentation folder (issued: 73,311) 9
— Proof *FDC* (in 1996 set, See PS57) * £12
— Proof in silver *FDC* (Issued: 39,336) £32
— Proof in gold *FDC* (Issued: 2,127) £600

** Coins marked thus were originally issued in Royal Mint Sets.*

4304

4304 Five pounds (crown). Golden Wedding of Queen Elizabeth II and Prince Philip. Conjoint portraits of The Queen and Prince Philip. R. Royal Arms and Arms of Prince Philip surmounted by St. Edward's crown which divides the dates 1947 and 1997 20 November, and an anchor below with the denomination.

1997 7

— Specimen in presentation folder 9

— Proof *FDC* (in 1997 set, See PS59)* £12

— Proof in silver *FDC* (Issued: 33,689) £32

— Proof in gold *FDC* (Issued: 2,574) £650

NICKEL-BRASS

4311

	UNC £		*UNC* £
4311 Two pounds. R. St. Andrew's cross surmounted by a thistle of Scotland. Edge XIII COMMONWEALTH GAMES SCOTLAND 1986			5
— Specimen in presentation folder	5	— Proof in silver *FDC* (Issued: 59,779) £20	
— .500 silver (Issued: 58,881)	12	— Proof in gold *FDC* (Issued: 3,277) £200	
— Proof *FDC** £6			

* *Coins marked thus were originally issued in Royal Mint Sets.*

4312

4313

4312 **Two pounds** 300th Anniversary of Bill of Rights. R Cypher of William and Mary, House of Commons mace and St. Edward's crown.
1989.. 4 — Proof in silver *FDC* (Issued: 25,000) £23
— Specimen in presentation folder 5 — Proof piedfort in silver *FDC** £45
— Proof *FDC** £6

4313 **Two pounds** 300th Anniversary of Claim of Right (Scotland). R. As 4312, but with crown of Scotland.
1989.. 8 — Proof in silver *FDC* (Issued: 24,852) £23
— Specimen in presentation folder 10 — Proof piedfort in silver *FDC** £45
— Proof *FDC** £10

4314

4314 **Two pounds** 300th Anniversary of the Bank of England. R: Bank's original Corporate Seal, with Crown & Cyphers of William III & Mary II. Edge SIC VOC NON VOBIS.
1994.. 5 — Proof piedfort in silver *FDC* (Issued: 9,569) £50
— Specimen in presentation folder 5 — Proof in gold *FDC* (Issued: 1,000) £400
— Proof *FDC** £6.................. — gold error. Obverse as 4251 (Included in above) £800
— Proof in silver *FDC* (Issued: 27, 957) £30

** Coins marked thus were originally issued in Royal Mint sets.*

4315

UNC
£

4315 **Two pounds** 50th Anniversary of the End of World War II. R: A Dove of Peace. Edge 1945 IN PEACE GOODWILL 1995
1995 5
— Specimen in presentation folder 5
— Proof *FDC* *£6 .... — Proof piedfort in silver *FDC* (Edition: 10,000) £50
— Proof in silver *FDC* (Issued: 35,751) £30 — Proof in gold *FDC* (Issued: 2,500) £350

4316

4316 **Two pounds** 50th Anniversary of the Establishment of the United Nations. R: 50th Anniversary symbol and an array of flags. Edge NATIONS UNITED FOR PEACE 1945-1995.
1995 5
— Specimen in presentation folder 5
— Proof in silver *FDC* (Edition: 175,000) £30 — Proof in gold *FDC* (Edition: 17,500) £350
— Proof piedfort in silver *FDC* (Edition: 10,000) £50

4317

4317 **Two pounds** European Football Championships. R: A stylised representation of a football. Edge: TENTH EUROPEAN CHAMPIONSHIP.
1996 5
— Specimen in presentation folder 5
— Proof *FDC** £6 .... — Proof piedfort in silver *FDC* (Issued: 7,634) £55
— Proof in silver *FDC* (Issued: 25,163) £26 — Proof in gold *FDC* (Issued: 2,098) £295

** Coins marked thus were originally issued in Royal Mint Sets.*

4318

UNC £ | *UNC* £

4318 **Two pounds** Bimetallic currency issue. R. Four concentric circles representing the Iron Age, 18th century industrial development, silicon chip, and Internet. Edge: STANDING ON THE SHOULDERS OF GIANTS

1997 4
— Specimen in presentation folder 6
— Proof *FDC** £6
— Proof in silver FDC (Issued: 29,910) £29
— Proof piedfort in silver *FDC* (Issued: 10,000) £50
— Proof in gold *FDC* (Issued: 2,482) £325

4331

4332

4331 **One pound** (Welsh design). Edge PLEIDIOL WYF I'M GWLAD

1985 4
— Specimen in presentation folder (Issued: 24,850) 4
— Proof *FDC** £5
— Proof in silver *FDC* (Issued: 50,000) £21
— Proof piedfort in silver *FDC* (Issued: 15,000) £45
1990 5
— Proof *FDC** £6
— Proof in silver *FDC* (Issued: 23,277) £21

4332 **One pound** (Northern Irish design). Edge DECUS ET TUTAMEN

1986 5
— Specimen in presentatioon folder (Issued: 19,908) 5
— Proof *FDC** £4
— Proof in silver *FDC* (Issued: 37, 958) £20
— Proof piedfort in silver *FDC* (Issued: 15,000) £45
1991 5
— Proof *FDC** £6
— Proof in silver *FDC* (Issued: 22,922) £20

* *Coins marked thus were originally issued in Royal Mint sets.*

4333

4334

4333 **One pound** (English design). Edge DECUS ET TUTAMEN
1987 4
— Specimen in presentation folder (Issued: 72,607) 4
— Proof *FDC** £6
— Proof in silver *FDC* (Issued: 50,000) £20
— Proof piedfort in silver *FDC* (Issued: 15,000) £45
1992 5
— Proof *FDC** £6
— Proof in silver *FDC* (Issued: 13,065) £21

4334 **One pound** (Royal Shield). Edge DECUS ET TUTAMEN
1988 5
— Specimen in presentation folder (Issued: 29,550) 5
— Proof *FDC** £6
— Proof in silver *FDC* (Issued: 50,000) £25
— Proof piedfort in silver *FDC* (Issued: 10,000) £45

4335 **One pound** (Scottish design). Edge NEMO ME IMPUNE LACESSIT (Illus. as 4222)
1989 5
— Proof FDC* £6
— Proof in silver *FDC* (Issued: 22,275) £20
— Proof piedfort in silver *FDC* (Issued: 10,000) £50

4336 **One pound** (Royal Arms design). Edge DECUS ET TUTAMEN (Illus. as 4221)
1993 5
— Proof FDC* £6
— Proof in silver *FDC* (Issued: 16,526) £30
— Proof piedfort in silver *FDC* (Issued: 12,500) £50

4337

4338

4339

4340

4337 **One pound** (Scottish design). R: Lion rampant within a double tressure. Edge NEMO ME IMPUNE LACESSIT
1994 4
— Specimen in presentation folder 5
— Proof *FDC** £6
— Proof in silver *FDC* (Issued: 25,000) £50
— Proof piedfort in silver *FDC* (Issued: 11,722) £50

4338 **One pound** (Welsh design). R. Heraldic dragon Edge PLEIDIOL WYF I'M GWLAD
1995 4
— Specimen in presentation folder (Issued: 23,728) £5
— Proof *FDC** £5
— Proof in silver *FDC* (Issued: 27,445) £23
— Proof in piedfort in silver *FDC* (Issued: 8,458) £50

** Coins marked thus were originally issued in Royal Mint sets.*

4339 **One pound** (Northern Irish design). R. A Celtic cross incorporating a pimpernel at its centre. Edge DECUS ET TUTAMEN

1996.. 4
— Specimen in presentation folder 6
— Proof *FDC** £6
— Proof in silver *FDC* (Issued: 25,000) £24
— Proof piedfort in silver *FDC* (Issued: 10,000) £50

4340 **One pound** (English design) R. Three lions. Edge: DECUS ET TUTAMEN.

1997.. 4
— Specimen in presentation folder (Issued 56,996) £5
— Proof *FDC** £5
— Proof in silver *FDC* (Issued: 20,137) £25
— Proof piedfort in silver *FDC* (Issued: 10,000) £45

4351

4351 **Fifty pence.** R. Britannia r. (4341)

1985 5
— Proof *FDC** £3
1986* 3
— Proof *FDC** £3
1987* 3
— Proof *FDC** £3
1988* 3
— Proof *FDC** £4
1989* 4
— Proof *FDC** £3....
1990*........................ 4
— Proof *FDC** £5....
1991*........................ 4
— Proof *FDC** £5....
1992*........................ 4
— Proof *FDC** £5....
1993*........................ 4
— Proof *FDC** £4
1995*........................ 3
— Proof *FDC** £4
1996*........................ 3
— Proof *FDC** £4
— Proof in silver *FDC** £15
1997.......................... 3
— Proof *FDC** £4
— Proof in silver *FDC** £24

4352

4352 **Fifty pence** Presidency of the Council of European Community Ministers and completion of the Single Market. R Conference table top and twelve stars

1992-1993 5
— Proof *FDC** £5.................
— Proof in silver *FDC** (Issued: 26,890) £24
— Proof piedfort in silver *FDC* (Issued: 10,993) £45
— Proof in gold *FDC* (Issued: 1,864) £400

4352A — Specimen in presentation folder with 1992 date 4351 5

** Coins marked thus were originally issued in Royal Mint sets.*

4353

4353 **Fifty pence** 50th Anniversary of the Normandy Landings on D-Day. R: Allied Invasion Force.

1994.. 2

— Specimen in presentation folder 3

— Proof *FDC** £5

— Proof in silver *FDC* (Issued: 40,000) £30

— Proof piedfort in silver *FDC* (Issued: 10,000) £50

— Proof in gold *FDC* (Issued: 1,877) £375

4354 **Fifty pence** R. Britannia: diam 27.3mm

1997.. 1

— Proof *FDC** £4

— Proof in silver *FDC* (Issued: 1,632) £27

— Proof piedfort in silver *FDC* (Issued: 7,192) £46

4361

4361 **Twenty pence.** R. Crowned double rose

1985 ....

— Proof *FDC** £2

1986* 1

— Proof *FDC** £2

1987 ....

— Proof *FDC** £2

1988 ....

— Proof *FDC** £3

1989 ....

— Proof *FDC** £3.....

1990..........................

— Proof *FDC** £3.....

1991..........................

— Proof *FDC** £3.....

1992..........................

— Proof *FDC** £3.....

1993..........................

— Proof *FDC** £3.....

1994..........................

— Proof *FDC** £3

1995..........................

— Proof *FDC** £3

1996..........................

— Proof *FDC** £3

— Proof in silver *FDC** £15

1997..........................

— Proof *FDC** £3

4366

UNC £   *UNC* £   *UNC* £

4366 **Ten pence.** R. Lion passant guardant

1985* 3

— Proof *FDC* * £2

1986* 2

— Proof *FDC** £2

1987* 3

— Proof *FDC** £3

1988*........................ 3

— Proof *FDC** £3....

1989*........................ 4

— Proof *FDC** £3.....

1990*........................ 4

— Proof *FDC** £3

1991*........................ 4

— Proof *FDC** £3

1992*........................ 3

— Proof *FDC** £4

— Proof in silver *FDC** £14

** Coins marked thus were originally issued in Royal Mint sets.*

4367

4367 **Ten pence** R Lion passant guardant: diam. 24.5mm

1992.......................................
— Proof *FDC** £3.................
— Proof in silver *FDC** £14..
— Proof piedfort in silver *FDC** (Issued: 14,167) £30
1993*.....................................
— Proof *FDC** £2.................
1994*.....................................
— Proof *FDC** £2.................
1995......................
— Proof *FDC** £2
1996......................
— Proof *FDC** £2
— Proof in silver *FDC** £15
1997......................
— Proof *FDC** £2

4371

4371 **Five pence.** R. Crowned thistle

1985* 1
— Proof *FDC** £1
1986* 1
— Proof *FDC** £1
1987 ....
— Proof *FDC** £2....
1988..........................
— Proof *FDC** £2....
1989..........................
— Proof *FDC** £2
1990*........................ 2
— Proof *FDC** £3
— Proof in silver *FDC** £12

4372

4372 **Five pence.** R. Crowned thistle: diam 18mm

1990 ....
— Proof *FDC** £2
— Proof in silver *FDC** £12
— Proof piedfort in silver *FDC* (Issued: 20,000) £25
1991 ....
— Proof *FDC** £2
1992 ....
— Proof *FDC** £2....
1993*........................
— Proof *FDC** £2....
1994..........................
— Proof *FDC** £2....
1995..........................
— Proof *FDC** £2
1996..........................
— Proof *FDC** £2
— Proof in silver *FDC** £15
1997..........................
— Proof *FDC** £2

** Coins marked thus were originally issued in Royal Mint sets.*

BRONZE

4376

4381

4376 **Two pence.** R. Plumes

1985	1988..........................	1991..........................
— Proof *FDC** £1	— Proof *FDC** £1....	— Proof *FDC** £1
1986	1989..........................	1992* ....
— Proof *FDC** £1	— Proof *FDC** £1....	— Proof *FDC** £1
1987	1990..........................	
— Proof *FDC** £1	— Proof *FDC** £1	

4381 **One penny.** R. Portcullis with chains

1985	1988..........................	1991..........................
— Proof *FDC** £1	— Proof *FDC** £1....	— Proof *FDC** £1
1986	1989..........................	1992*........................
— Proof *FDC** £1	— Proof *FDC** £1....	— Proof *FDC** £1
1987	1990..........................	
— Proof *FDC** £1	— Proof *FDC** £1	

COPPER PLATED STEEL

4386 **Two pence** R. Plumes

1992	— Proof *FDC** £1....	— Proof *FDC** £1
1993	1995..........................	— Proof in silver *FDC** £15
— Proof *FDC** £1	— Proof *FDC** £1....	1997..........................
1994	1996..........................	— Proof *FDC** £1

4391 **One penny** R. Portcullis with chains

1992	— Proof *FDC** £1....	— Proof *FDC** £1
1993	1995..........................	— Proof in silver *FDC** £15
— Proof *FDC** £1	— Proof *FDC** £1....	1997..........................
1994	1996..........................	— Proof *FDC** £1

** Coins marked thus were originally issued in Royal Mint sets.*

GOLD

4400

4400 **Five pounds.** R. St George
1998 Proof *FDC** £650
1999 Proof *FDC** £650
2000 Proof *FDC** £650
2001 Proof *FDC** £650

4410 **Five pounds.** R. St. George, 'U' in a circle to left of date
1998 (Issued: 825) £300
1999 (Edition:1,000) £300
2000 (Edition:1,000) £300

4420 **Two pounds.** R. St. George
1998 Proof *FDC** £300
1999 Proof *FDC** £300
2000 Proof *FDC** £300

4430 **Sovereign.** R. St. George
1998 Proof *FDC* (Issued: 10,000) £160
1999 Proof *FDC* (Issued: 10,000) £185
2000.. BV
— Proof *FDC* (Edition 10,000) £150
2001 .... BV
— Proof *FDC* (Edition 12,500) . £130

4440 **Half sovereign.** R. St. George
1998 Proof *FDC* (Issued: 6,147) £85
1999 Proof *FDC* (Issued: 7,500) £90
2000.. BV
— Proof *FDC* (Edition 7,500) £69
2001 .... BV
— Proof *FDC* (Edition 7,500)... £75

4450

4450 **Britannia. One Hundred pounds.** (1oz fine gold, alloyed with silver) R. Standing figure of Britannia
1998 Proof *FDC** £500
1999 ....BV
1999 Proof *FDC** £500
2000 Proof *FDC** £500

4460

4460 **Britannia. Fifty pounds.** (1/2 oz of fine gold, alloyed with silver) R. Standing figure of Britannia
1998 Proof *FDC** £275
1999 ....BV
1999 Proof *FDC** £275
2000 Proof *FDC** £275

4470

4470 **Britannia. Twenty five pounds.** (1/4 oz of fine gold, alloyed with silver) R. Standing figure of Britannia
1998 Proof *FDC* (Issued: 560) £125
1999 ....BV
1999 Proof *FDC* (Edition: 1,000) £125
2000 Proof *FDC* (Edition: 500) £125

4480 **Britannia. Ten pounds.** (1/10 oz of fine gold, alloyed with silver) R. Standing figure of Britannia
1998 Proof *FDC* (Issued: 392) £50
1999 ....BV
1999 Proof *FDC* (Edition: 5,000) £50
2000 Proof *FDC* (Edition: 5,000) £50

SILVER

4500

4500 **Britannia. Two pounds.** (1 oz of fine silver) R. Standing figure of Britannia
1998 (Issued: 88,909).. £10
— Proof *FDC* (Issued: 2,168) £35
2000.. £10

** Coins marked thus were originally issued in Royal Mint sets.*

4501 **Britannia. Two pounds.** (1 oz of fine silver) R. Standing figure of Britannia in horse drawn chariot (Illus. as 4300)
1999 (Edition: 100,000) £10

4510

4510 **Britannia. One pound.** (1/2 oz of fine silver) R. Standing figure of Britannia
1998 — Proof *FDC** £25

4520

4520 **Britannia. Fifty pence.** (1/4 oz of fine silver) R. Standing figure of Britannia
1998 — Proof *FDC** £20

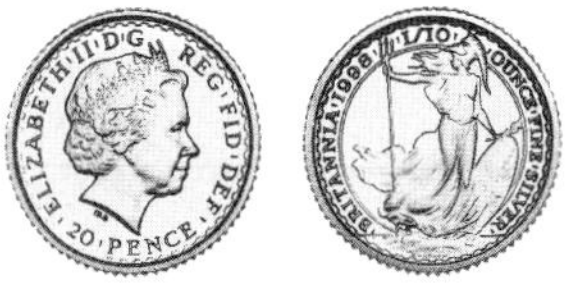

4530

4530 **Britannia. Twenty pence.** (1/10 oz of fine silver) R. Standing figure of Britannia
1998 — Proof *FDC* (Issued: 2,724) £15

* *Coins marked thus were originally issued in Royal Mint sets.*

CUPRO-NICKEL

4550

4550 **Five pounds** (crown). Prince of Wales 50th Birthday. R. Portrait of The Prince of Wales with the inscriptions 'The Prince's Trust' and 'Helping young people to succeed' on a ribbon at the base of the portrait with the denomination 'Five Pounds' and the dates 1948 and 1998.

1998 .... £7

— Specimen in presentation folder £10

— Proof *FDC* (in 1998 set, see PS 61)* £12

— Proof in silver *FDC* (Issued: 13,379) £40

— Proof in gold *FDC* (Issued: 773) £600

4551

4551 **Five pounds** (crown). Diana, Princess of Wales Memorial. R. Portrait of Diana, Princess of Wales with the inscription 'In memory of Diana, Princess of Wales' with the denomination 'Five Pounds' and the dates 1961 and 1997

1999 .... £7

— Specimen in presentation folder £10

— Proof *FDC* (in 1999 set, see PS63)* £12

— Proof in silver *FDC* (Edition: 350,000) £33

— Proof in gold *FDC* (Issued: 7,500) £600

* *Coins marked thus were originally issued in Royal Mint sets.*

4552

4552A

4552 **Five pounds** (crown). Millennium commemorative. R. In the centre, on a patterned circle, a representation of the British Isles with a pair of clock hands emanating from Greenwich, set at 12 o'clock with the inscription 'Anno Domini' with the denomination 'Five Pounds' and the dates 1999 and 2000

1999 .... £7

— Specimen in presentation folder £10

— Proof in silver *FDC* (Edition: 75,000) £33

— Proof in gold *FDC* (Issued: 2,500) £600

2000 .... £7

— Specimen in presentation folder £10

— Proof *FDC* (in 2000 set, see PS65)* £12

— Proof in gold *FDC* (Edition: 2,500) £495

4552A

—Specimen in presentation folder with Dome mint mark £10

4552B

—Proof in silver FDC (Edition: 50,000) £37

(The reverse design is the same as the 1999 issue but with the British Isles coloured with 22 carat gold)

* *Coins marked thus were originally issued in Royal Mint sets.*

4553

4553 **Five pounds** (crown). Queen Mother commemorative. R Portrait of the Queen Mother with Inscription "Queen Elizabeth the Queen Mother" and cheering crowds in 19th Century and modern day dress with the Queen Mother's signature below and the denomination 'Five Pounds' and the dates 1900 and 2000.

2000 .... £7

— Specimen in presentation folder £10

— Proof in silver *FDC* (Edition: 100,000) £35

— Proof piedfort in silver *FDC* (Edition: 20,000) £68

— Proof in gold *FDC* (Edition: 3,000) £495

4554

4554 **Five pounds** (crown) Victorian anniversary. R. A classic portrait of the young Queen Victoria based on the Penny Black postage stamp with a V representing Victoria, and taking the form of railway lines and in the background the iron framework of the Crystal Palace, and the denomination "Five Pounds" and the dates 1901 and 2001.

2001 .... £7

— Specimen in presentation folder £10

— Proof *FDC* (in 2001 set, see PS68)* £10

— Proof in silver *FDC* (Edition: 19,250) £35

— Proof in gold *FDC* (Edition: 2,750) £525

4554A — Proof in silver FDC with reverse frosting (Edition: 750 - Issued with sovereigns dated 1901 and 2001) * £60

4554B — Proof in gold FDC with reverse frosting (Edition: 750 - Issued with four different type sovereigns of Victoria, - Young Head with shield, and St.George reverse, Jubilee Head and Old Head.)* £750

** Coins marked thus were originally issued in Royal Mint sets.*

NICKEL-BRASS

4570

4570 **Two pounds.** Bimetallic currency issue. R. Four concentric circles, representing the Iron Age, 18th century industrial development, silicon chip and Internet. Edge: STANDING OF THE SHOULDERS OF GIANTS

1998.. £4

— Proof *FDC** £6

— Proof in silver *FDC* (Issued: 19,978) £29

— Proof PIEDFORT in silver *FDC* (Issued: 7,646) £50

2000

— Proof *FDC** £6

— Proof in silver *FDC** £30

2001

— Proof *FDC** £6

4571

4571 **Two pounds.** Rugby World Cup. R. In the centre a rugby ball and goal posts surrounded by a styalised stadium with the denomination 'Two Pounds' and the date 1999

1999.. £4

— Specimen in presentation folder £6

— Proof *FDC* (in 1999 set, see PS63)* £6

— Proof in silver *FDC* (Edition: 25,000) £29

— Proof piedfort in silver *FDC* (Issued: 10,000) £100

— Proof in gold *FDC* (Edition: 2,000) £300

** Coins marked thus were originally issued in Royal Mint sets.*

4572

4572 **Two pounds.** Marconi commemorative. R. Decorative radio waves emanating from a spark of electricity linking the zeros of the date to represent the generation of the signal that crossed the Atlantic with the date 2001 and the denomination "Two Pounds". Edge: WIRELESS BRIDGES THE ATLANTIC… MARCONI 1901
2001
— Specimen in presentation folder £7
— Proof *FDC* (in 2001 set, see PS68)* £10
— Proof in silver *FDC* (Edition: 25,000) £29
— Proof piedfort in silver *FDC*
— Proof in gold *FDC* (Edition: 2,500) £295

4590

4590 **One pound** (Royal Arms design). Edge: DECUS ET TUTAMEN (Illus. as 4221)
1998*.......... £10
— Proof *FDC** £6
— Proof in silver *FDC* (Issued: 13,863) £25
— Proof piedfort in silver *FDC* (Issued: 7,894) £45

4591 **One pound.** (Scottish lion design). Edge: NEMO ME IMPUNE LACESSIT (Illus as 4337)
1999
— Specimen in presentation folder £4
— Proof *FDC* (in 1999 set, see PS63)* £6
— Proof in silver *FDC* (Edition: 23,000) £25
— Proof piedfort in silver *FDC* (Edition: 10,000) £45

4591A — Proof in silver FDC, with reverse frosting, (Edition: 2,000)* £40

4592 **One pound.** (Welsh design). Edge: PLEIDIOL WYF I'M GWLAD (Illus. as 4338)
2000
— Proof *FDC* (in 2000 set, see PS65)* £6
— Proof in silver *FDC* (Edition: 23,000) £25
— Proof piedfort in silver *FDC* (Edition: 10,000) £47

4592A — Proof in silver FDC, with reverse frosting, (Edition: 2,000)* £40

4593 **One pound** (Northern Irish design). Edge: DECUS ET TUTAMEN (Illus. as 4339)
2001
— Proof *FDC** £6
— Proof in silver *FDC* (Edition: 25,000) £27
— Proof piedfort in silver *FDC*

** Coins marked thus were originally issued in Royal Mint sets.*

4610 Fifty pence. R. Britannia. (Illus. as 4351)

1998
— Proof *FDC** £3

1999
— Proof *FDC** £3

2000
— Proof *FDC** £3
— Proof in silver *FDC** £25

2001
— Proof *FDC** £3

4611

4611 Fifty pence. R. Celebratory pattern of twelve stars reflecting the European flag with the dates 1973 and 1998 commemorating the 25th Anniversary of the United Kingdom's membership of the European Union and Presidency of the Council of Ministers.

1998 .... £2
— Proof *FDC** £5
— Proof in silver *FDC* (Issued: 8,859) £25
— Proof piedfort in silver *FDC* (Issued: 8,440) £45
— Proof in gold *FDC* (Issued: 1,177) £250

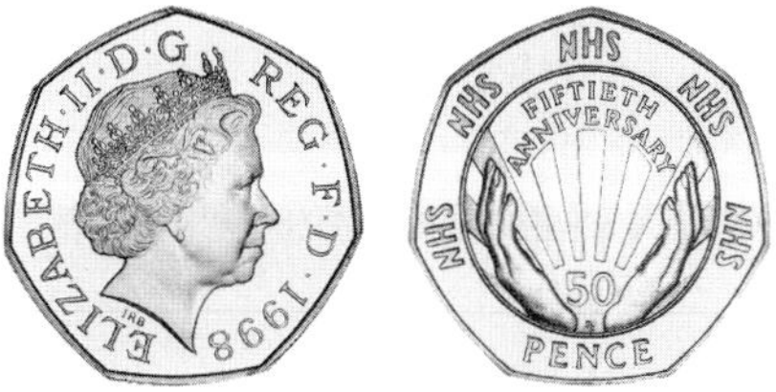

4612

4613

4612 Fifty pence. R. A pair of hands set against a pattern of radiating lines with the words Fiftieth Anniversary and the value 50 pence with the initials NHS.

1998 .... £2
— Specimen in presentation folder £3
— Proof *FDC** £5
— Proof in silver *FDC* (Issued: 9,032) £25
— Proof piedfort in silver *FDC* (Issued: 5,117) £45
— Proof in gold *FDC* (Issued: 651) £250

4613 Fifty pence. Library commemorative. R. The turning pages of a book above the pediment of a classical library building which contains the inscription 'Public Libraries' and the denomination'50 pence' and the dates 1850 and 2000

2000 .... £2
— Specimen in presentation folder £5
— Proof *FDC** £5
— Proof in silver *FDC* (Edition: 25,000) £25
— Proof piedfort in silver *FDC* (Edition: 10,000) £47
— Proof in gold *FDC* (Edition: 2,000) £250

**Coins marked thus were originally issued in Royal Mint sets.*

4630 **Twenty pence.** R. Crowned double rose. (Illus. as 4230)

1998	2000	2001
— Proof *FDC** £3	— Proof *FDC** £3	— Proof *FDC** £3
	— Proof in silver *FDC**	
1999		
— Proof *FDC** £3		

4650 **Ten pence.** R. Lion passant guardant. (Illus. as 4232)

1998*	1999*	2000	2001
— Proof *FDC** £3	— Proof *FDC** £3	— Proof *FDC** £3	— Proof *FDC** £3
		— Proof in silver *FDC**	

4670 **Five pence.** R. Crowned thistle. (Illus. as 4234)

1998	1999	2000	2001
— Proof *FDC** £3	— Proof *FDC** £3	— Proof *FDC** £3	— Proof *FDC** £3
		— Proof in silver *FDC**	

COPPER PLATED STEEL

4690 **Two pence.** R. Plumes. (Illus. as 4376)

1998	1999	2000	2001
— Proof *FDC** £3	— Proof *FDC** £3	— Proof *FDC** £3	— Proof *FDC** £3
		— Proof in silver *FDC**	

BRONZE

4700 **Two pence.** R. Plumes. (Illus. as 4376)
1998

COPPER PLATED STEEL

4710 **One pence.** R. Portcullis with chains. (Illus. as 4381)

1998	1999	2000	2001
— Proof *FDC** £3	— Proof FDC* £3	— Proof in silver *FDC** £3	— Proof *FDC** £3

** Coins marked thus were originally issued in Royal Mint sets*

The practice of issuing annual sets of coins was started by the Royal Mint in 1970 when a set of the £SD coins was issued as a souvenir prior to Decimalisation. There are now regular issues of brilliant uncirculated coin sets as well as proofs in base metal, and issues in gold and silver. In order to simplify the numbering system, and to allow for the continuation of the various issues in the future, the Prefix letters have been changed. The base metal proof sets will continue the series of numbers from the 1970 set, PS20. For ease of reference, where collectors have the 2001 Edition of the Catalogue, the previous numbers are shown in brackets.

Uncirculated Sets

US01–**1982** (PS21)	Uncirculated (specimen) set in Royal Mint folder, 50p to 1/2p, new reverse type, including 20 pence (Issued: 205,000)	(7)	9
US02–**1983** (PS22)	'U.K.' £1 (4221) to 1/2p (Issued: 637,100)	(8)	15
US03–**1984** (PS23)	'Scottish' £1 (4222) to 1/2p (Issued: 158,820)	(8)	13
US04–**1985** (PS24)	'Welsh' £1 (4331) to 1p, new portrait of The Queen (Issued: 102,015).	(7)	13
US05–**1986** (PS25)	Commonwealth Games £2 (4311) plus 'Northern Irish' £1 (4332) to 1p, ((Issued: 167,224)	(8)	14
US06–**1987** (PS26)	'English' £1 (4333) to 1p, (Issued: 172,425)	(7)	12
US07–**1988** (PS27)	'Arms' £1 (4334) to 1p, (Issued: 134,067)	(7)	15
US08–**1989** (PS28)	'Scottish' £1 (4335) to 1p, (Issued: 77,569)	(7)	22
US09–**1989** (PS29)	Bill of Rights and Claim of Right £2s (4312 and 4313) in Royal Mint folder (Issued: not known)	(2)	15
US10–**1990** (PS30)	'Welsh' £1 (4331) to 1p plus new 5p, (Issued: 102,606)	(8)	20
US11–**1991** (PS31)	'Northern Irish' £1 (4332) to 1p, (Issued: 74,975)	(7)	20
US12–**1992** (PS32)	'English' £1 (4333), 'European Community' 50p (4352) and Britannia 50p, 20p to 1p plus new 10p (Issued: 78,421)	(9)	20
US13–**1993** (PS33)	'UK' £1 (4336), 'European Community' 50p to 1p ((Issued: 56,945)...	(8)	25
US14–**1994** (PS34)	'Bank' £2 (4314), 'Scottish' £1 (4337) and 'D-Day' 50p (4353) to 1p, (Issued: 177,971)	(8)	15
US15–**1995** (PS35)	'Peace' £2 (4315) and 'Welsh' £1 (4338) to 1p (Issued: 105, 647)	(8)	15
US16–**1996** (PS36)	'Football' £2 (4317) and 'Northern Irish' £1 (4339) to 1p (Issued: 86,501)	(8)	15
US17–**1997** (PS37)	'Bimetallic' £2 (4318), 'English' £1 (4340) to 1p plus new 50p (Issued: 109,557)	(9)	15
US18–**1998** (PS38)	'Bimetallic' £2 (4570), 'UK' £1 (4590) and 'EU' 50 pence (4611) to 1 pence (Issued: 96,192)	(9)	15
US19–**1998** (PS39)	'EU' and Britannia 50 pence (4611 and 4610) in Royal Mint folder.	(2)	6
US20–**1999** (PS40)	'Bimetallic' £2 (4571), 'Scottish' £1 (4591) to 1p (Issued: 136,492).	(8)	15
US21–**2000** (PS41)	'Bimetallic' £2 (4570), 'Welsh' £1 (4592) to 1p plus 'Library' 50 pence	(9)	15
US22–**2001**	'Bimetallic' £2 (4570), 'Bimetallic' £2 (4572), 'Irish' £1 (4594) to 1p	(9)	14

Proof Sets

PS21–**1971** (PS47)	Decimal coinage set, 50 new pence ('Britannia' to 1/2 new pence, plus medallion in sealed plastic case with card wrapper (Issued: 350,000)	(6)	15
PS22–**1972** (PS48)	Proof 'Silver Wedding' Crown struck in c/n (4226) plus 50p to 1/2p (Issued: 150,000)	(7)	20
PS23–**1973** (PS49)	'EEC' 50p (4224) plus 10p to 1/2p, (Issued: 100,000)	(6)	15
PS24–**1974** (PS50)	Britannia 50p to 1/2p, as 1971 (Issued: 100,000)	(6)	12
PS25–**1975** (PS51)	50p to 1/2p (as 1974), (Issued: 100,000)	(6)	12
PS26–**1976** (PS52)	50p to 1/2p, as 1975, (Issued: 100,000)	(6)	12

PS27–**1977** (PS53)	Proof 'Silver Jubilee' Crown struck in c/n (4227) plus 50p to 1/2p, (Issued: 193,000)	(7)	12
PS28–**1978** (PS54)	50p to 1/2p, as 1976, (Issued: 86,100)	(6)	12
PS29–**1979** (PS55)	50p to 1/2p, as 1978, (Issued: 81,000)	(6)	12
PS30–**1980** (PS56)	50p to 1/2p, as 1979, (Issued: 143,000)	(6)	10
PS31–**1981** (PS57)	50p to 1/2p, as 1980, (Issued: 100,300)	(6)	10
PS32–**1982** (PS58)	50p to 1/2p including 20 pence (Issued: 106,800)	(7)	12
PS33–**1983** (PS59)	'U.K.' £1 (4221) to 1/2p in new packaging (Issued: 107,800)	(8)	17
PS34–**1984** (PS60)	'Scottish' £1 (4222) to 1/2p, (Issued: 106,520)	(8)	16
PS35–**1985** (PS61)	'Welsh' £1 (4331) to 1p, (Issued: 102,015)	(7)	16
PS36–**1985** (PS62)	As last but packed in deluxe red leather case (Included above)	(7)	20
PS37–**1986** (PS63)	Commonwealth games £2 (4311) plus 'Northern Irish' £1 (4332) to 1p, (Issued: 104,597)	(8)	20
PS38–**1986** (PS64)	As last but packed in deluxe red leather case (Included above)	(8)	23
PS39–**1987** (PS65)	'English' £1 (4333) to 1p, (Issued: 88,659)	(7)	20
PS40–**1987** (PS66)	As last but packed in deluxe leather case (Included above)	(7)	24
PS41–**1988** (PS67)	'Arms' £1 (4334) to 1p, (Issued: 79,314)	(7)	25
PS42–**1988** (PS68)	As last but packed in deluxe leather case (Included above)	(7)	29
PS43–**1989** (PS69)	Bill of Rights and Claim of Right £2s (4312 and 4313), 'Scottish' £1 (4335) to 1p, (Issued: 85,704)	(9)	30
PS44–**1989** (PS70)	As last but packed in red leather case, (Included above)	(9)	35
PS45–**1990** (PS71)	'Welsh' £1 (4331) to 1p plus new 5p, (Issued: 79,052)	(8)	27
PS46–**1990** (PS72)	As last but packed in red leather case (Included above)	(8)	32
PS47–**1991** (PS73)	'Northern Irish' £1 (4332) to 1p, (Issued: 55,144)	(7)	27
PS48–**1991** (PS74)	As last but packed in red leather case (Included above)	(7)	33
PS49–**1992** (PS75)	'English' £1 (4333), 'European community' 50p (4352) and Britannia 50p, 20p to 1p plus new 10p, (Issued: 44,337)	(9)	28
PS50–**1992** (PS76)	As last but packed in red leather case (Issued: 17,989)	(9)	33
PS51–**1993** (PS77)	'Coronation Anniversary' £5 struck in c/n (4302), 'U.K.' £1 (4336), 50p to 1p, (Issued: 43,509)	(8)	30
PS52–**1993** (PS78)	As last but packed in red leather case (Issued: 22,571)	(8)	35
PS53–**1994** (PS79)	'Bank' £2 (4314), 'Scottish' £1 (4337), 'D-Day' 50p (4353) to 1p, (Issued: 44,643)	(8)	30
PS54–**1994** (PS80)	As last but packed in red leather case (Issued: 22,078)	(8)	35
PS55–**1995** (PS81)	'Peace' £2 (4315), 'Welsh' £1 (4338) to 1p, (Issued: 42,842)	(8)	32
PS56–**1995** (PS82)	As last but packed in red leather case (Issued: 17,797)	(8)	35
PS57–**1996** (PS83)	Proof '70th Birthday' £5 struck in c/n (4303), 'Football' £2 (4317), 'Northern Irish' £1 (4339) to 1p, (Issued: 46,295)	(9)	32
PS58–**1996** (PS84)	As last but packed in red leather case (Issued: 21,286)	(9)	37
PS59–**1997** (PS85)	Proof 'Golden Wedding' £5 struck in c/n (4304), 'Bimetallic' £2 (4318), 'English' £1 (4340) to 1p plus new 50p (Issued: 48,761)	(10)	33
PS60–**1997** (PS86)	As last but packed in red leather case (Issued: 31,987)	(10)	40
PS61–**1998** (PS87)	Proof £5 'Prince of Wales 50th Birthday', struck in c/n (4550), 'Bimetallic' £2 (4570), 'UK'. £1 (4590), 'EU' 50 pence (4611) to 1 pence. (Issued: 36,907)	(10)	33
PS62–**1998** (PS88)	As last, but packed in red leather case. (Issued: 26,763)	(10)	40
PS63–**1999** (PS89)	Proof £5 'Diana, Princess of Wales', struck in c/n (4551), 'Bimetallic' 'Rugby' £2 (4571), 'Scottish' £1 (4591) to 1p. (Issued: 40,024)	(9)	34
PS64–**1999** (PS90)	As last, but packed in red leather case. (Issued: 39,377)	(9)	40

PS65–**2000** (PS91)	Proof £5 'Millennium', struck in c/n (4552), 'Bimetallic' £2 (4570), 'Welsh' £1 (4592), 'Library' 50 pence (4613) and 'Britannia' 50 pence (4610) to 1p Standard Set, (Edition: 90,000)	(10)	£30
PS66–**2000** (PS92)	As last, but Deluxe set (Edition: included above)	(10)	£40
PS67–**2000** (PS93)	As last, but Executive set (Edition: 10,000)	(10)	£70
PS68–**2001**	Proof £5 'Victoria', struck in c/n (4554), 'Bimetallic' £2 (4570), 'Bimetallic' £2 (4572), 'Irish' £1 (4594) to 1p. Standard Set. (Edition: 60,000)	(10)	34
PS69–**2001**	As last, but Gift Set (Edition: included above)	(10)	43
PS70–**2001**	As last, but packed in red leather case (Edition: 30,000)	(10)	48
PS71–**2001**	As last, but Executive Set (Edition: 10,000)	(10)	75

Silver Sets

PSS01–**1989** (PS96)	Bill of Rights and Claim of Right £2s (4312 and 4313), Silver piedfort proofs (Issued: 10,000)	(2)	85
PSS02–**1989** (PS97)	As last but Silver proofs (Issue figure not known)	(2)	42
PSS03–**1990** (PS98)	2 x 5p Silver proofs (4371 and 4372), (Issued: 35,000)	(2)	24
PSS04–**1992** (PS99)	2 x 10p Silver proofs (4366 and 4367), (Not known)	(2)	28
PSS05–**1996** (PS100)	25th Anniversary of Decimal Currency (4339, 4351, 4361, 4367, 4372, 4386, 4391) in Silver proof (Edition: 15,000)	(7)	100
PSS06–**1997** (PS101)	2 x 50p silver proofs (4351 and 4354) (Issued: 10,304)	(2)	48
PSS07–**1997** (PS102)	Britannia proofs, £2 – 20 pence (4300, 4300A, 4300B, 4300C) (Issued: 11,832)	(4)	85
PSS08–**1998** (PS103)	Britannia proofs, £2 – 20 pence (4500, 4510, 4520, 4530) (Issued: 3,044)	(4)	100
PSS09–**1998** (PS104)	'EU' and 'NHS' Silver proofs (4611 and 4612)	(2)	50
PSS10–**2000** (PS105)	'Millennium' £5, 'Bimetallic' £2, 'Welsh' £1, 50p to 1p, and Maundy coins, 4p-1p in silver poof (4552, 4570, 4592, 4610, 4630, 4650, 4670, 4212-4215) (Edition: 15,000)	(13)	245

Gold Sovereign Proof Sets

PGS01–**1980** (PS111)	Gold £5 to half-sovereign (4201, 4203-4205) (Issued: 10,000)	(4)	750
PGS02–**1981** (PS112)	U.K. Proof coin Commemorative collection. (Consists of £5, sovereign, 'Royal Wedding' Crown (4229) in silver, plus base metal proofs 50p to 1/2p), (Not known)	(9)	600
PGS03–**1982** (PS113)	Gold £5 to half-sovereign (Issued: 2,500)	(4)	800
PGS04–**1983** (PS114)	Gold £2, sovereign and half-sovereign, (Not known)	(3)	325
PGS05–**1984** (PS115)	Gold £5, sovereign and half-sovereign, (Issued: 7,095)	(3)	600
PGS06–**1985** (PS116)	Gold £5 to half-sovereign (4251, 4261, 4271, 4276) (Issued: 5,849)	(4)	750
PGS07–**1986** (PS117)	Gold Commonwealth games £2, (4311) sovereign and half-sovereign (Issued: 12,500)	(3)	325
PGS08–**1987** (PS118)	Gold £2 (4261), sovereign and half-sovereign (Issued: 12,500)	(3)	325
PGS09–**1988** (PS119)	Gold £2 to half-sovereign (Issued: 11,192)	(3)	325
PGS10–**1989** (PS120)	Sovereign Anniversary Gold £5 to half-sovereign (4254, 4263, 4272, 4277), (Issued: 5,000)	(4)	900
PGS11–**1989** (PS121)	Gold £2 to half-sovereign (Issued: 7,936)	(3)	450
PGS12–**1990** (PS122)	Gold £5 to half-sovereign (as 1985 issue), (Issued: 1,721)	(4)	775
PGS13–**1990** (PS123)	Gold £2 to half-sovereign (as 1988 issue), (Issued: 1,937)	(3)	375
PGS14–**1991** (PS124)	Gold £5 to half-sovereign (Issued: 1,336)	(4)	750
PGS15–**1991** (PS125)	Gold £2 to half-sovereign (Issued: 1,152)	(3)	400
PGS16–**1992** (PS126)	Gold £5 to half-sovereign (Issued: 1,165)	(4)	750
PGS17–**1992** (PS127)	Gold £2 to half-sovereign (Issued: 967)	(3)	425

PGS18–**1993** (PS128) Gold £5 to half-sovereign with silver Pistrucci medal in case (Issued: 1,078) .... (5) 800
PGS19–**1993** (PS129) Gold £2 to half-sovereign (Issued: 663) .... (3) 425
PGS20–**1994** (PS130) Gold £5, £2 (as 4314), sovereign and half-sovereign (Issued: 918)..... (4) 850
PGS21–**1994** (PS131) Gold £2, (as 4314), sovereign and half-sovereign (Issued: 1,249)... (3) 500
PGS22–**1995** (PS132) Gold £5, £2 (as 4315), sovereign and half-sovereign (Issued: 718). (4) 900
PGS23–**1995** (PS133) Gold £2 (as 4315), sovereign and half-sovereign (Issued: 1,112).... (3) 500
PGS24–**1996** (PS134) Gold £5 to half-sovereign (as 1992 issue) (Issued: 742) .... (4) 900
PGS25–**1996** (PS135) Gold £2 to half-sovereign (as 1992 issue) (Issued: 868) .... (3) 500
PGS26–**1997** (PS136) Gold £5, £2 (as 4318), sovereign and half-sovereign (Issued: 860) .... (4) 900
PGS27–**1997** (PS137) Gold £2 (as 4318) to half-sovereign (Issued: 817) .... (3) 500
PGS28–**1998** (PS138) Gold £5 to half sovereign (4400, 4420, 4430, 4440) (Issued: 789) .... (4) 900
PGS29–**1998** (PS139) Gold £2 to half sovereign (4420, 4430, 4440) (Issued: 560)........ (3) 495
PGS30–**1999** (PS140) Gold £5, £2 (as 4571), sovereign and half sovereign (Edition: 1,000) .. (4) 1000
PGS31–**1999** (PS141) Gold £2 (as 4571), sovereign and half sovereign (Edition: 1,250)... (3) 495
PGS32–**2000** (PS142) Gold £5 to half-sovereign (as 1998 issue) (Issued: 1,000) .... (4) 950
PGS33–**2000** (PS143) Gold £2 to half-sovereign (as 1998 issue) (Issued: 1,250) .... (3) 395
PGS34–**2001** Gold £5, £2 (as 4572), sovereign and half sovereign (Edition: 1,000) . (4) 965
PGS35–**2001** Gold £2 (as 4572), sovereign and half sovereign (Edition: 1,500)... (3) 415

Britannia Series

PBS01–**1987** (PS147) Britannia Gold Proofs £100, £50, £25, £10 (4281, 4286, 4291, 4296), (Issued: 10,000) .... (4) 650
PBS02–**1987** (PS148) Britannia Gold Proofs £25, £10 (4291 and 4296) (Issued: 11,100) . (2) 125
PBS03–**1988** (PS149) Britannia Proofs £100–£10 (as 1987 issue) (Issued: 3,505) .... (4) 650
PBS04–**1988** (PS150) Britannia Proofs £25, £10 (as 1987 issue) (Issued: 894) .... (2) 125
PBS05–**1989** (PS151) Britannia Proofs £100 – £10 (as 1987) (Issued: 2,268) .... (4) 675
PBS06–**1989** (PS152) Britannia Proofs £25, £10 (as 1987 issue) (Issued: 451) .... (2) 150
PBS07–**1990** (PS153) Britannia Proofs, £100-£10, gold with the addition of silver alloy (4282, 4287, 4292, 4297) (Issued: 527)........ (4) 775
PBS08–**1991** (PS154) Britannia Proofs, as PS153 (Issued: 509) .... (4) 775
PBS09–**1992** (PS155) Britannia Proofs, as PS153 (Issued: 500) .... (4) 900
PBS10–**1993** (PS156) Britannia Proofs, as PS153 (Issued: 462) .... (4) 900
PBS11–**1994** (PS157) Britannia Proofs, as PS153 ((Issued: 435)........ (4) 900
PBS12–**1995** (PS158) Britannia Proofs, as PS153 (Issued: 500) .... (4) 1000
PBS13–**1996** (PS159) Britannia Proofs, as PS153 (Issued: 483) .... (4) 1000
PBS14–**1997** (PS160) Britannia proofs £100, £50, £25, £10 (4283, 4288, 4293, 4298) (Issued: 892) .... (4) 1000
PBS15–**1998** (PS161) Britannia proofs £100, £50, £25, £10 (4450, 4460, 4470, 4480) (Issued: 750) .... (4) 1000
PBS16–**1999** (PS162) Britannia Proofs, as PS161 (Edition: 750)........ (4) 1000
PBS17–**2000** (PS163) Britannia Proofs, as PS161 (Issued: 750) .... (4) 900

APPENDIX 1

A SELECT NUMISMATIC BIBLIOGRAPHY

Listed below is a selection of general books on British numismatics and other works that the specialist collector will need to consult.

General Books:

BROOKE, G. C. *English Coins*. 3rd ed., 1966.

CHALLIS, C. E. (ed.) *A New History of the Royal Mint*. 1992

GRUEBER, H. A. *Handbook of the Coins of Great Britain and Ireland*. Revised 1970

KENYON, R. Ll. *Gold Coins of England*. 1884

NORTH, J. J. *English Hammered Coinage*, Vol. I, c. 650-1272. 1994; Vol. II, 1272-1662. 1991

SUTHERLAND, C. H. V. *English Coinage, 600-1900*. 1972

Specialist Works:

ALLEN, D. *The Origins of Coinage in Britain: A Reappraisal*. Reprint 1978

ALLEN, D. F. *The Coins of the Coritani*. (SCBI no. 3) 1963

ALLEN, D. F. *English Coins in the British Museum: The Cross-and-Crosslets ('Tealby') type of Henry II*. 1951

ARCHIBALD, M. M. and BLUNT, C. E. *British Museum. Anglo-Saxon Coins. Athelstan to the reform of Edgar. 924-c 973*. 1986

ASKEW, G. *The Coinage of Roman Britain*. (1951) Reprinted 1980.

BESLY, E. M. *Coins and Medals of the English Civil War*. 1990

BLACKBURN, M. A. S. *Anglo-Saxon Monetary History*. 1986

BLUNT, C. E. and WHITTON, C. A. *The Coinages of Edward IV and of Henry VI (Restored)*.

BLUNT, C. E., STEWART, B.H.I.H. and LYON, C.S.S. *Coinage in Tenth-Century England. From Edward the Elder to Edgar's Reform*. 1989

BRAND, J.D. *The English Coinage 1180-1247: Money, Mints and Exchanges* 1994

BROOKE, G. C. *English Coins in the British Museum: The Norman Kings*. 1916

BROWN, I. D. and DOLLEY, M. *Bibliography of Coin Hoards of Great Britain and Ireland 1500-1967*. 1971

CARSON, R. A. G. *Mints, Dies and Currency. Essays in Memory of Albert Baldwin*. 1971

DE JERSEY, P. *Coinage in Iron Age Armorica*. 1994

DOLLEY, R. H. M. (ed.). *Anglo-Saxon Coins; studies presented to Sir Frank Stenton*. 1964

GRIERSON, P. and BLACKBURN, M. A. S. *Medieval European Coinage, vol. 1, The Early Middle Ages*. 1986

HOBBS, R. *British Iron Age Coins in the British Museum*. 1996

KEARY, C. and GREUBER, H. *English Coins in the British Museum: Anglo-Saxon Series*. 1887, reprinted, 1970, 2 volumes.

LAKER, A. J. *The portrait Groats of Henry VIII*. 1978

LAWRENCE, L. A. *The Coinage of Edward III from 1351*.

LINECAR, H. W. A. *The Crown Pieces of Great Britain and the British Commonwealth*. 1962

— — *English Proof and Pattern Crown-Size Pieces*. 1968

MACK, R. P. *The R. P. Mack Collection, Ancient British, Anglo-Saxon and Norman Coins*. (SCBI no. 20) 1973

MANVILLE, H. E. *Encyclopedia of British Numismatics. Numismatic Guide to British and Irish Periodicals 1731-1991*. 1993

MANVILLE, H. E. and ROBERTSON, T. J. *An Annotated Bibliography of British Numismatic Auction Catalogues from 1710 to the Present*. 1986

MARSH, M. A. *The Gold Half Sovereign*. 1982

MARSH, M. A. *The Gold Sovereign*. 2nd Edition 1999

NORTH, J. J. *Edwardian English Silver Coins 1279-1351. (SCBI 39)* 1989

NORTH, J. J. and PRESTON-MORLEY, P. J. *The John G. Brooker Collection: Coins of Charles I. (SCBI 33)* 1984

PECK, C. W. *English Copper, Tin and Bronze Coins in the British Museum, 1558-1958*. 1970

RAYNER, P.A. *The English Silver Coinage from 1649*. 5th ed. 1992

REECE, R. *Coinage in Roman Britain,* 1987.

ROBINSON, Dr. B. *The Royal Maundy*. 1992

RUDING, REV. R. *Annals of the Coinage of Great Britain*. 3rd Edition 1840

SEAR, D. R. *Roman Coins and their Values. 4th Edition* (1999) Reprinted 2000

SEAR, DAVID R. *The History and Coinage of the Roman Imperators 49-27 BC*. 1998

THOMPSON, J. D. A. *Inventory of British Coin Hoards, A.D. 600-1500*. 1956

VAN ARSDELL, R. *Celtic Coinage of Britain*. 1989.

VAN ARSDELL, R. D. *The Coinage of the Dobunni*. 1994

WHITTON, C. A. *The Heavy Coinage of Henry VI.*

WOODHEAD, P. *English Gold Coins 1257-1603. The Herbert Schneider Collection, vol. 1 (SCBI 47)* 1996

WREN, C. R. *The Short-cross coinage 1180-1247. Henry II to Henry III. An illustrated Guide to Identification*. 1992

— — *The Voided Long-Cross Coinage 1247-1279. Henry III and Edward I*. 1993

— — *The English Long-Cross Pennies 1279-1489. Edward I-Henry VII*. 1995

For further references to British hammered coinage see *Sylloge of Coins of the British Isles,* a serial publication now comprising 53 volumes cataloguing collections in private hands and institutions. For full list of the 53 volumes published to date in this series, please contact Spink at the address below.

Other authoritative papers are published in the *Numismatic Chronicle, British Numismatic Journal and Spink's Numismatic Circular*. A complete book list is available from Spink & Son Ltd., 69 Southampton Row, Bloomsbury, London WC1B 4ET. Tel: 020 7563 4046 Fax: 020 7563 4068.

LATIN OR FOREIGN LEGENDS ON ENGLISH COINS

A DOMINO FACTUM EST ISTUD ET EST MIRABILE IN OCULIS NOSTRIS. (This is the Lord's doing and it is marvellous in our eyes: *Psalm 118.23.*) First used on 'fine' sovereign of Mary.

AMOR POPULI PRAESIDIUM REGIS. (The love of the people is the King's protection.) Reverse legend on angels of Charles I.

ANNO REGNI PRIMO, etc. (In the first year of the reign, etc.) Used around the edge of many of the larger milled denominations.

CHRISTO AUSPICE REGNO. (I reign under the auspice of Christ.) Used extensively in the reign of Charles I.

CIVIUM INDUSTRIA FLORET CIVITAS. (By the industry of its people the State flourishes.) On the 1951 Festival Crown of George VI.

CULTORES SUI DEUS PROTEGIT. (God protects His worshippers.) On gold double crowns and crowns of Charles I.

DECUS ET TUTAMEN. (An ornament and a safeguard: Virgil, *Aenid,* v.262.) This inscription on the edge of all early large milled silver was suggested by Evelyn, he having seen it on the vignette in Cardinal Richelieu's Greek Testament, and of course refers to the device as a means to prevent clipping. This legend also appears on the edge of U.K. and Northern Ireland one pound coins.

DIEU ET MON DROIT. (God and my right.) On halfcrowns of George IV and later monarchs

DIRIGE DEUS GRESSUS MEOS. (May the Lord direct my steps.) On the 'Una' Five pounds of Queen Victoria.

DOMINE NE IN FURORE TUO ARGUAS ME. (O Lord, rebuke me not in Thine anger: *Psalm 6, 1.).* First used on the half-florin of Edward III and then on all half-nobles.

D*omi*N*us* D*eus* O*mnipotens* REX. (Lord God, Almighty King.) Viking coins.

DUM SPIRO SPERO. (Whilst I live, I hope.) On the coins struck at Pontefract Castle during the Civil War after Charles I had been imprisoned.

EXALTABITUR IN GLORIA. (He shall be exalted in glory.) On all quarter-nobles.

EXURGAT DEUS ET DISSIPENTUR INIMICI EIUS. (Let God arise and let His enemies be scattered: *Psalm* 68, 1.) On the Scottish ducat and early English coins of James I (VI) and was chosen by the King himself. Also on Charles I, civil war, and Declaration coins,

FACIAM EOS IN GENTEM UNAM. (I will make them one nation: *Ezekiel, 37, 22.)* On unites and laurels of James I.

FLORENT CONCORDIA REGNA. (Through concord kingdoms flourish.) On gold unite of Charles I and broad of Charles II.

HANC DEUS DEDIT. (God has given this, i.e. the crown .) On siege-pieces of Pontefract struck in the name of Charles II.

HAS NISI PERITURUS MIHI ADIMAT NEMO. (Let no one remove these [letters] from me under penalty of death.) On the edge of crowns and half-crowns of Cromwell.

HENRICUS ROSAS REGNA JACOBUS. (Henry united the roses, James the kingdoms.) On English and Scottish gold coins of James I (VI).

HONI SOIT QUI MAL Y PENSE. (Evil to him who evil thinks.) The Motto of the Order of the Garter, first used on the Hereford (?) halfcrowns of Charles I. It also occurs on the Garter Star in the centre of the reverse of the silver coins of Charles II, but being so small it is usually illegible; it is more prominent on the coinage of George III.

ICH DIEN. (I serve.) Aberystwyth Furnace 2d, and Decimal 2p. The motto of The Prince of Wales.

INIMICOS EJUS INDUAM CONFUSIONE. (As for his enemies I shall clothe them with shame: *Psalm* 132, 18.) On shillings of Edward VI struck at Durham House, Strand.

JESUS AUTEM TRANSIENS PER MEDIUM ILLORUM IBAT. (But Jesus, passing through the midst of them, went His way: *Luke iv. 30.)* The usual reverse legend on English nobles, ryals and hammered sovereigns before James I; also on the very rare Scottish noble of David II of Scotland and the unique Anglo-Gallic noble of Edward the Black Prince.

JUSTITIA THRONUM FIRMAT. (Justice strengthens the throne.) On Charles I half-groats and pennies and Scottish twenty-penny pieces.

LUCERNA PEDIBUS MEIS VERBUM EST. (Thy word is a lamp unto my feet: *Psalm 119, 105.)* Obverse legend on a rare half-sovereign of Edward VI struck at Durham House, Strand.

MIRABILIA FECIT. (He made marvellously.) On the Viking coins of (?) York.

NEMO ME IMPUNE LACESSIT. (No-one provokes me with impunity.) On the 1984 Scottish one pound. Motto of The Order of the Thistle.

NUMMORUM FAMULUS. (The servant of the coinage.) The legend on the edge of the English tin coinage at the end of the seventeenth century.

O CRUX AVE SPES UNICA. (Hail! O Cross, our only hope.) On the reverse of all half-angels.

PAX MISSA PER ORBEM. (Peace sent throughout the world.) The reverse legend of a pattern farthing of Anne.

PAX QUÆRITUR BELLO. (Peace is sought by war.) The reverse legend of the Cromwell broad.

PER CRUCEM TUAM SALVA NOS CHRISTE REDEMPTOR. (By Thy cross, save us, O Christ, our Redeemer.) The normal reverse of English angels.

PLEIDIOL WYF I'M GWLAD. (True am I to my country.) Used on the 1985 Welsh one pound. Taken from the Welsh National Anthem.

POST MORTEM PATRIS PRO FILIO. (After the death of the father for the son.) On siege-pieces struck at Pontefract in 1648 (old style) after the execution of Charles I.

POSUI DEUM ADJUTOREM MEUM. (I have made God my Helper: *comp. Psalm* 54, 4.) Used on many English and Irish silver coins from Edward III until 1603. Altered to POSUIMUS and NOSTRUM on the coins of Philip and Mary.

PROTECTOR LITERIS LITERÆ NUMMIS CORONA ET SALUS. (A protection to the letters [on the face of the coin], the letters [on the edge] are a garland and a safeguard to the coinage.) On the edge of the rare fifty-shilling piece of Cromwell.

QUÆ DEUS CONJUNXIT NEMO SEPARET. (What God hath joined together let no man put asunder: *Matthew 19, 6.)* On the larger silver English and Scottish coins of James I after he succeeded to the English throne.

REDDE CUIQUE QUOD SUUM EST. (Render to each that which is his own.) On a Henry VIII type groat of Edward VI struck by Sir Martin Bowes at Durham House, Strand.

RELIGIO PROTESTANTIVM LEGES ANGLIÆ LIBERTAS PARLIAMENTI. (The religion of the Protestants, the laws of England, the liberty of the Parliament.) This is known as the 'Declaration' and refers to Charles I's declaration to the Privy Council at Wellington, 19 September, 1642; it is found on many of his coins struck at the provincial mints during the Civil War. Usually abbreviated to REL:PROT:LEG: ANG:LIB:PAR: ROSA SINE SPINA. (A rose without a thorn.) Found on some gold and small coins of Henry VIII and later reigns.

RUTILANS ROSA SINE SPINA. (A dazzling rose without a thorn.) As last but on small gold only.

SCUTUM FIDEI PROTEGET EUM or EAM. (The shield of faith shall protect him, or her.) On much of the gold of Edward VI and Elizabeth.
SIC VOC NON VOBIS (Thus we labour but not for ourselves). 1994 £2 Bank of England.
TALI DICATA SIGNO MENS FLUCTUARI NEQUIT. (Consecrated by such a sign the mind cannot waver: from a hymn by Prudentius written in the fourth century, entitled 'Hymnus ante Somnum'.) Only on the gold 'George noble' of Henry VIII.
TIMOR DOMINI FONS VITÆ. (The fear of the Lord is a fountain of life: *Proverbs, 14, 27.)* On many shillings of Edward VI.
TVAETUR UNITA DEUS. (May God guard these united, i.e. kingdoms.) On many English Scottish and Irish coins of James I.
VERITAS TEMPORIS FILIA. (Truth, the daughter of Time.) On English and Irish coins of Mary Tudor.

Some Royal Titles:

REX ANGL*orum*—King of the English.
REX SAXONUM OCCIDENTA LIM —King of the West Saxons.
DEI GRA*tia ANGLiae ET FRANCiae DomiNus HYBerniae ET AQVITaniae*—By the Grace of God, King of England and France, Lord of Ireland and Aquitaine.
D*ei GRAtia Magnae Britanniae, FRanciae ET Hiberniae REX Fidei Defensor BRunsviciensis ET Luneburgen-sis Dux, Sacri Romani Imperii Archi-THesaurarius ET ELector*=By the Grace of God, King of Great Britain, France and Ireland, Defender of the Faith, Duke of Brunswick and Luneburg, High Treasurer and Elector of the Holy Roman Empire.
BRITANNIARUM REX —King of the Britains (i.e. Britain and British territories overseas).
BRITT:OMN:REX:FID:DEF:IND:IMP: —King of all the Britains, Defender of the Faith, Emperor of India.
VIVAT REGINA ELIZABETHA — Long live Queen Elizabeth. On the 1996 £5 Queen's 70th birthday £5 crown.

APPENDIX III

NUMISMATIC CLUBS AND SOCIETIES

Coins News is the major monthly numismatic magazine. Spink's *Numismatic Circular* is long established, its first issue appeared in December 1892, and is now published 6 times a year. There are many numismatic magazines which carry articles of interest, such as the *CNG Review*. Many local clubs and societies are affiliated to the British Association of Numismatic Societies, (B.A.N.S) which holds an annual Congress. Details of your nearest numismatic club can be obtained from the Hon. Secretary, Philip Mernick, British Association of Numismatic Societies, c/o Bush, Boake Allen Ltd. Blackhorse Lane, London E17 5QP.

The two principal learned societies are the Royal Numismatic Society, c/o Department of Coins and Medals, the British Museum, Great Russell Street, Bloomsbury, London WC1B 3DG, and the British Numismatic Society, c/o Graham Dyer, The Royal Mint, Llantrisant, Pontyclun, mid Glamorgan, Wales. Both these societies publish an annual journal.

APPENDIX IV

MINTMARKS AND OTHER SYMBOLS ON ENGLISH COINS

A Mintmark *(mm.),* is a term borrowed from Roman and Greek numismatics where it showed the place of mintage; it was generally used on English coins to show where the legend began (a religious age preferred a cross for the purpose). Later, this mark, since the dating of coins was not usual, had a periodic significance, changing from time to time. Hence it was of a secret or 'privy' nature; other privy marks on a coin might be the code-mark of a particular workshop or workman. Thus a privy mark (including the *mintmark.)* might show when a coin was made, or who made it. In the use of precious metals this knowledge was necessary to guard against fraud and counterfeiting.

Mintmarks are sometimes termed 'initial marks' as they are normally placed at the commencement of the inscription. Some of the symbols chosen were personal badges of the ruling monarch, such as the rose and sun of York, or the boar's head of Richard III, the dragon of Henry Tudor or the thistle of James I; others are heraldic symbols or may allude to the mint master responsible for the coinage, e.g. the *mm.* bow used on the Durham House coins struck under John Bowes and the WS mark of William Sharrington of Bristol.

A table of mintmarks is given on the next page. Where mintmarks appear in the catalogue they are sometimes referred to only by the reference number, in order to save space, i.e. *mm. 28* (=mintmark Sun), *mm.28/74 (=mm. S*un on obverse, *mm.* Coronet on reverse), *mm.* 28/- (=*mm.* Sun on obverse only).

MINTMARKS AND OTHER SYMBOLS

1 Edward III, Cross 1 (Class B+C).
2 Edward III, broken Cross 1 (Class D).
3 Edward III, Cross 2 (Class E)
4 Edward III, Cross 3 (Class G)
5 Cross Potent (Edw. III Treaty)
6 Cross Pattee (Edw. III Post Treaty Rich. III).
7 (a) Plain of Greek Cross. (b) Cross Moline.
8 Cross Patonce.
9 Cross Fleuree.
10 Cross Calvary (Cross on steps).
11 Long Cross Fitchee.
12 Short Cross Fitchee.
13 Restoration Cross (Hen. VI).
14 Latin Cross.
15 Voided Cross (Henry VI).
16 Saltire Cross.
17 Cross and 4 pellets.
18 Pierced Cross.
19 Pierced Cross & pellet.
20 Pierced Cross & central pellet.
21 Cross Crosslet.
22 Curved Star (rayant).
23 Star.
24 Spur Rowel.
25 Mullet.
26 Pierced Mullet.
27 Eglantine.
28 Sun (Edw. IV).
29 Mullet (Henry V).
30 Pansy.
31 Heraldic Cinquefoil (Edw. IV).
32 Heraldic Cinquefoil (James I).
33 Rose (Edw. IV).
34 Rosette (Edw. IV).
35 Rose (Chas. I).
36 Catherine Wheel.
37 Cross in circle.
38 Halved Sun (6 rays) & Rose.
39 Halved Sun (4 rays) & Rose.
40 Lis-upon-Half-Rose.
41 Lis-upon-Sun & Rose.
42 Lis-Rose dimidiated.
43 Lis-issuant-from-Rose.
44 Trefoil.
45 Slipped Trefoil, James I (1).
46 Slipped Trefoil, James I (2).
47 Quatrefoil.
48 Saltire.
49 Pinecone.
50 Leaf (-mascle, Hen. VI).
51 Leaf (-trefoil, Hen. VI).
52 Arrow.
53 Pheon.
54 A.
55 Annulet.
56 Annulet-with-pellet.
57 Anchor.
58 Anchor & B.
59 Flower & B.
60 Bell.
61 Book.
62 Boar's Head (early Richard III).
63 Boar's Head (later Richard III).
64 Boar's Head, Charles I.
65 Acorn (a) Hen. VIII (b) Elizabeth.
66 Bow.
67 Br. (Bristol, Chas. I).
68 Cardinal's Hat.
69 Castle (Henry VIII).
70 Castle with H.
71 Castle (Chas. I).
72 Crescent (a) Henry VIII (b) Elizabeth.
73 Pomegranate. (Mary; Henry VIII's is broader).
74 Coronet.
75 Crown.
76 Crozier (a) Edw. III (b) Hen. VIII.
77 Ermine.
78 Escallop (Hen. VII).
79 Escallop (James I).
80 Eye (in legend Edw. IV).
81 Eye (Parliament).
82 Radiate Eye (Hen. VII).
83 Gerb.
84 Grapes.
85 Greyhound's Head.
86 Hand.
87 Harp.
88 Heart.
89 Helmet.
90 Key.
91 Leopard's Head.
91A Crowned Leopard's Head with collar (Edw. VI).
92 Lion.
93 Lion rampant.
94 Martlet.
95 Mascle.
96 Negro's Head.
97 Ostrich's Head.
98 P in brackets.
99 Pall.
100 Pear.
101 Plume.
102 Plume. Aberystwyth and Bristol.
103 Plume. Oxford.
104 Plume. Shrewsbury.
105 Lis.
106 Lis.
107 Portcullis.
108 Portcullis, Crowned.
109 Sceptre.
110 Sunburst.
111 Swan.
112 R in brackets.
113 Sword.
114 T (Henry VIII).
115 TC monogram.
116 WS monogram.
117 y or Y.
118 Dragon (Henry VII).
119 (a) Triangle (b) Triangle in Circle.
120 Sun (Parliament).
121 Uncertain mark.
122 Grapple.
123 Tun.
124 Woolpack.
125 Thistle.
126 Figure 6 (Edw. VI).
127 Floriated cross.
128 Lozenge.
129 Billet.
130 Plume. Bridgnorth or late declaration
131 Two lions.
132 Clasped book.
133 Cross pomee.
134 Bugle.
135 Crowned T (Tournai, Hen VIII)
136 An incurved pierced cross

The reign listed after a mintmark indicates that from which the drawing is taken. A similar mm. may have been used in another reign and will be found in the chronological list at the beginning of each reign.

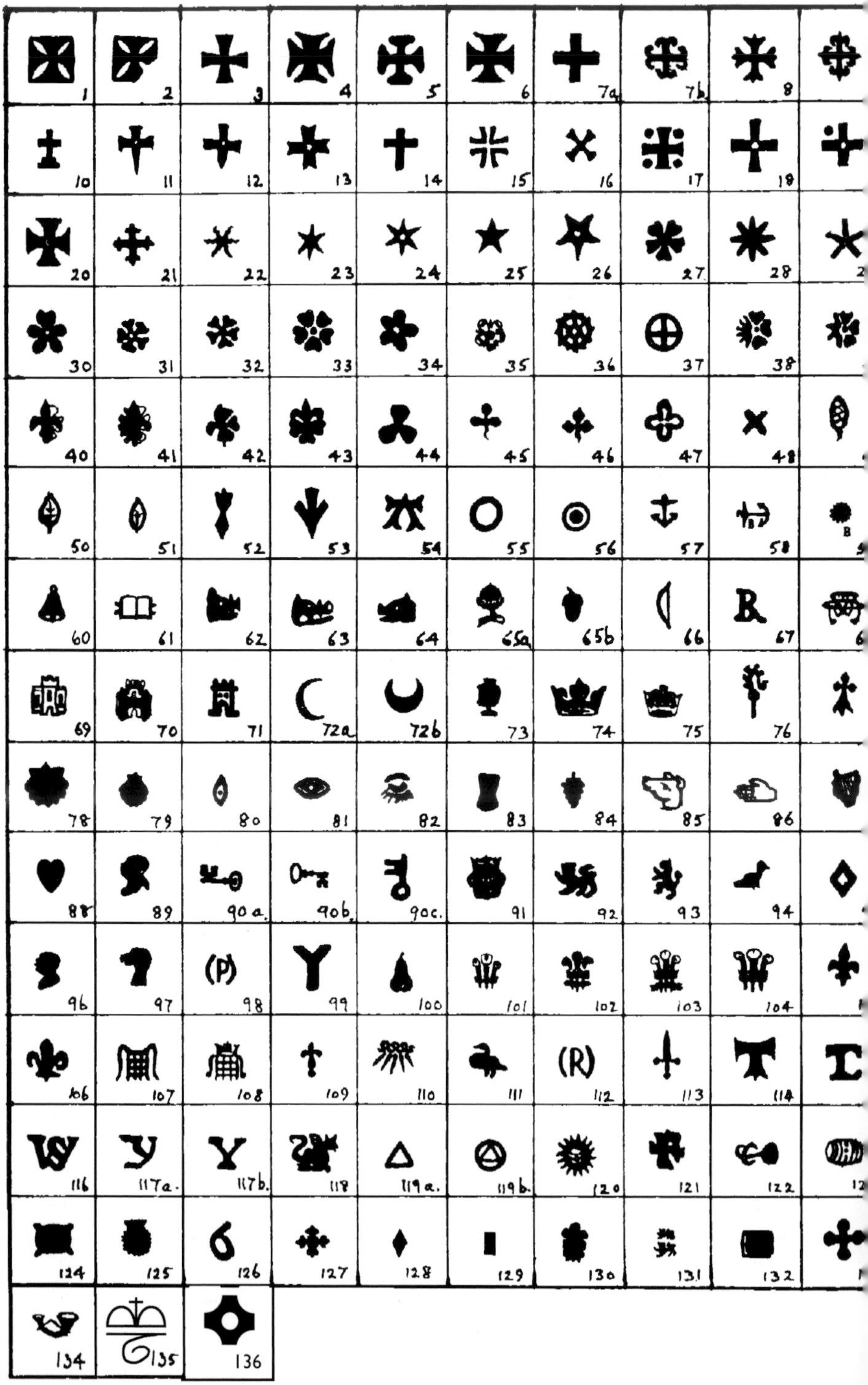
1 2 3 4 5 6 7a 7b 8
10 11 12 13 14 15 16 17 18
20 21 22 23 24 25 26 27 28
30 31 32 33 34 35 36 37 38
40 41 42 43 44 45 46 47
50 51 52 53 54 55 56 57 58
60 61 62 63 64 65a 65b 66 67
69 70 71 72a 72b 73 74 75 76
78 79 80 81 82 83 84 85 86
88 89 90a. 90b. 90c. 91 92 93 94
96 97 98 99 100 101 102 103 104
106 107 108 109 110 111 112 113 114
116 117a. 117b. 118 119a. 119b. 120 121 122
124 125 126 127 128 129 130 131 132
134 135 136

ALPHABETICAL INDEX OF RULERS AND COIN ISSUES